REFERENCE CATALOGUE
OF BRIGHT GALAXIES

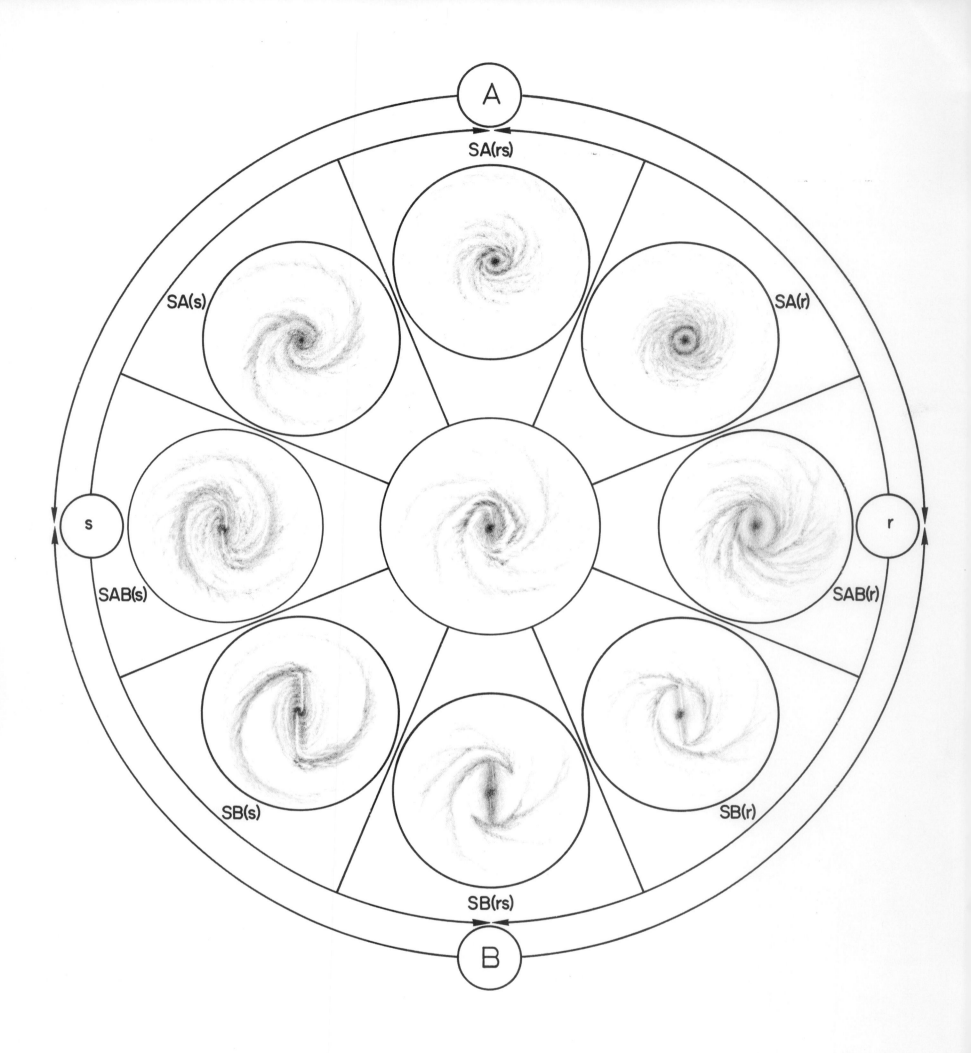

Fig. 1. Cross section of three-dimensional classification system of morphological types at stage Sb, showing (a) the two main <u>families</u> of ordinary spirals SA (above), barred spirals SB (below) and intermediate types SAB on horizontal axis; (b) the two main <u>varieties</u> of s-shaped spirals S(s) (left), ringed spirals S(r) at right, and intermediate types S(rs) on vertical axis. Note outer (R) ring structure in types SA(r) and SA(rs). For details of the 3D system see *Handbuch der Physik,* vol. 53, 1959.

REFERENCE CATALOGUE
OF BRIGHT GALAXIES

being the Harvard Survey of galaxies brighter than
the 13th magnitude of H. Shapley and A. Ames,
Revised, corrected and enlarged, with
Notes, Bibliography and Appendices

Gerard de Vaucouleurs
and
Antoinette de Vaucouleurs

First Edition
January 1, 1964

THE UNIVERSITY OF TEXAS PRESS · AUSTIN · 1964

Table of Contents

REFERENCE CATALOGUE OF BRIGHT GALAXIES

1. Introduction

The Harvard "Survey of Galaxies Brighter than the 13th Magnitude" by H. Shapley and A. Ames (1932) has been the standard reference list of bright galaxies for three decades. Nearly all objects listed in it were selected from earlier surveys and catalogues; the more important of these were various older Harvard lists of nebulae for the southern sky, the Helwan lists (1911-1935) in the zone $-45° < \delta < 0°$, and, especially the Heidelberg survey "Die Herschel Nebel" by K. Reinmuth (1926) which is a photographic revision of the old "General Catalogue" of J. Herschel (1864) — supplemented by J. L. E. Dreyer (1878) — for the zone of declinations $\delta > -20°$. Except for a few large or faint objects newly discovered in the course of these photographic surveys, nearly all had been found visually during the 19th century, mainly by W. and J. Herschel and their successors and are listed in the "New General Catalogue" or the "Index" catalogues of J. Dreyer (1888, 1895, 1908). The selection rule used by Shapley and Ames for inclusion of an object in the Harvard Survey was that 1) it should be known or presumed to be extragalactic, and 2) the integrated photographic magnitude estimated visually by inspection of small scale plates be $m_{pg} \leq 12.9$. However, some two hundred marginal cases of estimated magnitude $12.9 < m \leq 13.2$ were also included. Altogether 1249 objects presumed to be galaxies are listed in the Shapley-Ames survey.

Together with the photographic magnitude, the Hubble type and apparent photographic dimensions were given whenever available, mainly from the early reflector surveys at Lick (Curtis (1918), Mt. Wilson (Hubble 1926), and from (Harvard) Boyden Station plates. These data are heterogeneous and often incomplete or missing. This is especially true in the southern hemisphere in declinations $\delta < -20°$.

Despite the usefulness of the Shapley-Ames Catalogue as a finding list, e.g. for photometric, spectroscopic and more recently radio surveys of the brighter galaxies, the need for a revision, and a more complete and homogeneous catalogue, became clear after a decade or so. H. Shapley himself had started to collect additions and corrections to the Harvard Survey which he kindly communicated to us when he was informed of our intention to prepare a completely revised, enlarged version of the catalogue, including new observations of the poorly explored southern galaxies.

The present project was started in 1949 at the Institute of Astrophysics in Paris and at the Péridier Observatory, Le Houga, with the assistance of Mr. P. Griboval. The first step was to prepare a card index of all Shapley-Ames galaxies and to record all known corrections and sources of information for each object (monographs, photographs, photometry, diameters, magnitudes, colors, spectroscopy, velocities, supernovae, radio emission, etc.). This index was progressively enlarged to include all bright galaxies for which at least *one* significant piece of information (e.g. diameters > 1', magnitudes, photoelectric colors, velocities < 15,000 km/sec, radio emission) is known. For several hundred objects of $\delta < -35°$ new observations were made with the 30-inch and 74-inch reflectors of Mount Stromlo Observatory between 1952 and 1956 (G. de Vaucouleurs, 1956a; G. and A. de Vaucouleurs, 1961). Then, nearly all existing collections of large-scale reflector plates, including the 20-inch I. Roberts collection now at Paris Observatory, the 36-inch Crossley collection at Lick Observatory, the 60-inch Boyden collection at Harvard, and the 60-inch, 100-inch, and 200-inch collections at Mt. Wilson-Palomar were inspected to provide revised types and additional diameter estimates. Eventually

over 2800 galaxies were included in the card index and all available data were processed and reduced to standard systems of classification, diameters, magnitudes, colors, etc., as nearly homogeneous and uniform over the whole sky as can be presently devised. A special effort was made to include all anonymous objects of large diameter and low surface brightness discovered during the past 30 years. The data were checked and revised several times and new data, e.g. on velocities, magnitudes and colors, incorporated as they became available. During the preparation of the final listing galaxies which were either too small, (D < 0'5) or too faint, (m > 15), or with large velocities (V > 15,000 km/sec) or for which too little information was available were rejected and the number of entries reduced to 2599, over twice the number in the original Harvard Survey. Even though the Harvard survey attempted to include all galaxies brighter than m = 13.0, we know now that some large objects much brighter than this limit but of low surface brightness (e.g. the Sculptor and Fornax systems) had been missed; in fact, the Harvard survey is 50 per cent complete near m ≃ 12.5 (de Vaucouleurs, 1956b, 1957a). At the other end of the range some very small, compact ellipticals of high surface brightness which are easily mistaken for stars on small-scale survey plates may have been missed also, unless previously recognized as nebulae by visual observers. It is fairly generally acknowledged now that it is impossible in practice to produce a galaxy catalogue complete to any specified limit of magnitude or diameter. Recognition of a galaxy for inclusion in a catalogue depends not only on total magnitude but also on many other factors, of which the main ones are diameter and/or surface brightness, structure and shape, and declination (because of incompleteness and scarcity of southern surveys). We have, therefore, made no attempt to be complete to any specified limit of magnitude, diameter or velocity. The present catalogue is merely a selection of the brighter, larger and best observed galaxies. As a rough indication, however, we expect the 50 per cent completeness level to be reached near B ≃ 13.0. A statistical analysis to be published elsewhere gives quantitative estimates of the selection and completeness factors of magnitudes, diameters, velocities, etc.

Except for this unavoidable incompleteness the present "Reference Catalogue of Bright Galaxies" is intended to render services similar to Schlesinger's "Bright Star Catalogue". It replaces a provisional revision of the Harvard Survey prepared at Mt. Stromlo Observatory in 1953 (de Vaucouleurs 1953a). The present catalogue consists of two main parts: 1) the Catalogue proper includes all classification and quantitative data presentable in tabular form, 2) the Notes include whenever possible an abbreviated description from our inspection of original reflector plates, data on pair membership, corrections to earlier catalogues, and all significant references (monographs, photographs, photometry, magnitude and colors, spectroscopy, star counts, rotation and mass, clusters, HII regions, radio emission, HI emission, supernovae, etc.) published before January 1, 1964. Four Appendices give detailed magnitude and color data, and a listing by right ascension.

Section 2 gives a succinct description of the information given in each column of the Catalogue; section 3 gives a more detailed explanation of the sources of the material and of the methods of reduction to homogeneous systems; section 4 gives explanation of the notes and appendices to the catalogue.

2. The Catalogue

The data for each galaxy occupy two lines of two pages face to face. The entries on the <u>left page</u> are as follows:

Column 1: NGC identification (N), IC identification (I), where available, or A (for anonymous) followed by 4 digits being the hours and minutes of right ascension (1950). Some anonymous objects close to NGC or IC objects have been given the corresponding NGC or IC numbers followed by a letter A, B, C, etc.

Column 2: line 1, RA = right ascension (1950) to 0.1 min.; line 2, 100 P = precession in right ascension for 100 years in the same units.

Column 3: line 1, D = declination (1950) to 1'; line 2, 100 P = precession in declination for 100 years in the same units.

Column 4: line 1, L^I = old galactic longitude in Harvard-Lund system; (See explanation in section 3.1,a). line 2, B^I = old galactic latitude (both to $0°.01$).

Column 5: line 1, L^{II} = new galactic longitude in Leiden-Sydney (I.A.U. 1958) system; (section 3.1.b). line 2, B^{II} = new galactic latitude (both to $0°.01$).

Column 6: line 1, SGL = supergalactic longitude as defined by de Vaucouleurs (1956c, 1958a, 1959c); (see section 3.1,c). line 2, SGB = supergalactic latitude (both to $0°.1$).

Column 7: line 1, Revised morphological type in *Handbuch der Physik* system (de Vaucouleurs 1959d, 1963) and source (S) of plate material both coded as explained in Tables 1a, 1b of section (3.2,a); Fig. 1 is a revised illustration of a cross-section of the classification volume near stage Sb = S3 showing the two main families SA, SB and varieties S(r), S(s) and transition types. line 2, DDO (T,L) = David Dunlap Observatory (DDO) type and luminosity class L (van den Bergh 1960) coded as explained in Table 2 of (3.2,b).

Column 8: line 1, Y1 = type and color class in Yerkes list 1 (Morgan 1958); line 2, Y2 = type and color class in Yerkes list 2 (Morgan 1959), both coded as explained in (3.2,c).

Column 9: line 1, H-S = Hubble-Sandage type as given in the "Hubble Atlas of Galaxies" (Sandage 1961), and coded as explained in (3.2,d); line 2, Ho = revised Hubble type according to Holmberg (1958) and coded as explained in (3.2,e).

Column 10: line 1, log D = decimal logarithm of mean major diameter measured visually on photographs and reduced to standard "corrected" Heidelberg system following the precepts given by de Vaucouleurs (1959a, b) as specified in (3.3,a) below. Unit of D is $0'.1$ to avoid negative entries; line 2, w = weight of log D computed as explained in section (3.3,b); unit weight is for mean error of (log D) = 0.10 in the mean, depending slightly on galaxy type (cf. sect. 3.3,b).

Column 11: line 1, log R = decimal logarithm of mean ratio of major diameter D to minor diameter d derived from visual measurements of photographs; this ratio was corrected for subjective systematic errors following the precepts of Holmberg (1946) and de Vaucouleurs (1959a, b) as specified in section (3.3,c); line 2, w = weight of log R (usually same as for log D) computed as explained in section (3.3,c); unit weight for m.e. (log R) $\simeq$ 0.10.

Column 12: line 1, log D(0) = decimal logarithm of major diameter (in $0'.1$) statistically corrected to "face on" by the relation

$$\log D(0) = \log D - 0.4 \log R$$

following the precepts given by de Vaucouleurs (1959a, b) as explained in (3.3,d).

Column 13: lines 1, 2, S(D,R) = the sources of log D, log R coded as explained in section (3.3,e).

The entries on the <u>right page</u> are:

Column 14: repeats NGC, IC or Anon. identification.

Column 15: line 1, m_H = Harvard photographic apparent magnitude from HA 88,2; this entry identifies objects listed in the original Shapley-Ames catalogue (see section 3.4,a). line 2, m_c = Harvard photographic magnitude statistically corrected to the B(0) system as specified in section (3.4,b). The mean error of the corrected Harvard magnitude is of the order of ± 0.2 to ± 0.3 mag. depending on magnitude, diameter and axis ratio (de Vaucouleurs, 1956b).

Column 16: line 1, B(0) = integrated magnitude in the B system within a circle of diameter D(0) derived by interpolation or extrapolation from photoelectric and modern photographic data in (or reduced to) the standard B system following the precepts of de Vaucouleurs (1961) as explained in section (3.4,c). The total or asymptotic magnitude $B_T = B(\infty)$ is approximately from 0.4 to 0.6 mag. brighter than B(0), depending on galaxy type (cf. section 3.4,c). line 2, w = weight of B(0) computed as explained in section (3.4,c); unit weight for m.e. = 0.10 mag.

Column 17: line 1, B'(0) = mean B surface brightness in magnitude per square minute of arc within a circle of diameter D(0), as given by the relation

$$B'(0) = B(0) + 5 \log D(0) - 5.26$$

line 2, m'_c = mean B surface brightness derived from the corrected Harvard magnitude

$$m'_c = m_c + 5 \log D(0) - 5.26$$

Column 18: lines 1, 2, S(B) = sources of B magnitude coded as explained in section (3.4,c).

Column 19: line 1, (B-V)(0) = integrated color index in the standard B,V system within the circle of diameter D(0) derived following the precepts of de Vaucouleurs (1961) and as specified in section (3.5,a). For most galaxy types (B-V)(0) is very close to and for many purposes practically identical with the total or asymptotic color (B-V)(∞) (cf. section 3.5,a); line 2, w = weight of (B-V)(0) computed as explained in section (3.5,a); unit weight for m.e. = 0.10 mag.

Column 20: line 1, $C_0(0)$ = "intrinsic" color index derived from (B-V)(0) statistically corrected for galactic absorption to "outside" the Galaxy, for internal absorption to "face on" orientation, and for red shift to zero velocity following the precepts of de Vaucouleurs (1961) and as explained in section (3.5,b); line 2, available to fill in the similar information from (U-B)(0) when available.

Column 21: lines 1, 2, S(C) = sources of B-V, and where given after a diagonal sign (/), sources of U-B coded as explained in section (3.5,a).

Column 22: line 1, (U-B)(0) = integrated color index in the standard U-B system within the circle of diameter D(0) derived following the precepts of de Vaucouleurs (1961) and as specified in section (3.5,c). For most galaxy types (U-B)(0) is close to the asymptotic value (U-B)(∞).

line 2, w = weight of (U–B)(0) to be filled in when enough duplicate data have been obtained to permit reliable estimates of standard errors.

Column 23: line 1, V = observed radial velocity in kilometers per second, being the weighted mean of optical and, where available, radio determinations with weights derived from the precepts of Page (1961) and G. and A. de Vaucouleurs (1963) as specified in section (3.6,a); line 2, w = weight of V computed as explained in section (3.6,b); unit of w for m.e. (V) = ± 100 km/sec.

Column 24: line 1, V_o = radial velocity corrected for solar motion (relative to the Local Group of galaxies) through the relation

$$V_o = V + \Delta V = V + 300 \cos A$$

where A is the angular distance to the conventional extragalactic solar apex at $L^I = 55°$, $B^I = 0°$, following the precepts of Humason and Wahlquist (1955) and Humason, Mayall and Sandage (1956).
line 2, $\Delta V = 300 \cos A$ (in km/sec); the solar motion correction is listed for all galaxies even if the velocity has not yet been determined.

Column 25: lines 1, 2, S(V) = sources of radial velocities coded as explained in section (3.6,a).

Column 26: line 1, ϕ_r = radio (continuum) flux at some standard wavelength, to be filled in when available; this column was left blank as no definitive standard system of radio flux or magnitudes, nor a sufficient number of reliable determinations of such magnitudes were available during the preparation of this catalogue. References to radio data published prior to January 1, 1964, will be found in the Notes to the Catalogue.
line 2, n = radio (continuum) spectral index between two standard wavelengths, to be filled in when available, same remarks.

Column 27: line 1, ϕ (21) = integrated flux in the 21-cm HI emission line to be filled in when available; same remarks as for 26.1. Published radio data are given in the Notes.
line 2, blank, available for additional line emission information.

Column 28: lines 1, 2, blank, available for any other future radio or optical information (e.g. radio apparent diameter or optical effective diameter).

Column 29: lines 1, 2, Photo = references to best sources of published direct photographs of each object, coded as explained in section (3.7).

3. Explanation of Sources, and Reduction of Data

This section gives more detailed information on the catalogue entries which are not self-explanatory.

3.1. Coordinates.

a) Old Galactic Coordinates L^I, B^I (Column 4; lines 1, 2).

This column was added after a circular letter sent in 1960 to request suggestions for additions and improvements to a provisional list of catalogue entries disclosed interest in retaining L^I, B^I in addition to L^{II}, B^{II}. Recent work (unpublished) indicates that the old galactic coordinates system (Ohlsson 1932) is somewhat better than the new system to compute galactic absorption corrections; this is consistent with the fact that galactic obscuration of external galaxies occurs mainly in nearby interstellar clouds rather than in the distant inner regions of the Galaxy. Also, computations of standard corrections of radial velocities for solar motion (col. 24) and of supergalactic coordinates are simpler in the old coordinates system with respect to which they were defined.

b) New Galactic Coordinates L^{II}, B^{II} (column 5, lines 1, 2).

This is the system mainly derived from HI studies (Blaauw, Gum, Pawsey and Westerhout 1960) and adopted by the I.A.U. in 1958; the new pole is at RA = $12^h 46^m.6$, D = $+27°40'$ (1900), or $L^I = 347°.7$, $B^I = +88°.51$, the origin of longitudes at the galactic center of old coordinates $L^I = 327°.69$, $B^I = -1°.40$.

c) Supergalactic Coordinates SGL, SGB (Column 6, lines 1, 2).

The majority of bright galaxies lie in an equatorial belt within ± 30° from the equator of this coordinate system which is useful for studies of their apparent surface density and velocity distribution. It is the natural reference system for the study of nearby galaxies if the Local Supercluster is a significant physical and dynamical entity (de Vaucouleurs 1953b, 1956c, 1959c). North supergalactic pole is at $L^I = 15°$, $B^I = +5°$, origin of SGL at $L^I = 105°$, $B^I = 0°$.
The distribution maps in Fig. 2, 3, 4, 5 and 6 are in supergalactic coordinates. On these maps the Milky Way and zone of avoidance are along the periphery and vertically across the center of the chart; the northern galactic hemisphere is to the right of the center line where the concentration of the Virgo cluster(s) is in evidence.

3.2. Types.

a) Revised Types (Column 7, line 1).

Source of type indicates the origin of the best plate or plates from which the revised type was estimated as shown in Table 1a.

TABLE 1a. SOURCES OF REVISED TYPES

SOURCE		CODE	SOURCE		CODE
Palomar	200''	P200	Palomar	48''	P048
Mount Wilson	100''	W100	Lick	36''	L036
Radcliffe	74''	R074	Helwan	30''	H030
Mount Stromlo	74''	S074	Mount Stromlo	30''	S030
Boyden	60''	B060	I. Roberts	20''	R020
Mount Wilson	60''	W060			

When no other source was available and an approximate type was needed for the reduction of diameters, magnitudes, or colors, the Hubble type listed by Pettit (1954) or Humason et al. (1956) was adopted and coded W (Mt. Wilson) or L (Lick) without telescope size.

The revised morphological type in the Handbuch der Physik system was coded as shown in Table 1b to make the notation compatible with the symbols available on the IBM printer.

In all cases the number of symbols used gives an indication of the degree of resolution available and of the reliability of the classification.

To facilitate the reading of the coded symbols an interpretation table is given on a loose leaf insert.

Example: NGC 23, coded type SBS1 stands for type SB(s)a, i.e. early type barred spiral of the s-shaped variety.

TABLE 1b. CODING OF REVISED MORPHOLOGICAL TYPES

CLASSES	FAMILIES	VARIETIES	STAGES	TYPE	CODE
Ellipticals				E	. E . . .
			Ellipt.(0-7)	E0	. E . 0 .
			Intermediate	E0-1	. E . 0 +
			Late Ellip.	E$^+$	. E + . .
Lenticulars	Ordinary			S0	. L
	Barred			SA0	. L A
	Mixed			SB0	. L B
				SAB0	. L X
		Inner ring		S(r)0	. L . R
		S-shaped		S(s)0	. L . S
		Mixed		S(rs)0	. L . T
			Early	S0$^-$	. L . . $-$
			Interm.	S0°	. L . . 0
			Late	S0$^+$	. L . . +
Spirals	Ordinary			SA	. S A
	Barred			SB	. S B
	Mixed			SAB	. S X
		Inner ring		S(r)	. S . R
		S-shaped		S(s)	. S . S
		Mixed		S(rs)	. S . T
			0/a	S0/a	. S . . 0
			a	Sa	. S . . 1
			ab	Sab	. S . . 2
			b	Sb	. S . . 3
			bc	Sbc	. S . . 4
			c	Sc	. S . . 5
			cd	Scd	. S . . 6
			d	Sd	. S . . 7
			dm	Sdm	. S . . 8
			m	Sm	. S . . 9
Irregulars	Ordinary			IA	. I A
	Barred			IB	. I B
	Mixed			IAB	. I X
		S-shaped		I(s)	. I . S
			Magellanic	Im	. I . . 9
			Non-Magell.	I0	. I . 0
Peculiars				P	. P
Peculiarities			Peculiarity	P	. . . . . P
(all types)			Uncertain	:	. . . . . *
			Doubtful	?	. . . . . $
			Spindle	sp	. . . . . /
			Outer ring	(R)	R . . . . .
			Pseudo outer ring	(R')	P . . . . .

b) <u>DDO Types and Luminosity Classes</u> (Column 7, line 2).

The DDO types and luminosity classes of van den Bergh (1960) are coded as shown in Table 2.

TABLE 2. CODING OF DDO (VAN DEN BERGH) TYPES

CLASSES	FAMILIES	STAGES	TYPE	CODING	NOTES
Elliptical		Ellipticity (0-9)	E0	E 0	(1)
Spiral	Ordinary		S	S	
	Barred		SB	S B	
	Intermediate		S(B)	S X	
		a	Sa	S 0	
		b$^-$	Sb$^-$	S 2	
		b	Sb	S 3	
		b$^+$	Sb$^+$	S 4	
		c	Sc	S 5	
		$-$	S$^-$	S 6	
		$+$	S$^+$	S 7	
Irregular			Ir	I	
			Ir$^+$	I 9	
Peculiar			P	P	
Peculiarities		Bright nucleus	N	N	
		Nebulous arms, mild case	(n)	N $-$	(2)
		" " , normal	n	N	
		" " , extreme	nn	N +	
		Patchy arms, mild case	(*)	K $-$	
		" " , normal	*	K	
		" " , extreme	**	K +	
		Distorted arms, mild case	(t)	T $-$	
		" " , normal	t	T	
		" " , extreme	tt	T +	
		Peculiarity	p	P	
		Uncertain ? , : , ( )		* * *	(3)
LUMINOSITY CLASSES		I		1	
		I-II		2	
		II		3	
		II-III		4	
		III		5	
		III-IV		6	
		IV		7	
		IV-V		8	
		V		9	

(1) Includes lenticulars, especially in E8, E9. (2) Combined cases are coded NK, NT, etc., (3) Applies to symbol or group of symbols immediately preceding it.

The correlation between DDO types and the revised types was studied by de Vaucouleurs (1963) and the code numbers for DDO spiral stages chosen accordingly. In the DDO notation system n stands for fuzzy or nebulous arms, * for patchy arms, t for distorted arms; mild cases (coded $-$) are shown in parenthesis, extreme cases (coded +) are denoted by double symbols. A loose leaf interpretation table is inserted.

<u>Example</u>: NGC 157, code: S 5 K $-$ 1, stands for Sc(*)I, i.e. ordinary late-type spiral with moderately patchy arms, luminosity class I.

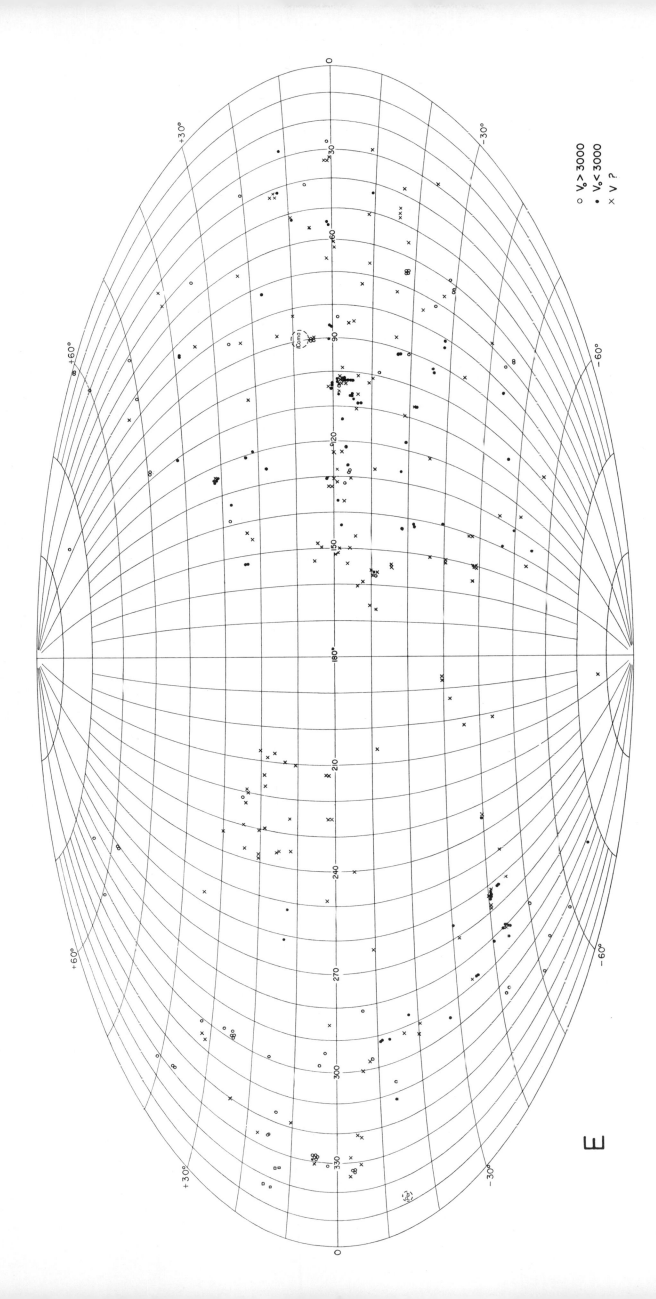

Fig. 2. Distribution of elliptical galaxies in supergalactic coordinates. Dots and circles denote objects having known redshifts respectively smaller or greater than 3000 km sec^{-1}; crosses objects whose velocity is unknown. The north pole of the supergalactic coordinate system is at (old) galactic coordinates $l^I = 15°$, $b^I = +5°$; the northern galactic hemisphere is at right where the clustering in Virgo is in evidence.

E

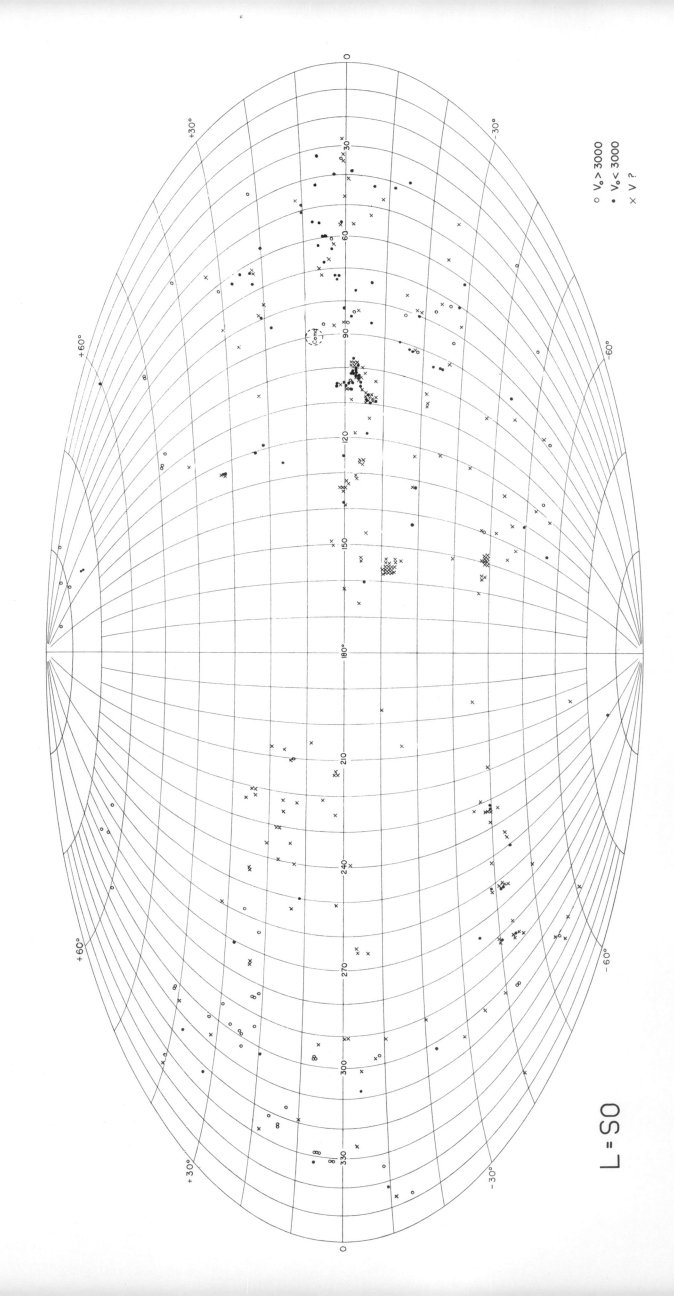

L = SO

Fig. 3. Distribution of lenticular galaxies in supergalactic coordinates.

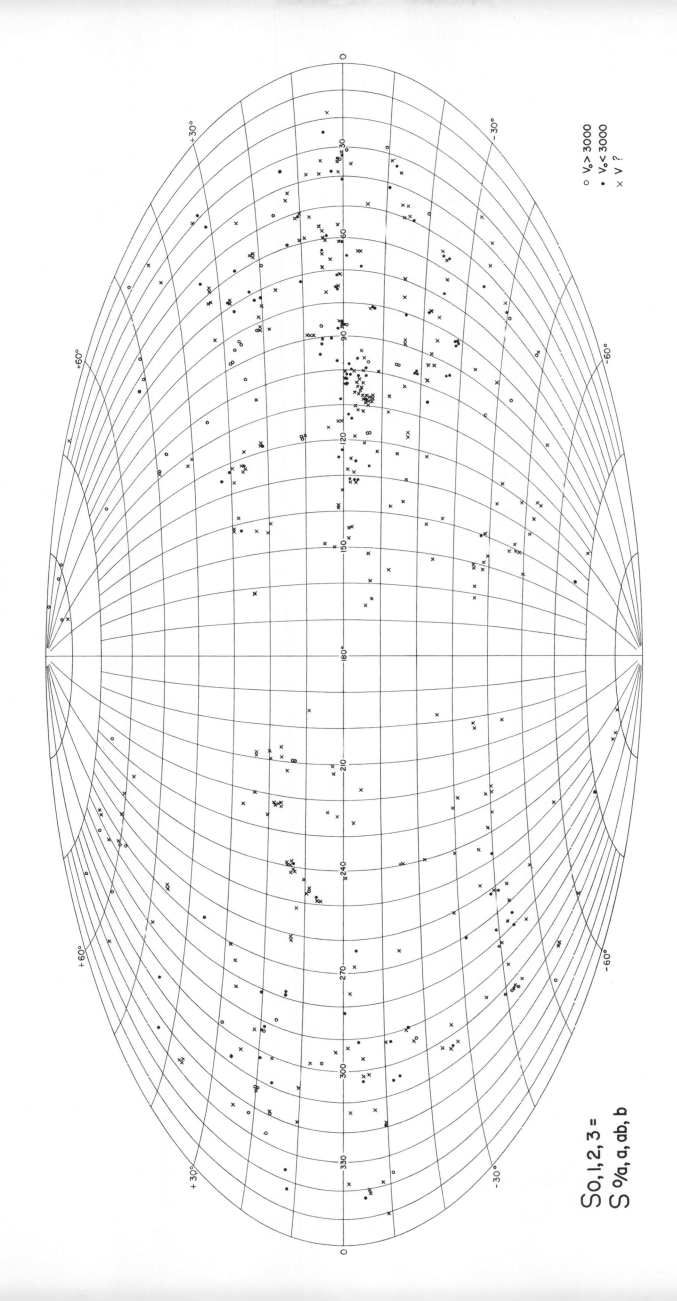

$$So, 1, 2, 3 =$$
$$S o/a, a, ab, b$$

○ = $V_o > 3000$
• = $V_o < 3000$
× = V?

Fig. 4. Distribution of "early-type" spirals in supergalactic coordinates.

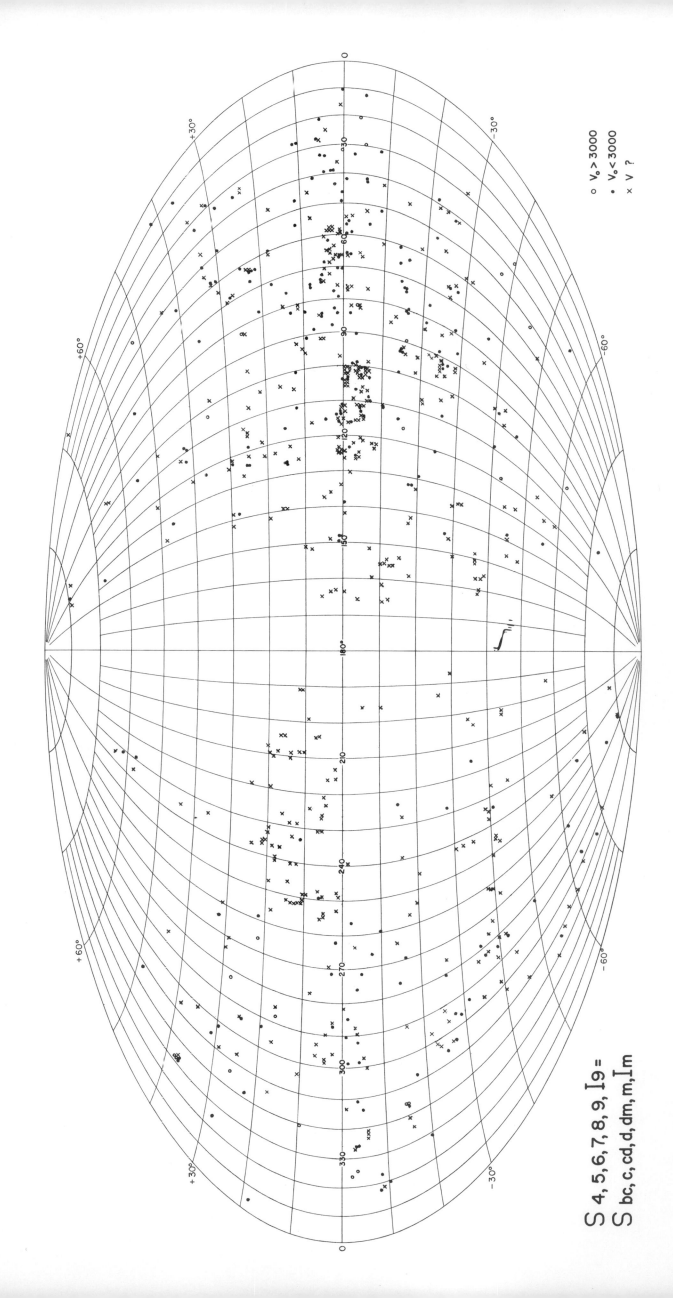

S 4, 5, 6, 7, 8, 9, I9 =
S bc, c, cd, d, dm, m, Im

○ $v_o > 3000$
● $v_o < 3000$
× v ?

Fig. 5. Distribution of "late-type" spirals and magellanic irregulars in supergalactic coordinates.

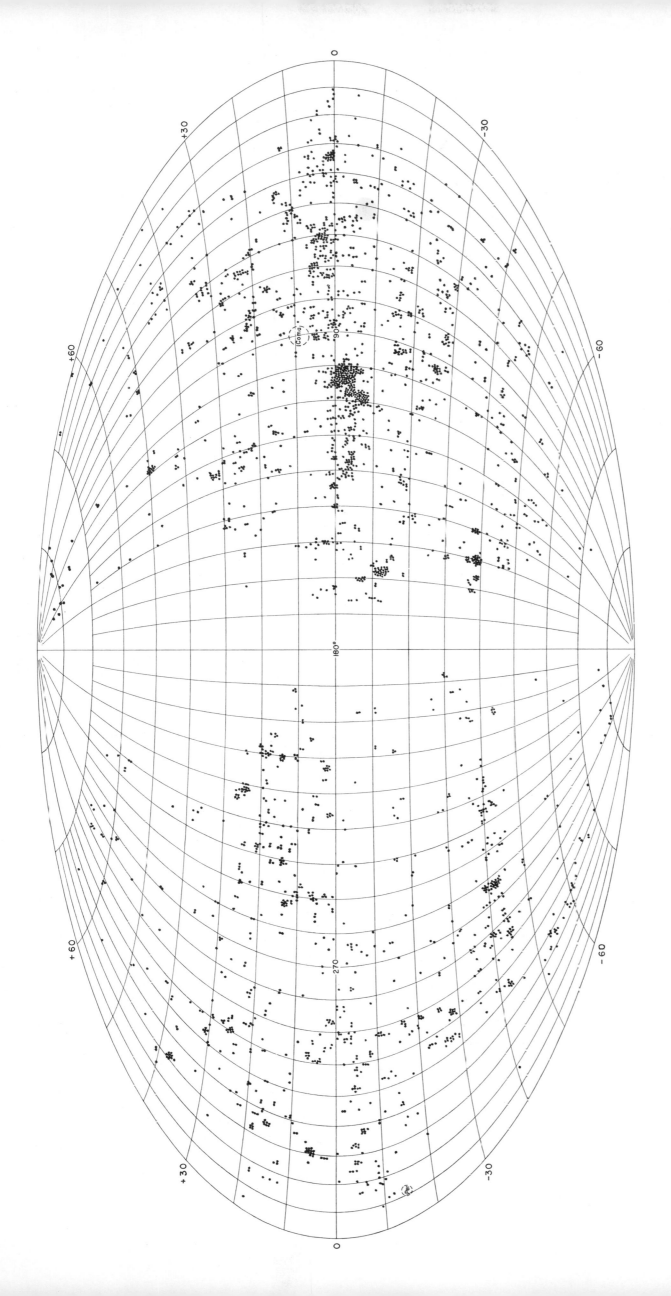

Fig. 6. Distribution of 2599 bright galaxies in supergalactic coordinates. Note the concentration to the supergalactic equator, especially in the northern galactic hemisphere. Some symbols have been slightly displaced for greater clarity in crowded areas.

9

c) <u>Yerkes Types and Color Classes</u> (Column 8, lines 1 and 2).

Yerkes types and color classes, list 1 from Mt. Wilson-Palomar reflector plates (Morgan 1958), list 2 from 48-inch Schmidt plates (Morgan 1959) are coded as shown in Table 3.

TABLE 3. CODING OF YERKES (MORGAN) TYPES

CLASSES	TYPE	CODE	COLOR CLASSES	CODE
Elliptical	E(0-7)	E0	a	A
	E-D	ED	af	AF
	D-E	DE	f	F
	S-E	SE	fg	FG
Dusty	D	D	g	G
	D-S	DS	gk	GK
	S-D	SD	k	K
Spiral	S	S	:	*
Barred	B	B		
	(B)	SX		
	B-S	BS		
	S-B	SB		
Irregular	I	I		
	S-I	SI		
	I-S	IS		
	I-B	IB		
	B-I	BI		

CLASSES	TYPE	CODE
Peculiarities	L (1)	. . L
	P	. . P
	?,:	*

(1) Low surface brightness.

The Yerkes system and the revised (*Handbuch der Physik*) system have been compared by de Vaucouleurs (1963). Several of the Yerkes types are not directly translatable into revised types, but Yerkes color classes are fairly closely correlated with stages of the spiral sequence from Sa to Sm (loc. cit. Table 13).

d) <u>Hubble-Sandage Types</u> (Column 9, line 1).

Hubble Atlas (Sandage 1961) types are coded as shown in Table 4.

TABLE 4. CODING OF HUBBLE-SANDAGE TYPES

CLASSES	TYPE	CODE	TYPE	CODE
E	E (0-7)	E 0	E0/S0$_1$	E+0
S0	S0	L	S B0	LB
	S0$_1$	L 1	S B0$_1$	LB1
			S B0$_{1/2}$	LB1+
	S0$_2$	L 2	S B0$_2$	LB2
			S B0$_{2/3}$	LB2+
	S0$_3$	L 3	S B0$_3$	LB3
	S0$_3$/Sa(s)	S S0	S B0$_3$/SBa(s)	S BS0
	S0$_2$/Sa(r)	S R0	S B0$_3$/SBa(r)	S BR0
S	Sa	S 1	S Ba(s)	S BS1
			S Ba(r)	S BR1
			S Ba	S B 1
			S a/SBa	S X 1
	Sa/Sb	S 2		
	Sb	S 3	S Bb(s)	S BS3
			S Bb(r)	S BR3
			S Bb(rs) or (sr)	S BT3
			S Bb(s)/Sb	S XS3
			S b/SBb	S X 3
	Sc/Sb	S 4		
	Sc	S 5	S Bc(s)	S BS5
			S Bc(r)	S BR5
			S Bc(rs) or (sr)	S BT5
			S c/SBc	S X 5
	Sc/Irr	S 9		
I	Irr I	I 9	Irr II	I 0
Pec.	(p)	P		

The Hubble Atlas and revised types were compared by de Vaucouleurs (1963); the correlation is generally good for spiral stages and is reflected in the numerical coding of the stages; the correlation is poorer for lenticulars and no simple correspondence exists between H-S stages 1, 2, 3 and stages -, 0, + of the revised system (loc. cit. Table III,2).

e) <u>Holmberg Types</u> (Column 9, line 2).

Holmberg types were compared with the revised types by de Vaucouleurs (1963) and are, accordingly, coded as shown in Table 5.

TABLE 5. CODING OF HOLMBERG (Ho) TYPES

TYPE	CODE
E	E
S 0	L
S a	S 1
S b$^-$	S 3
S b$^+$	S 4
S c$^-$	S 5
S c$^+$	S 6
Ir I	I 9
Ir II	I 0
S	S .
P	P

3.3. Diameters.

a) <u>Mean corrected log D</u> (Column 10, line 1).

The systematic errors of micrometric-photographic diameters have been investigated by Holmberg (1946) and de Vaucouleurs (1959a, b). Major diameters were corrected for scale error and reduced to a uniform mean system through relations of the form

$$\log D \text{ (corr.)} = A \log (D + 0.3S) + B \qquad (1)$$

where A, B, are constants and S the plate scale in minutes of arc per mm. The values of the constants are given in Table 6.

The log D value listed in column 10, line 1 is the weighted mean of the values derived from the individual sources, with weights computed as explained in the following section.

b) <u>Weights</u> (Column 10, line 2).

The weight given is the sum of the individual weights w_i. The weights w_i of the individual log D values were computed through the formula

$$w_i = w_D (D/S)^{\frac{1}{2}} \qquad (2)$$

w_D is the relative weight of the input D: $w_D = 1$ unless marked :, ( ), or ? in original data when $w_D = 1/2, 1/3, 1/5$; D/S is the linear size of the image of the galaxy in millimeters on the plate. This second factor was derived from a study of the residuals vs. log D and source in a first approximation of the reduction. Where D_m values were formed they were assigned weights $w_m = 0.5 (w_i + w_o)$.

The mean error for unit weight is $\sigma_1 (\log D) = 0.10$ on the average; it is about 0.08 for type S, and 0.12 for types E, L, and I (cf. de Vaucouleurs 1959b, p. 33). The diameter data were reduced in two successive approximations and aberrant values leaving residuals > 0.25 in log D (e.g. from underexposed plates) were rejected prior to the second run.

Log D values are listed for 2300 objects or 88.5 per cent of the total and weights range from 0.3 to about 30, with an average $\overline{w} (\log D) = 4.0$ corresponding to a mean error $\overline{\sigma} (\log D) = 0.05$.

c) <u>Means Axis Ratios and Weights</u> (Column 11, lines 1, 2).

The systematic errors in the axis ratio R = D/d derived from major and minor diameters measured visually on photographs have been investigated by Holmberg (1946) and de Vaucouleurs (1959a, b). R is usually too large (d measured too small), the magnitude of the error depending slightly on galaxy type. Errors of this type are present in the Heidelberg data and several other series. Accordingly, measured values of $r = R^{-1} = d/D$ which are subject to

TABLE 6. REDUCTION CONSTANTS FOR LOG D

CODE	SOURCE	A	B	0.3 S	CODE	SOURCE	A	B	0.3 S
A	Heidelberg 9	1	0	0.50	N	Lick 36" b,c	1	0	0.19
B	Lund 6	1	0	0.50	O	Pretoria 74"	1	0*	0.11
C	Lund 9	1	+0.10	0.50	P	Boyden 60"	1	0	0.13
D	HA 88,2	1	0	0.30	Q	Mt. Wilson 60"	1	0*	0.13
E	HA 88,4	(*)	-0.10	0.30	R	Pease 60"	1	0	0.13
F	Helwan b,c,d	1	0	0.27	S	Lundmark	1	0	0.2:
G	Helwan a	1	+0.10	0.27	T	Lund 10a	1	0	0.27
H	Roberts	1	0	0.41	U	Lund 10b	1	0	0.19
I	Mt. Stromlo 30"	1	0*	0.33	V	Lund 10c	1	0	0.1:
J	Mt. Stromlo 74"	1	0*	0.11	W	Mt. Wilson 100"	1	0*	0.08
K	DDO II,6	1	0	0.33	X	Lund 136	see	notes	
L	Lick 13	1	+0.10	0.19	Y	Patterson	see	notes	
M	Lick 36" a	1	0	0.19	Z	Palomar 200"	1	0*	0.06

NOTES. (*) Source E (HA 88,4): A = 0.86 for type E, 0.93 for L, and 1.00 for all other types. Sources I, J, O, Q, W, Z: "inner" and "outer" diameters D_i, D_o were measured; the corrections were applied to the (geometric) mean diameter defined by $\log D_m = 0.5 (\log D_i + \log D_o)$. Sources X, Y: these give diameters from microphotometer tracings, which are much larger than those of the photographic mean diameter system and not directly comparable or reducible to it. These values were not used in deriving the mean photographic system.

(Sources are identified in Table 8.)

errors of the Heidelberg system were corrected by means of the relations given by Holmberg (1946, Table 10; see also de Vaucouleurs 1959 b, p. 41).

For computation purposes these corrections were approximated by the following formulae:

for type E

$$\log R = - \log r_c = - \log [0.86r - 0.14 (1 - r)^6 + 0.14] \quad (3)$$

for other types

$$\log R = - \log r_c = - \log [0.81r - 0.19 (1 - r)^6 + 0.19] \quad (4)$$

The corrections applied to various catalogues are listed in Table 7.

The log R value listed in column 11, line 1 is the weighted mean of the values derived from the individual sources, with the weights shown on line 2. These weights are generally the same as for the log D values (column 10); where w(log R) is less than w(log D) it indicates that one of the sources gives D only. The mean error of log R for unit weight is about 0.10 and is independent of type (de Vaucouleurs 1959b, p. 33).

Log R values are listed for 2282 objects or 87.9 per cent of the total and weights range from 0.3 to over 30 with an average $\overline{w}$(log R) = 3.8 corresponding to $\overline{\sigma}$ (log R) $\simeq$ 0.05.

d) Mean "Face On" Diameters Log D(0) (Column 12).

The statistical relation between axis ratio and apparent major diameter was investigated by Holmberg (1946), Wyatt and Brown (1955) and de Vaucouleurs (1956a, 1957b). Galaxies of a given type and apparent magnitude appear larger when seen edgewise because of the greater optical path through the system and correspondingly increased surface brightness at a given radial distance. In the range of radial distances corresponding to the standard diameters the relative variation of D is conveniently independent of galaxy type and a function of axis ratio R only, with the constant slope

TABLE 7. CORRECTIONS TO AXIS RATIO r = d/D

CODE	SOURCES	CORRECTIONS
A	Heidelberg 9	eq. (3), (4)
B	Lund 6	as A
C	Lund 9	add 0.02 to r and treat as A
D	HA 88,2	no correction
E	HA 88,4	no correction
F	Helwan 21-35	as A
G	Helwan 9, 15	as A
H	Roberts	as A
I, J	Mt. Stromlo 30, 74	no correction
K	DDO II, 6	Type E: no correction; Type L: see note (1); other types: as A
L, M, N	Lick 13, 36	as A
O	Pretoria 74	no correction
P	Boyden 60	as A
Q, W	Mt. Wilson 60, 100	as A
R	Pease 60	as A
S	Lundmark	Type E: see note (2); other types: as A
T	Lund 10	as A
U	Lund 10	Type E: as A; other types: see note (3)
V	Lund 10	as A
Z	Palomar 200	as A

NOTES. For further details and justification of procedures see de Vaucouleurs (1959b, pp. 27 - 29). (1) Source K, for type L: $\log R = -\log A [0.9 r - 0.1 (1-r)^6 + 0.1]$. (2) Source S, for type E: if $r \geq 0.7$, as A; if $r < 0.7$, add 0.1 and treat as A. (3) Source U, for other types: if $r \geq 0.6$, as A, if $r < 0.6$, add 0.08 and treat as A.

$d(\log D)/d(\log R) = + 0.40$ (de Vaucouleurs 1957b). The "face on" diameter is then computed through the relation

$$\log D(0) = \log D - 0.40 \log R \quad (5)$$

for all 2282 galaxies having both D and R values. D(0) is a better distance indicator than D and a convenient parameter for the reduction of magnitudes and colors to standard conditions (col. 16, 19, 22).

TABLE 8. SOURCES OF DIAMETER DATA

CODE	SERIES*	OBSERVATORY	TEL.	SCALE ʹ/mm	No. of GALAXIES TOTAL	No. of GALAXIES H.A. 88,2	REFERENCE	SOURCE	NOTES
A	Ia	Heidelberg	16"r	1ʹ7	3500±	776	Reinmuth 1926	(1)	
B	Ib	—	—	—	827	149	Holmberg 1937	(2)	
C	Ic	—	—	—	4666	426	Reiz 1941	(3)	
D	IIa	Harvard-Boyden	24"r	1ʹ0	243	243	Shapley-Ames 1932	(4)	(1)
E	IIb	—	—	—	488	488	Shapley 1934	(5)	
F	IIIb	Helwan	30"R	0ʹ9	184	91	Gregory 1920, 1921	(6)	
	IIIc	—	—	—	169	60	Knox-Shaw 1924, Madwar 1935	(7)	
G	IIIa	—	—	—	58	40	Know-Shaw 1912, 1915	(8)	
H	IV	Roberts	20"R	1ʹ37	600	289	de Vaucouleurs 1952	(9)	(2)
I	V	Mt. Stromlo	30"R	1ʹ12	460	205	de Vaucouleurs 1956	(10)	(3)
J	Va	Mt. Stromlo	74"R	0ʹ38	47	40	de Vaucouleurs 1961	(11)	(3)
K	XIV	Palomar	48"S	1ʹ12	935	935	van den Bergh 1960	(12)	(4)
L	X	Lick	36"R	0ʹ63	477	257	Curtis 1918	(13)	
M	VIa	—	—	—		105	de Vaucouleurs 1955	(14)	(5)
N	VIb	—	—	—	494	54	— —		(6a)
	VIc	—	—	—		59	— —		(6b)
O	Vb	Pretoria	74"R	0ʹ38	34	19	— 1961	(11)	(7)
P	Vc	Harvard-Boyden	60"R	0ʹ44	101	61	de Vaucouleurs 1958	(15)	
Q	VIIa	Mt. Wilson	60"R	0ʹ45		68	de Vaucouleurs 1957	(15)	(3,8)
	VIIb	—	—	—	384	166			
	VIIc	—	—	—		53			
R	XIa	Mt. Wilson	60"R	0ʹ45	101	29	Pease 1917, 1920	(16)	
S	XII	—	—	—	122	96	Lundmark 1927	(17)	(9)
T	XIIIa	Helwan	30"R	0ʹ9			Danver 1942	(18)	
U	XIIIb	Lick	36"R	0ʹ63	202	162			
V	XIIIc	Mt. Wilson	60"R	0ʹ45					
			100"R	0ʹ27					
W	VIIIa	Mt. Wilson	100"R			51	de Vaucouleurs 1957	(15)	(3,10)
	VIIIb	—	—	0ʹ27	503	182			
	VIIIc	—	—			167			
X	XV	Mt. Wilson	60"R	0ʹ45	300	280	Holmberg 1958	(19)	(11)
			100"R	0ʹ27					
Y	XVI	Harvard	16"r	1ʹ67	123	123	Patterson 1941	(20)	(11,12)
Z	IXa	Palomar	200"R	0ʹ20	262	118	de Vaucouleurs 1957	(15)	(3,13)
	IXb	—	—	—		57	— —		

* Refers to notation previously used (de Vaucouleurs 1956b, 1957a).

NOTES. (1) Noted authority "a" only in HA 88,2 (fully exposed 24" Bruce plates). (2) Measured on prints x1.5, x4, or x8 from I. Roberts original plates. (3) D_m computed from measured D_i and D_0. (4) Measured on NGS-Palomar Sky Survey prints. (5) Crossley plates of 1933-1939. (6a) Crossley plates of 1940-42. (6b) Crossley plates of 1946-1953. (7) Measured on prints of "Cape Atlas of Southern Galaxies". (8) Series VIIa, b, c refer respectively to plates exposed prior to 1930, from 1930 to 1939, and after 1940. (9) Includes some values measured on Franklin-Adams 10"r plates (S = 3'0/mm). (10) Series VIIIa, b, c refer respectively to plates exposed prior to 1930, from 1930 to 1939, and after 1940. (11) Maximum detectable dimensions on microphotometer tracings, not reduced to standard system. (12) Unpublished Radcliffe thesis, cf. de Vaucouleurs 1957b. (13) Series IXa, b refer respectively to 103a-O plates without filter or with minus UV filter.

SOURCES. (1) Reinmuth, K., 1926, Veröff. Heidelberg, vol. 9. (2) Holmberg, E., 1937, Ann. Lund Obs., No. 6. (3) Reiz, A., 1941, Ann. Lund Obs., No. 9. (4) Shapley, H. and Ames, A., 1932, Harvard Ann., 88, No. 2. (5) Shapley, H., 1934, Harvard Ann., 88, No. 4. (6) Gregory, C. C. L., 1920, Helwan Obs. Bull., No. 21, 201; 1921, ibid., No. 22, 219. (7) Knox-Shaw, H., 1924, Helwan Obs. Bull., No. 30, 71. Madwar, M. R., 1935, Helwan Obs. Bull., No. 38, 1. (8) Knox-Shaw, H., 1912, ibid., No. 9, 69; 1915, ibid., No. 15, 129. (9) Vaucouleurs, G. de, 1952, unpublished. (10) Vaucouleurs, G. de, 1956, Mem. Commonwealth Obs., III, No. 13. (11) Vaucouleurs, G. and A. de, 1961, Mem. R.A.S., 68, 69. (12) van den Bergh, S., 1960, Pub. David Dunlap Obs., vol. II, no. 6. (13) Curtis, H. D., 1918, Publ. Lick Obs., XIII, part I. (14) Vaucouleurs, G. de, 1955, unpublished. (15) Vaucouleurs, G. de, 1957, unpublished. (16) Pease, F. G., 1917, Ap. J., 46, 24 = MWC No. **132**; 1920, ibid., 51, 276 = MWC No. **186**. (17) Lundmark, K., 1927, Medd. Upsala, No. 21. (18) Danver, C. G., 1942, Ann. Lund Obs., No. 10. (19) Holmberg, E., 1958, Medd. Lund, Ser. II, Nr 136. (20) Patterson, F. S., 1941, Unpubl. Harvard Univ. (Radcliffe College) Thesis.

e) <u>Sources of Diameters</u> (Column 13, lines 1, 2).

The sources of diameters and axis ratios have been described in detail by de Vaucouleurs (1957a, 1957b, 1963); all photographs used for D, R data are on ordinary (blue sensitive) emulsions; Table 8 gives a summary of the material and coding.

An effort was made to achieve a homogeneous system over the whole sky, but only a few series provide enough overlap for a good tie between the northern and southern hemispheres and residual systematic differences of the order of a few hundredths in log D depending on declination may be present, especially in the poorly observed zone $-35° < \delta < -20°$ between the northern limit of the Mt. Stromlo surveys and the practical southern limits of the Heidelberg, Lick and Mt. Wilson surveys. The surface brightness corresponding to the standard photographic diameter system is not known precisely; preliminary estimates are $\mu_D \simeq 23.0$ mag sec^{-2} for ellipticals and lenticulars, $\mu_D \simeq 24.2$ mag sec^{-2} for spirals (de Vaucouleurs 1957a). Programs of detailed isophotometry in progress at McDonald Observatory will provide a more precise calibration.

3.4. Magnitudes.

a) <u>Harvard Magnitudes m_H</u> (Column 15, line 1).

The Harvard photographic magnitude is given for all objects listed in H.A. 88,2; in addition Harvard magnitudes (presumably on the same system) are given for the Sculptor system (A0058), the Fornax system (A0239), A0255 from H.B. 914, A0143 from H.B. 919, and for I.C. 1613. An * indicates uncertain values (:), which apply in general to the larger and brighter galaxies or to systems of low surface brightness.

b) <u>Corrected Harvard Magnitudes m_c</u> (Column 15, line 2).

The systematic errors of the Harvard magnitudes have been investigated by de Vaucouleurs (1956b, 1957a) and Holmberg (1958). The errors depend mainly on surface brightness and luminosity gradient, i.e. type; there is no true scale error. For the present catalogue the Harvard magnitudes were reduced to the B(0) system—as defined in section 3.4,c, below—through relations of the form

$$m_c = m_H - \alpha(m'_H - \mu) \qquad (6)$$

where

$$m'_H = m_H + 5 \log D(0) - 5.26 \qquad (7)$$

is a measure of the average surface brightness, and α and μ are constants derived by least squares for each galaxy type. In a first trial solution an additional term, $\beta(\text{cosec } b - 1)$, was included, but solutions showed that the coefficient β does not differ significantly from zero. Another trial solution showed that there was no advantage in using the measured (D,R) instead of the derived D(0) parameter to compute m'_H. From plots of α, μ versus revised morphological type $\tilde{\sigma}$ the smoothed values listed in Table 9 were adopted for the final reduction.

TABLE 9. CONSTANTS FOR REDUCTION OF
HARVARD MAGNITUDES

TYPE	E	L	I, I0	S0	S1	S2	S3
α	0.34	0.34	0.40	0.46	0.46	0.46	0.46
μ	13.05	13.30	13.5 :	13.65	13.75	13.80	13.85

TYPE	S4	S5	S6	S7	S8	S9	I9
α	0.46	0.46	0.46	0.46	0.46	0.34	0.34
μ	13.90	13.95	14.05	14.20	14.20	14.30	13.50

Plots of B(0) minus m_c versus cosec b, log R, log D(0), and m'_H for all types indicate no systematic trend; the range of residuals is $\pm$ 0.9 mag., indicating a mean error of the order of 0.2 to 0.3 mag. for the corrected Harvard magnitudes. These magnitudes, although of much lower accuracy than B(0), should be useful until photoelectric observations are secured for all the Shapley-Ames galaxies, especially in the southern hemisphere.

Corrected Harvard magnitudes are given for 1193 objects or 95.4 per cent of the Shapley-Ames galaxies and 45.9 per cent of the present catalogue.

c) <u>Integrated B(0) Magnitudes and Weights</u> (Column 16, lines 1, 2).

The integrated magnitude B(0) was derived from photoelectric or modern photographic magnitudes measured in the B system or reduced to the B system through the relations given in Table 10.

Sources E, L, M are direct photoelectric observations in the U,B,V system; all others were in various photographic or photoelectric systems and the transformations to the B system were derived from comparisons with source E (de Vaucouleurs 1961) by means of graphs of B or m plotted for each galaxy versus X = log A/D(0), where A is the field aperture of the photometer. For source G an "equivalent" aperture was defined by log A = log D - 0.4 log R. For source K, the transformation from Pe to B was derived from the North Polar Sequence and standard stars. For source C, the NPS comparison gives B = m_{pg} + 0.10, but for galaxies in common this relation leads to $<(m_{pg} + 0.10) - B> = +0.12$ and the transformation formula derived from the direct comparison of galaxy magnitudes was preferred.

The B(X) values so computed are listed in Appendix I for 954 galaxies or 36.8 per cent of the catalogue. From plots of B(X) vs. X for well observed galaxies mean integrated luminosity curves were derived for each galaxy type, i.e., $\Delta B(X) = B(X) - B(0)$, where B(0) is the integrated magnitude for a circular field aperture equal to the "face on" diameter A = D(0). Over the useful range $-1 < X < +1$ the integrated luminosity curves are very nearly parabolic, i.e.

$$B(0) - B(X) = \beta X (2X_0 - X) \qquad (8)$$

and to the degree of accuracy justified by the data two standard curves sufficed to represent the main galaxy types as follows

(I) Types E, L, S0, S3, I0: $\beta = 0.75$, $X_0 = +1.0$ $(X > -0.5)$ (8a)

(II) Types S4 to S9, I9: $\begin{cases} \beta = 1.30, X_0 = +0.5 & (X > -0.5) \\ \beta = 2.60, X_0 = +0.5 & (X \leq -0.5) \end{cases}$ (8b)

The first relation agrees almost perfectly with the luminosity curve derived by integration of the ellipsoidal luminosity law (de Vaucouleurs 1957a, 1959d)

$$\log B = -3.33 (\alpha^{1/4} - 1)$$

which leads to

$$\Delta m(\alpha) = -2.5 \log k(\alpha)$$

where

$$k(\alpha) = 1 - e^{-x}\left(1 + \sum_{1}^{7} \frac{x^n}{n!}\right)$$

with

$$x = 7.668 \, \alpha^{1/4}$$

The second agrees only in the outer regions of spirals (X > 0) with the tentative exponential law (de Vaucouleurs 1957a, 1962)

$$k(\alpha) = 1 - (1 + x)e^{-x}$$

where

$$x = 1.6785\alpha$$

this is not unexpected since the exponential law applies only to late-type spirals (de Vaucouleurs 1959e). The correction curves are shown in Fig. 7; over the useful range the corrections $\Delta B(X)$ range from -0.8 to +0.5 mag. for type (I), and from -1.0 to +0.3 mag. for types (II). According to relations (8a, 8b) above the total or asymptotic magnitude $B_T = B(\infty)$ is practically reached at $X_0 = +1.0$, i.e. A = 10 D(0), where $B_T - B(0) = -0.65$ mag., for galaxies of classes E, and L and for spirals of type Sb and earlier;

TABLE 10. SOURCES OF B MAGNITUDES

CODE	REFERENCE	SOURCE	METHOD	TRANSFORMATION	σ_0	N	NOTES
A	Stebbins and Whitford 1937	(1)	Pe	$B = Pe + 0.08$	0.06	165	
B	Stebbins and Whitford 1952	(2)	Pe	$B = Pg + 0.07$	0.07	176	
C	Pettit 1954	(3)	Pe	$B = m_{pg} + 0.20 - 0.26\ C\dot{I}$	0.07	561	
D	Tifft 1958	(4,5)	Pe	$B = [4] + 13.71 + 1.26\ (B-V)$	0.05	68	(a)
	— 1963	—	—	$B = [4] + 0.21 + 1.26\ (B-V)$	—	—	—
E	de Vaucouleurs 1959, -61	(6,7,8)	Pe	$B = V + (B-V)$	0.06	130	
F	Bigay 1951	(9)	Pg	$B = m_{pg} - 0.03$	0.10	175	
G	Holmberg 1958	(10)	Pg	$B = m_{pg} + 0.19 - 0.13\ C$	0.08	300	
H	Bigay *et al.*	(11,12,13)	Pe	$B = m_{pg} + 0.26 - 0.22\ C\dot{I}$	0.06 :	48	
K	Whitford 1936	(14)	Pe	$B = P_e + 0.08 + 0.09\ (B-V)$	0.06 :	11	(b)
L	Hodge 1963	(15)	Pe	$B = V + (B-V)$	0.07 :	60	
M	Shobbrook 1964	(16)	Pe	$B = V + (B-V)$	0.07 :	53	

NOTES. (a) $B-V = 0.043 + 0.63\ [2-4]$. (b) B-V derived or estimated from other sources.

SOURCES. (1) *Ap.J.*, 86, 247, 1937. (2) *Ap.J.*, 108, 413, 1948. (3) *Ap.J.*, 120, 413, 1954. (4) *A.J.*, 66, 390, 1961. (5) *A.J.*, 68, 302, 1963. (6) *Lowell Obs. Bull.*, vol. 4, No. 97, 1959. (7) *Lowell Obs. Bull.*, Vol. 4, No. 98, 1959. (8) *Ap.J., Suppl.*, Vol. V, No. 48, 233, 1961. (9) *Ann. d'Ap.*, 14, 319, 1951. (10) *Lund Medd.*, II, Nr. 136, 1958. (11) *Ann. d'Ap.*, 16, 133, 1953. (12) *Ann. d'Ap.*, 17, 78, 1954. (13) *Ann. d'Ap.*, 18, 141, 1955, (14) *Ap.J.*, 83, 424, 1936. (15) *A.J.*, 68, 237, 1963. (16) *Australian Nat. Univ. Thesis*, Canberra, 1964.

it is reached at $X_0 = + 0.5$, i.e. $A \simeq 3\ D(0)$, where $B_T - B(0) = -0.33$ mag. for spirals of type later than Sb. Attempts at empirical extrapolation of the individual luminosity curves B(X) for a number of well-observed galaxies lead to estimates of B_T about 0.1 to 0.2 mag. fainter in the mean than the computed values; this result could be expected since very few galaxies have been observed with large enough field apertures to permit a reliable extrapolation to "infinity". For the available data the maximum values of X are generally $X < +0.4$, except for source G for which $+0.2 < X < +0.6$. To avoid excessive extrapolations magnitudes for which $X < -1.0$ were not used in the derivation of B(0); however these magnitudes are listed in Appendix I.

In a first approximation provisional unweighted mean values of $\overline{B(0)} = \langle B(X) + \Delta B(X)\rangle$ and residuals $\delta B(0)_X = B(0)_X - \overline{B(0)}$ were computed; plots of $\delta B(0)_X$ versus X show that residuals are at a minimum for $X = 0$, as could be expected since no correction is needed when $A = D(0)$, and that the scatter increases in direct proportion with $|X|$. Thus both the intrinsic mean error σ_0 of each series, and the mean error α_X introduced by the reduction to $X = 0$ could be estimated. The total variance of a reduced value of B(0), then is

$$\sigma^2 = \sigma_0^2 + 0.04\ X^2 \qquad (9)$$

where the values of σ_0 for the different sources are listed in Table 10 above.

In a second approximation provisional weighted means B_0 of the B(0) values having $w > 0.5$ were computed; the weighted mean residuals and standard error were formed for each source from the residuals $\delta B(0) = B_0 - B(0)$ for multiply observed objects. This led to small zero point corrections as follows:

SOURCE	A	B	C	D	E	F
Corr.: $-\overline{\delta B(0)}$	+0.05	-0.05	-0.02	+0.02	-0.02	+0.02
$\overline{\sigma}$	0.16	0.16	0.18	0.17	0.15	0.29

SOURCE	G	H	K	L	M
Corr.: $-\overline{\delta B(0)}$	-0.01	+0.01	-0.06	+0.08	0.00?
$\overline{\sigma}$	0.21	0.15	0.22	—	—

The values of B(0) listed in column 16, line 1 are the weighted means of B(0) corr. $= B(0) - \overline{\delta B(0)}$, using only B(0) values for which $w > 0.5$ and $|\delta B(0)| < 0.30$ mag. The total weight of the mean B(0) corr. is shown on line 2; the unit of weight is for a m.e. $\sigma[B(0)] = 0.10$ mag.

B(0) values are given for 873 objects or 33.6 per cent of the catalogue; the range of weights is from about 1 to 20, and averages 4.0 corresponding to an average m.e.: $\overline{\sigma}[B(0)] = 0.05$ mag.; in the few cases where only one B(0) value of $w < 0.5$ is available, it is given in the notes and the source shown in column 18.

3.5. Colors.

a) Integrated (B-V)(0) colors and weights (Column 19, lines 1, 2).

The integrated color index was derived from photoelectric observations in the B-V system (sources E, L, M) or reduced to this system by comparison with source E through the relations listed in Table 11 (after de Vaucouleurs 1961).

The colors so derived are listed in Appendix II for 900 objects or 34.6 per cent of the catalogued systems. Because integrated colors depend on the relative size of the field aperture, all colors reduced to the (B-V) scale were corrected to $A/D(0) = 1.0$ through standard relations approximating the color-aperture curves derived in Ap.J. Suppl. No. 48. No correction was applied when $X = \log A/D(0) > 0.0$, i.e. the asymptotic color is essentially reached for $X = 0$. For $-1.0 < X < 0.0$ the corrected color was computed through the relation

$$(B-V)(0) = (B-V)(X) - S(T)\cdot X \qquad (10)$$

where the coefficient $S(T) = d(B-V)/dX$ varies with galaxy type as follows:

TYPE	E	L	S0	S1	S2	S3	S4
S(T)	-0.03	-0.05	-0.07	-0.09	-0.11	-0.13	-0.15

TYPE	S5	S6	S7	S8	S9	I9
S(T)	-0.17	-0.11	-0.04	+0.03	+0.10	+0.17

Colors measured for X < -1.0, i.e. A < 0.1 D(0), refer mainly to the nucleus and were not used in deriving (B-V)(0) to avoid excessive extrapolation; however, these colors are listed in Appendix II. In a few cases of well observed galaxies such as NGC 205, 221, 278, 2633, 2681, 2903, 3031, 3338, 3351, 4214, 4244, etc., whose color trend clearly departs from the normal or average trend for the type, the observed color curve was used to derive (B-V)(0). For the Large and Small Magellanic Clouds, M 31 and M 33 the integrated B-V was derived from detailed surface photometry (de Vaucouleurs 1958b, 1959e, 1960b). In several cases apparently discordant values, especially low weight values from source C, were rejected. In all other cases the weighted mean values of (B-V)(0) is listed in column 19, line 1; the total weight is in line 2 with unit weight for m.e. = 0.10 mag. Colors are given for 841 objects or 32.4 per cent of the catalogue; weights range from 0.9 to 80 with an average $\overline{w} \simeq 6.9$ corresponding to $\overline{m.e.} \simeq 0.04$ mag. Colors of southern galaxies from source M only have no assigned weight, but from internal evidence an average weight of the order of 4 to 6 may be provisionally assumed.

b) Intrinsic colors $C_O(0)$ (Column 20, line 1).

The relations between apparent and intrinsic colors of galaxies have been investigated by Holmberg (1958) and de Vaucouleurs (1961). The observed color index C(0) = (B-V)(0) can be statistically corrected for internal absorption, galactic absorption, and red shift through the relation (de Vaucouleurs 1961)

$$C_o(0) = C(0) - \Sigma \Delta C(0) \qquad (11)$$

where

$$\Sigma \Delta C(0) = \Delta C(0)_v + \Delta C(0)_b + \Delta C(0)_r$$
$$= 0.012 \times 10^{-3} V + 0.05 \ |\text{cosec } b| + 0.4 \ \gamma(1-r) \qquad (12)$$

if V is the observed red shift in km/sec (col. 23), b the galactic latitude b^{II}, r = 1/R is the axis ratio (col 11) and γ the internal absorption coefficient which depends on galaxy type as follows:

γ	0.0	0.1	0.2	0.3	0.4
Type	E / I9	L / S8,S9	S0,I0 / S6,S7	S1 / S4,S5	S2 / S3

The total corrections range from -0.05 mag. for ellipticals of small velocity near the galactic pole, to values in excess of -0.4 mag. for edge-on spirals having large velocities in low galactic latitudes. Obviously the larger corrections are proportionately more uncertain, especially for axis ratios r < 0.2 and in galactic latitudes |b| < 20° because of the patchiness of interstellar absorption. Nevertheless the corrected color is generally more useful than the observed color as an additional classification and luminosity criterion (cf de Vaucouleurs 1961). Corrected C_O colors are listed for 650 objects or 25.0 per cent of the catalogue.

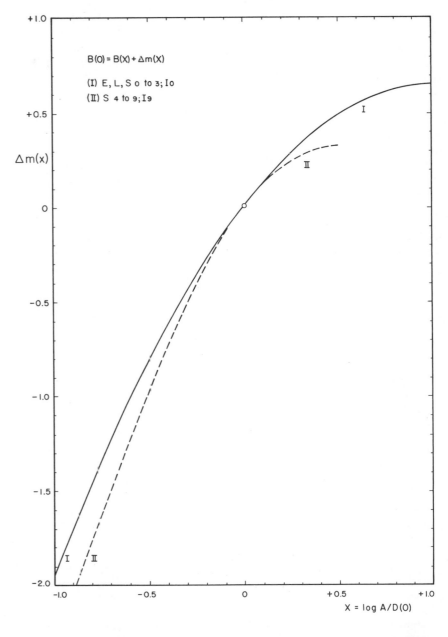

Fig. 7. Standard integrated luminosity curves $\Delta B(X) = B(X) - B(0)$ for the derivation of B(0). X = log A/D(0), if A = diameter of field aperture, D(0) = standard "face on" diameter.

TABLE 11. SOURCES OF B-V COLORS (*)

CODE	SOURCE	TRANSFORMATION	σ	w
A	Stebbins and Whitford 1937	$B-V = +0.834 + 1.477 \ C_2$	0.047	4.4
B	— — 1952	$B-V = +0.189 + 0.856 \ C_p$	0.041	6.2
C	Pettit 1954	$B-V = +0.218 + 0.742 \ CI$	0.071	1.9
D	Tifft 1958-63	$B-V = +0.043 + 0.631 \ [2-4]$	0.032	9.4
E	de Vaucouleurs 1959-61	$B-V = B-V$	0.040	6.2
G	Holmberg 1958	$B-V = +0.209 + 0.871 \ C$	0.065	2.5
H	Bigay *et al.* 1953, 54, 55	$B-V = +0.278 + 0.779 \ CI$	0.055 :	3.1
L	Hodge 1963	$B-V = B-V$	0.073	(1)
M	Shobbrook 1964	$B-V = B-V$	?	(2)

(*) For references see Table 10, Sources of B magnitudes.

(1) w = 0.9 (σ = 0.105) for n = 1, and $\overline{n} \simeq 2$ obs. per object. (2) No relative weight can yet be derived for this series of southern observations which have little or no overlap with northern hemisphere data.

The sources of B-V colors (column 21, lines 1,2) and, where shown after the diagonal sign (/), of U-B colors (see below), are coded as indicated in Tables 10 and 11. Sources F and K give no colors.

c) Integrated (U-B)(0) Colors (Column 22, line 1).

Photoelectric colors in the U-B system are available in sources E, L, and M and ultraviolet colors denoted [1-3] in source D can be transformed to U-B through the relation (de Vaucouleurs 1961)

$$U-B = -0.715 + 0.778\,[1-3] \tag{13}$$

The number of multiply observed galaxies is too small yet to permit reliable estimates of mean errors of individual sources; however, the r.m.s. residual between the observed (U-B) from source E and the (U-B) derived from source D through eq. (13) above is $\sigma_{D,E}$ (U-B) = 0.052 mag., while the corresponding residuals for (B-V) colors give $\sigma_{D,E}$ (B-V) = 0.051 mag. (de Vaucouleurs 1961, p. 288). Hence the mean errors of (U-B) data are about equal to those of the (B-V) data. The observed or derived values of (U-B)(X) are listed in Appendix III for 269 objects or 10.3 per cent of the catalogue. In the same manner as for the (B-V) data the observed colors (U-B)(X) were reduced to X = 0 through equations of the form

$$(U-B)(0) = (U-B)(X) - S(T)(X) \tag{14}$$

approximating the color-aperture relations over the useful range (-1 < X < 0) with the following coefficients

TYPE	E	I0,S0	S1,S2	S3,S4	S5
S(T)	-0.10	-0.12	-0.15	-0.18	-0.20

TYPE	S6	S7	S8	S9	I9
S(T)	-0.10	-0.05	+0.05	+0.10	+0.14

Colors observed with X < -1, i.e. A < 0.1 D(0), were not used to avoid excessive extrapolation; however, these colors are listed in Appendix III. The values of (U-B)(0) listed in column 22 are the simple arithmetic means of the individual (U-B)(0) so derived, except for source L where the mean is weighted by the number of observations. For NGC 224 and 598 the integrated (U-B) was derived from the detailed surface photometry (de Vaucouleurs 1958b, 1959e). In a few cases, such as NGC 4051, 4151, 4156, where the color-aperture relation is clearly abnormal (usually because of strong nuclear emission), the corrected color was derived by graphical interpolation or extrapolation of the observed color trend. Altogether (U-B)(0) data are listed for 253 objects or only 9.7 per cent of the catalogue. There is clearly a need for more observations of this useful index; such observations are in progress at McDonald Observatory.

3.6. Velocities.

a) Mean Observed Velocities (Column 23, line 1).

The accidental and systematic errors of galaxy red shift measurements have been investigated by Holmberg (1961), Page (1961) and G. and A. de Vaucouleurs (1963). The latter two investigations were used as the basis for the reduction to a homogeneous system. After excluding all velocities possibly affected by rotational motions as indicated in the Notes, weighted means were formed with weights w = $(100/\sigma)^2$, where the standard errors are computed as explained in section 3.6,b. The sources are listed in Table 12.

b) Weights (Column 23, line 2)

Following the precepts of Page (1961) and de Vaucouleurs (1963) the mean errors σ(in km sec^{-1}) or weights w = $(100/\sigma)^2$ of observed velocities were computed as follows:

TABLE 12. SOURCES OF VELOCITY DATA

CODE	SOURCE	No.	REF.
A	Lowell 1925	41	(1)
B	Mt. Wilson 1956	583	(2)
C	Lick (1) 1956, 1960	300+22	(2,3)
D	Lick (2) 1962	92	(4)
E	McDonald (1) 1952, 1961	41+29	(5,6)
F	McDonald (2) 1959-63	52	(7)
G	McDonald (3) 1963	1	(8)
H	Mt. Stromlo 1961	11	(9,10)
I	Radcliffe 1952-61	10	(11,12)
J	Haute Provence 1961	6	(13)
K	Mt. Wilson-Palomar 1960-63	29	(14,15,16,17)
L	Mt. Stromlo 1964	19	(18)
M	Radcliffe 1963	34	(19)
R	21 cm 1963	28	(20)

REFERENCES. (1) G. Strömberg, *Ap.J.*, 61, 352, 1925; zero point correction: + 67 km sec^{-1}). (2) M. L. Humason, N. U. Mayall and A. R. Sandage, *A.J.*, 61, 97, 1956. (3) J. L. Lovasich, N. U. Mayall, J. Neyman, and E. Scott., *Proc. Fourth Berkeley Symp. on Mathematical Statistics and Probability*, Univ. of California Press, vol. III, 187-227, 1961. (4) N. U. Mayall and A. de Vaucouleurs, *A.J.*, 67, 360, 1962. (5) T. page, *Ap.J.*, 116, 63, 1952; O. Struve, *P.A.S.P.*, 52, 40, 1940. (6) T. Page, *Proc. Fourth Berkeley Symp. on Mathematical Statistics and Probability*, Univ. of California Press, vol. III, 277-306, 1961. (7) G. R. Burbidge, E. M. Burbidge *et al.*, 1959-1963, *Ap.J.*, 129, 271; 130, 12, 26, 629, 739; 131, 282, 549; 132, 30, 640, 654, 661; 133, 726, 814; 134, 232, 237, 244, 248, 874; 135, 366; 136, 119, 128, 339, 704; 137, 376, 1022; 138, 375, 873. (8) G. and A. de Vaucouleurs, *Ap.J.*, 137, 363, 1963. (9) G. and A. de Vaucouleurs, *Mem. R.A.S.*, 68, 69, 1961. (10) G. de Vaucouleurs, *Ap. J.*, 131, 265, 1960; 133, 405, 1961. (11) D. S. Evans, *Observatory*, 72, 164, 1952, *M.N.R.A.S.*, 116, 659, 1956, D. S. Evans *et al.*, *M.N. Ast. Soc. South Africa*, 17, 137, 1958; 20, 64, 1961. (12) M. W. Feast, A. D. Thackeray and A. J. Wesselink, *M.N.R.A.S.*, 122, 433, 1961. (13) R. Duflot-Augarde, *Comptes Rendus*, 253, 224, 1961. (14) J. L. Greenstein, *Ap.J.*, 133, 335, 1961; 135, 679, 1962. (15) R. Minkowski, *Ap.J.*, 130, 1028, 1959. *A. J.*, 66, 558, 1961. (16) G. Munch, *P.A.S.P.*, 71, 101, 1959. (17) F. Zwicky and M. L. Humason, *P.A.S.P.*, 72, 108, 1960; 73, 185, 1961; *Ap.J.*, 132, 627, 1960; 133, 794, 804, 1961. (18) R. Shobbrook, *Australian Nat. Univ. Thesis*, Canberra, 1964. (19) D. S. Evans, *M. N. Ast. Soc. South Africa*, 22, 140, 1963. (20) E. Epstein, *Harvard Univ. Thesis*, Cambridge, 1963.

Source A: σ = 100, or 150 if value marked (:), or 200 if marked (::).

Source B: the "estimated error" as given by Humason was taken as σ.

Source C: $w = \Sigma_j \left[(\sigma_m^2 + \sigma_p^2) \Big/ \left(\dfrac{\sigma_m^2}{w_s w_j} + \sigma_p^2 \right) \right]$, where w_s is the combined (emulsion + slit width) weighting factor, as given by Page (1961, Table 6), w_j the sum of the line weights in the jth spectrum as listed by Mayall (Humason et al., 1956, Table V), σ_m = 83 (for w_s = 1), and σ_p = 46. The range of σ values so computed is about 30 to 100 in Mayall's list (Lick 1).

Source D: same as C, except that the Lick (2) w_j's were multiplied by 2 to make them consistent with the weighting system used in Lick (1). The average ratio of the p.e.'s listed in Lick (2) from internal evidence to the σ's so computed is 0.59 vs. 0.67 expected; the agreement is satisfactory. The range of σ values in the Lick (2) list is about 40 to 140.

Source E: Page's (1961) list of pairs gives only the mean velocities $\overline{V}$ and velocity differences ΔV with their weights w_V and w_Δ; the weights of the individual velocities cannot be derived separately and the same value of σ was assigned to both members of a pair, through the relation

$$\sigma^2 = \frac{(104)^2}{w_v} + \frac{(45)^2}{w_\Delta}$$

The range of σ's so computed is about 30 to 170.

Source F: there is not enough overlap with the other data for a detailed estimate of errors; by analogy with source E (using the same spectrograph) values of σ ranging from 30 to 100 were adopted depending on the number of plates and lines measured.

Source G: only one galaxy (NGC 4631, σ = 21) was published prior to 1964; this new series of red shift observations in progress at McDonald Observatory was coded for future reference.

Source H: values of σ ranging from 15 to 140 were estimated from the published average deviation with allowance for plate dispersion, number of plates and lines measured. The velocity of the Large Cloud (A0524) at the optical center of the bar (5^h24^m, -69°8) was taken as +259 ± 5 after de Vaucouleurs (1960).

Source I: A value of σ = 50 was assumed more or less arbitrarily. The velocities of the Small Cloud (A0051) and of the Large Cloud at the optical centers were taken as +166 ± 3 and +260 ± 2 after (Feast *et al.* 1961).

Source J: values of σ ranging from 10 to 25 were adopted from the published estimated errors.

Source K: values of σ ranging from 10 to 100 were adopted from the published errors or estimated from dispersion, number of plates and lines.

Source L: the mean errors for unit relative weight derived from the published internal average deviations are σ_a = 73 for absorption lines, and σ_e = 40 for emission lines, then, $w = (100)^2 / [(\sigma_a^2/n_a) + (\sigma_e^2/n_e)]$, if n_a, n_e = number of absorption and emission lines measured. The σ's so computed range from about 20 to 70.

Source M: values of σ ranging from 14 to 100 were estimated depending on the number of absorption and emission lines. Comparison with other sources, mainly Mount Stromlo, gives only weak confirmation of a zero point error of -40 suspected by Evans; the systematic difference (Pretoria minus other source) is -24 for 17 pairs, or + 16 for 14 pairs, rejecting 3 residuals greater than 150 (NGC 1553, 7590). The average deviation ± 88 (n = 17), or ± 68 (n = 14) is consistent with the estimated errors of the series compared. No zero point correction was applied.

Source R: values of σ ranging from 3 to 30 (and in one case, NGC 4631, to 80) were adopted after Epstein (1963). For the Magellanic Clouds + 161 ± 3 and + 276 ± 3 were adopted after Kerr and de Vaucouleurs (1955, 1956).

Altogether systemic velocities are listed for 959 galaxies or 36.9 per cent of the catalogue; weights range from 0.4 for galaxies having poor absorption lines observed with very low dispersion to 4000 for a few galaxies with precise 21-cm data; the average weight is about 12 corresponding to a mean error of 30 km sec^{-1}.

3.7. Photographs.

References to published photographs are coded as shown in Table 13.

TABLE 13. SOURCES OF PHOTOGRAPHS

CODE	SOURCES
A	(J. E. Keeler), Lick Obs. Publ. vol. VIII, 1908.
B	H. D. Curtis, Lick Obs. Publ., vol. XIII, Part II, 1918.
C	F. G. Pease, Ap.J., 46, 24, 1917 = MWC No. 132.
D	F. G. Pease, Ap.J., 51, 276, 1920 = MWC No. 186.
E	C. C. L. Gregory, Helwan Obs. Bull., No. 22, 219, 1921.
F	G. de Vaucouleurs, Mem. Commonwealth Obs., No. 13, 1956.
G	G. and A. de Vaucouleurs, Mem. R.A.S., vol. 68, p. 69, 1961.
H	D. S. Evans, Cape Atlas of Southern Galaxies, 1957.
I	D. S. Evans, Vistas in Astronomy, vol. 2, p. 1553, 1956.
J	W. W. Morgan and N. U. Mayall, P.A.S.P., 69, 291, 1957.
K	W. W. Morgan, P.A.S.P., 70, 364, 1958.
L	G. de Vaucouleurs, Handbuch d. Phys., 53, 275, 1959.
M	G. de Vaucouleurs, Ap.J., 127, 487, 1958.
P	A. Sandage, The Hubble Atlas of Galaxies, Carnegie Inst. of Washington, Publ. 618, 1961.

4. Explanation of Notes and Appendices

The Notes to the catalogue collect all information not presentable in tabular form as follows:

1) abbreviated description of object mainly from our inspection of original reflector plates; the NGC-style abbreviations are explained in Table 14; it is similar to that used in the Mt. Stromlo survey (de Vaucouleurs 1956a). This description includes also dimension data for the nucleus or nuclear region, for the lens, if any, for inner and outer rings (r), (R), where present, and for outer irregular extensions. Membership in pairs whether optical or physical is noted by P(a) for no apparent interaction, P(b) for mild interaction, e.g. tidal distorsion of outer parts, P(c) for strong interaction, e.g. collision or disrupted main bodies, and with corresponding identification in Holmberg's catalogue (1937).

2) bibliographical references additional to the standard sources of tabulated material, in particular to monographs, surveys, special photographs, detailed isophotometry and luminosity distribution studies, integrated magnitudes and colors, polarization, star counts in resolved systems, clusters, HII regions, spectral analysis and spectrum description, spectroscopic rotation and rotational mass estimates, continuum radio emission, 21-cm (HI) emission, novae and supernovae, etc. The bibliography is substantially complete for original research papers published prior to January 1, 1964. Reviews and semi-popular papers or books were included only occasionally. For the Magellanic Clouds, only the more recent and complete surveys and reviews are listed in which complete references to earlier papers are given.

TABLE 14. ABBREVIATIONS

abs.	absorption
anom.	anomalous
anon.	anonymous
asym.	asymmetrical
att.	attached
B	bright
bet.	between
branch.	branching (or branches)
br.	brightness

(continued)

cent.	center or central
cl.	cluster
class.	classification
coll.	colliding
coord.	coordinates
comp.	component (or companion)
compl.	complex
condens.	condensation (or condensed)
corr.	correction or corrected
dble	double
def.	defined
diff.	diffuse
desc.	description
dim.	dimensions
dist.	distance
dk	dark
e	extremely
elong.	elongated
emiss.	emission
envel.	envelope
extens.	extensions
f	following
F	faint
filam.	filamentary
gal.	galaxy (or galaxies)
glob.	globular
Heid. 9	Heidelberg Veröff., vol. 9, 1926.
hexag.	hexagonal
identif.	identification (or identified)
inv.	involved
irreg.	irregular
isol.	isolated
L	large
m.	much (or many)
M	middle (or in the middle)
mag.	magnitude
mark.	markings
matt.	matter
n	north
N	nucleus
narr.	narrow
nf	north-following
np	north preceding
neb.	nebulous or nebulosity
obj.	object
out.	outer
p	preceding
part.	partly
patt.	pattern
pec.	peculiar
poor.	poorly
prob.	probably
P. w.	pair with
P(a)	non-interacting pair
P(b)	interacting pair
P(c)	colliding or strongly interacting pair
(r)	inner ring
(R)	outer ring
reg.	region (or regular)
rej.	rejected
res.	resolved (or resolution)
resid.	residual
s	small (in description), or south
sf	south following
sp	south preceding

sev.	several
sh.	short
spir.	spiral
struct.	structure
SN	supernova
superp.	superposed
surf.	surface
v	very
vel.	velocity
w	with
*	star
DI	Dreyer's corr. in NGC
DII	— — in IC I
DIII	— — in IC II
DIV	— — in M.N., 73, 37, 1912.

The notes also call attention to corrections to NGC, Harvard 88,2, or Mt. Stromlo 13 coordinates; to corrections to revised morphological type if it is significantly different from de Vaucouleurs (1963); to probable misidentifications in earlier catalogues or papers; to special procedures used in the reduction of diameters, magnitudes or colors for some objects.

In the field of NGC 4341, 4342, 4343 we have adopted, after consultation with Dr. N. U. Mayall, the identifications marked in Fig. 8. There has been much confusion in this field originating in the NGC and compounded by inconsistencies in the identifications used at various times at Heidelberg and Mt. Wilson. We are not certain that we have succeeded in sorting out the earlier identifications in all cases.

All Shapley-Ames objects, except three, are included in the present catalogue; the three exceptions are NGC 2149, found to be a star + galactic nebulosity (N. U. Mayall, private communication to H. Shapley, 1952), NGC 643, an outlying cluster of the Small Magellanic Cloud (de Vaucouleurs 1957b), and NGC 6026, a galactic planetary nebula (de Vaucouleurs 1955).

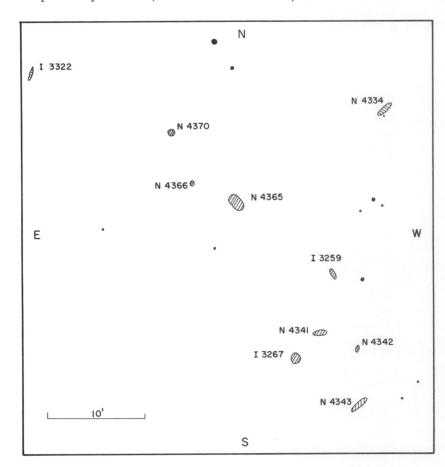

Fig. 8. Identifications in field of NGC 4341-42-43.

Several of the NGC identifications of HA 88,2 were corrected and in particular

For NGC 1048	2:38.2,	−8°45'	read NGC 1042	2:38.0,	−8°40'
— NGC 1270	3:15.6,	+41°18'	— NGC 1275	3:16.5,	+41°20'
— NGC 4160	—	—	— NGC 4183	—	—
— New 2	12:32.9,	−39°31'	— NGC 4507	12:32.9,	−39°38'
— NGC 4872	12:57.2,	+28°43'	— NGC 4889	12:57.2,	+28°15' = N4884

The Appendices list the following information:

Appendix I. Integrated Magnitudes in B System.

Blocks of 9 digits give $X = \log A/D(0)$, where A is the field aperture, $D(0)$ the "face on" diameter, in hundredths; source coded as in Table 10; B magnitude in hundredths; example:

$$\text{NGC 16: } X = +0.08, \quad \text{source C, } B(X) = 13.20;$$
$$X = +0.38, \quad \text{source C, } B(X) = 13.15.$$

(Source C is Pettit 1954).

An asterisk (*) after the B value denotes lower weight in the original magnitude measure, or an uncertainty in the reduction to the B system.

Where $\log D(0)$ is not known, the actual diameter of the photometer field aperture is given in minutes of arc with decimal point shown, thus NGC 72A has A = 0.'61, source C, B(A) = 15.80.

When two galaxies in a close pair were in the aperture this is recorded by a dot (period) after the NGC number, and since no $D(0)$ can be attached, A itself is given as above; thus after separate entries for NGC 750, and NGC 751 measured through small apertures, the catalogue gives NGC 750 + 751 measured together through a larger aperture:

$$\text{NGC 750. A = 1.'15, source C, B(A) = 13.25; etc.}$$

Where no X or A value is given an asterisk is entered instead, and the magnitude is the total or asymptotic value derived by integration of detailed isophotes; examples are NGC 224, 598. For the Magellanic Clouds, see Notes.

Appendix II. Integrated Colors in (B-V) System.

Blocks of 9 digits give $X = \log A/D(0)$ in hundredths (or A in minutes and hundredths with decimal point), source, color index $(B-V)(X)$ in hundredths (always positive). Special cases noted as in Appendix I.

Example: NGC 16, X = +0.08, source C, $(B-V)(X)$ = +0.96; etc.

Appendix III. Integrated Colors in (U-B) System.

Same scheme as Appendix II; except that sign of $(U-B)(X)$ is shown where negative (zero in column if positive). Special cases as in Appendix I.

Example: NGC 125, X = −0.06, source L, $(U-B)(X)$ + 0.37.

Appendix IV. Listing of Right Ascension.

A list of all NGC, IC and anonymous objects in order of (1950) right ascension. Gives RA and D. Pairs may be more easily identified from this list.

LIST OF MESSIER OBJECTS

Messier No.	NGC No.	Messier No.	NGC No.
31	224	82	3034
32	221	83	5236
33	598	84	4374
49	4472	85	4382
51	5194	86	4406
58	4579	87	4486
59	4621	88	4501
60	4649	89	4552
61	4303	90	4569
63	5055	94	4736
64	4826	95	3351
65	3623	96	3368
66	3627	98	4192
74	628	99	4254
77	1068	100	4321
81	3031	101	5457

FINDING LIST OF VORONTSOV-VELYAMINOV INTERACTING GALAXIES

VV	NGC IC,A	VV	NGC IC,A	VV	NGC IC,A	VV	NGC IC,A
1	5194-5	67	7727	150	A1130A-B	247	6621-22
5	7752-3	68	7393	166	0070	249	3994-5
7	5829	73	4618	172	A1129	251	3664
8	3981	75	3509	175	0741-2	252	3447-47A
9	2535-6	76	4496A-B	188	4438	261	4194
11	3432	77	5613-4-5	189	0750-1	280	7625
14	3445	78	1487	193	0382-3	288	7317-18-19-20
19	5278-9	79	2623	201	4782-3	297	6872-I4970
21	5426-7	81	0274-5	206	4647-49	304	6769-70
22	3656	82	2944	207	0507-8	307	3187-90
30	4485-90	86	6052	209	3226-7	308	3627-28
31	3921	95	3239	210	5544-45	310	5403
33	5216-18	104	4190	213	6041	313	4809-10
43	I3481-83	109	A1444	217	0942-3	329	7679-82
48	5394-95	115	6027A-D	219	4567-8	334	1241-42-43
50	2798-99	116	A0937A-B-C-D	224	4676,I819-20	338	0672-I1727
51	7714-15	117	2444-45	228	3786-88	344	5457-74
55	5257-58	118	3690-I694	231	0520	350	3799-800
56	4651	123	A0708	244	5953-4		
65	3256	138	2537	245	4038-9		
66	4027	140	A1447	246	3395-6		

5. Acknowledgements

In the span of 15 years covered by the preparation of this catalogue we have received support and assistance from many people and institutions whose cooperation and hospitality are hereby gratefully acknowledged.

The project was started in 1949 at the Péridier Observatory, Le Houga and at the Institute of Astrophysics in Paris where Mr. P. Griboval assisted in the preparation of the initial card index. The historic I. Roberts plate collection was examined by courtesy of Prof. P. Couderc, Chief of the "Carte du Ciel" office at Paris Observatory. The survey of southern galaxies with the 30-in. and 74-in. reflectors of Mount Stromlo Observatory between 1951 and 1956 was made possible by invitation of Prof. (now Sir Richard) Woolley and a Research Fellowship of the Australian National University. The revised classification of northern galaxies in the Crossley plate collection by kind permission of former Director C. D. Shane and Dr. N. U. Mayall at the Lick Observatory in the summer of 1955 was supported by the University of California and by a travel grant of Commission 38 of the International Astronomical Union when the late Prof. F. J. M. Stratton was Chairman. The major source of revised types for northern galaxies was found in the 200-in., 100-in., and 60-in. plate collections of the Mount Wilson and Palomar Observatories generously made available by Director I. S. Bowen and by Dr. A. R. Sandage in the summer of 1957 during a period as Guest Investigator supported by a travel grant from Lowell Observatory. The Boyden Observatory 60-in. plate collection was examined at Harvard Observatory in 1958-59 by permission of Prof. D. H. Menzel. Dr. E. Epstein and Dr. R. Shobbrook kindly made available data from their dissertations in advance of publication.

Photoelectric observations with the 20-in. reflector of Lowell Observatory in 1957-58, and the 36-in. reflector of McDonald Observatory since 1960 were started with the advice and encouragement of Dr. H. L. Johnson. The investigation of diameter data at Harvard Observatory was supported by the National Science Foundation as part of the publication grant for this Catalogue. The new observations and reduction of older magnitude and color data were supported in part by the National Science Foundation and in part by the Research Institute of the University of Texas. The study of accidental and systematic errors in galaxy velocities was supported by the Office of Naval Research as part of the current red-shift program of McDonald Observatory.

The lengthy and tedious statistical analysis and extensive computations required for the reduction of the raw data to homogeneous systems was greatly alleviated through the skillful cooperation of Dr. A. T. Young who programmed and processed the diameter data reductions with the IBM 7090 computer at Harvard Observatory in 1960-61. Messrs. J. Copeland, E. McDonald, J. Vallée, and G. Malik programmed and processed most of the coordinates, magnitudes, colors and velocity data with the CDC 1604 Computer at the University of Texas. The Director of the Computing Center Prof. D. M. Young generously provided much free machine time and Mr. C. B. Williams gave every facility to produce the near perfect listings required for the photo-offset reproduction of the tabular material of the catalogue and appendices.

Apart from the authors, two persons have carried the main burden of keeping order and continuity in a project involving at times a dozen different collaborators and the handling of some one hundred thousand separate pieces of information and tens of thousands of punched cards. At Harvard Observatory (1958-60) Mrs. Carol Smith gave able and devoted assistance throughout the lengthy preparation of the raw input data prior to punching and in checking the punched cards. At the University of Texas (1961-1963) Mrs. Judith Weiss contributed much to the final stages of preparation of the catalogue for publication, not only by the quality of her typescript of the extensive Notes also reproduced by photo off-set, but even more through her efficient participation in the large amount of card handling, processing and proofreading required to obtain listings of the 70,000 odd tabular entries as nearly error-free as man and machine can contrive to produce.

We are much obliged to Dr. F. Kerr for his careful reading of the manuscript of this introduction and several helpful suggestions for improvements.

It is a pleasure to thank the University of Texas Press for its excellent cooperation and for the quality of production of this volume, which was subsidized in part by a Publication Grant from the National Science Foundation.

General References

Blaauw, A., Gum, C. S., Pawsey, J. L. and Westerhout, G. 1960, "The New I.A.U. System of Galactic Coordinates (1958 Revision)," *Monthly Notices R. Ast. Soc.*, **121**, 123.

Dreyer, J. L. E. 1878, *Trans. R. Irish Acad.*, **XXVI**, p. 381.

—— 1888, "New General Catalogue of Nebulae and Star Clusters," *Memoirs R. Ast. Soc.*, **XLIX**, Part I.

—— 1895, "Index Catalogue . . .," *Memoirs R. Ast. Soc.*, **LI**, p. 185.

—— 1908, "Second Index Catalogue . . .," *Memoirs R. Ast. Soc.*, **LIX**, p. 105.

Epstein, E. 1963, Harvard Univ. Thesis (unpublished).

Feast, M. W., Thackeray, A. D. and Wesselink, A. J. 1961, "Analysis of Radial Velocities of Stars and Nebulae in the Magellanic Clouds," *Monthly Notices of the R. Ast. Soc.*, **122**, 433.

Herschel, J. 1864, "A General Catalogue of Nebulae and Star Clusters," *Philosophical Transactions*, **CXIX**, p. 27.

Holmberg, E. 1937, "A Study of Double and Multiple Galaxies," *Annals Lund Obs.*, No. 6.

—— 1946, "On the Apparent Diameters and the Orientation and Space of Extragalactic Nebulae," *Meddelande Lund Ast. Obs.*, Ser. II, Nr. 117.

—— 1958, "A Photographic Photometry of Extragalactic Nebulae," *Meddelande Lund Ast. Obs.*, Ser. II, Nr. 136.

—— 1961, "A Systematic Effect in the Redshifts of Extragalactic Nebulae," *Arkiv f. Astronomi*, Bd. 2, Nr. 51 = Medd. Upsala Ast. Obs., No. 138.

Hubble, E. 1926, "Extragalactic Nebulae," *The Astrophysical Journal*, **66**, 321 = Mt. Wilson Cont., No. 324.

Humason, M. L., Mayall, N. U. and Sandage, A. R. 1956, "Redshifts and Magnitudes of Extragalactic Nebulae," *The Astronomical Journal*, **61**, 97, = Lick Obs. Bull., No. 542.

Humason, M. L. and Wahlquist, H. D. 1955, "Solar Motion with Respect to the Local Group of Nebulae," *The Astronomical Journal*, **60**, 254.

Kerr, F. J. and Vaucouleurs, G. de 1955, "Rotation and Other Motions of the Magellanic Clouds from Radio Observations," *Australian Journal of Physics*, **8**, 508.

—— 1956, "The Masses of the Magellanic Clouds from Radio Observations," *Australian Journal of Physics*, **9**, 90.

Morgan, W. W. 1958, "A preliminary Classification of the Forms of Galaxies According to their Stellar Population. I.," *Publications of the Astron. Soc. of the Pacific*, **70**, 364.

—— 1959, "A preliminary Classification of the Forms of Galaxies According to Their Stellar Population. II.," *Publications of the Astron. Soc. of the Pacific*, **71**, 394.

Ohlsson, J. 1932, "Tables for the Conversion of Equatorial Coordinates into Galactic Coordinates," Annals Lund Obs., vol. 3.

Page, Th. 1961, "Average Masses of the Double Galaxies," *Proc. Fourth Berkeley Symp. on Mathematical Statistics and Probability*, **III**, p. 277.

Pettit, E. 1954, "Magnitudes and Color Indices of Extragalactic Nebulae Determined Photoelectrically," *The Astrophysical Journal*, **120**, 413.

Reinmuth, K. 1926, "Die Herschel-Nebel," *Veröffentlichugen. . .Sternwarte zu Heidelberg*, Bd. 9.

Sandage, A. R. 1961, *The Hubble Atlas of Galaxies*, (Carnegie Institution of Washington) Publ. No. 618.

Shapley, H. and Ames, A. 1932, "A Survey of the External Galaxies Brighter than the Thirteenth Magnitude," *Annals of the Harvard College Obs.*, **88**, No. 2.

van den Bergh, S. 1960, "A Reclassification of the Northern Shapley-Ames Galaxies," *Publications of the D. Dunlap Obs.*, **II**, Nr. 6.

Vaucouleurs, G. de 1953a, "A Revision of the Harvard Survey of Bright Galaxies," Australian National Univ. Mimeogram.

—— 1953b, "Evidence for a Local Supergalaxy," *The Astronomical Journal*, **58**, 29.

—— 1955, "NGC 6026: A New Planetary Nebula," *Publications of the Astron. Soc. of the Pacific*, **67**, 418.

—— 1956a, Survey of Bright Galaxies South of −35° Declination," *Memoirs of the Commonwealth (Mount Stromlo) Observatory*, **III**, No. 13.

—— 1956b, "Photographic Magnitudes of the Brighter External Galaxies," *Astronomical Journal*, **61**, 430.

—— 1957a, "Etudes sur les Galaxies Brillantes, I. Magnitudes Photographiques," *Annales de l'Obs. du Houga*, **II**, Part 1.

—— 1957b, "NGC 643: A New Outlying Cluster of the Small Magellanic Cloud," *Publications of the Astron. Soc. of the Pacific*, **69**, 252.

—— 1958a, "Further Evidence for a Local Super-Cluster of Galaxies: Rotation and Expansion," *The Astronomical Journal*, **63**, 253.

—— 1958b, "Photoelectric Photometry of the Andromeda Nebula in the U,B,V System," *The Astrophysical Journal*, **128**, 465.

—— 1959a, "Photographic Dimensions of the Brighter Galaxies," *Astronomical Journal*, **64**, 397.

—— 1959b, "Etudes sur les Galaxies Brillantes, II. Dimensions Photographiques," *Annales de l'Obs. du Houga*, **II**, Part 2.

—— 1959c, "The Local Super-Cluster of Galaxies," *Astronomicheskii Zhurnal*, **36**, 977 = Soviet Astronomy 1960, 3, 897.

—— 1959d, "Classification and Morphology of External Galaxies," *Handbuch der Physik*, (Springer-Verlag: Berlin), **53**, 275.

—— 1959e, "Photoelectric Photometry of Messier 33 in the U,B,V System," *The Astrophysical Journal*, **130**, 728.

—— 1960a, "Rotation and Mass of the Large Magellanic Cloud," *The Astrophysical Journal*, **131**, 265.

—— 1960b, "Magnitudes and Colors of the Magellanic Clouds," *The Astrophysical Journal*, **131**, 574.

—— 1961, "Integrated Colors of Bright Galaxies in the U,B,V System," *Astrophysical Journal Suppl. No. 48*, **5**, p. 233.

—— 1962, "Classification of Galaxies by Form, Luminosity and Color," *Problems of Extragalactic Research*, I.A.U. Symp. No. 15, (Edit. G. C. McVittie), (Macmillan: New York) pp. 3-21.

—— 1963, "Revised Classification of 1500 Bright Galaxies," *Astrophysical Journal, Suppl. No. 74*, **8**, p. 31.

Vaucouleurs, G. and A. de 1961, "Classification and Radial Velocities of Bright Galaxies," *Memoirs of the R. Ast. Soc.*, **LXVIII**, p. 69.

—— 1963, "Search for Systematic Errors in Galaxy Redshift Measurements," *The Astronomical Journal*, **68**, 96.

Vorontsov-Velyaminov, B. A. 1959, *Atlas and Catalogue of Interacting Galaxies* (Sternberg Institute, Moscow Univ.: Moscow).

Wyatt, S. P. and Brown, F. G. 1955, "Position Angles and Shapes of Galaxies in Cetus," *The Astronomical Journal*, **60**, 415.

Zwicky, F., Herzog, E. and Wild, P. 1961, *"Catalogue of Galaxies and of Clusters of Galaxies*, (Calif. Inst. of Technology).

CATALOGUE

NGC (IC, A)	RA (1950) 100 P	Dec 100 P	L^I B^I	L^{II} B^{II}	SGL SGB	Rev. type (S) DDO (T, L)	Yerkes (1) Yerkes (2)	Hu-San Ho	log D w	log R w	log D(O)	S (D,R)
(1)	(2)	(3)	(4)	(5)	(6)	(7)	(8)	(9)	(10)	(11)	(12)	(13)
N0001	0 4.7	27 26	79.82	111.11	321.8				.96	.00	.96	AB
	5.1	33	−34.10	−34.14	17.6				.96	.96		
N0002	0 4.7	27 24	79.81	111.10	321.8				1.08	.20	1.00	AB
	5.1	33	−34.13	−34.18	17.6				1.28	1.28		
N0007	0 5.8	−30 11	340.72	14.05	265.3				1.40			F
	5.1	33	−81.62	−80.14	1.9				1.05			
N0008	0 6.1	23 34	79.36	110.50	317.9				.91	.00	.91	AB
	5.1	33	−37.96	−37.99	16.6				.83	.83		
N0009	0 6.3	23 33	79.41	110.55	317.9				1.16	.30	1.04	AB
	5.1	33	−37.99	−38.02	16.6				1.49	1.49		
N0010	0 6.1	−34 9	318.18	354.12	261.6	.S....$H030			1.36	.25	1.26	F
	5.1	33	−79.91	−78.59	0.6				1.49	1.49		
N0012	0 6.1	4 20	73.24	103.29	298.5	.S....*R020			1.21	.08	1.17	AH
	5.1	33	−56.75	−56.61	12.4				1.74	1.74		
N0013	0 6.2	33 9	81.31	112.80	327.8	.L.....R020			1.43	.66	1.17	H
	5.2	33	−28.51	−28.59	18.1				1.30	1.30		
N0016	0 6.5	27 27	80.30	111.59	321.9	.LX.-./W100 E 3	B *K		1.09	.28	.98	AKW
	5.2	33	−34.15	−34.21	17.2				2.49	2.49		
N0020	0 7.0	33 1	81.47	112.96	327.7	.E....*R020			.96	.00	.96	AH
	5.2	33	−28.66	−28.75	17.9				.70	.70		
N0021	0 7.8	32 51	81.63	113.11	327.6				.98	.16	.92	H
	5.2	33	−28.86	−28.95	17.7				.63	.63		
N0023	0 7.3	25 39	80.15	111.37	320.1	.SBS1..P200 S T -*	SBP*G	S 3	1.16	.19	1.08	AHZ
	5.2	33	−35.96	−36.01	16.7				4.22	4.22		
N0024	0 7.4	−25 15	15.47	43.64	270.1	.SAS5..W100 S 3 5			1.65	.60	1.40	DEFKW
	5.1	33	−81.78	−80.44	3.2				11.21	11.21		
N0026	0 7.8	25 34	80.27	111.48	320.0	.SAT2..P200	S AF		1.15	.11	1.10	AHZ
	5.2	33	−36.06	−36.11	16.6				4.11	4.11		
N0029	0 8.2	33 4	81.77	113.25	327.8	.SX.3*.L036			1.22	.34	1.08	AHLU
	5.2	33	−28.67	−28.76	17.6				3.95	3.95		
N0045	0 11.4	−23 27	29.63	55.88	272.1	.SAS8..P200 S 6 8	S F	S 5	1.93	.16	1.87	EFKMZ
	5.1	33	−81.80	−80.64	2.9				16.72	16.72		
N0048	0 11.5	47 58	84.61	116.54	343.5				.94	.15	.89	R
	5.2	33	−13.99	−14.16	18.4				1.29	1.29		
N0051	0 12.0	47 59	84.70	116.63	343.5				.80	.18	.73	R
	5.3	33	−13.98	−14.16	18.3				1.05	1.05		
N0055	0 12.5	−39 30	295.84	332.75	256.9	.SBS9*/S030	I A		2.48	.79	2.16	FGTI
	5.0	33	−76.69	−75.72	−2.4				17.78	17.78		
N0067	0 15.7	29 48	83.09	114.46	324.7				.90	.00	.90	AB
	5.2	33	−32.12	−32.25	15.6				.84	.84		
N0068	0 15.8	29 48	83.11	114.48	324.7	.L.....W			1.28	.14	1.22	LS
	5.2	33	−32.12	−32.25	15.6				2.36	1.59		
N0069	0 15.8	29 46	83.11	114.48	324.6	.LB....W			.88	.00	.88	AB
	5.2	33	−32.15	−32.28	15.5				.76	.76		
N0070	0 15.9	29 49	83.14	114.51	324.7				.93	.00	.93	AB
	5.2	33	−32.11	−32.24	15.5				.90	.90		
N0071	0 15.9	29 48	83.14	114.51	324.7	.E.2...W			.90	.00	.90	AB
	5.2	33	−32.12	−32.25	15.5				.84	.84		
N0072	0 15.9	29 46	83.13	114.50	324.6	.SB.2..W			.93	.00	.93	AB
	5.2	33	−32.16	−32.29	15.5				.90	.90		
N0072A	0 16.0	29 45	83.15	114.52	324.6	.E.4..*W						
	5.2	33	−32.17	−32.30	15.5							
N0080	0 18.6	22 5	82.74	113.80	316.9	.L.....W			1.00	.00	1.00	A
	5.2	33	−39.86	−39.97	13.5				.54	.54		
N0083	0 18.8	22 9	82.81	113.87	317.0	.E.0...W			.94	.00	.94	AL
	5.2	33	−39.80	−39.92	13.5				.91	.91		
N0095	0 19.6	10 12	80.85	111.27	305.2	.SXT5P.W060 S 5 K *	S F		1.18	.10	1.14	AKMQ
	5.2	33	−51.67	−51.73	10.6				4.03	4.03		
N0100	0 21.4	16 13	82.69	113.46	311.2				1.48	.50	1.28	B
	5.2	33	−45.76	−45.87	11.6				1.21	1.21		
N0105	0 22.7	12 37	82.53	113.10	307.7	.SA.1..W						
	5.2	33	−49.37	−49.48	10.5							
N0120	0 25.0	−1 47	80.05	109.34	293.8	.L....*.H030			1.10			F
	5.1	33	−63.72	−63.75	6.2				1.05			
N0124	0 25.4	−2 5	80.17	109.42	293.6	.SAS5..P200			1.11	.17	1.04	FZ
	5.1	33	−64.03	−64.06	6.0				3.91	3.91		
N0125	0 26.3	2 33	81.98	111.76	298.1	.L.....W			.90	.00	.90	A
	5.1	33	−59.46	−59.54	7.1				.42	.42		
N0127	0 26.6	2 36	82.14	111.92	298.2	.L...*.P200	DSP*K		.85	.00	.85	A
	5.1	33	−59.43	−59.52	7.0				.34	.34		
N0128	0 26.7	2 35	82.18	111.96	298.2	.L...P/P200 E 8	D P K	L 1 P	1.44	.64	1.18	AK
	5.1	33	−59.54	−59.54	7.0				2.61	2.61		
N0131	0 27.1	−33 33	298.54	339.14	263.5	.SBS3*/W100			1.26	.58	1.03	VW
	4.9	33	−83.31	−82.25	−3.4				3.31	3.31		
N0132	0 27.7	1 49	82.50	112.20	297.5	.SXS4..W060			1.26	.18	1.18	AMQ
	5.1	33	−60.24	−60.34	6.5				3.29	3.29		
N0134	0 27.9	−33 32	297.36	338.24	263.5	.SXS4..W100	S F		1.86	.56	1.64	GVW
	4.9	33	−83.40	−82.37	−3.6				7.98	7.98		
N0145	0 29.2	−5 26	81.30	110.01	290.6	.SBS8..P200			1.23	.19	1.15	AZ
	5.1	33	−67.49	−67.53	4.2				3.72	3.72		

NGC (IC, A) (14)	mH / mC (15)	B(O) / w (16)	B'(O) / m'C (17)	S(B) (18)	(B-V)(O) / w (19)	Co(O) (20)	S(C) (21)	(U-B)(O) / w (22)	V / w (23)	Vo / ΔV (24)	S(V) (25)	φr / n (26)	φ(21) (27)	(28)	Photo. (29)
N0001										226					
N0002										225					
N0007										12					
N0008										215					
N0009										215					
N0010										−6					
N0012										156					
N0013										236					
N0016	13.0	13.36	13.00	C	.95	.80	C		3110	3334	B				
	13.22	2.88	12.86		3.75				4.0	224					
N0020										236					
N0021										235					
N0023	12.7	13.12	13.21	C	.81	.63	C		4568	4788	B				P
	13.14	3.17	13.23		5.63				1.0	220					
N0024	12.2														
	12.20		13.94							33					
N0026										219					
N0029										235					
N0045	12.1								450	489	B				LP
	11.21		15.25						11.1	39					
N0048										253					
N0051										253					
N0055	7.8								131	97	HR				FIL
	8.13		13.67						416.0	−34					
N0067										224					
N0068		14.05	14.89	C	.87	.70	C		5787	6011	B				
		0.96			1.88				2.4	224					
N0069		15.75	14.84	C	1.00	.83	C		6637	6861	B				
		2.01			1.88				.4	224					
N0070										224					
N0071		14.62	13.86	C	1.08	.91	C		6591	6815	B				
		3.21			3.75				.4	224					
N0072		14.91	14.30	C	1.06	.89	C		6976	7200	B				
		3.43			3.75				.4	224					
N0072A				C*			C*		6807	7031	B				
									.6	224					
N0080		13.74	13.48	C	1.00	.85	C		5586	5790	B				
		1.72			1.88				1.0	204					
N0083		14.21	13.60	C	1.07	.91	C		6541	6745	B				
		1.86			1.88				.4	204					
N0095	13.1	13.59	14.03	A						167					
	13.29	1.98	13.73												
N0100										185					
N0105				C*			C*			173					
N0120										120					
N0124										119					
N0125		13.83	13.07	C*L	.91	.79	C*L	.33	5289	5425	B				
		5.30			8.30		/L		4.0	136					
N0127		15.43	14.02	L	.96	.85	L	.41	4094	4230	B				P
		3.39			5.40		/L		6.3	136					
N0128	12.9	12.92	13.56	ACL	1.00	.86	CL	.56	4250	4386	B				P
	12.82	5.88	13.46		9.20		/L		4.0	136					
N0131										−16					
N0132										132					
N0134	11.4								1681	1665	C				I
	11.22		14.11						1.9	−16					
N0145										103					

25

NGC (IC, A)	Coordinates					Classification			Diameters			
	RA (1950) 100 P	Dec 100 P	L^I B^I	L^{II} B^{II}	SGL SGB	Rev. type (S) DDO (T,L)	Yerkes (1) Yerkes (2)	Hu-San Ho	log D w	log R w	log D(O)	S (D,R)
(1)	(2)	(3)	(4)	(5)	(6)	(7)	(8)	(9)	(10)	(11)	(12)	(13)
N0147	0 30.4	48 14	87.87	119.81	344.0	.E.5.P.W060	L		1.78	.22	1.70	AKXQ
	5.5	33	-13.99	-14.25	15.3	E 4P	L	E P	3.02	3.02		
N0148	0 31.8	-32 4	297.30	340.61	265.2	.L...$.H030			1.10			F
	4.9	33	-85.08	-84.03	-3.9				1.05			
N0150	0 31.8	-28 5	350.70	21.83	269.0	.SBT3*.W100			1.45	.31	1.32	GW
	5.0	33	-87.62	-86.13	-2.8				3.56	3.56		
N0151	0 31.6	-9 58	81.24	108.94	286.4	.SBR4..P200	S FG		1.51	.32	1.38	AEFKLTZ
	5.1	33	-72.06	-72.09	2.3	S 4 3*		S 5	12.46	12.46		
N0157	0 32.3	-8 40	82.30	110.32	287.7	.SXT4..P200	S AF		1.54	.17	1.47	AEKLXZ
	5.1	33	-70.79	-70.86	2.5	S 5 K - 1	S A	S5	9.14	8.14		
N0160	0 33.4	23 41	87.29	118.42	319.3	RLA.+P.W100			1.36	.20	1.28	ALUW
	5.3	33	-38.54	-38.78	10.5				4.91	4.06		
N0163	0 33.5	-10 24	82.58	110.15	286.1	.E...$.H030			.90	.00	.90	A
	5.1	33	-72.55	-72.61	1.8				.42	.42		
N0165	0 33.9	-10 24	82.91	110.47	286.1	.S...$.H030			1.13	.08	1.10	FL
	5.1	33	-72.56	-72.63	1.7				1.68	1.05		
N0169	0 34.3	23 43	87.56	118.68	319.4	.S..3./L036			1.24	.69	.96	ALU
	5.3	33	-38.52	-38.76	10.3				3.12	2.43		
N0175	0 34.9	-20 12	76.64	98.14	276.8	.SBR2..P200		SBS1	1.26	.06	1.24	DK
	5.0	33	-82.28	-82.11	-1.3	SB3 1	B G		2.38	2.38		
N0178	0 36.6	-14 27	83.79	109.81	282.4	.SBS9..W100			1.28	.23	1.18	KW
	5.0	33	-76.65	-76.73	-.1	P T -*	I P A *		2.29	2.29		
N0182	0 35.7	2 28	86.59	116.35	298.7	.S...1..W /			1.40	.18	1.32	A
	5.1	33	-59.76	-59.96	4.8				1.08	1.08		
N0185	0 36.1	48 4	88.85	120.77	344.0	.E+3.P.W060	E P	E P	1.73	.07	1.70	AKLXQ
	5.5	33	-14.19	-14.48	14.3	E 0*	DE GK	E P	4.03	2.94		
N0191	0 36.4	-9 17	85.23	113.09	287.4	.S...$.H030			1.16	.07	1.13	ABF
	5.1	33	-71.50	-71.64	1.4				2.88	2.88		
N0194	0 36.8	2 46	87.16	116.96	299.0	.E.1...W			.89	.00	.89	AL
	5.1	33	-59.48	-59.69	4.6				.83	.83		
N0195	0 37.1	-9 28	85.74	113.54	287.2	.SB..$.H030			.88	.13	.83	AF
	5.1	33	-71.70	-71.85	1.2				1.40	1.40		
N0198	0 36.9	2 32	87.19	116.96	298.8	.SAR5..W100			1.14	.01	1.14	ALW
	5.1	33	-59.71	-59.92	4.5				2.31	1.68		
N0200	0 37.1	2 37	87.30	117.08	298.9	.SBS4..W100			1.32	.38	1.17	ALW
	5.1	33	-59.63	-59.85	4.5				2.94	2.94		
N0205	0 37.6	41 25	88.97	120.71	337.2	.E+5.P.....	E P	E+ P	2.00	.29	1.88	ABEHKLR SX
	5.4	33	-20.85	-21.13	13.1	E 6*T -*	D G	E P	19.39	19.39		
N0210	0 38.0	-14 9	85.35	111.50	282.8	.SXS3..P200		S 3	1.68	.18	1.61	AFKMZ
	5.0	33	-76.38	-76.50	-.3	S 2 1	SDP*GK		13.35	13.35		
N0214	0 38.7	25 14	88.88	120.07	321.1	.SXR5..W100	S G		1.20	.15	1.14	AKW
	5.3	33	-37.03	-37.31	9.7	S 3 1			4.25	4.25		
N0221	0 40.0	40 36	89.44	121.16	336.5	.E.2.......	E3 K	E	1.56	.12	1.51	ABEHKLS XY
	5.5	33	-21.67	-21.97	12.5	E 2	E3 K		9.61	9.61		
N0224	0 40.0	41 0	89.45	121.17	336.9	.SAS3......	S K	S 3	3.20	.49	3.00	ABKT
	5.5	33	-21.27	-21.57	12.6	S 3 2	S GK	S3				
N0227	0 40.1	-1 48	88.60	117.86	294.8	.E.4...W			1.09	.13	1.04	AK
	5.1	33	-64.07	-64.31	2.6	E 2*			1.02	1.02		
N0237	0 40.9	-0 24	89.09	118.54	296.2	.SXT6..W100			1.15	.19	1.08	KW
	5.1	33	-62.66	-62.92	2.8	S 5 3*			3.20	3.20		
N0244	0 43.3	-15 51	90.93	116.18	281.5				.90	.00	.90	A
	5.0	33	-78.13	-78.38	-2.0				.42	.42		
N0245	0 43.7	-1 59	90.66	119.92	294.9	.SAT3P*W100			1.14	.05	1.12	AKW
	5.1	33	-64.26	-64.55	1.6	I *	I P A *		2.67	2.67		
N0247	0 44.6	-21 1	94.22	113.84	276.6	.SXS7..W100	SI *A		2.32	.45	2.14	EFGKLUX W
	5.0	33	-83.27	-83.54	-3.7	S 6 7		S6	25.80	25.80		
N0252	0 45.4	27 20	90.73	122.01	323.5				1.20	.23	1.11	AB
	5.4	33	-34.92	-35.25	8.7				1.20	1.20		
N0253	0 45.1	-25 34	105.41	97.34	272.2	.SXS5..W100	S AF*	S 5	2.38	.58	2.15	DEFKLMU OW
	4.9	33	-87.76	-87.97	-5.0	S 5PK -			45.43	45.43		
N0254	0 45.2	-31 42	261.58	313.64	266.3	.LB..$.H030			1.18	.32	1.05	F
	4.9	33	-85.98	-85.62	-6.6				1.18	1.18		
N0255	0 45.2	-11 45	92.38	119.56	285.6	.SXT4..P200			1.41	.08	1.38	AEKLW
	5.0	33	-74.01	-74.32	-1.4	S 4 N 3*	SX G		7.46	7.46		
N0259	0 45.5	-3 3	91.76	120.88	294.0				1.38	.65	1.12	AB
	5.1	33	-65.31	-65.64	0.9				2.11	2.11		
N0260	0 45.9	27 24	90.86	122.15	323.6				1.02	.00	1.02	AB
	5.4	33	-34.86	-35.18	8.6				1.14	1.14		
N0268	0 47.6	-5 28	93.32	122.07	291.8				1.16	.08	1.13	AK
	5.1	33	-67.71	-68.06	-.2	S 5 3			1.76	1.76		
N0273	0 48.3	-7 10	94.07	122.50	290.2	.L..../W060			1.25	.46	1.06	AFQ
	5.1	33	-69.39	-69.77	-.9				3.01	1.72		
N0274	0 48.5	-7 20	94.24	122.64	290.1	.LXR-P.P200			1.03	.03	1.02	ABEFKSQ
	5.1	33	-69.56	-69.93	-1.0	E 1	D K		5.32	5.32		
N0275	0 48.5	-7 20	94.24	122.64	290.1	.SBT6P.P200			1.18	.15	1.12	ABFKSQ
	5.1	33	-69.56	-69.93	-1.0	S T	I P		5.86	5.86		
N0278	0 49.2	47 18	91.13	123.03	343.5	.SXT3..P200	SD *F		1.19	.01	1.18	AKLRQ
	5.6	33	-14.96	-15.30	12.0	E OP	SI F		5.98	4.22		
N0289	0 50.4	-31 29	245.74	298.81	266.8	.SBT4..W100			1.56	.14	1.50	FGW
	4.8	33	-85.87	-85.91	-7.6				6.12	6.12		

26

NGC (IC, A) (14)	Magnitudes				Colors				Velocities			Radio			
	m_H / m_c (15)	B(O) w (16)	B'(O) m'_c (17)	S(B) (18)	(B-V)(O) w (19)	C_o(O) (20)	S(C) (21)	(U-B)(O) w (22)	V w (23)	V_o ΔV (24)	S(V) (25)	ϕ_r n (26)	ϕ(21) (27)	(28)	Photo. (29)
N0147	12.1	11.48	14.67	BCG	.93		BCG								
	11.34	3.30	14.53		16.87					244					
N0148	12.9														
	12.95		13.19							-12					
N0150	12.2														
	12.34		13.68							5					
N0151	12.5	12.52	14.16	C	.91		C								E
	12.39	1.72	14.03		3.75					83					
N0157	11.1	11.23	13.32	CG	.64*	.52	CG*		1748	1336	BF				KP
	11.43	6.15	13.52		5.63				3.0	88					
N0160		13.77	14.86	C	1.00	.84	C		5255	5453	B				
		1.89			3.75				4.0	198					
N0163															
										80					
N0165															
										79					
N0169															B
										198					
N0175	12.8														P
	12.85		13.74							37					
N0178	12.9	13.29	13.93	C	.58		C								
	13.16	1.54	13.80		1.88					61					
N0182		13.51	14.85	C	.85	.69	C		5234	5353	B				
		2.03			1.88				4.0	129					
N0185	11.8	10.92	14.11	BCGH	.93	.74	BCGHL	.28	-252	-10	BCD				P
	11.14	11.69	14.33	L*	27.10		/L		8.8	242					
N0191															
										82					
N0194		13.65	12.79	C	.94	.82	C		5105	5234	B				
		2.38			3.75				4.0	129					
N0195															
										81					
N0198															
										128					
N0200															
										128					
N0205	10.8	9.71	13.85	BCDEF	.81*	.67	BCDEG	.10	-239	-5	BC				P
	10.16	8.77	14.30	GL*	36.25		/DEL		74.4	233					
N0210	12.5	12.00	14.74	C	.77	.65	C		1768	1829	C				P
	11.86	3.08	14.60		3.75				3.7	61					
N0214	12.8	13.17	13.61	C	.73	.56	C		4521	4720	BC				
	13.13	1.50	13.57		3.75				5.6	199					
N0221	9.5	9.39	11.68	ABCDE	.93*	.80	ABCDE	.46	-213	17	ABC				*
	9.93	11.41	12.22	GKL*	49.00		G/DEL		109.6	23C					
N0224	5.0	4.61	14.35	ABDEG	.92	.68	ABDEG	.50	-299	-68	ABCR				ABKP
	4.59	6.12	14.33	K	15.00		/DE		1171	231					
N0227	13.1	13.51	13.40	C	.92	.80	C		5315	5424	B				
	13.12	2.03	13.01		1.88				2.4	109					
N0237	13.2	14.05	14.14	A											
	13.55	1.64	13.64							114					
N0244									971	1021	D				
									2.3	50					
N0245	12.9														
	13.18		13.52							106					
N0247	10.7	9.93	15.32	CG	.71	.61	C		-156	-129	R				
	9.83	2.99	15.22		1.88				44.4	27					
N0252															
										200					
N0253	7.0	8.19	13.68	K					96	104	FI				AHIM
	7.67	3.70	13.16						8.0	7					P
N0254	12.8														
	12.97		12.96							-19					
N0255	12.8	12.64	14.28	C	.59	.50	C		1921	1987	C				
	12.55	1.08	14.19		3.75				2.8	66					
N0259															
										100					
N0260															
										200					
N0268	13.2														
	13.37		13.76							89					
N0273															
										82					
N0274	13.0								1890	1971	D				
	13.16		13.00						3.8	81					
N0275	13.0								1773	1854	D				
	13.33		13.67						4.7	81					
N0278	11.6	11.85	12.49	CH	.66	.46	CH		633	867	ABC				C
	12.34	4.75	12.98		10.00				15.9	234					
N0289	12.1								1928	1907	C				
	11.92		14.11						1.9	-21					

NGC (IC, A)	Coordinates					Classification			Diameters			
	RA (1950) Dec 100 P / 100 P	L^I B^I	L^{II} B^{II}	SGL SGB	Rev. type (S) DDO (T,L)	Yerkes (1) Yerkes (2)	Hu-San Ho	log D w	log R w	log D(0)	S (D,R)
(1)	(2)	(3)	(4)	(5)	(6)	(7)	(8)	(9)	(10)	(11)	(12)	(13)
N0300	0 52.6 4.7	−37 58 32	258.86 −79.54	299.13 −79.41	260.5 −9.5	.SAS7..RO74 S A			2.30 23.28	.15 23.28	2.24	FGTIJO
N0309	0 54.0 5.0	−10 13 32	99.31 −72.28	127.16 −72.78	287.7 −3.0	.SXR5..P200 S 5 2	S F	S 5	1.44 10.41	.06 10.41	1.41	ABEFKZ
N0315	0 55.1 5.4	30 5 32	93.17 −32.11	124.56 −32.50	326.7 7.3				1.24 1.71	.28 1.71	1.13	AB
N0327	0 55.4 5.1	−5 24 32	98.37 −67.46	127.25 −67.95	292.4 −2.1				1.19 1.57	.32 1.57	1.06	AB
N0329	0 55.5 5.1	−5 20 32	98.42 −67.39	127.30 −67.88	292.5 −2.1				1.22 1.64	.37 1.64	1.07	AB
N0337	0 57.3 5.0	−7 51 32	100.65 −69.82	129.12 −70.35	290.2 −3.2	.SBS7..LO36 S 5 N 4*	S A *		1.39 3.15	.16 3.15	1.33	AF
N0337A	0 59.2 5.0	−7 52 32	102.00 −69.75	130.52 −70.32	290.3 −3.7	.S.....HO30						
N0352	0 59.6 5.1	−4 31 32	100.68 −66.43	129.77 −66.98	293.5 −2.9	.S...*.HO30			1.36 2.52	.36 2.52	1.21	AF
N0357	1 0.8 5.1	−6 37 32	102.43 −68.45	131.21 −69.03	291.6 −3.7	.SBRO*.W100 SBO	B K *		1.27 1.88	.10 1.88	1.23	EK
N0375	1 4.3 5.5	32 5 32	95.28 −29.96	126.76 −30.40	329.1 5.9	.E.5...W			.88 .38	.00 .38	.88	A
N0379	1 4.5 5.5	32 15 32	95.31 −29.79	126.79 −30.24	329.3 5.9	.L.....W			.95 .48	.25 .48	.86	A
N0380	1 4.5 5.5	32 13 32	95.32 −29.83	126.79 −30.27	329.3 5.9	.E.2...W			.90 .42	.00 .42	.90	A
N0382	1 4.6 5.5	32 8 32	95.35 −29.91	126.83 −30.35	329.2 5.8	.E.0...W			.81 .30	.00 .30	.81	A
N0383	1 4.6 5.5	32 9 32	95.35 −29.89	126.82 −30.33	329.2 5.8	.L.....W			.90 .42	.00 .42	.90	A
N0384	1 4.6 5.5	32 2 32	95.36 −30.01	126.83 −30.45	329.1 5.8	.L.....W			.88 .38	.00 .38	.88	A
N0385	1 4.7 5.5	32 3 32	95.38 −29.99	126.86 −30.43	329.1 5.8	.E.3...W			.88 .38	.00 .38	.88	A
N0386	1 4.7 5.5	32 5 32	95.38 −29.96	126.85 −30.40	329.2 5.8	.E.3...W			.85 .34	.00 .34	.85	A
N0388	1 5.0 5.5	32 2 32	95.46 −30.00	126.93 −30.44	329.1 5.7	.E.3...W			.85 .34	.00 .34	.85	A
N0403	1 6.4 5.5	32 29 32	95.75 −29.51	127.24 −29.96	329.7 5.5	.S.....*			1.31 1.71	.42 .94	1.15	AL
N0404	1 6.6 5.6	35 27 32	95.44 −26.57	127.02 −27.01	332.5 6.3	.LAS-*.W100 E 0	E P	L 3 L	1.29 8.71	.03 8.71	1.28	AKLMSXW
N0406	1 5.8 3.4	−70 9 32	267.02 −47.44	300.90 −47.18	228.0 −15.8	.SAS5*.SO30			1.55 4.03	.45 4.03	1.37	DEI
N0407	1 7.8 5.5	32 52 32	96.04 −29.09	127.55 −29.55	330.1 5.3	.S.....$			1.08 1.11	.10 .48	1.04	AL
N0410	1 8.2 5.5	32 53 32	96.13 −29.08	127.62 −29.54	330.1 5.3	.E.2.*.W			1.12 2.49	.33 1.86	.98	ALS
N0428	1 10.4 5.1	0 43 32	104.37 −60.78	134.24 −61.42	299.3 −4.1	.SXS9..W100 S 5P 6	I L*AF* S P AF	S6	1.64 7.41	.10 7.41	1.60	AEKLXW
N0434	1 10.2 4.0	−58 31 32	262.94 −58.83	297.68 −58.66	240.1 −15.6	.SXS2..RO74			1.20 3.01	.25 3.01	1.10	IO
N0434A	1 10.5 4.0	−58 29 32	262.86 −58.86	297.59 −58.69	240.2 −15.6	.SBSOP/RO74			.92 .68	.50 .68	.72	O
N0439	1 11.5 4.7	−32 0 32	215.87 −82.39	257.63 −83.29	267.2 −12.1							
N0440	1 10.9 4.0	−58 33 32	262.78 −58.78	297.51 −58.62	240.1 −15.7	.SAS4*.RO74			.97 2.22	.22 2.22	.88	IO
N0442	1 11.9 5.1	−1 17 32	106.12 −62.63	135.83 −63.31	297.5 −5.0	.S..0./W060			.96 .58	.63 .58	.71	Q
N0450	1 13.0 5.1	−1 7 32	106.61 −62.40	136.35 −63.09	297.7 −5.2	.SXS6*.W060 S 8	SD F		1.48 6.61	.11 6.61	1.44	AEFKYQ
N0467	1 16.6 5.2	3 3 32	106.25 −58.14	136.40 −58.83	302.0 −4.9	.LASOP$P200 E1 K			1.06 3.59	.02 3.59	1.05	AQZ
N0470	1 17.1 5.2	3 9 31	106.43 −58.02	136.60 −58.71	302.1 −5.0	.SAT3..P200 S 5 K	SD *F SI *AF		1.37 7.57	.18 6.77	1.30	AKLYQZ
N0473	1 17.5 5.3	16 14 31	101.93 −45.23	132.84 −45.82	314.7 −1.4	.SXRO*.W060 E 4P	D *G *		1.05 2.09	.21 2.09	.96	AKQ
N0474	1 17.5 5.2	3 10 31	106.61 −57.97	136.78 −58.67	302.2 −5.1	.LASO..P200 E T	SE *K *		1.47 5.73	.04 5.73	1.45	AYQZ
N0488	1 19.1 5.2	5 0 31	106.46 −56.10	136.78 −56.79	304.0 −5.0	.SAR3..P200 S 2 1	S K S GK	S 3 S3	1.61 11.28	.11 11.28	1.56	AKLUXYZ
N0491	1 19.1 4.6	−34 19 31	222.24 −79.76	261.83 −80.54	265.2 −14.1	.SBR3*.SO30			1.10 1.96	.04 1.96	1.08	FI
N0491A	1 17.6 4.6	−34 8 31	222.50 −80.12	262.40 −80.89	265.3 −13.7	.SB.5$.SO30			1.46 1.08	.31 1.08	1.33	I
N0495	1 20.1 5.6	33 12 31	98.90 −28.41	130.44 −28.94	331.1 3.0	.L.....W...			1.18 .77	.26 .77	1.08	A
N0499	1 20.4 5.6	33 11 31	98.97 −28.41	130.51 −28.94	331.1 2.9	.L.....W...			1.04 .30	.00 .30	1.04	A
N0507	1 20.8 5.6	32 59 31	99.10 −28.60	130.64 −29.13	331.0 2.8	.E.3...W...			1.08 .64	.00 .64	1.08	A

NGC (IC, A)	Magnitudes				Colors				Velocities			Radio			
	m_H / m_c	B(O) / w	B'(O) / m'_c	S(B)	(B-V)(O) / w	C_o(O)	S(C)	(U-B)(O) / w	V / w	V_o / ΔV	S(V)	ϕ_r / n	ϕ(21)		Photo.
(14)	(15)	(16)	(17)	(18)	(19)	(20)	(21)	(22)	(23)	(24)	(25)	(26)	(27)	(28)	(29)
N0300	11.3								145	95	R				EFHI
	9.90		15.84						100.0	-50					L
N0309	12.5									65					P
	12.34		14.13												
N0315										200					
N0327										84					
N0329										84					
N0337	12.2									72					
	12.50		13.84												
N0337A									388	459	D				
									1.3	71					
N0352										84					
N0357	13.0	13.16	14.00	C	1.05	.95	C		2541	2616	B				
	12.91	3.54	13.75		3.75				4.0	75					
N0375		15.73	14.82	C	1.02	.85	C		6011	6209	B				
		2.03			1.88				6.3	198					
N0379		14.16	13.15	CL	1.03	.85	CL	.54	5374	5573	B				
		8.21			12.80		/L		2.4	199					
N0380		14.05	13.29	CL	1.03	.88	CL	.59	4341	4539	B				
		8.31			12.80		/L		.4	193					
N0382		14.67	13.46	L	.97	.81	L	.52	5156	5354	B				
		3.53			4.50		/L		4.0	198					
N0383		13.59	12.83	CL	1.02	.86	CL	.58	4888	5086	B				
		2.87			7.3Q		/L		4.0	198					
N0384		14.45	13.54	CL	.96	.81	CL	.54	4401	4599	B				
		4.83			9.10		/L		1.0	198					
N0385		14.38	13.47	CL	.97	.82	CL	.48	4845	5043	B				
		6.18			10.10		/L		.4	198					
N0386		15.43	14.37	CL	.96	.79	CL	.59	5555	5753	B				
		5.43			8.20		/L		.4	198					
N0388		15.86	14.80	CL	1.04	.88	CL	.50	5114	5312	B				
		6.79			11.00		/L		1.0	198					
N0403										198					
N0404	11.9	11.47	12.56	CGH	.91	.80	CGH		-36	169	ABD				P
	12.01	7.51	13.10		10.63				14.9	204					
N0406	12.9														
	12.67		14.21							-172					
N0407										198					
N0410										197					
N0428	11.9	12.11	14.85	ACG	.49	.42	CG		1078	1173	C				
	11.78	7.23	14.52		6.25				1.0	95					
N0434	13.0									-137					H
	13.26		13.50												
N0434A										-137					H
N0439	13.0									-38					
N0440										-138					H
N0442										87					
N0450	12.6									86					
	12.37		14.31												
N0467										99					
N0470	12.4	12.75	13.94	AL	.72		L	-.01		99					
	12.52	3.50	13.71		2.70		/L								
N0473	13.1		13.10							144					
	13.56														
N0474	12.6	12.51	14.50	ACL	.87	.78	CL	.39	2306	2405	B				
	12.16	2.88	14.15		4.70		/L		6.3	99					
N0488	11.8	11.41	13.95	ACGH	.88	.76	CGH		2180	2284	B				KLP
	11.57	9.83	14.11		8.75				.4	104					
N0491	13.0									-52					
	13.05		13.19												
N0491A										-50					
N0495									4114	4304	B				
									4.0	190					
N0499		13.54	13.48	L	1.05	.89	L	.61	4375	4565	B				
		1.24			0.90		/L		4.0	190					
N0507		13.33	13.47	L	1.00	.84	L	.57	4929	5118	B				
		1.11			0.90		/L		4.0	189					

NGC (IC, A) (1)	RA (1950) 100 P (2)	Dec 100 P (3)	L^I / B^I (4)	L^II / B^II (5)	SGL / SGB (6)	Rev. type (S) DDO (T, L) (7)	Yerkes (1) Yerkes (2) (8)	Hu-San Ho (9)	log D w (10)	log R w (11)	log D(O) (12)	S (D,R) (13)
N0509	1 20.7	9 10	105.36	135.95	308.2	.S....$R020			1.23	.42	1.06	AH
	5.2	31	-51.95	-52.62	-4.2				1.02	1.02		
N0514	1 21.3	12 39	104.34	135.11	311.5	.SXT5..W100	S AF		1.45	.10	1.41	AKLSW
	5.3	31	-48.54	-49.19	-3.3	S 5 2*			8.81	8.81		
N0516	1 21.5	9 18	105.62	136.22	308.4	.S....$R020			1.13	.33	.99	AH
	5.3	31	-51.77	-52.45	-4.3				.85	.85		
N0518	1 21.6	9 3	105.76	136.34	308.1	.S....$R020			1.23	.41	1.07	AH
	5.2	31	-52.01	-52.69	-4.4				1.02	1.02		
N0520	1 22.0	3 32	108.45	138.71	302.8	.P.....P200	I P F *	I 0	1.54	.51	1.34	AXY
	5.2	31	-57.32	-58.06	-6.1	P	I P K *	I0	1.33	1.33		
N0521	1 22.0	1 28	109.59	139.70	300.8	.SBR4..W100	B K		1.40	.04	1.38	AEW
	5.1	31	-59.30	-60.06	-6.6	SX3 N -*	SX F		4.91	4.91		
N0522	1 22.1	9 44	105.68	136.31	308.8	.S.....*			1.28	.73	.99	AS
	5.3	31	-51.32	-52.00	-4.3				2.51	1.19		
N0524	1 22.1	9 16	105.88	136.48	308.3	.LAT+..P200		L 2	1.20	.01	1.19	AHKLS
	5.2	31	-51.78	-52.47	-4.5	E 1	D K		4.05	4.05		
N0532	1 22.7	9 0	106.20	136.80	308.1	.S....$R020			1.44	.47	1.25	AH
	5.2	31	-51.99	-52.68	-4.7				1.39	1.39		
N0533	1 22.9	1 30	109.99	140.12	300.9	.E.3.*.W100	E4 K		1.05	.21	.97	AEK
	5.1	31	-59.20	-59.97	-6.8	E 2*	E4 K		1.48	1.48		
N0545	1 23.4	-1 36	112.25	142.17	297.9	.LA.-..P200			1.17	.17	1.10	ABZ
	5.1	31	-62.10	-62.92	-7.8				3.15	3.15		
N0547	1 23.4	-1 36	112.25	142.17	297.9	.E.1...P200			.85	.03	.83	ABZ
	5.1	31	-62.10	-62.92	-7.8				1.80	1.80		
N0550	1 24.1	1 46	110.38	140.56	301.3	.S..3.*P048			1.20	.44	1.02	A
	5.1	31	-58.85	-59.63	-7.1				.80	.80		
N0560	1 24.9	-2 11	113.44	143.34	297.5	.L.....W			1.15	.63	.90	A
	5.1	31	-62.52	-63.36	-8.3				.73	.73		
N0564	1 25.2	-2 9	113.57	143.48	297.5	.E.3...W			.92	.00	.92	AB
	5.1	31	-62.46	-63.30	-8.4				.87	.87		
N0578	1 28.0	-22 56	157.49	188.29	277.1	.SXT5..W100	BS *AF		1.66	.18	1.59	DEFKMTX
	4.8	31	-78.65	-80.11	-13.9	S 5 3		S5	15.71	15.71		W
N0584	1 28.8	-7 7	120.13	149.77	292.9	.E.4...W100	E4 K		1.32	.23	1.23	ABEFKLW
	5.0	31	-66.65	-67.63	-10.5	E 4	E4 K		8.25	5.87		
N0586	1 29.1	-7 9	120.34	149.99	292.9	.SAS1*W100			1.10	.34	.96	ABFW
	5.0	31	-66.65	-67.63	-10.6				4.53	3.48		
N0596	1 30.3	-7 17	121.16	150.85	292.8	.E.0...W			1.28	.23	1.18	AEK
	5.0	31	-66.63	-67.63	-11.0	E 2	ED K		2.35	2.35		
N0598	1 31.1	30 24	102.14	133.63	329.2	.SAS6......	S F	S 5	2.79	.21	2.70	AHKLUXY
	5.6	31	-30.72	-31.33	-.1	S 5 4	S F	S6	26.92	26.92		
N0600	1 30.8	-7 35	121.79	151.48	292.6	.SB..*.H030			1.35	.13	1.30	AFH
	5.0	31	-66.84	-67.85	-11.1				3.06	3.06		
N0613	1 32.0	-29 40	193.01	229.03	270.4	.SBT4..W100	BS *F		1.72	.15	1.66	FGLTOW
	4.6	31	-78.97	-80.29	-16.0				12.58	11.32		
N0615	1 32.6	-7 35	122.78	152.54	292.7	.SAT3..P200		S 3	1.50	.40	1.34	AEHKZ
	5.0	31	-66.62	-67.65	-11.1	S 3 4	SD G		9.22	9.22		
N0625	1 32.9	-41 41	236.78	273.66	258.0	.SB.9$/S030			1.46	.40	1.30	EFI
	4.3	31	-72.66	-73.13	-17.7				4.11	4.11		
N0628	1 34.0	15 32	107.62	138.61	315.2	.SAS5..P200	S FG	S 5	1.98	.03	1.97	AHKLSVX
	5.4	31	-44.97	-45.70	-5.4	S 5 1		S5	23.35	23.35		YZ
N0636	1 36.6	-7 45	125.14	155.04	292.8	.E+3...W100			1.14	.10	1.10	AKW
	5.0	30	-66.27	-67.35	-12.6	E 1	E3 K		3.26	3.26		
N0643B	1 38.4	-75 16	265.20	298.82	222.6	.S...*.S030			1.12	.57	.90	I
	1.6	30	-41.94	-41.73	-18.0				.67	.67		
N0643C	1 41.2	-75 31	265.08	298.68	222.3	.S...*.S030			1.17	.66	.91	I
	1.4	30	-41.65	-41.44	-18.2				.73	.73		
N0660	1 40.2	13 21	110.62	141.57	313.6	.SBS1P.W060			2.02	.36	1.87	XQ
	5.3	30	-46.61	-47.40	-7.5			S P	2.12	2.12		
N0661	1 41.4	28 25	105.26	136.72	328.0				1.08	.08	1.05	AS
	5.6	30	-32.09	-32.77	-2.9				1.86	.54		
N0670	1 44.5	27 38	106.29	137.74	327.5	.E.6...R020			1.17	.30	1.05	AHKS
	5.6	30	-32.67	-33.38	-3.8	E 4	E7 *K		3.49	2.11		
N0672	1 45.0	27 11	106.57	138.01	327.1	.SBS6..P200	B A		1.79	.43	1.61	ABHKMSX
	5.6	30	-33.07	-33.78	-4.0	SB5 5	B *AF	S6	19.52	17.00		Z
N0676	1 46.3	5 40	117.14	147.86	306.6	.S..0*.W060			1.38	.66	1.12	AHQ
	5.2	30	-53.22	-54.15	-11.3				3.26	3.26		
N0678	1 46.6	21 46	108.98	140.26	322.1	.S..../R020			1.68	.77	1.37	AHLU
	5.5	30	-38.14	-38.90	-6.2				7.23	6.05		
N0680	1 47.0	21 44	109.12	140.40	322.1	.E.2..*R020			1.12	.11	1.07	AHL
	5.5	30	-38.14	-38.90	-6.3				2.06	1.61		
N0681	1 46.7	-10 40	134.56	164.81	290.5	.SXS2./W100			1.28	.25	1.19	AKW
	4.9	30	-67.23	-68.46	-15.7	S 2	DS K		4.72	4.72		
N0684	1 47.4	27 24	107.11	138.56	327.5	.L....*R020			1.37	.83	1.03	AHS
	5.6	30	-32.71	-33.43	-4.5				3.94	2.68		
N0685	1 45.9	-53 2	249.38	284.48	246.1	.SXR5..S030			1.58	.01	1.58	I
	3.8	30	-62.10	-62.28	-20.4				1.78	1.78		
N0691	1 47.9	21 31	109.44	140.73	322.0	.S..5..R020			1.50	.10	1.46	AHLU
	5.5	30	-38.28	-39.05	-6.6				5.75	5.75		
N0693	1 47.9	5 54	117.57	148.33	307.0	.S....*R020			1.12	.36	.97	AH
	5.2	30	-52.85	-53.79	-11.6				1.50	1.50		

NGC (IC, A) (14)	Magnitudes m_H m_C (15)	B(O) w (16)	B'(O) m'_C (17)	S(B) (18)	Colors (B-V)(O) w (19)	C_o(O) (20)	S(C) (21)	(U-B)(O) w (22)	Velocities V w (23)	V_o ΔV (24)	S(V) (25)	Radio ϕ_r n (26)	ϕ(21) (27)	(28)	Photo. (29)
N0509										118					
N0514	12.4	12.56	14.35	C	.67	.55	C		2541	2670	BC				
	12.29	1.05	14.08		1.88				5.2	129					
N0516										118					
N0518										117					
N0520	12.4	12.75	14.19	ACGL*	.85*	.71	CGL*	*	2223	2320	CD				P
		2.77			8.13		/L		4.7	96					
N0521	13.0	12.75	14.34	A											
	12.68	2.70	14.27							89					
N0522										119					
N0524	12.0	12.11	12.80	ACL	1.03	.93	ACL	.61	2470	2587	B				P
	12.21	9.21	12.90		15.40		/L		2.4	117					
N0532										116					
N0533	13.0	13.44	13.03	A											
	13.16	1.14	12.75							88					
N0545										76					
N0547										76					
N0550										88					
N0560		14.41	13.60	CL	.97	.82	CL	.49	5503	5576	B				
		3.22			4.70		/L		.4	72					
N0564		14.02	13.31	C	.97	.84	C		5851	5923	B				
		1.91			1.88				.4	72					
N0578	11.7	11.80	14.49	CG	.58	.47	CG		2017	2004	C				E
	11.50	5.00	14.19		8.13				2.0	-13					
N0584	11.6	11.71	12.55	AC	.91	.84	AC		1835	1885	AB				
	11.81	9.03	12.65		6.25				2.2	50					
N0586										50					
N0596	12.2	12.31	12.95	C	.86	.78	C		2049	2097	B				
	12.27	1.83	12.91		1.88				2.4	48					
N0598	7.8	6.47	14.71	AEGK	.55	.42	ABEG*	-.10	-186	-11	BR				AP
	6.88	6.56	15.12		15.00		/E*		444.4	175					
N0600										47					
N0613	11.1	11.02	14.01	C	.77	.67	C		1558	1515	C				HI
	11.01	1.24	14.00		1.88				2.1	-43					
N0615	12.6								1946	1991	D				P
	12.51		13.95						1.6	45					
N0625	12.3														
	12.58		13.77							-89					
N0628	11.2	10.07	14.66	ACFG	.61	.53	CG		653	782	BR				AKP
	10.35	7.24	14.94		8.13				404.0	129					
N0636	12.6	12.66	12.85	C	.94	.86	C		1941	1982	B				
	12.69	1.32	12.88		1.88				4.0	41					
N0643B										-193					
N0643C										-194					
N0660		11.90	15.99	G	.84		G								
		1.56			2.50					116					
N0661										162					
N0670	13.0														
	13.04		12.98							158					
N0672	11.9	11.76	14.55	CG	.59	.44	CG		340	496	C				J
	11.61	2.86	14.40		4.38				3.6	156					
N0676										84					
N0678										139					B
N0680										138					
N0681	12.9	13.03	13.67	C	.86	.72	C		1784	1805	BD				
	13.02	1.65	13.66		3.75				3.7	21					
N0684										155					
N0685	12.7														F
	12.06		14.70							-136					
N0691										137					
N0693										83					

NGC (IC, A) (1)	Coordinates					Classification			Diameters			
	RA (1950) Dec 100 P (2)	100 P (3)	L^I B^I (4)	L^{II} B^{II} (5)	SGL SGB (6)	Rev. type (S) DDO (T, L) (7)	Yerkes (1) Yerkes (2) (8)	Hu-San Ho (9)	log D w (10)	log R w (11)	log D(O) (12)	S (D,R) (13)
N0694	1 48.2	21 44	109.44	140.73	322.2	.S..5..R020			1.57	.23	1.48	HU
	5.5	30	-38.05	-38.82	-6.6				3.90	3.90		
N0695	1 48.4	22 20	109.27	140.58	322.8	.E....*R020			.90	.00	.90	AHL
	5.5	30	-37.46	-38.23	-6.4				.89	.89		
N0697	1 48.5	22 6	109.38	140.68	322.6	.S..4..L036			1.62	.46	1.44	AHLU
	5.5	30	-37.68	-38.45	-6.5				6.76	6.76		
N0701	1 48.6	-9 57	134.34	164.66	291.3	.SBT5..W060	ISP A *		1.30	.34	1.16	ABEKQ
	4.9	30	-66.38	-67.60	-16.0	S NK-			5.83	5.83		
N0702	1 48.8	-4 18	126.90	157.32	297.0	.SBS.P.P200			1.17	.09	1.13	AZ
	5.0	30	-61.74	-62.85	-14.6				3.41	3.41		
N0706	1 49.2	6 4	117.95	148.72	307.3	.S....*R020			1.20	.22	1.11	AH
	5.2	30	-52.56	-53.51	-11.8				1.72	1.72		
N0718	1 50.7	3 57	120.05	150.78	305.3	.SXS1..P200	S P GK	S 1	1.29	.10	1.25	AKZ
	5.2	30	-54.31	-55.30	-12.8	S 3 N			4.62	4.62		
N0720	1 50.6	-13 59	142.49	173.03	287.3	.E.5..W060	E6 K		1.38	.23	1.29	HK
	4.9	30	-69.02	-70.35	-17.4	E 3			1.20	1.20		
N0721	1 51.9	39 8	104.32	136.09	338.8	.SB.3..W			1.26	.10	1.22	A
	6.0	29	-21.20	-21.87	-1.2				.44	.44		
N0731	1 52.5	-9 15	135.07	165.54	292.3	.E.0...L036			.99	.00	.99	AF
	5.0	29	-65.23	-66.47	-16.8				1.40	1.40		
N0736	1 53.8	32 48	106.76	138.38	333.1	.E.1...W			.89	.00	.89	AL
	5.8	29	-27.15	-27.86	-3.8				.82	.42		
N0740	1 54.0	32 47	106.81	138.44	333.1	.S....$			1.30	.61	1.06	AL
	5.8	29	-27.15	-27.86	-3.9				1.69	1.69		
N0741	1 53.8	5 23	120.14	150.96	306.9	.E.0.*.W100	E1 K		1.15	.04	1.14	AK
	5.2	29	-52.68	-53.67	-13.1	E 1	E3 K		.55	.55		
N0750	1 54.6	32 58	106.88	138.51	333.3	.E...P.P200	D G	E 0	.95	.10	.91	A
	5.8	29	-26.94	-27.65	-3.9	E	DE K		.48	.48		
N0751	1 54.6	32 58	106.88	138.51	333.3	.E...P.P200	D GK	E 0	.88	.00	.88	A
	5.8	29	-26.94	-27.65	-3.9				.38	.38		
N0753	1 54.6	35 41	105.97	137.66	335.8	.SXT4..W060	S F		1.34	.14	1.29	AKMXQ
	5.9	29	-24.35	-25.05	-2.9	S 5 3*		S5	5.99	5.99		
N0755	1 53.8	-9 18	135.74	166.25	292.3	.S...$.H030			1.60	.51	1.39	AF
	4.9	29	-65.06	-66.31	-17.1				3.26	3.26		
N0759	1 54.6	36 6	105.87	137.58	336.2	.E.0.*.L036			.89	.08	.86	AM
	5.9	29	-23.94	-24.63	-2.8				.91	.91		
N0761	1 54.9	33 9	106.89	138.52	333.5	.S....*			1.18	.48	.98	AL
	5.8	29	-26.74	-27.46	-3.9				1.40	.77		
N0770	1 56.5	18 43	113.13	144.39	320.0	.SB.1..W			.83	.17	.76	ALS
	5.5	29	-40.22	-41.07	-9.4				1.58	1.18		
N0772	1 56.6	18 46	113.14	144.39	320.1	.SAS3..W060	S P F		1.73	.22	1.64	AELSUXQ
	5.5	29	-40.16	-41.01	-9.4	S 3 NT 1	S G	S4	13.36	13.36		
N0777	1 57.3	31 12	108.12	139.72	331.8	.E.1...W060			1.03	.05	1.01	AKQ
	5.8	29	-28.43	-29.18	-5.1	E 2	E K		1.09	1.09		
N0779	1 57.2	-6 12	132.86	163.48	295.6	.SXR3..W060	S G		1.51	.52	1.30	AFHKLQ
	5.0	29	-62.11	-63.32	-17.1	S 2 4			8.52	8.52		
N0782	1 56.1	-58 1	252.01	286.61	240.6	.SBR3..S030			1.25	.03	1.24	I
	3.4	29	-57.09	-57.20	-21.6				1.14	1.14		
N0784	1 58.4	28 36	109.37	140.90	329.5				1.81	.67	1.55	AX
	5.7	29	-30.81	-31.58	-6.3			S6	1.88	1.88		
N0788	1 58.6	-7 3	134.58	165.24	294.9	.SAS0*.W060			1.09	.08	1.06	AKQ
	5.0	29	-62.57	-63.80	-17.7	S 0			2.65	2.65		
N0803	2 1.0	15 47	115.96	147.17	317.6				1.40	.48	1.21	AX
	5.4	29	-42.51	-43.42	-11.5			S5	1.08	1.08		
N0808	2 1.6	-23 32	171.16	203.76	277.8	.S.....H030			1.10	.25	1.01	F
	4.6	29	-71.70	-73.18	-21.6				.53	.53		
N0818	2 5.7	38 32	107.25	139.05	339.3	.SX.5*.L036			1.49	.34	1.36	AL
	6.0	28	-20.94	-21.67	-3.9				2.15	2.15		
N0821	2 5.6	10 46	120.41	151.52	313.1	.E+6..$W060			1.20	.25	1.10	AK
	5.3	28	-46.56	-47.56	-14.2	E 2	E6 *K		1.22	1.22		
N0829	2 6.2	-8 2	139.04	169.92	294.3	.S...$.H030			1.11	.25	1.01	AF
	5.0	28	-62.08	-63.38	-19.8				1.74	1.74		
N0833	2 7.0	-10 22	142.91	173.89	292.0	.S...P*P048			1.08	.20	1.00	A
	4.9	28	-63.62	-64.96	-20.5				.64	.64		
N0835	2 7.0	-10 22	142.91	173.89	292.0	.S...P*P048			.93	.00	.93	A
	4.9	28	-63.62	-64.96	-20.5				.45	.45		
N0838	2 7.2	-10 23	143.02	174.00	292.0	.E....*P048			.90	.00	.90	A
	4.9	28	-63.60	-64.94	-20.5				.42	.42		
N0839	2 7.3	-10 26	143.14	174.12	291.9	.L....*P048			1.04	.39	.88	A
	4.9	28	-63.61	-64.96	-20.6				.60	.60		
N0842	2 7.4	-8 0	139.45	170.37	294.5	.E...$.H030			1.04	.28	.93	A
	5.0	28	-61.86	-63.16	-20.0				.60	.60		
N0848	2 8.2	-10 34	143.70	174.71	291.8	.S.....*P048						
	4.9	28	-63.55	-64.90	-20.8							
N0864	2 12.8	5 45	126.46	157.55	308.8	.SXT5..P200			1.60	.09	1.56	AKMZ
	5.2	28	-50.05	-51.15	-17.5	S 5 3	S AF		10.10	10.10		
N0871	2 14.5	14 19	120.80	152.09	317.4	.SBS5*.W100			1.08	.47	.89	AMW
	5.4	28	-42.41	-43.41	-15.1				2.81	2.81		
N0876	2 15.2	14 18	121.02	152.31	317.4	.SA.5*/L036			1.32	.77	1.02	AM
	5.4	28	-42.34	-43.35	-15.2				1.05	1.05		

NGC (IC, A) (14)	Magnitudes				Colors				Velocities			Radio			
	m_H m_C (15)	B(O) w (16)	B'(O) m'_C (17)	S(B) (18)	(B-V)(O) w (19)	C_O(O) (20)	S(C) (21)	(U-B)(O) w (22)	V w (23)	V_O ΔV (24)	S(V) (25)	ϕ_r n (26)	ϕ(21) (27)	(28)	Photo. (29)
N0694										137					
N0695										139					
N0697										138					B
N0701	12.7 13.03		13.57							22					
N0702										44					
N0706										83					
N0718	12.7 12.73	12.81 5.27	13.80 13.72	AC	.81 3.75	.70	C		1802 3.1	1876 74	C				P
N0720	11.7 11.75	11.47 3.57	12.66 12.94	AC	.97 6.25	.89	AC		1808 1.0	1813 5	B				
N0721		14.12 1.91	14.91	C	.70 1.88		C			182					
N0731										22					
N0736		13.86 3.67	13.00	C	.95 3.75	.79	C		4366 6.3	4531 165	B				
N0740										165					
N0741	13.0 12.88	13.12 6.37	13.51 13.27	AC	1.02 3.75	.90	C		5559 4.0	5636 76	B				
N0750	12.9 13.19	13.67 4.03	12.96 12.48	C*L	1.04 3.70	.87	C*L /L	.58	5130 6.3	5295 165	B				P
N0751		13.98 4.26	13.07	C*L	.97 3.70	.80	C*L /L	.72*	5126 2.8	5291 165	3				P
N0753	13.0 12.89	13.25 7.83	14.39 14.03	CGH	.69 10.63	.49	CGH		4766 4.2	4938 172	C				
N0755										20					
N0759										173					
N0761										165					
N0770		14.42 1.76	12.91	C	1.14 1.88		C			121					
N0772	12.0 11.50	11.42 3.03	14.36 14.44	CFG	.79 4.38	.62	CG		2431 .4	2552 121	B				
N0777	13.0 13.09		12.88							158					
N0779	11.8 12.17	12.20 2.80	13.44 13.41	C	.85 5.63		C			30					
N0782	12.7 12.82		13.71							-156					
N0784		12.47 1.22	14.91	G	.51 2.50		G			150					
N0788	13.1 13.36	13.20 2.04	13.19 13.35	C	.74 1.88	.62	C		4137 2.4	4162 25	B				
N0803		13.30 0.91	14.04	G	.66 1.88		G			107					
N0808										-42					
N0818										172					
N0821	12.7 12.75	12.59 8.12	12.78 12.94	AC	.99 9.38	.90	C		1778 1.0	1864 86	B				
N0829										15					
N0833										5					
N0835										5					
N0838										5					
N0839										4					
N0842										14					
N0848										3					
N0864	12.3 11.89	11.73 2.00	14.27 14.43	C	.60 3.75	.50	C		1583 2.4	1644 61	C				
N0871		14.30 1.39	13.44	C	.63 1.88	.43	C		3731 4.1	3821 90	CD				
N0876										90					

33

NGC (IC, A) (1)	RA (1950) 100 P (2)	Dec 100 P (3)	L^I B^I (4)	L^II B^II (5)	SGL SGB (6)	Rev. type (S) DDO (T, L) (7)	Yerkes (1) Yerkes (2) (8)	Hu-San Ho (9)	log D w (10)	log R w (11)	log D(O) (12)	S (D,R) (13)
N0877	2 15.3	14 19	121.04	152.33	317.4	.SXT4..W100	SI *AF		1.32	.12	1.27	AKMU
	5.4	28	-42.32	-43.33	-15.2	S 5 1*	SI AF		6.92	6.92		
N0890	2 19.1	33 2	112.20	143.91	335.4	.LXR-$.W100	D P K *		1.17	.26	1.07	AKQW
	5.9	27	-25.05	-25.89	-8.6	E 4			4.71	4.71		
N0891	2 19.3	42 7	108.46	140.36	343.6	.SAS3$/....	S GK*	S 3	2.09	.79	1.78	AHKLX
	6.3	27	-16.67	-17.43	-4.7	S 3	S G *	S4	10.81	10.81		
N0895	2 19.1	-5 45	140.61	171.77	297.6	.SAS6..W060			1.53	.13	1.47	AHKLRVQ
	5.0	27	-58.23	-59.55	-22.3	S 4 3	S F		12.17	10.91		
N0898	2 20.9	41 43	108.90	140.80	343.4	.S....*R020			1.34	.57	1.12	H
	6.3	27	-16.92	-17.69	-5.2				1.15	1.15		
N0907	2 20.7	-20 56	168.45	200.80	281.3				1.20	.51	.99	F
	4.6	27	-66.66	-68.15	-25.7				1.20	1.20		
N0908	2 20.8	-21 27	169.69	202.12	280.8	.SAS5..W100	S AF		1.71	.36	1.57	FKLTXW
	4.6	27	-66.83	-68.31	-25.8	S 5 1		S5	9.91	9.91		
N0918	2 23.2	18 17	120.76	152.19	322.0	.SXS5..L036			1.49	.25	1.39	A
	5.6	27	-37.92	-38.93	-15.5				1.24	1.24		
N0922	2 22.9	-25 1	178.84	211.88	276.9	.SBS6P.W100			1.28	.05	1.25	KW
	4.5	27	-67.38	-68.84	-26.6	S 5P 4*			2.29	2.29		
N0925	2 24.3	35 22	112.24	144.02	338.0	.SXS7..P200	B AF	SX 5	1.93	.24	1.83	AKMSXZ
	6.1	27	-22.48	-23.32	-8.6	SX5 4	BS AF	S6	18.37	13.78		
N0926	2 23.5	-0 37	135.99	167.19	303.2	.S....$R020			1.28	.30	1.16	AH
	5.1	27	-53.66	-54.91	-22.0				1.11	1.11		
N0936	2 25.1	-1 22	137.34	168.57	302.6	.LBT+..P200	B K		1.61	.10	1.57	AFGKLMX
	5.1	27	-53.97	-55.25	-22.6	SB0	B K	S1	15.53	15.53		QZ
N0941	2 26.0	-1 22	137.63	168.87	302.6	.SXT5..W060			1.38	.09	1.34	AFHKLMX
	5.1	27	-53.83	-55.11	-22.8	S 5 6		S6	8.07	7.18		Q
N0942	2 26.6	-11 3	150.76	182.25	292.4							
	4.9	27	-60.43	-61.85	-25.3							
N0943	2 26.6	-11 3	150.76	182.25	292.4							
	4.9	27	-60.43	-61.85	-25.3							
N0945	2 26.2	-10 45	150.16	181.63	292.7	.SB.5*.H030			1.36	.13	1.31	ABF
	4.9	27	-60.32	-61.74	-25.2				3.58	3.58		
N0948	2 26.3	-10 44	150.16	181.64	292.7	.S.....H030			1.16	.05	1.14	BF
	4.9	27	-60.29	-61.71	-25.2				1.89	1.89		
N0949	2 27.6	36 56	112.19	144.01	339.7	.SAT3*$W060			1.20	.33	1.07	AHKLQ
	6.1	27	-20.78	-21.62	-8.5	S *	DE K *		5.12	4.49		
N0955	2 28.0	-1 19	138.21	169.48	302.8	.S..3*/L			1.34	.65	1.08	AFHKR
	5.1	27	-53.46	-54.75	-23.3	E 8			7.01	5.52		
N0958	2 28.1	-3 9	140.34	171.63	300.9	.SB.5*.H030			1.39	.40	1.23	AFKT
	5.0	27	-54.80	-56.12	-23.8	SX4* 2	B *F		6.11	6.11		
N0972	2 31.3	29 6	116.71	148.40	332.9	.I.0...P200	I A *	S 3	1.44	.27	1.33	AHKLRZ
	5.9	26	-27.49	-28.42	-12.7	S 5 N - 3*			10.20	10.20		
N0976	2 31.2	20 44	121.33	152.86	325.1	.SAT5*.W100	S *F		1.07	.08	1.04	AKW
	5.6	26	-34.87	-35.89	-16.2	S 3 N 3*	S K *		3.50	3.50		
N0986	2 31.6	-39 15	213.99	248.65	260.8	.SBT2..W100	B G		1.48	.14	1.43	IOW
	4.0	26	-64.63	-65.64	-28.8				7.68	7.68		
N0986A	2 30.7	-39 32	214.75	249.45	260.5	.S....$.S030			1.21	.47	1.02	I
	4.0	26	-64.70	-65.69	-28.7				.77	.77		
N0991	2 33.2	-7 22	147.31	178.78	296.8	.SXT5..W100			1.34	.03	1.33	AEFKYW
	4.9	26	-56.83	-58.22	-26.1	S 7*	S AF		7.36	7.36		
N1003	2 36.1	40 40	112.08	144.00	343.8	.SAS6..P200			1.68	.49	1.48	AXWZ
	6.3	26	-16.70	-17.54	-8.2			S6	10.59	10.59		
N1022	2 36.1	-6 53	147.51	179.01	297.5	PSBS1..P200			1.23	.12	1.18	AEHKMUY
	5.0	26	-55.97	-57.36	-26.7	S 3 N	S P G		5.71	5.71		
N1023	2 37.2	38 52	113.11	145.00	342.3	.LBT-..P200	D P K	L	1.75	.49	1.55	AHKLRVX
	6.3	26	-18.22	-19.08	-9.3	E 7P			18.35	18.35		Z
N1035	2 37.0	-8 20	149.76	181.34	296.0	.SAS5.$W100			1.31	.44	1.13	AEFKMY
	4.9	26	-56.73	-58.15	-27.2	P	SI *F *		7.03	7.03		
N1042	2 38.0	-8 40	150.52	182.12	295.7	.SXT6..W100			1.60	.10	1.56	EFKTXYW
	4.9	26	-56.75	-58.17	-27.6	S 5 N	S F	S5	12.05	12.05		
N1047	2 38.2	-8 23	150.18	181.77	296.0	.S....*/W100			1.03	.35	.89	FMW
	4.9	26	-56.54	-57.95	-27.5				2.98	2.98		
N1048A	2 38.2	-8 46	150.72	182.33	295.6	.S..../W100			1.05	.42	.88	FW
	4.9	26	-56.78	-58.19	-27.6				1.83	1.83		
N1048B	2 38.2	-8 46	150.72	182.33	295.6	.SBS5*.W100			1.08	.38	.92	FW
	4.9	26	-56.78	-58.19	-27.6				1.91	1.91		
N1052	2 38.6	-8 28	150.41	182.01	295.9	.E.4...W100	E4 K		1.21	.16	1.14	AEFKMXY
	4.9	26	-56.51	-57.93	-27.7	E 2	E4 K	E	7.21	7.21		W
N1055	2 39.2	0 16	139.87	171.30	305.4	.S..3./R020			1.83	.49	1.63	AEHKLX
	5.1	26	-50.41	-51.72	-25.5	S 3 4	S G	S4	6.37	6.37		
N1058	2 40.2	37 8	114.50	146.37	341.1	.SAT5..P200	S AF		1.39	.03	1.38	AMUXZ
	6.2	26	-19.50	-20.38	-10.6	S 5 K 6*	D F	S5	8.21	8.21		
N1063	2 39.7	-5 47	147.10	178.63	298.9	.S...$.H030			1.10	.25	1.01	F
	5.0	26	-54.57	-55.96	-27.3				1.05	1.05		
N1068	2 40.1	-0 14	140.65	172.09	304.9	RSAT3..W100	SD *G	S 3	1.72	.07	1.69	AEHKLRU
	5.1	25	-50.62	-51.94	-25.8	S 3P	S P G	S3	14.44	14.44		XW
N1072	2 41.0	0 5	140.56	172.02	305.4	.S....*R020			1.15	.37	1.00	H
	5.1	25	-50.23	-51.55	-26.0				.16	.16		
N1073	2 41.2	1 10	139.49	170.94	306.5	.SBT5..P200	B AF	SBT5	1.65	.02	1.64	AEKMXZ
	5.2	25	-49.41	-50.71	-25.7	SX5 3	B F	S6	11.90	11.90		

NGC (IC, A) (14)	m_H / m_c (15)	B(O) / w (16)	B'(O) / m'_c (17)	S(B) (18)	(B-V)(O) / w (19)	C_o(O) (20)	S(C) (21)	(U-B)(O) / w (22)	V / w (23)	V_o / ΔV (24)	S(V) (25)	ϕ_r / n (26)	ϕ(21) (27)	(28)	Photo. (29)
N0877	12.4	12.76	13.85	AC	.69	.54	C		4016	4106	C				
	12.59	3.38	13.68		1.88				2.0	90					
N0890	12.7	13.15	13.19	CHL	.97	.79	CHL	.50	4043	4190	B				
	12.89	7.59	12.93		8.70		/L		2.4	147					
N0891	12.2	11.24	14.83	CG	.92	.62	CG		72	243	B				ABLP
	11.31	3.04	14.90		4.38				1.0	171					
N0895	12.2														
	12.09		14.18							12					
N0898										169					
N0907										−47					
N0908	11.1	11.14	13.68	CG	.68	.54	CG		1734	1685	C				
	11.24	2.70	13.78		6.25				1.5	−49					
N0918										97					
N0922	12.3	12.52	13.51	C	.70		C								
	12.65	1.89	13.64		1.88					−64					
N0925	12.6	10.96	14.85	CG	.60*	.43	CG		568	718	BC				P
	11.55	4.47	15.44		8.13				2.2	150					
N0926										28					
N0936	11.5	11.28	13.82	ACG	.97	.88	ACG		1348	1371	AB				
	11.25	7.87	13.79		8.75				5.0	24					
N0941	13.3	13.20	14.64	G	.55		G								
	12.94	1.17	14.38		1.88					23					
N0942										−15					
N0943										−15					
N0945										−13					
N0948										−13					
N0949	12.8	13.14	13.23	H	.63		H								
	13.24	3.94	13.33		6.25					152					
N0955	13.1														
	13.38		13.52							21					
N0958	13.0														
	13.03		13.92							14					
N0972	12.6	12.33	13.67	C	.85	.69	C		1555	1681	BD				BCP
	12.42	2.03	13.76		1.88				4.0	126					
N0976	12.7														
	13.30		13.24							99					
N0986	11.8								2073	1953	M				H
	11.87		13.71						1.0	−120					
N0986A										−120					
N0991	12.7														
	12.64		14.03							−7					
N1003		12.45	14.59	CG	.57	.34	CG		585	741	B				
		2.87			5.00				2.8	156					
N1022	12.0														
	12.51		13.15							−7					
N1023	11.2	10.65	13.14	ACFG	1.00	.81	ACG		573	729	ABD				
	11.07	8.39	13.56		9.38				5.5	151					
N1035	12.8														
	13.15		13.54							−14					
N1042	12.5	11.81	14.30	CG	.57	.49	CG		355	339	C				
	12.07	1.10	14.56		2.50				1.0	−16					
N1047										−15					
N1048A				C*			C*								
										−16					
N1048B				C*			C*								
										−16					
N1052	11.6	12.12	12.56	CG	.92	.84	CG		1460	1444	BC				
	11.94	2.23	12.38		4.38				8.3	−16					
N1055	12.0	11.77	14.66	G	.89		G								
	11.52	1.05	14.41		2.50					17					
N1058	12.7	12.26	13.85	CGH	.63	.48	CGH		80	223	C *				K
	12.54	7.87	14.13		10.63				2.2	144					
N1063										−6					
N1068	10.0	9.81	13.00	ACFG	.74*	.64	ACG		1080	1094	ABCFJ				ACKP
	10.30	6.28	13.49		10.63				36.7	14					
N1072										15					
N1073	12.0	11.80	14.74	CG	.55	.46	CG		1874	1893	C				P
	11.54	3.25	14.48		4.38				1.5	19					

NGC (IC, A) (1)	RA (1950) Dec 100 P / 100 P (2)(3)	L^I B^I (4)	L^{II} B^{II} (5)	SGL SGB (6)	Rev. type (S) DDO (T,L) (7)	Yerkes (1) Yerkes (2) (8)	Hu-San Ho (9)	log D w (10)	log R w (11)	log D(0) (12)	S (D,R) (13)
N1079	2 41.6 −29 13 / 4.3 25	190.35 −63.84	223.89 −65.21	272.4 −31.1	RSXTOP.P200			1.44 7.10	.23 7.10	1.35	FOZ
N1084	2 43.5 −7 47 / 4.9 25	150.81 −55.14	182.46 −56.56	297.0 −28.7	.SAS5..W100 S 5 2	S A S P*A	S 5	1.42 8.82	.31 8.82	1.29	AEHKLUY W
N1087	2 43.9 −0 42 / 5.1 25	142.23 −50.30	173.73 −51.63	304.8 −26.9	.SXT5..W100 S 5 K 5*	SI *A IS A	S 5 S5	1.48 9.83	.20 9.83	1.40	AEFHKLT XW
N1090	2 44.0 −0 27 / 5.1 25	141.99 −50.10	173.49 −51.44	305.0 −26.8	.SBT4..W100 S 6 N 7*	S F S F	S4	1.57 10.67	.39 10.67	1.42	AEFKLTX W
N1094	2 44.8 −0 28 / 5.1 25	142.23 −49.97	173.74 −51.31	305.1 −27.0	.SXS2..W100			1.05 3.49	.11 2.86	1.00	AFLW
N1097	2 44.3 −30 29 / 4.3 25	193.26 −63.32	226.91 −64.66	270.9 −31.7	.SBS3..W100	B P G	SBS3	1.90 16.72	.17 16.72	1.83	FGTOW
N1097A	2 44.3 −30 29 / 4.3 25	193.26 −63.32	226.91 −64.66	270.9 −31.7	.E.5...						
N1104	2 46.0 −0 29 / 5.1 25	142.58 −49.77	174.10 −51.12	305.2 −27.3				1.02 .93	.33 .93	.89	F
N1136	2 49.4 −55 16 / 3.0 25	239.11 −54.22	273.39 −54.67	242.2 −29.3	.SBR1$.B060			1.11 1.62	.07 1.62	1.08	P
N1140	2 52.2 −10 14 / 4.8 24	156.47 −54.87	188.34 −56.33	294.8 −31.3	.I..9..W060 P	I P*K *		1.06 2.94	.30 2.94	.94	AKQ
N1143	2 52.6 −0 22 / 5.1 24	144.22 −48.52	175.83 −49.88	305.9 −28.9	.L...P.P200			.77 .78	.00 .78	.77	AZ
N1144	2 52.6 −0 22 / 5.1 24	144.22 −48.52	175.83 −49.88	305.9 −28.9	.S...P.P200			.95 .98	.16 .98	.88	AZ
N1156	2 56.7 25 3 / 5.8 24	124.54 −28.11	156.28 −29.20	331.9 −19.6	.IBS9..P200 I 9 7*	I A I9	I 9	1.42 8.81	.20 7.81	1.34	AHLSXZ
N1169	3 0.1 46 12 / 6.8 24	113.33 −9.77	145.41 −10.63	350.9 −9.0	.SXR3..W060 SX2 3*	S FG		1.47 5.21	.12 5.21	1.42	AKQ
N1172	2 59.3 −15 2 / 4.7 24	165.29 −55.86	197.49 −57.34	289.6 −33.9	E 1			1.12 .53	.05 .53	1.10	AK
N1175	3 1.3 42 8 / 6.6 23	115.64 −13.15	147.66 −14.06	347.6 −11.5	.LAR+..W060 S NN *	D *K		1.24 1.96	.68 1.96	.97	AK
N1179	2 59.7 −19 6 / 4.6 24	172.09 −57.47	204.58 −58.95	284.7 −34.5	.SXR6..W100 S P	S F		1.72 4.02	.11 4.02	1.67	KW
N1186	3 2.3 42 38 / 6.6 23	115.54 −12.63	147.56 −13.54	348.1 −11.4	.S.....W			1.41 3.44	.40 3.44	1.25	AR
N1187	3 0.4 −23 4 / 4.5 24	179.28 −58.60	212.10 −60.06	279.9 −35.0	.SBR5..W060 SX5* 1	SB *AF S AF		1.66 13.67	.09 13.67	1.62	FGKMTQ
N1199	3 1.3 −15 48 / 4.7 23	166.89 −55.77	199.16 −57.26	288.8 −34.5	.E.3.*.W060 E 2	E3 K		1.10 1.41	.08 1.41	1.06	AKQ
N1201	3 2.0 −26 15 / 4.3 23	185.42 −58.98	218.52 −60.39	276.0 −35.5	.LARO*.P200 S 0		L 1	1.45 7.25	.23 7.25	1.36	KNZ
N1209	3 3.8 −15 48 / 4.7 23	167.36 −55.24	199.65 −56.72	288.9 −35.1	.E.6...W E 5	ED *K		1.17 .77	.28 .77	1.05	AK
N1232	3 7.5 −20 46 / 4.5 23	176.12 −56.34	208.77 −57.81	282.9 −36.5	.SXT5..P200 S 5 1	S F S F	S 5 S5	1.85 18.10	.06 18.10	1.82	FKMTXZ
N1232A	3 8.0 −20 47 / 4.5 23	176.22 −56.23	208.87 −57.70	282.9 −36.6	.SBS9..P200			.96 3.97	.06 3.97	.93	FMZ
N1241	3 8.8 −9 7 / 4.9 23	158.71 −50.85	190.72 −52.32	297.2 −35.1	.SBT3..W060 S 4 T	SX F		1.31 7.31	.23 7.31	1.21	ABEFKQ
N1242	3 8.9 −9 6 / 4.9 23	158.71 −50.82	190.72 −52.29	297.2 −35.1	.SBT5*.W060			.98 1.21	.10 1.21	.94	ABQ
N1248	3 10.3 −5 25 / 5.0 22	154.36 −48.42	186.26 −49.87	301.6 −34.5	.LASO*.P200			.93 2.47	.09 2.47	.90	AZ
N1249	3 8.6 −53 32 / 2.9 23	234.09 −52.83	268.22 −53.41	243.2 −32.5	.SBS6..S030			1.69 5.33	.33 5.33	1.55	DEI
N1255	3 11.4 −25 58 / 4.3 22	185.67 −56.86	218.71 −58.27	276.4 −37.6	.SXT4..W100 S 5 3			1.55 10.40	.19 10.40	1.47	DEKNW
N1270	3 15.6 41 18 / 6.6 22	118.41 −12.41	150.45 −13.38	348.4 −14.1	.E.3...W E 2			.97 .75	.08 .75	.94	AK
N1272	3 15.7 41 16 / 6.6 22	118.44 −12.43	150.48 −13.40	348.4 −14.2	.L.....W			1.00 .54	.00 .54	1.00	A
N1273	3 16.1 41 22 / 6.6 22	118.45 −12.30	150.49 −13.27	348.6 −14.2	.E.1...W			.90 .42	.00 .42	.90	A
N1274	3 16.4 41 22 / 6.6 22	118.49 −12.25	150.54 −13.22	348.6 −14.2							
N1275	3 16.5 41 20 / 6.6 22	118.53 −12.29	150.57 −13.26	348.6 −14.3	.P.....P200	E2P K		1.16 4.54	.12 4.54	1.11	AMZ
N1277	3 16.5 41 24 / 6.6 22	118.49 −12.23	150.54 −13.20	348.6 −14.2	.E.3...W			.95 .48	.32 .48	.83	A
N1278	3 16.5 41 23 / 6.6 22	118.50 −12.25	150.55 −13.22	348.6 −14.2	.E.1...W			.95 .48	.00 .48	.95	A
N1281	3 16.7 41 27 / 6.6 22	118.49 −12.17	150.54 −13.14	348.7 −14.2	.E.2...W			.88 .38	.00 .38	.88	A
N1282	3 16.6 41 8 / 6.6 22	118.66 −12.44	150.70 −13.42	348.4 −14.4	.E.3...W						
N1288	3 15.3 −32 46 / 4.0 22	198.21 −56.79	231.71 −58.06	267.8 −38.1	.S....*.H030			1.28 2.07	.01 2.07	1.27	EF
N1291	3 15.5 −41 17 / 3.6 22	213.57 −55.02	247.51 −57.04	257.1 −36.9	RSBS0..S030			1.76 5.58	.17 5.58	1.69	EFI

36

NGC (IC, A) (14)	m_H / m_C (15)	B(O) w (16)	B'(O) m'_C (17)	S(B) (18)	(B-V)(O) w (19)	C_O(O) (20)	S(C) (21)	(U-B)(O) w (22)	V w (23)	V_O ΔV (24)	S(V) (25)	ϕ_r n (26)	φ(21) (27)	(28)	Photo. (29)
N1079	12.6	12.47	13.91	C	.95	.85	C		2252	2158	B				H
	12.35	2.03	13.79		1.88				.2	-94					
N1084	11.2	11.38	12.57	AC	.63	.49	AC		1465	1448	BF				LP
	11.92	10.53	13.11		8.13				5.0	-17					
N1087	11.2	11.74	13.48	CG	.61	.48	CG		1824	1833	B				EKP
	11.66	4.33	13.40		6.25				.3	9					
N1090	12.8	11.89	13.68	G	.67		G								
	12.48	0.98	14.27		2.50					10					
N1094															
										9					
N1097	10.6	10.39	14.28	C	.79*	.67	C		1373	1272	BCF				EHIP
	10.31	2.94	14.20		3.75				6.6	-101					
N1097A				C*			C*								HIP
										-101					
N1104															
										8					
N1136															
										-175					
N1140	13.0	12.89	12.28	CL	.43	.35	CL		1544	1510	B				
	13.38	1.89	12.77		2.80				6.3	-34					
N1143															
										3					
N1144															
										3					
N1156	12.9	12.71	14.15	CGL	.56	.45	CGL		405	497	B				P
	12.61	3.86	14.05		7.20				6.3	92					
N1169	13.0	12.80	14.59	H	.89		H								
	12.57	3.16	14.36		6.25					155					
N1172	13.1														
	13.00		13.24							-58					
N1175	13.0	14.31	13.85	H	.99		H								
	13.26	4.12	12.80		6.25					143					
N1179	13.0														
	12.06		15.15							-73					
N1186															D
										144					
N1187	11.3								1579	1491	C				E
	11.21		14.05						3.6	-88					
N1199	12.7	13.02	13.06	L	1.01	.92	L		2581	2518	B				
	12.81	1.18	12.85		0.90				4.0	-63					
N1201	12.0	11.88	13.37	CL	.92	.82	CL	.49	1722	1622	B				P
	11.94	2.56	13.43		2.80		/L		4.0	-100					
N1209	12.5	12.86	12.85	CL	.96	.87	CL	.60	2568	2503	B				
	12.69	5.00	12.68		6.50		/L		.4	-65					
N1232	11.1	10.73	14.57	CG	.70*	.60	CG		1820	1734	C				P
	10.64	3.35	14.48		4.38				1.6	-86					
N1232A															
										-86					
N1241	13.0														
	13.03		13.82							-45					
N1242															
										-45					
N1248															
										-32					
N1249	12.3														F
	11.96		14.45							-181					
N1255	12.1														
	11.97		14.06							-107					
N1270		14.39	13.78	C	1.13	.85	C		4905	5036	B				
		1.91			1.88				2.4	131					
N1272		13.91	13.65	CH	1.13	.86	CH		4172	4303	D				
		3.81			11.25				.7	131					
N1273		14.70	13.94	CH	1.15	.87	CH		5354	5485	B				
		6.18			8.13				4.0	131					
N1274									6447	6578	D				
									.6	131					
N1275	12.7	13.14	13.43	AC	.85*	.57	AC		5160	5291	B				
	12.72	3.03	13.01		6.25				6.3	131					
N1277		14.75	13.59	AC	1.09	.81	AC		4974	5105	B				
		4.48			6.25				4.0	131					
N1278		14.22	13.71	AC	1.01	.72	AC		6115	6246	B				
		3.64			6.25				4.0	131					
N1281		14.87	13.96	A	1.11		A								
		2.16			4.38					131					
N1282				C*			C*								
										130					
N1288	13.0														
	13.07		14.16							-132					
N1291	10.2								802	646	HM				FL
	10.17		13.36						31.2	-156					

NGC (IC, A) (1)	Coordinates					Classification			Diameters			
	RA (1950) Dec 100 P (2)	Dec 100 P (3)	L^I B^I (4)	L^II B^II (5)	SGL SGB (6)	Rev. type (S) DDO (T, L) (7)	Yerkes (1) Yerkes (2) (8)	Hu-San Ho (9)	log D w (10)	log R w (11)	log D(O) (12)	S (D,R) (13)
N1292	3 16.0 4.2	-27 48 22	189.27 -56.18	222.43 -57.55	274.1 -38.6	.SAS5..W100			1.38 3.76	.38 3.76	1.23	EW
N1293	3 17.9 6.6	41 10 22	118.85 -12.28	150.89 -13.25	348.6 -14.6	.E.3...W			.90 .42	.00 .42	.90	A
N1294	3 18.0 6.6	41 8 22	118.88 -12.29	150.93 -13.27	348.6 -14.6	.E.....W			.90 .42	.00 .42	.90	A
N1297	3 17.0 4.5	-19 16 22	175.00 -53.73	207.57 -55.20	285.0 -38.6	.S.....R020 E 2	D GK*		1.16 1.15	.08 1.15	1.13	HK
N1300	3 17.5 4.5	-19 35 22	175.57 -53.73	208.16 -55.20	284.6 -38.8	.SBT4..P200 SB3 1	B F B G	SBS3 S4	1.80 12.83	.19 12.83	1.73	HKLUXZ
N1302	3 17.7 4.3	-26 14 22	186.65 -55.52	219.68 -56.93	276.1 -39.0	RSBRO..P200 SX0	B K	S 1	1.46 8.91	.03 8.91	1.44	DEKPZ
N1305	3 18.8 5.0	-2 30 22	152.85 -44.97	184.76 -46.40	305.8 -35.7				.91 .87	.04 .87	.90	AF
N1309	3 19.8 4.6	-15 35 21	169.84 -51.67	202.21 -53.16	289.8 -38.9	.SAS4*.W060 S 5 4	S F DS G		1.23 7.08	.03 7.08	1.22	AFKMUQ
N1310	3 19.1 3.8	-37 19 22	206.38 -55.88	240.10 -57.03	261.9 -38.3	.SAS5*.W100			1.35 1.30	.14 1.30	1.29	I
N1313	3 17.6 1.2	-66 40 22	249.60 -44.47	283.35 -44.66	228.7 -28.2	.SBS7..S074			1.89 11.79	.13 11.79	1.83	EIJO
N1313A	3 9.4 1.3	-66 52 23	250.55 -44.95	284.33 -45.12	228.9 -27.4	.S...*.S030			1.12 .95	.57 .95	.90	I
N1315	3 20.9 4.4	-21 33 21	179.15 -53.63	211.87 -55.08	282.2 -39.7	.LBT+$.W060						
N1316	3 20.7 3.8	-37 25 21	206.51 -55.56	240.22 -56.70	261.7 -38.6	.LXSOP.W100			1.60 12.54	.13 12.54	1.55	DEFIOW
N1316C	3 23.0 3.8	-37 12 21	206.07 -55.12	239.75 -56.27	261.9 -39.1	.S...$.S030			1.10 .91	.43 .91	.92	I
N1317	3 20.8 3.8	-37 17 21	206.27 -55.55	239.98 -56.70	261.9 -38.6	PSXTO*.W100			1.30 4.81	.05 4.81	1.28	EIOW
N1319	3 21.7 4.4	-21 41 21	179.46 -53.49	212.19 -54.94	282.0 -39.9	.L...../W060			1.09 .69	.36 .69	.95	Q
N1325	3 22.3 4.4	-21 43 21	179.58 -53.37	212.31 -54.82	282.0 -40.0	.SAS4..W060 S 3 NK-	SD F	S4	1.58 7.49	.46 7.49	1.40	DEKXQ
N1325A	3 22.7 4.4	-21 31 21	179.31 -53.22	212.03 -54.67	282.2 -40.1	.SBR3.$W060		S5	1.41 1.03	.00 1.03	1.41	XQ
N1326	3 22.0 3.8	-36 39 21	205.13 -55.35	238.79 -56.52	262.6 -39.0	RLBR+..W100	B *K *		1.44 8.47	.14 8.47	1.39	DEFIW
N1326A	3 23.1 3.8	-36 31 21	204.88 -55.14	238.52 -56.31	262.7 -39.2	.SB.9P$S030			1.14 .98	.06 .98	1.12	I
N1326B	3 23.3 3.8	-36 31 21	204.87 -55.10	238.51 -56.27	262.7 -39.3	.SB.5*/S030			1.55 1.70	.60 1.70	1.31	I
N1331	3 23.9 4.4	-21 32 21	179.48 -52.96	212.20 -54.41	282.2 -40.4	.E.2.*.W100			.78 .61	.05 .61	.76	W
N1332	3 24.1 4.4	-21 31 21	179.48 -52.91	212.20 -54.36	282.2 -40.4	.L.S-*/W100 E 7	D K DE K		1.47 9.07	.50 9.07	1.27	EKMQW
N1337	3 25.6 4.9	-8 34 21	161.41 -47.06	193.53 -48.54	299.0 -39.0	.SAS6..W060 S 6 7*	S AF	S6	1.80 6.60	.58 6.60	1.56	EKLXQ
N1339	3 26.1 4.0	-32 27 21	197.82 -54.50	231.21 -55.78	267.8 -40.4	.E...*.			1.05 1.57	.06 1.57	1.03	DE
N1341	3 26.1 3.8	-37 19 21	206.20 -54.49	239.85 -55.65	261.6 -39.7	.SBS1..S030			1.09 .90	.01 .90	1.09	I
N1344	3 26.7 4.1	-31 14 21	195.75 -54.29	229.07 -55.59	269.4 -40.7	.E.5...W100	E5 K		1.33 5.10	.25 5.10	1.23	DEW
N1350	3 29.1 3.9	-33 47 20	200.15 -53.93	233.59 -55.18	266.0 -40.9	.SB.4..H030			1.58 3.80	.28 3.80	1.47	DEG
N1351	3 28.6 3.9	-35 2 20	202.27 -54.06	235.78 -55.27	264.4 -40.6	.E+4..$S030			1.03 2.33	.20 2.33	.95	DEI
N1351A	3 26.9 3.9	-35 21 21	202.81 -54.40	236.36 -55.61	264.1 -40.2	.S...../S030			1.52 .72	.76 .72	1.22	I
N1353	3 29.8 4.4	-21 0 20	179.35 -51.48	212.05 -52.94	283.0 -41.7	.SBT3*.W060 S 3 4	S FG		1.46 8.12	.38 8.12	1.30	DEFKQ
N1355	3 30.9 5.0	-5 10 20	158.37 -44.10	190.43 -45.56	303.7 -39.4	.L...../W060			.99 .99	.67 .99	.72	Q
N1357	3 30.9 4.7	-13 50 20	169.20 -48.49	201.55 -49.98	292.6 -41.3	.SAS2..W060 S	S GK		1.27 2.19	.14 2.19	1.21	AKQ
N1358	3 31.2 5.0	-5 16 20	158.54 -44.09	190.61 -45.56	303.6 -39.5	.SXRO..W060 SX2 3*			1.38 2.36	.15 2.36	1.32	KQ
N1359	3 31.5 4.5	-19 41 20	177.59 -50.67	210.21 -52.14	284.8 -42.1	.SBS9P$P200 SB7P 7	SIP*A *		1.31 8.83	.08 8.83	1.28	DFKMZ
N1365	3 31.8 3.8	-36 18 20	204.40 -53.40	237.94 -54.58	262.6 -41.0	.SBS3..W100	B FG		1.97 21.26	.26 21.26	1.87	DEFGTIO W
N1366	3 32.0 4.0	-31 23 20	196.18 -53.17	229.47 -54.47	269.1 -41.8				1.22 .67	.41 .67	1.06	E
N1371	3 32.8 4.3	-25 6 20	186.02 -51.96	218.95 -53.36	277.5 -42.5	.SXT1..P200 SX0			1.58 7.80	.13 7.80	1.53	DKZ
N1374	3 33.7 3.9	-35 24 20	202.89 -53.08	236.38 -54.28	263.7 -41.5	.E.0...S030			1.01 2.24	.01 2.24	1.00	DEI
N1375	3 33.3 3.9	-35 26 20	202.95 -53.10	236.43 -54.30	263.6 -41.5	.L...*/S030			1.10 .92	.54 .92	.89	I

NGC (IC, A) (14)	m_H m_C (15)	B(O) w (16)	B'(O) m'_C (17)	S(B) (18)	(B-V)(O) w (19)	C_o(O) (20)	S(C) (21)	(U-B)(O) w (22)	V w (23)	V_o ΔV (24)	S(V) (25)	φ_r n (26)	φ (21) (27)	(28)	Photo. (29)
N1292	12.8 12.92		13.81							-117					
N1293		14.60 1.96	13.84	C	1.04 1.88		C			129					
N1294		14.55 1.96	13.79	C	1.10 1.88		C			129					
N1297	13.0 12.99		13.33							-89					
N1300	11.8 11.23	11.34 3.51	14.68 14.57	CG	.69 4.38	.57	CG		1625 5.2	1535 -90	C				BKP
N1302	11.9 11.81	11.62 1.11	13.56 13.75	C	.68 1.88	.59	C		1730 1.8	1617 -113	B				P
N1305										-29					
N1309	11.8 12.40		13.19							-78					E
N1310										-148					
N1313	10.8 10.57		14.46						254 44.4	47 -207	H				FHL
N1313A										-205					
N1315										-100					
N1316	10.1 10.34	9.90 2.03	12.39 12.83	C	.82 1.88	.73	C		1864 3.8	1715 -149	BHM				H
N1316C										-150					
N1317	12.2 12.37	11.96 1.72	13.05 13.46	C	.69 3.75	.60	C		2060 1.0	1911 -149	B				H
N1319										-101					
N1325	12.9 12.58	12.56 1.12	14.25 14.27	G	.78 2.50		G			-102					
N1325A		13.45 1.50	15.19	G	.62 2.50		G			-101					
N1326	11.8 11.75		13.39							-148					F
N1326A										-148					
N1326B										-148					
N1331		15.09 1.96	13.63	C	.77 1.88	.69	C		1408 1.3	1305 -103	C				
N1332	11.4 11.68	11.59 2.00	12.68 12.77	CL	.98 4.70	.88	CL /L	.82	1599 5.6	1497 -102	BC				
N1337	12.7 12.15	12.50 1.45	15.04 14.69	G	.58 2.50		G			-58					
N1339	12.8 12.94		12.78							-139					
N1341	13.1 13.33		13.47							-153					
N1344	11.6 11.79		12.68							-136					
N1350	11.8 11.80		13.89						1802 12.8	1657 -145	DK				
N1351	12.8 13.06		12.55						1589 1.0	1441 -148	D				
N1351A										-148					
N1353	12.4 12.50		13.74							-105					
N1355										-50					
N1357	12.5 12.73		13.52							-82					
N1358	13.1 12.74		14.08							-50					
N1359	12.8 12.94	12.85 1.08	13.94 14.03	C	.39 1.88	.30	C		1992 2.8	1890 -102	C				
N1365	11.2 10.56	10.20 1.64	14.24 14.60	E	.67 6.25	.52	E /E	.12	1724 8.3	1571 -154	DFHI				FHL
N1366	13.0									-140					
N1371	12.2 11.81		14.20							-121					
N1374	12.4 12.71		12.45						1289 1.3	1136 -153	D				
N1375										-153					

NGC (IC, A) (1)	RA (1950) 100 P (2)	Dec 100 P (3)	L^I B^I (4)	L^II B^II (5)	SGL SGB (6)	Rev. type (S) DDO (T,L) (7)	Yerkes (1) Yerkes (2) (8)	Hu-San Ho (9)	log D w (10)	log R w (11)	log D(O) (12)	S (D,R) (13)
N1376	3 34.7	-5 12	159.14	191.23	304.0	.SAS6..W100	S AF		1.27	.04	1.25	KMW
	5.0	20	-43.33	-44.80	-40.3	S 5 4*			5.37	5.37		
N1379	3 34.2	-35 37	203.25	236.74	263.4	.E.0...S030			1.05	.02	1.04	DEI
	3.8	20	-52.92	-54.12	-41.6				2.41	2.41		
N1380	3 34.6	-35 9	202.48	235.94	263.9	.LA....S030			1.50	.46	1.32	DEI
	3.9	20	-52.83	-54.04	-41.8				4.40	4.40		
N1380A	3 34.8	-34 53	202.04	235.49	264.3	.S...*/S030			1.36	.70	1.08	I
	3.9	20	-52.79	-54.01	-41.9				.29	.29		
N1380B	3 35.1	-35 21	202.81	236.28	263.7							
	3.8	20	-52.73	-53.94	-41.8							
N1381	3 34.7	-35 28	203.00	236.48	263.5	.LA.../S030	D K		1.31	.63	1.06	DEI
	3.8	20	-52.81	-54.02	-41.7				3.40	3.40		
N1385	3 35.2	-24 40	185.56	218.45	278.1	.SBS6..W100	SI *AF		1.44	.22	1.35	DFKTW
	4.3	20	-51.32	-52.74	-43.0	S 5 2	S P A *		10.09	10.09		
N1386	3 35.0	-36 10	204.16	237.67	262.6	.LA....S030			1.42	.44	1.24	DEI
	3.8	20	-52.75	-53.94	-41.7				3.63	3.63		
N1387	3 35.1	-35 41	203.36	236.85	263.2	.L..-..S030			1.17	.03	1.16	DEI
	3.8	20	-52.73	-53.93	-41.8				2.80	2.80		
N1389	3 35.3	-35 55	203.75	237.24	262.9	.E+4.*.S030			1.10	.19	1.02	DEI
	3.8	20	-52.69	-53.89	-41.8				2.60	2.60		
N1393	3 36.4	-18 36	176.64	209.22	286.4	.LAR+*.W			1.05	.07	1.03	FL
	4.5	20	-49.21	-50.68	-43.1				1.51	.94		
N1394	3 36.9	-18 27	176.50	209.07	286.6	.L....$.H030			1.05			FL
	4.5	19	-49.04	-50.51	-43.2				1.51			
N1395	3 36.3	-23 11	183.39	216.20	280.1	.E.2...W100	E2 K		1.26	.12	1.21	DKW
	4.3	20	-50.69	-52.12	-43.3	E 3	E3 K		4.18	4.18		
N1398	3 36.8	-26 30	188.55	221.54	275.5	PSBR2..P200	B K	SBR3	1.73	.11	1.69	DFKMZ
	4.2	19	-51.39	-52.77	-43.3	SX2 1			14.67	12.31		
N1399	3 36.6	-35 37	203.26	236.72	263.2	.E.0...S030	E1 K		1.26	.02	1.25	DEI
	3.8	20	-52.43	-53.63	-42.1				3.33	3.33		
N1400	3 37.2	-18 51	177.10	209.70	286.1	.LA.-..W060			1.07	.06	1.05	FKLQ
	4.5	19	-49.12	-50.59	-43.3	E 1	E2 K		3.95	2.41		
N1401	3 37.2	-22 53	183.02	215.82	280.5	.L..../L036						
	4.4	19	-50.41	-51.84	-43.5							
N1404	3 37.0	-35 45	203.47	236.94	263.0	.E.1...S030	E1 K		1.14	.03	1.13	DEI
	3.8	19	-52.35	-53.55	-42.1	E 1			2.78	2.78		
N1406	3 37.5	-31 28	196.51	229.76	268.7	.S....*/			1.50	.59	1.26	DE
	4.0	19	-52.01	-53.31	-43.0				2.65	2.65		
N1407	3 37.9	-18 44	177.03	209.62	286.2	.E+0...W060	ED *K		1.16	.00	1.16	FKLQ
	4.5	19	-48.92	-50.39	-43.5	E 0			3.92	3.92		
N1411	3 37.1	-44 15	217.23	251.00	252.1	.LA....S030			1.26	.10	1.22	I
	3.4	19	-51.57	-52.52	-39.9				.58	.58		
N1415	3 38.7	-22 43	182.93	215.71	280.7	RSXS0..W100	DS GK*		1.40	.27	1.29	DKW
	4.4	19	-50.03	-51.46	-43.8	S 4 T -*5			5.80	5.80		
N1416	3 38.8	-22 56	183.26	216.05	280.4	.E.1.*.W100			.68	.00	.68	W
	4.4	19	-50.07	-51.50	-43.9				.53	.53		
N1417	3 39.5	-4 52	159.67	191.77	304.8	.SXT3..P200	SX FG		1.37	.19	1.29	ABKWZ
	5.0	19	-42.15	-43.63	-41.4	S 3 2*			7.51	7.51		
N1418	3 39.8	-4 53	159.74	191.85	304.9	.SBS3*.P200			1.11	.12	1.06	ABWZ
	5.0	19	-42.10	-43.57	-41.5				3.43	3.43		
N1421	3 40.2	-13 40	170.46	202.84	293.3	.SXT4*.W060	S A		1.52	.59	1.28	AKLUQ
	4.7	19	-46.39	-47.88	-43.5	S 4 1*			8.74	8.74		
N1422	3 39.3	-21 51	181.71	214.45	281.9	.S...*.W060			1.25	.58	1.02	Q
	4.4	19	-49.65	-51.09	-44.0				1.36	1.36		
N1424	3 40.8	-4 53	159.93	192.04	304.9	.SXT3*.W100			1.25	.32	1.12	AW
	5.0	19	-41.89	-43.37	-41.7				1.27	1.27		
N1425	3 40.1	-30 4	194.37	227.54	270.5	.SAS3..W100			1.66	.33	1.53	DW
	4.1	19	-51.29	-52.61	-43.7				6.17	6.17		
N1426	3 40.6	-22 16	182.46	215.22	281.4	.E.4...W060	E4 K		1.08	.17	1.02	DKQ
	4.4	19	-49.48	-50.92	-44.3	E 2			1.97	1.97		
N1427	3 40.4	-35 34	203.19	236.62	263.1	.E.3...S030			1.20	.16	1.13	EI
	3.8	19	-51.66	-52.86	-42.8				1.88	1.88		
N1427A	3 37.7	-35 47	203.53	236.99	262.9	.I...*.S030			1.30	.23	1.21	I
	3.8	19	-52.21	-53.40	-42.3				1.23	1.23		
N1428	3 40.5	-35 19	202.79	236.21	263.4	.L...$.S030			1.08	.43	.90	I
	3.8	19	-51.63	-52.84	-42.9				.63	.63		
N1433	3 40.4	-47 24	221.93	255.72	248.1	.SBR1..S074			1.78	.08	1.75	DEJ
	3.1	19	-50.35	-51.20	-39.3				7.68	7.68		
N1437	3 41.7	-36 1	203.92	237.36	262.4	.SBT1..S030			1.34	.15	1.28	EI
	3.8	19	-51.40	-52.59	-43.0				2.09	2.09		
N1439	3 42.6	-22 5	182.40	215.15	281.6	.E.1...W060	E1 K		1.12	.03	1.11	DKQ
	4.4	19	-48.99	-50.42	-44.7	E 1			2.06	2.06		
N1440	3 42.8	-18 27	177.26	209.84	286.7	.L...*.L036	B K		1.14	.14	1.09	KL
	4.5	19	-47.74	-49.20	-44.6	SX0			1.57	.94		
N1441	3 43.2	-4 15	159.66	191.78	306.0	.SBS3..W100			1.13	.46	.94	AW
	5.0	19	-41.04	-42.52	-42.1				2.30	2.30		
N1448	3 42.9	-44 48	217.80	251.52	251.0	.SA.6*.S030			1.87	.76	1.57	DEI
	3.3	19	-50.45	-51.39	-40.7				6.71	6.71		
N1449	3 43.5	-4 18	159.77	191.89	305.9	.L.....W100			.74	.27	.63	W
	5.0	19	-41.01	-42.48	-42.2				1.32	1.32		

NGC (IC, A) (14)	m_H / m_c (15)	B(O) / w (16)	B'(O) / m'_c (17)	S(B) (18)	(B-V)(O) / w (19)	C_0(O) (20)	S(C) (21)	(U-B)(O) / w (22)	V / w (23)	V_0 / ΔV (24)	S(V) (25)	ϕ_r / n (26)	ϕ(21) (27)	(28)	Photo. (29)
N1376	12.9									−53					
	12.97		13.96												
N1379	12.3								1457	1303	D				
	12.58		12.52						1.1	−154					
N1380	11.4	11.30	12.59	CL	.86	.75	CL	.37	1865	1712	BD				
	11.61	2.15	12.90		2.80		/L		4.1	−153					
N1380A										−152					
N1380B										−154					
N1381	12.6								1871	1717	D				
	12.82		12.86						1.1	−154					
N1385	11.8	11.79	13.28	C	.66	.54	C		2012	1890	C				
	12.15	2.03	13.64		1.88				1.9	−122					
N1386	12.4														
	12.40		13.29							−156					
N1387	12.1								1274	1119	D				
	12.34		12.83						2.1	−155					
N1389	12.8								1070	915	D				
	12.94		12.78						.7	−155					
N1393										−103					
N1394										−103					
N1395	11.2	11.65	12.44	C	.92	.84	C		1721	1603	BC				
	11.56	1.72	12.35		1.88				8.2	−118					
N1398	11.3	10.73	13.87	C	.97	.85	C		1524	1395	C				JKP
	11.01	1.94	14.15		1.88				3.1	−129					
N1399	10.9	11.15	12.14	CL	.85	.77	CL	.44	1466	1311	BD				
	11.29	2.48	12.28		5.60		/L		1.6	−156					
N1400	12.5	12.34	12.33	AC	.88	.80	AC		483	379	B				
	12.78	7.81	12.77		10.00				6.3	−104					
N1401										−118					
N1404	11.5	11.34	11.73	CL	.89	.80	CL	.47*	1985	1828	BD				
	11.89	3.65	12.28		4.20		/L		2.2	−156					
N1406	12.7														
	12.89		13.93							−145					
N1407	11.5	11.43	11.97	AC	1.03	.95	AC		1811	1707	B				
	11.84	8.85	12.38		8.13				4.0	−105					
N1411	12.0														
	12.16		13.00							−178					
N1415	12.8								1508	1390	B				
	12.67		13.81						4.0	−118					
N1416										−119					
N1417	12.9								4101	4045	B				
	12.79		13.98						4.0	−56					
N1418										−57					
N1421	12.0														
	12.37		13.46							−89					
N1422										−116					
N1424										−58					
N1425	12.1														
	11.81		14.20							−142					
N1426	12.8	12.86	12.65	C	.86	.78	C		1358	1240	B				
	12.96	4.25	12.75		7.50				4.0	−119					
N1427	12.4								1681	1523	D				
	12.49		12.88						2.0	−158					
N1427A										−157					
N1428										−158					
N1433	11.4								974	787	H				GL
	10.90		14.34						8.2	−186					
N1437	12.9														
	12.77		13.91							−160					
N1439	12.9	12.90	13.19	C	.88	.79	C		1997	1377	B				
	12.85	2.00	13.14		1.88				1.0	−120					
N1440	13.0														
	13.04		13.23							−108					
N1441		14.11	13.55	C	1.00	.77	C		4262	4205	B				
		1.83			1.88				.4	−57					
N1448	11.8														F
	11.67		14.21							−182					
N1449		14.84	12.68	C	.89	.75	C		4176	4118	B				
		1.46			1.88				1.0	−58					

NGC (IC, A)	Coordinates					Classification			Diameters			
	RA (1950) 100 P	Dec 100 P	L^I B^I	L^II B^II	SGL SGB	Rev. type (S) DDO (T, L)	Yerkes (1) Yerkes (2)	Hu-San Ho	log D w	log R w	log D(O)	S (D, R)
(1)	(2)	(3)	(4)	(5)	(6)	(7)	(8)	(9)	(10)	(11)	(12)	(13)
N1451	3 43.6 5.0	-4 14 19	159.72 -40.95	191.83 -42.42	306.1 -42.2	.L...$.W100			.68 .53	.38 .53	.53	W
N1452	3 43.1 4.5	-18 47 19	177.76 -47.79	210.36 -49.26	286.3 -44.7	.SBR.$.L036 SB0	B K		1.27 1.84	.23 1.24	1.18	KL
N1453	3 44.0 5.0	-4 8 19	159.68 -40.81	191.80 -42.29	306.2 -42.2	.E.2+..W100 E 2	E3 K		1.08 2.53	.13 2.53	1.03	AKW
N1461	3 46.1 4.6	-16 32 18	175.09 -46.29	207.60 -47.76	289.5 -45.3	.LARO..W100 S 0	DS *K		1.32 3.98	.48 3.98	1.12	KW
N1469	3 54.2 9.9	68 29 17	106.13 12.43	138.71 11.72	12.5 0.0							
N1482	3 52.5 4.4	-20 39 18	181.45 -46.35	214.13 -47.79	283.7 -47.0	.S..1P.W						
N1483	3 51.2 3.1	-47 38 18	221.68 -48.52	255.37 -49.37	246.8 -40.9	.S...4..B						
N1485	3 59.5 10.7	70 55 17	104.77 14.53	137.40 13.84	14.5 1.5							
N1487	3 54.1 3.4	-42 31 17	213.90 -48.74	247.46 -49.76	252.9 -43.4	.P.....W100			1.23 3.55	.15 3.55	1.17	IW
N1493	3 55.9 3.1	-46 21 17	219.57 -47.95	253.20 -48.86	247.9 -42.2	.SBR6..S030			1.40 1.40	.06 1.40	1.37	I
N1494	3 56.2 2.9	-49 3 17	223.50 -47.42	257.17 -48.24	244.7 -41.0	.SAS7..S030			1.39 1.38	.18 1.38	1.31	I
N1507	4 1.8 5.0	-2 20 16	160.88 -36.11	193.05 -37.59	310.6 -45.9	.SBS9P$W100 S	I *A		1.51 8.85	.66 8.85	1.25	AEKMW
N1510	4 1.9 3.3	-43 33 16	215.26 -47.23	248.78 -48.22	250.8 -44.3	.E.0.*.S030			.83 .56	.00 .56	.83	I
N1511	3 59.3 0.4	-67 46 17	247.81 -40.50	281.37 -40.74	225.1 -31.0	.SA.2*.S030			1.43 3.87	.49 3.87	1.23	DEI
N1511A	4 0.1 0.4	-67 56 17	247.96 -40.36	281.51 -40.59	224.8 -30.9	.S...$.S030			1.10 .91	.53 .91	.88	I
N1511B	4 0.7 0.4	-67 45 17	247.71 -40.39	281.26 -40.63	225.0 -31.1	.S...*/S030			1.20 .76	.73 .76	.91	I
N1512	4 2.3 3.3	-43 29 16	215.15 -47.17	248.66 -48.16	250.9 -44.4	.LBR+..S030			1.52 3.13	.10 3.13	1.48	FI
N1515	4 2.7 2.4	-54 14 16	230.44 -45.21	264.10 -45.87	238.1 -39.3	.SXS4..R074			1.70 9.08	.67 9.08	1.44	DEIO
N1515A	4 2.5 2.4	-54 14 16	230.46 -45.23	264.11 -45.90	238.7 -39.3	.SBR3$.R074			.97 1.46	.05 1.46	.95	O
N1518	4 4.7 4.4	-21 18 16	183.61 -43.86	216.32 -45.29	282.8 -49.9	.SBS8..W100 S 5P	I A I P*A *		1.50 4.87	.38 4.87	1.35	FKW
N1521	4 6.2 4.4	-21 11 16	183.62 -43.49	216.32 -44.92	282.9 -50.2	.E+3.*.W100 E 3	ED K		1.11 .39	.15 .39	1.05	K
N1527	4 6.9 2.9	-48 1 16	221.56 -45.85	255.13 -46.72	244.8 -43.1	.LA.-..S030			1.32 2.58	.45 2.58	1.14	DI
N1530	4 16.9 12.7	75 11 14	102.47 18.39	135.21 17.76	18.1 4.0	.SBT3..W060			1.66 4.31	.30 2.90	1.54	LQ
N1530A	4 38.2 13.3	75 37 12	103.00 19.71	135.77 19.06	19.5 3.6							
N1531	4 10.1 3.8	-32 59 15	200.01 -45.34	233.14 -46.59	264.6 -49.4				1.13 .59	.30 .59	1.01	E
N1532	4 10.2 3.8	-33 0 15	200.03 -45.32	233.17 -46.57	264.6 -49.4	.SBS2*$H030			1.88 2.77	.67 2.77	1.61	EG
N1533	4 8.8 2.2	-56 15 16	232.83 -43.82	266.45 -44.43	235.3 -38.9	.LB.-..S030			1.35 3.29	.04 3.29	1.33	DEI
N1536	4 10.0 2.1	-56 36 15	233.24 -43.56	266.84 -44.16	234.9 -38.8	.SBS5*.S030			1.16 1.00	.17 1.00	1.09	I
N1537	4 11.8 3.9	-31 41 15	198.26 -44.80	231.34 -46.07	266.4 -50.1	.L..-.$W100						
N1543	4 11.7 2.0	-57 52 15	234.82 -42.99	268.41 -43.55	233.4 -38.3	RLBS0..S030			1.49 3.87	.28 3.87	1.38	DEI
N1546	4 13.6 2.1	-56 11 15	232.50 -43.20	266.08 -43.81	234.9 -39.5	.L...*.S030			1.31 2.80	.35 2.80	1.18	DEI
N1549	4 14.7 2.2	-55 42 15	231.81 -43.17	265.38 -43.80	235.3 -39.9	.E.0+..S030			1.39 3.49	.04 3.49	1.37	DEI
N1553	4 15.2 2.2	-55 54 15	232.05 -43.05	265.62 -43.68	235.0 -39.8	.LARO..B060			1.46 6.60	.17 6.60	1.39	DEPI
N1558	4 17.7 3.1	-45 9 14	217.26 -44.30	250.69 -45.25	247.0 -46.1	.S...$.						
N1559	4 17.0 1.2	-62 55 14	240.98 -40.78	274.53 -41.19	228.0 -35.5	.SBS6..S030			1.44 2.36	.23 2.36	1.35	EI
N1560	4 26.1 11.3	71 48 13	105.61 16.68	138.29 15.98	16.7 0.9	.SAS7./W060		S6	1.97 6.24	.68 6.24	1.70	LXQ
N1566	4 18.9 2.2	-55 4 14	230.78 -42.73	264.32 -43.39	235.5 -40.8	.SXS4..S030			1.86 5.88	.10 5.88	1.82	DEI
N1569	4 26.0 9.5	64 45	111.11 12.07	143.67 11.24	12.6 -4.9	.IB.9..P200 I P 6*	I A	I9	1.40 7.88	.34 7.88	1.26	AKMXZ
N1574	4 21.0 2.0	-57 5 14	233.35 -41.99	266.88 -42.58	233.2 -39.7	.LAS-..S030			1.10 2.23	.02 2.23	1.09	DEI
N1587	4 28.1 5.1	0 33 13	162.24 -29.03	194.46 -30.51	318.5 -50.8	.E.1...W			.93 .90	.00 .90	.93	AB

42

NGC (IC, A) (14)	Magnitudes				Colors				Velocities			Radio			
	m_H m_c (15)	B(O) w (16)	B'(O) m'_c (17)	S(B) (18)	(B-V)(O) w (19)	C_o(O) (20)	S(C) (21)	(U-B)(O) w (22)	V w (23)	V_o ΔV (24)	S(V) (25)	$φ_r$ n (26)	φ(21) (27)	(28)	Photo. (29)
N1451		14.79	12.13	C	1.06	.92	C		3927	3869	B				
		1.11			1.88				1.8	−58					
N1452	13.0														
	12.88		13.52							−109					
N1453	12.8	13.10	12.94	CL	1.06	.94	CL	.64	3952	3894	BC				
	12.94	3.31	12.78		3.70		/L		8.7	−58					
N1461	12.8														
	12.85		13.19							−104					
N1469										184					
N1482										−123					
N1483										−193					
N1485										188					
N1487	12.6									−185					F
N1493	11.8														
	12.10		13.69							−194					
N1494	12.2														F
	12.53		13.82							−199					
N1507	12.9														
	13.06		14.00							−66					
N1510										−192					
N1511	12.1														
	12.47		13.36							−222					
N1511A										−223					
N1511B										−223					
N1512	11.8								734	542	H				FL
	11.58		13.72						3.3	−192					
N1515	12.1	12.02	13.96	M	.85		M	.21							FH
	12.06	2.21	14.00				/M			−211					
N1515A										−211					H
N1518	12.1	12.49	13.98	C	.62	.51	C		1027	892	C				EJ
	12.38	1.32	13.87		1.88				2.4	−135					
N1521	13.0								4222	4086	B*				
	13.02		13.01						4.0	−136					
N1527	12.1														
	12.36		12.80							−203					
N1530										192					B
N1530A										189					
N1531	13.0														
										−173					
N1532	11.8														
	11.44		14.23							−173					
N1533	12.3	12.02	13.41	M	.95		M	.52							
	12.17	2.82	13.56				/M			−216					
N1536	13.2														
	13.46		13.65							−217					
N1537	12.0														
										−171					
N1543	12.0	11.71	13.35	M	.96		M	.44	1400	1181	L				
	11.88	2.55	13.52				/M		2.8	−219					
N1546	12.5	12.71	13.35	M	.89		M	.25							
	12.57	3.37	13.21				/M			−219					
N1549	11.0	11.05	12.64	M	.92	.83	M	.47	1160	942	LM				
	11.16	2.60	12.75				/M		29.0	−218					
N1553	10.2	10.57	12.26	M	.93	.83	M	.46	1264	1033	HLM				L
	10.68	2.49	12.37				/M		24.4	−219					
N1558										−204					
N1559	11.1	11.06	12.55	M	.44		M	−.06							
	11.79	1.86	13.28				/M			−226					
N1560		12.37	15.61	G	.73		G								
		1.50			2.50					182					
N1566	10.5	10.09	13.93	M	.70	.59	M	−.14	1393	1173	HL				FIL
	10.32	0.54	14.16				/M		19.5	−220					
N1569	12.4	12.02	13.06	CG	.75	.50	CG		−42	121	BC				
	12.42	2.62	13.46		4.38				16.8	164					
N1574	12.2	11.62	11.81	M	.87	.78	M	.40	890	667	L				F
	12.53	3.44	12.72				/M		4.7	−223					
N1587		13.45	12.84	C	.96	.81	C		3890	3812	B				
		1.94			1.88				1.3	−78					

NGC (IC, A)	Coordinates					Classification			Diameters			
	RA (1950) 100 P	Dec 100 P	L^I B^I	L^{II} B^{II}	SGL SGB	Rev. type (S) DDO (T, L)	Yerkes (1) Yerkes (2)	Hu-San Ho	log D W	log R W	log D(O)	S (D,R)
(1)	(2)	(3)	(4)	(5)	(6)	(7)	(8)	(9)	(10)	(11)	(12)	(13)
N1596	4 26.6 2.2	−55 7 13	230.54 −41.64	264.04 −42.31	234.5 −41.6	.LA..*/B060			1.40 6.18	.57 6.18	1.17	DEPI
N1599	4 29.2 5.0	− 4 41 13	167.59 −31.50	199.89 −32.99	310.8 −53.1				.98 .90	.00 .37	.98	FL
N1600	4 29.2 4.9	− 5 10 13	168.08 −31.74	200.39 −33.23	310.1 −53.3	.E.3...W100 E 2	DE K		1.14 1.35	.15 1.35	1.08	AKL
N1601	4 29.2 4.9	− 5 10 13	168.08 −31.74	200.39 −33.23	310.1 −53.3	.L...*/W100			.81 .30	.00 .30	.81	A
N1602	4 26.8 2.2	−55 10 13	230.60 −41.60	264.10 −42.27	234.4 −41.6	.SBR.*.S030			1.20 1.06	.28 1.06	1.08	I
N1606	4 29.5 4.9	− 5 9 13	168.11 −31.67	200.42 −33.15	310.1 −53.3	.LXR+..W100						
N1614	4 31.9 4.8	− 8 41 12	172.12 −32.83	204.49 −34.31	304.7 −54.9	.SBS.P.P200			1.03 2.26	.15 2.26	.97	Z
N1615	4 33.1 5.9	19 51 12	146.01 −16.70	178.14 −18.08	342.2 −40.6	.L.....L036						
N1617	4 30.6 2.2	−54 42 13	229.86 −41.15	263.33 −41.83	234.4 −42.3	.SBS1..S030			1.56 4.53	.34 4.53	1.42	DEI
N1618	4 33.7 5.0	− 3 15 12	166.80 −29.81	199.09 −31.30	313.7 −53.6	.SBR3*.W100			1.40 2.37	.33 2.37	1.26	AW
N1620	4 34.0 5.1	− 0 14 12	163.89 −28.20	196.14 −29.68	318.4 −52.5	.S....*R020			1.47 2.54	.42 2.54	1.30	AH
N1622	4 34.1 5.0	− 3 17 12	166.89 −29.74	199.18 −31.23	313.7 −53.7	.SXR2*.W100			1.44 3.28	.53 3.28	1.22	ABW
N1625	4 34.6 5.0	− 3 24 12	167.08 −29.69	199.37 −31.18	313.6 −53.9	.SBT3*.W100 S N −			1.42 3.85	.60 3.85	1.18	AKW
N1635	4 37.6 5.1	− 0 38 12	164.81 −27.64	197.07 −29.12	318.4 −53.4				1.13 1.54	.15 1.54	1.07	AH
N1637	4 38.9 5.0	− 2 56 12	167.24 −28.53	199.53 −30.02	315.1 −54.7	.SXT5..P200 S 5 N	S F S F	S 5 S5	1.59 10.08	.08 8.99	1.55	AHKLXZ
N1638	4 39.1 5.1	− 1 53 11	166.24 −27.96	198.52 −29.44	316.8 −54.3	.LA.−*.L036 E 2			1.06 1.45	.08 .82	1.02	AKL
N1640	4 40.1 4.3	−20 32 11	186.23 −35.80	218.88 −37.21	283.6 −58.2	.SBR3..P200 SB2 3	B G		1.34 7.63	.18 7.63	1.26	DKMZ
N1642	4 40.3 5.1	0 31 11	164.10 −26.46	196.35 −27.94	320.7 −53.5	.SA.5..L036			1.29 3.22	.10 2.40	1.25	ALU
N1659	4 44.0 4.9	− 4 53 11	169.88 −28.39	202.21 −29.87	312.7 −56.6	.SAR4P.W100 S 5 K 5	SD *F		1.22 2.56	.14 2.56	1.16	AKW
N1666	4 46.0 4.9	− 6 39 11	171.92 −28.79	204.28 −30.28	310.0 −57.7	.LBR+..W060			1.02 .62	.06 .62	1.00	Q
N1667	4 46.2 4.9	− 6 24 11	171.69 −28.63	204.05 −30.11	310.5 −57.6	.SXR5..W060 S 4 3*	S AF		1.15 1.73	.09 1.73	1.12	KQ
N1672	4 44.9 1.6	−59 20 11	235.37 −38.44	268.78 −38.99	228.2 −40.4	.SBS3..S030			1.64 3.03	.11 3.03	1.59	EI
N1688	4 47.6 1.5	−59 53 10	235.99 −38.01	269.38 −38.55	227.4 −40.3	.SBS5..S030			1.36 3.55	.11 3.55	1.32	DEI
N1699	4 54.5 4.9	− 4 50 9	171.25 −26.07	203.59 −27.55	314.7 −59.0	.SAT3..P200			.86 2.98	.16 2.98	.80	RZ
N1700	4 54.5 4.9	− 4 56 9	171.34 −26.12	203.69 −27.60	314.5 −59.1	.E.4...P200 E 1 T	E4 K		1.21 6.55	.17 6.55	1.14	AKMRZ
N1703	4 52.1 1.5	−59 49 10	235.79 −37.47	269.16 −38.01	226.9 −40.7	.SBR3..S030			1.43 .63	.05 .63	1.41	I
N1705	4 53.2 2.2	−53 26 10	227.74 −38.00	261.07 −38.73	232.5 −45.6	.LA.−P*S030			1.05 .60	.11 .60	1.01	I
N1720	4 56.5 4.8	− 7 55 9	174.55 −27.07	206.95 −28.55	309.3 −60.6	.SBS2..W100			1.14 4.07	.29 3.01	1.03	AFW
N1726	4 57.3 4.8	− 7 49 9	174.56 −26.85	206.95 −28.33	309.6 −60.7	.LAS0*.W100 E 2	E3 K		.98 3.96	.14 3.96	.92	AFKW
N1741	4 59.1 5.0	− 4 20 9	171.37 −24.82	203.71 −26.31	316.5 −59.9	.P.....P200						
N1744	4 57.9 4.1	−26 6 9	194.23 −33.70	226.99 −35.03	271.3 −61.3	.SBS7..W100 SX5 5*			1.72 12.25	.22 12.25	1.63	DEFKW
N1752	4 59.8 4.8	− 8 18 9	175.35 −26.52	207.76 −27.99	309.0 −61.4				1.40 2.62	.51 1.33	1.20	AF
N1771	4 58.5 0.9	−63 13 9	239.83 −36.17	273.17 −36.61	223.4 −38.4							
N1779	5 2.9 4.8	− 9 13 8	176.65 −26.25	209.07 −27.71	307.6 −62.4	.S....*H030			1.06 .62	.27 .62	.95	A
N1784	5 3.2 4.7	−11 56 8	179.43 −27.36	211.89 −28.82	301.9 −63.2	.SBR5..P200 SX5 3*	SB FG	S5	1.53 6.62	.19 5.85	1.45	KLXZ
N1792	5 3.5 3.4	−38 4 8	208.71 −35.35	241.72 −36.46	249.1 −57.1	.SAT4..W100 SI *AF			1.55 4.14	.32 4.14	1.42	GIW
N1796	5 2.1 1.2	−61 12 8	237.28 −36.05	270.61 −36.56	224.5 −40.3	.SBS3*.S030			1.24 2.99	.28 2.99	1.13	DEI
N1796A	5 4.6 1.2	−61 15 8	237.30 −35.75	270.61 −36.25	224.1 −40.5	.S...*.S030			1.08 .63	.40 .63	.92	I
N1796B	5 7.3 1.1	−61 31 8	237.58 −35.40	270.88 −35.89	223.6 −40.4				1.16 1.01	.71 1.01	.88	I
N1800	5 4.6 3.8	−32 1 8	201.57 −33.88	234.44 −35.11	258.9 −60.5	.S....$.						

NGC (IC, A)	Magnitudes				Colors				Velocities			Radio			
	m_H m_C	B(O) w	B'(O) m'_C	S(B)	(B-V)(O) w	C_o(O)	S(C)	(U-B)(O) w	V w	V_O ΔV	S(V)	ϕ_r n	ϕ(21)		Photo.
(14)	(15)	(16)	(17)	(18)	(19)	(20)	(21)	(22)	(23)	(24)	(25)	(26)	(27)	(28)	(29)
N1596	12.3 12.44	12.27 3.39	12.86 13.03	M	.92		M /M	.40*		-224					
N1599										-98					
N1600	12.7 12.77	12.55 13.31	12.69 12.91	ACL	.98 10.10	.83	AC*L /L	.58	4830 1.0	4730 -100	B				
N1601		14.98 3.51	13.77	CL	.95 3.70	.80	CL /L	.47	4997 1.0	4897 -100	B				
N1602										-224					
N1606										-100					
N1614										-115					
N1615										-5					
N1617	11.7 11.82	11.40 2.32	13.24 13.66	M	.94		M /M	.44		-225					L
N1618										-97					
N1620										-86					
N1622										-97					
N1625	13.1 13.15		13.79							-98					
N1635										-90					
N1637	11.6 11.54	11.63 9.30	14.12 14.03	ACG	.68 10.63	.55	ACG		661 5.0	561 -100	BC				P
N1638	13.1 13.22		13.06							-96					
N1640	12.6 12.70	12.66 1.91	13.70 13.74	C	.77 3.75	.61	C		1676 3.6	1516 -160	C				
N1642										-88					
N1659	12.9 13.11	13.43 1.46	13.97 13.65	C	.66 1.88		C			-111					
N1666										-119					
N1667	12.9 13.25		13.54							-118					
N1672	11.4 11.29		13.98							-235					F
N1688	12.7 12.66		14.00							-236					
N1699										-119					
N1700	12.4 12.47	12.39 11.52	12.83 12.91	AC	.98* 10.00	.82	AC		3976 6.3	3857 -120	B				
N1703										-238					
N1705	12.9 13.12		12.86							-235					
N1720										-132					
N1726	13.0 13.33		12.67							-132					
N1741										-121					
N1744	12.5 11.95	12.06 2.03	14.95 14.84	C	.51 1.88	.38	C		676 2.0	487 -189	C				
N1752										-136					
N1771										-241					
N1779										-141					
N1784	12.8 12.41	12.73 1.17	14.72 14.40	G	.71 2.50		G			-151					
N1792	10.7 11.33		13.17							-219					I
N1796	12.9 13.18		13.52							-242					
N1796A										-243					
N1796B										-244					
N1800	12.9									-208					

45

NGC (IC, A) (1)	RA (1950) Dec 100 P (2)	(3)	L^I B^I (4)	L^II B^II (5)	SGL SGB (6)	Rev. type (S) DDO (T, L) (7)	Yerkes (1) Yerkes (2) (8)	Hu-San Ho (9)	log D w (10)	log R w (11)	log D(O) (12)	S (D,R) (13)
N1808	5 5.9	-37 34	208.21	241.20	249.4	RSXS0..W100	S P F		1.72	.28	1.61	GIW
	3.5	8	-34.79	-35.91	-57.8				6.95	6.95		
N1832	5 10.0	-15 47	184.14	216.67	293.6	.SBR4..P200		S 3	1.39	.16	1.33	DKZ
	4.5	7	-27.45	-28.87	-65.3	S 5 3	S F		5.59	5.59		
N1888	5 20.2	-11 32	181.00	213.45	304.9	.SBS5P.W060			1.38	.66	1.11	FHLQ
	4.7	6	-23.43	-24.88	-67.2				5.78	3.40		
N1889	5 20.2	-11 32	181.00	213.45	304.9	.E.0...W060			.65	.03	.64	HQ
	4.7	6	-23.43	-24.88	-67.2				1.11	1.11		
N1947	5 26.0	-63 49	240.11	273.35	219.6	.L..-P.S074			1.20	.07	1.17	DEIJ
	0.6	5	-33.05	-33.49	-39.6				4.88	4.88		
N1954	5 30.6	-14 6	184.68	217.17	299.2	.SBT5*.H030			1.58	.20	1.50	F
	4.6	4	-22.22	-23.64	-70.1				2.63	2.63		
N1961	5 36.8	69 24	111.04	143.78	20.8	.SXT5..W060	S *F		1.62	.25	1.52	AKMXQ
	11.0	3	20.33	19.51	-3.9	S 3PNT 1*		S4	7.12	7.12		
N1964	5 31.2	-21 59	192.67	225.27	276.1	.SXS3..P200		S 3	1.71	.42	1.54	DEFGKXZ
	4.2	4	-25.17	-26.51	-69.7	S 3 3	S G	S4	13.97	13.97		
N2082	5 41.6	-64 20	240.65	273.82	217.3	.SBR3..B060			1.14	.01	1.13	DEPI
	0.5	3	-31.33	-31.75	-39.8				4.28	4.28		
N2090	5 45.2	-34 15	206.66	239.43	243.6	.SAT5..W100			1.62	.31	1.50	DEFPW
	3.6	2	-26.28	-27.43	-66.0				10.50	10.50		
N2139	5 59.0	-23 40	196.94	229.52	262.9	.SXT6..W100			1.29	.06	1.27	DEKNW
	4.1	0	-19.85	-21.14	-75.0	S 5P	I A *		7.58	7.58		
N2146	6 10.7	78 23	102.71	135.64	25.3	.SBS2P.P200	I A *		1.71	.25	1.61	AKLMRUX
	15.9	-1	25.54	24.90	4.2	S NT+	I P K *	S P	19.02	15.62		Z
N2146A	6 16.0	78 35	102.56	135.50	25.6	.S..5*.L036						R*
	16.1	-2	25.84	25.21	4.4							
N2179	6 5.9	-21 44	195.72	228.25	266.9	.SAS0..W100			1.03	.17	.96	KW
	4.2	0	-17.63	-18.94	-77.4	S 0	D G		2.74	2.74		
N2188	6 8.3	-34 5	208.12	240.82	233.9	.SBS9./W100			1.54	.57	1.31	EPW
	3.6	-1	-21.69	-22.82	-69.0				7.29	7.29		
N2196	6 10.1	-21 47	196.18	228.70	264.5	PSAS1..W100			1.35	.13	1.30	GKW
	4.2	-1	-16.76	-18.06	-78.2	S 3 2*	S K		4.81	4.81		
N2207	6 14.3	-21 21	196.18	228.69	263.9	.SXT4P.W100			1.58	.18	1.51	GKPW
	4.3	-2	-15.69	-16.99	-79.2	S 5 T 1*	S F		9.25	9.25		
N2217	6 19.7	-27 14	202.31	234.88	239.6	RLBT+..W100		SBR1	1.56	.05	1.54	DEFKW
	4.0	-3	-16.91	-18.13	-76.1	SB0			10.17	8.51		
N2223	6 22.5	-22 49	198.37	230.88	251.1	.SXR3..W060			1.54	.07	1.52	DEQ
	4.2	-3	-14.56	-15.83	-79.9	SX2 3*	S F		3.99	3.99		
N2256	6 40.8	74 17	107.56	140.49	26.6							
	12.9	-5	26.50	25.75	-.1							
N2258	6 42.4	74 33	107.28	140.21	26.7							
	13.0	-6	26.64	25.90	0.2							
N2268	7 1.3	84 30	96.15	129.19	27.6	.SXR4..W060	S F		1.44	.21	1.36	AKMXQ
	27.4	-8	28.04	27.56	10.2	S 3 N *		S5	6.48	6.48		
N2273B	6 42.2	60 24	122.62	155.37	26.1	.SB..*.						
	9.0	-6	23.83	22.78	-13.9							
N2276	7 11.0	85 52	94.59	127.64	27.8	.SXT5..W060	S AF		1.37	.02	1.36	AKXQ
	34.5	-10	28.17	27.72	11.5	S 5 K 1*		S6	3.32	3.32		
N2280	6 42.8	-27 35	204.79	237.30	217.9	.SAS6..W100			1.64	.28	1.53	FW
	4.0	-6	-12.37	-13.55	-77.8				5.97	5.97		
N2290	6 47.5	33 25	150.09	182.51	26.0				1.11	.27	1.00	AR
	6.6	-6	15.81	14.40	-40.9				1.95	1.95		
N2291	6 47.5	33 31	149.99	182.41	26.0				.91	.00	.91	AR
	6.6	-6	15.85	14.44	-40.8				1.70	.54		
N2294	6 47.7	33 31	150.01	182.43	26.0				.99	.46	.80	AR
	6.6	-6	15.89	14.47	-40.8				1.93	1.93		
N2300	7 16.5	85 50	94.61	127.67	27.9	.E+2...W060	E3 K		1.12	.10	1.08	AKXQ
	34.0	-10	28.27	27.83	11.5	E 1		E	2.62	2.62		
N2310	6 52.4	-40 48	218.07	250.71	207.6	.L..../S030			1.51	.68	1.24	I
	3.2	-7	-15.96	-16.90	-64.8				1.62	1.62		
N2314	7 3.8	75 19	106.56	139.54	28.1	.E.3...W060	E4 K		1.04	.10	1.00	KMQ
	13.3	-9	28.10	27.37	1.0	E 1P *			2.18	2.18		
N2325	7 0.7	-28 38	207.50	239.97	199.7	.E.4...W100			1.11	.21	1.03	NW
	3.9	-8	-9.27	-10.41	-76.9				2.27	2.27		
N2326A	7 4.9	50 44	133.76	166.42	29.5	.E.3...						
	7.7	-9	24.52	23.28	-23.6							
N2336	7 16.2	80 20	100.85	133.89	28.4	.SXR4..W060	S F		1.84	.26	1.73	AKMXQ
	17.5	-10	28.72	28.12	6.0	S 3 1	SX FG	S5	8.32	8.32		
N2339	7 5.4	18 52	165.51	197.83	32.7	.SXT4..W100	S AF		1.37	.10	1.33	AKMW
	5.9	-9	13.54	12.06	-55.4	S 5 4	S *AF*		5.49	5.49		
N2344	7 8.5	47 17	137.58	170.21	30.4	.SB.5..W						
	7.4	-9	24.20	22.91	-27.0							
N2347	7 11.6	64 54	118.39	151.27	29.4	PSAR3*.W060			1.16	.13	1.10	KMQ
	9.6	-10	27.97	26.99	-9.4	S 3 N *	E2 *K		4.08	4.08		
N2366	7 23.6	69 8	113.66	146.63	30.2	.IBS9..P200	L*A	I 9	1.86	.32	1.73	KLMXZ
	10.6	-11	29.41	28.53	-5.0	S 7 8		I9	10.38	10.38		
N2369	7 16.0	-62 16	240.48	273.32	203.7	.SBS1..B060			1.54	.50	1.34	PI
	1.1	-10	-20.59	-21.02	-43.2				4.39	4.39		
N2369A	7 18.3	-62 49	241.13	273.97	203.5	.S...*.S030			1.34	.19	1.26	I
	1.0	-11	-20.54	-20.96	-42.6				.56	.56		

NGC (IC, A) (14)	Magnitudes				Colors				Velocities			Radio				
	m_H / m_C (15)	B(O) w (16)	B'(O) m'_C (17)	S(B) (18)	(B-V)(O) w (19)	C_O(O) (20)	S(C) (21)	(U-B)(O) w (22)	V w (23)	V_o ΔV (24)	S(V) (25)	ϕ_r n (26)	ϕ(21) (27)	(28)	Photo. (29)
N1808	11.2 / 11.07		13.81						1039 / .8	819 / -220	D				HK
N1832	12.6 / 12.58	12.19 / 2.03	13.53 / 13.92	C	.78 / 3.75	.62	C		2037 / .3	1869 / -168	B				P
N1888				C*			C*		2557 / 2.4	2395 / -162	C				B
N1889		14.29 / 1.76	12.23	C*	.92 / 1.88	.77	C*		2496 / 8.7	2334 / -162	BC				B
N1947	12.2 / 12.39		12.93							-250					FL
N1954										-177					
N1961	11.6 / 11.63	12.19 / 4.53	14.48 / 13.92	CG	.75 / 6.25	.50	CG		3870 / 2.2	4027 / 157	C				
N1964	12.0 / 11.73	11.85 / 2.75	14.29 / 14.17	CG	.79 / 4.38	.56	CG		1849 / 1.2	1648 / -201	C				P
N2082	12.8 / 13.10		13.49							-255					
N2090	12.4 / 12.11		14.30							-237					
N2139	12.5 / 12.71	12.39 / 1.86	13.48 / 13.80	C	.28 / 1.88	.11	C		1913 / 2.5	1691 / -222	C				
N2146	11.6 / 11.33	11.60 / 2.98	14.39 / 14.12	BCFG*	.75 / 4.38	.55	CG		812 / 8.8	994 / 182	BCF				BD
N2146A										182					
N2179	13.0 / 13.51		13.05							-221					
N2188	12.6 / 12.74		14.03							-249					I
N2196	12.6 / 12.56		13.80							-224					
N2207	12.3 / 12.01	11.54 / 1.89	13.78 / 14.25	C	.74 / 3.75	.50	C		2680 / 2.8	2455 / -225	B				
N2217	12.6 / 12.01	11.69 / 1.69	14.13 / 14.45	C	.87 / 1.88	.69	C		1575 / 3.0	1334 / -242	BC				P
N2223	12.7 / 12.18		14.47							-233					
N2256										163					
N2258										164					
N2268	12.2 / 12.30	12.48 / 2.55	13.97 / 13.79	CG	.78 / 6.25	.59	CG		2337 / 1.9	2536 / 199	C				
N2273B										104					
N2276	12.4 / 12.40	12.25 / 2.06	13.79 / 13.94	CG	.59 / 4.38	.45	CG		2391 / 4.3	2595 / 204	C				
N2280	12.7 / 12.24		14.58							-253					
N2290										-26					D
N2291										-25					D
N2294										-25					D
N2300	12.2 / 12.44	12.58 / 3.92	12.72 / 12.58	BCG	1.03 / 10.63	.90	BCG		1986 / 15.4	2189 / 204	BC				
N2310	12.8 / 12.67		13.56							-276					
N2314	12.9 / 13.04	13.40 / 3.92	13.14 / 12.78	BC	.98 / 8.13	.82	BC		3860 / 13.1	4024 / 165	BC				
N2325	12.9 / 12.99		12.88							-263					
N2326A										53					
N2336	12.4 / 11.53	11.37 / 3.28	14.76 / 14.92	CG	.68 / 4.38	.49	CG		2252 / 1.6	2435 / 183	C				
N2339	12.7 / 12.64	12.68 / 3.31	14.02 / 13.98	C	.78 / 5.63	.49	C		2361 / 6.3	2259 / -102	B				
N2344										35					
N2347	12.7 / 13.12	13.21 / 2.53	13.45 / 13.36	C	.81 / 3.75	.60	C		4521 / 2.4	4640 / 119	C				
N2366	12.6 / 11.75	11.69 / 3.38	15.08 / 15.14	CG	.56 / 4.38	.45	CG			136	C				P
N2369	13.1 / 12.74		14.18							-280					
N2369A										-279					

NGC (IC, A) (1)	RA (1950) 100 P (2)	Dec 100 P (3)	L^I B^I (4)	L^II B^II (5)	SGL SGB (6)	Rev. type (S) DDO (T, L) (7)	Yerkes (1) Yerkes (2) (8)	Hu-San Ho (9)	log D w (10)	log R w (11)	log D(0) (12)	S (D,R) (13)
N2369B	7 19.8	-61 57	240.34	273.17	203.0	.SB.5*.S030			1.36	.03	1.35	I
	1.2	-11	-20.06	-20.50	-43.4				.29	.29		
N2379	7 24.2	33 55	152.49	184.95	35.9	.L...$.			.81	.00	.81	A
	6.5	-12	23.12	21.69	-39.9				.30	.30		
N2389	7 25.8	33 58	152.55	185.02	36.3	.SXT5..W060			1.28	.12	1.23	AMQ
	6.5	-12	23.45	22.02	-39.8				3.38	3.38		
N2397	7 21.5	-68 54	247.39	280.29	204.2	.SBS2..S030			1.26	.32	1.13	I
	-.3	-11	-22.33	-22.59	-36.5				1.16	1.16		
N2397A	7 21.4	-68 45	247.23	280.14	204.2	.SA.5*$S030			1.16	.13	1.11	I
	-.2	-11	-22.29	-22.55	-36.7				.71	.71		
N2403	7 32.0	65 43	117.62	150.56	31.5	.SXS6..P200	S A	S 5	2.19	.21	2.11	AHKLRVX
	9.7	-13	30.15	29.18	-8.3	S 5 5	S F	S6	29.60	29.60		YZ
N2415	7 33.7	35 20	151.67	184.16	38.0				.98	.00	.98	A
	6.6	-13	25.43	24.00	-38.1				.51	.51		
N2417	7 29.5	-62 09	241.00	273.80	201.6	.SA.4*.S030			1.30	.07	1.28	I
	1.2	-13	-19.09	-19.51	-43.1				.88	.88		
N2424	7 37.3	39 21	147.58	180.14	37.8	.SBR3*/W060			1.62	.74	1.33	HQ
	6.8	-13	27.21	25.81	-34.0				2.15	2.15		
N2427	7 35.1	-47 30	227.69	260.27	194.3	.SXS8..R074			1.74	.37	1.59	EIO
	2.9	-13	-11.94	-12.68	-57.0				6.63	6.63		
N2434	7 35.0	-69 10	248.12	281.00	202.8	.E.0+..S030			1.15	.00	1.15	I
	-.2	-13	-21.30	-21.54	-36.1				.99	.99		
N2441	7 47.1	73 6	108.97	142.03	31.3	.SXR3*.W060	S *AF		1.25	.07	1.22	KMQ
	11.7	-15	31.12	30.34	-.8	S 5 3*			4.62	4.62		
N2442	7 36.5	-69 25	248.42	281.30	202.7	.SBS3..S030			1.77	.06	1.75	I
	-.3	-13	-21.27	-21.50	-35.8				2.25	2.25		
N2444	7 43.5	39 9	148.13	180.69	39.3							
	6.7	-15	28.33	26.93	-33.9							
N2445	7 43.5	39 8	148.16	180.72	39.3	.I...P.						
	6.7	-15	28.32	26.92	-33.9							
N2460	7 52.7	60 31	123.72	156.66	34.9	.SAS1..W060	S G		1.51	.14	1.45	Q
	8.6	-15	32.44	31.37	-12.9	S 4 T 5*			2.58	2.58		
N2466	7 45.6	-71 17	250.59	283.47	202.4	.SA.5*.S030			1.15	.06	1.12	I
	-.8	-14	-21.31	-21.48	-33.8				.99	.99		
N2468	7 54.0	56 30	128.49	161.37	36.2				.95	.00	.95	A
	8.1	-15	32.55	31.39	-16.7				.09	.09		
N2469	7 54.0	56 50	128.09	160.98	36.1				1.18	.25	1.08	A
	8.1	-15	32.56	31.41	-16.4				.77	.77		
N2475	7 54.2	53 00	132.63	165.46	37.2	.E.3...L...						
	7.7	-16	32.39	31.17	20.1							
N2500	7 58.2	50 54	135.17	167.97	38.5	.SBT7..P200	SI *A		1.42	.04	1.40	KLXZ
	7.5	-16	32.84	31.58	-21.9	S 7 7		S6	5.88	5.08		
N2507	7 58.7	15 50	173.95	206.18	55.5	.S.....L...			1.28	.30	1.16	ABL
	5.7	-16	23.91	22.43	-54.5				2.51	1.82		
N2514	8 0.0	15 56	173.99	206.21	55.9	.S.....L...			1.18			L
	5.7	-16	24.23	22.76	-54.3				.63			
N2521	8 4.9	57 55	126.81	159.74	37.2							
	8.2	-17	34.04	32.91	-14.9							
N2523	8 9.2	73 45	107.91	141.01	32.7	.SBR4..P200	B FG	SBR3	1.42	.21	1.33	KMZ
	11.6	-17	32.56	31.80	0.2	SB2 1			6.99	6.99		
N2523A	7 58.4	74 14	107.52	140.61	31.8							
	12.0	-16	31.74	30.99	0.5							
N2523B	8 7.1	73 44	107.97	141.07	32.5	.SAS3*/P200			1.36	.77	1.05	Z
	11.6	-17	32.42	31.66	0.2				1.48	1.48		
N2523C	8 12.0	73 30	108.15	141.26	32.9	.E.4.*.						
	11.4	-18	32.81	32.05	0.1							
N2525	8 3.3	-11 17	199.71	231.86	105.3	.SBS5..W100		SBS5	1.40	.17	1.33	KNXW
	4.7	-17	12.06	10.80	-72.3	SX5P 3*	S PA *	S5	6.31	6.31		
N2532	8 7.0	34 8	155.08	187.57	46.7	.SXT5..P200			1.33	.05	1.31	AHLZ
	6.4	-17	31.69	30.24	-37.2				6.15	5.38		
N2534	8 9.1	55 50	129.32	162.24	38.5	.E.1.*.						
	7.9	-17	34.64	33.47	-16.7							
N2535	8 8.2	25 21	164.95	197.28	51.9	.SAR5P.L036			1.34	.32	1.21	ABS
	6.0	-17	29.44	27.96	-45.1				3.68	3.68		
N2536	8 8.3	25 20	164.97	197.31	51.9	.S...P.L036			.96	.00	.96	AB
	6.0	-17	29.46	27.97	-45.1				.96	.96		
N2537	8 9.7	46 9	141.06	173.80	42.1	.IBS9P.W100	I A		1.17	.07	1.14	AHKLRW
	7.1	-17	34.29	32.96	-25.8	S *			6.43	6.43		
N2537A	8 10.1	46 10	141.05	173.79	42.2	.SBT5..W100			.86	.13	.81	W
	7.1	-18	34.36	33.03	-25.8				.70	.70		
N2541	8 11.1	49 15	137.34	170.14	41.2	.SAS6..P200	S AF		1.78	.24	1.68	AHKXZ
	7.3	-18	34.78	33.49	-22.8	S 7 7		S6	5.89	5.89		
N2543	8 9.7	36 25	152.60	185.13	46.3	.SBS3..W060			1.30	.17	1.23	AHQ
	6.5	-18	32.74	31.31	-34.9				4.03	4.03		
N2544	8 15.7	74 8	107.34	140.46	33.0	.L...*.L036			1.04	.38	.88	M
	11.6	-18	32.91	32.16	0.8				1.19	1.19		
N2545	8 11.3	21 30	169.37	201.65	55.4	RSBR2..W100	DSP*G		1.10	.18	1.03	AKW
	5.9	-18	28.81	27.32	-48.2	S 3 T -*	S P*FG*		3.72	3.72		
N2549	8 14.9	57 58	126.68	159.65	38.5	.LAR0./P200	D GK		1.46	.46	1.28	KZ
	8.1	-18	35.36	34.23	-14.5	E 6			5.19	5.19		

| NGC (IC, A) | Magnitudes | | | | Colors | | | | Velocities | | | Radio | | | |
| | m_H m_c | B(O) w | B'(O) m'_c | S(B) | (B-V)(O) w | C_o(O) | S(C) | (U-B)(O) w | V w | V_o ΔV | S(V) | ϕ_r n | ϕ(21) | | Photo. |
(14)	(15)	(16)	(17)	(18)	(19)	(20)	(21)	(22)	(23)	(24)	(25)	(26)	(27)	(28)	(29)
N2369B										−231					
N2379		14.74 5.22	13.53	BC	.95 3.75	.77	C		4030 2.4	3994 −36	B				
N2389		13.52 3.68	14.41	C	.53 3.75	.32	C		3816 2.0	3780 −36	C*				
N2397	12.8 13.08		13.47							−271					
N2397A										−271					
N2403	10.2 9.54	9.07 4.59	14.36 14.83	CFG	.53 10.63	.40	BCG		136 406.3	255 119	BR				ACP
N2415									3822 2.4	3791 −31	D				
N2417										−282					
N2424										−12					
N2427	12.4 11.99		14.68							−291					FH
N2434	12.8 12.72		13.21							−272					
N2441	12.7 12.84	13.21 1.79	14.05 13.68	C	.82 1.88	.65	C		3623 1.4	3774 151	C				
N2442	11.8 11.14	11.81 0.65	15.39 14.63	M	.94		M /M	.18		−272					F
N2444									3965 2.0	3951 −14	F				
N2445										−15					
N2460	12.7 12.27	12.61 3.77	14.60 14.26	BC	.86 3.75	.71	C		1442 4.0	1534 92	B				
N2466										−269					
N2468										72					
N2469										74					
N2475									5019 2.0	5076 57	C				
N2500	12.6 12.56	12.39 3.31	14.08 14.25	CG	.61 4.38	.50	CG		470 5.4	513 43	C				
N2507										−133					
N2514										−133					
N2521										78					
N2523	12.7 12.61	13.01 1.99	14.40 14.00	C	.79* 3.75	.61	C		3448 2.6	3600 152	C				LP
N2523A										155					
N2523B										153					
N2523C										151					
N2525	12.2 12.39	12.44 3.12	13.78 13.73	CG	.70 4.38	.37	CG		2064 1.4	1825 −239	C				P
N2532		13.11 4.01	14.40	BC	.64 1.88	.47	C		5153 4.0	5108 −45	B				
N2534										67					
N2535		13.49 5.17	14.28	BC	.54 3.75	.32	C		4135 4.9	4046 −89	BE				
N2536		14.86 3.71	14.35	BC	.60 1.88	.44	C		4072 3.1	3983 −89	E				
N2537	12.2 12.49	12.55 9.21	12.99 12.93	BCE*	.64 16.25	.54	CE /E	−.10	404 29.1	422 17	BCD				BK
N2537A										17					
N2541	12.7 11.88	12.14 1.43	15.28 15.02	G	.55 2.50		G			33					
N2543										−33					
N2544										154					
N2545	13.0 13.42	13.64 2.56	13.53 13.31	C	.85 5.63		C			−108					
N2549	12.5 12.38	12.40 9.10	13.54 13.52	BCH	.96 10.00	.83	CH		1082 1.8	1159 77	B				

NGC (IC, A) (1)	RA (1950) 100 P (2)	Dec 100 P (3)	L^I / B^I (4)	L^II / B^II (5)	SGL / SGB (6)	Rev. type (S) / DDO (T, L) (7)	Yerkes (1) / Yerkes (2) (8)	Hu-San / Ho (9)	log D / w (10)	log R / w (11)	log D(O) (12)	S (D,R) (13)
N2550	8 18.7	74 10	107.24	140.37	33.2							
	11.6	-19	33.10	32.36	0.9							
N2550A	8 23.6	74 4	107.25	140.38	33.5	.S...*.						
	11.4	-19	33.45	32.71	0.9							
N2551	8 18.8	73 35	107.91	141.04	33.4	.SAS0..L036	SI *A		1.18	.16	1.11	KM
	11.3	-19	33.26	32.50	0.3	S 3 5*			2.47	2.47		
N2552	8 15.4	50 11	136.24	169.07	41.5	.SAS9.$P200			1.46	.15	1.39	HKZ
	7.3	-18	35.52	34.25	-21.7	I 9 8			5.53	5.53		
N2562	8 17.5	21 17	170.19	202.45	57.4	.S..1..W			.98	.29	.86	A
	5.8	-18	30.08	28.60	-47.6				.51	.51		
N2563	8 17.7	21 14	170.26	202.52	57.5	.L.....W			1.20	.28	1.09	A
	5.8	-18	30.11	28.62	-47.6				.80	.80		
N2565	8 16.9	22 10	169.17	201.45	56.6	.SB.3..W						
	5.9	-19	30.26	28.77	-46.9							
N2573	3 54.0	-89 52	270.01	303.07	207.7	.LA....S030			1.38	.45	1.19	I
	*	17	-28.01	-27.68	-15.6				1.35	1.35		
N2573A	22 30.0	-89 26	270.24	303.32	207.9	.S....*S030			1.32	.54	1.10	I
	91.3	31	-28.22	-27.89	-15.4				.63	.63		
N2573B	22 30.0	-89 26	270.24	303.32	207.9				1.06	.42	.89	I
	91.3	31	-28.22	-27.89	-15.4				.61	.61		
N2578	8 19.0	-13 9	203.46	235.54	113.4	.SBROP.W100			1.07	.13	1.02	W
	4.7	-19	14.28	13.07	-69.0				.44	.44		
N2591	8 30.9	78 12	102.41	135.56	32.3	.S.....			1.50	.63	1.25	A
	13.6	-20	32.54	31.91	4.9				1.26	1.26		
N2595	8 24.9	21 38	170.48	202.74	59.3	.SB...*R020			1.47	.25	1.37	AH
	5.8	-19	31.83	30.34	-46.4				1.89	1.89		
N2598	8 27.2	21 40	170.68	202.93	59.9	.S....*R020			1.08	.38	.93	AH
	5.8	-20	32.34	30.85	-46.1				1.41	1.41		
N2601	8 25.2	-67 57	249.26	282.00	197.0	.LA..*.S030			1.11	.14	1.05	I
	.7	-19	-16.69	-16.90	-35.6				.66	.66		
N2608	8 32.2	28 38	163.09	195.47	56.0	.SBS3*.W100	SIP*AF*		1.33	.26	1.23	AKS
	6.1	-20	35.52	34.03	-39.6	S 5 3*			4.01	2.23		
N2613	8 31.1	-22 48	213.24	245.35	138.4	.SAS3..W100	S GK		1.82	.58	1.59	DEGKMW
	4.4	-20	11.08	10.04	-65.7	S 3 3			15.57	15.57		
N2614	8 37.4	73 10	107.92	141.09	34.8	.S.....			1.43	.22	1.34	A
	10.8	-21	34.65	33.89	0.4				1.14	1.14		
N2623	8 35.4	25 56	166.51	198.83	58.8	.SB.3..W						
	6.0	-21	35.46	33.97	-41.5							
N2629	8 41.9	73 10	107.78	140.97	35.0				.95	.00	.95	A
	10.7	-21	34.96	34.20	0.6				.48	.48		
N2633	8 42.7	74 18	106.47	139.65	34.6	.SBS3..W060	B P*F		1.36	.19	1.28	KQ
	11.1	-21	34.60	33.88	1.6	SB3P	B P FG		3.52	3.52		
N2634	8 42.8	74 10	106.62	139.80	34.7	.E.1.*..W060			.92	.05	.90	Q
	11.1	-21	34.66	33.93	1.5				1.25	1.25		
N2634A	8 43.0	74 8	106.65	139.83	34.7	.SBS.*/W060			1.22	.73	.93	Q
	11.1	-22	34.68	33.95	1.5				.82	.82		
N2636	8 43.1	73 51	106.97	140.15	34.8	.E.0.*.W060			.73	.00	.73	Q
	10.9	-21	34.79	34.06	1.2				.41	.41		
N2639	8 40.1	50 24	135.93	168.85	45.2	RSAR1*$W100	E6P*K		1.18	.25	1.08	AHKW
	7.2	-21	39.46	38.19	-19.9	S 0			3.74	3.74		
N2642	8 38.3	-3 57	198.07	230.05	95.9	.SBR4..W100	SX *F		1.29	.01	1.29	AKNW
	5.0	-21	23.30	22.02	-61.5	SX3 1			6.46	6.46		
N2646	8 44.6	73 40	107.13	140.32	35.0	.LBR0*.W060			.91	.10	.87	KQ
	10.8	-22	34.96	34.22	1.1				1.19	1.19		
N2649	8 41.1	34 56	155.88	188.41	53.9	.SA.2..L036			1.26	.00	1.26	AL
	6.3	-21	38.72	37.27	-33.3				1.59	.87		
N2650	8 45.2	70 29	110.77	143.96	36.5	.SBR3*.W			.90	.00	.90	A
	9.8	-22	36.12	35.30	-1.7				.08	.08		
N2654	8 44.3	60 28	122.96	156.07	41.0	.S..1$.W	DS GK		1.60	.70	1.32	K
	8.1	-21	38.76	37.69	-10.7	S 2 4			1.82	1.82		
N2655	8 49.4	78 25	101.73	134.91	33.1	.SXS0..P200	E4P*	S1	1.57	.10	1.53	AHKLXZ
	13.2	-22	33.32	32.70	5.5	S N +			6.88	5.62		
N2672	8 46.6	19 16	175.30	207.46	67.1	.E.1+..W060	E2 K		1.09	.10	1.05	ABK
	5.7	-22	35.76	34.28	-45.2	E 1			1.68	1.68		
N2673	8 46.6	19 16	175.30	207.46	67.1	.E+0.*.W060			.89	.00	.89	AB
	5.7	-22	35.76	34.28	-45.2		E1 K		.80	.80		
N2681	8 50.0	51 31	134.32	167.31	46.1	PSXT0..P200	S K	S 1	1.45	.08	1.41	AHKXZ
	7.2	-22	40.93	39.69	-18.1	S 0		S1	7.70	7.70		
N2683	8 49.6	33 38	157.92	190.43	56.5	.SAT3..W100	S G	S3	1.93	.66	1.67	AHKLVXW
	6.2	-22	40.23	38.77	-33.4	S 2 4			21.76	21.76		
N2685	8 52.2	58 59	124.56	157.69	42.6	RLB..P.P200	D P K	L P	1.49	.23	1.40	KXZ
	7.8	-22	40.05	38.95	-11.5	S 3P 4*	D P K	L P	4.66	4.66		
N2692	8 53.4	52 16	133.24	166.26	46.2	.E....*R020			1.00	.17	.93	AH
	7.2	-23	41.37	40.13	-17.2				.87	.87		
N2693	8 53.5	51 33	134.20	167.20	46.6	.E.3.*.W060	E3 K		1.02	.11	.98	AHKQ
	7.2	-22	41.47	40.23	-17.8	E P			1.83	1.83		
N2694	8 53.5	51 32	134.21	167.21	46.6	.E.....R020			.90	.00	.90	AH
	7.2	-23	41.47	40.22	-17.9				.69	.69		
N2698	8 53.1	-2 59	199.39	231.30	97.4				1.11	.34	.97	A
	5.0	-22	26.93	25.66	-57.8				.69	.69		

NGC (IC, A) (14)	Magnitudes				Colors				Velocities			Radio			
	m_H m_C (15)	B(O) w (16)	B'(O) m'_C (17)	S(B) (18)	(B-V)(O) w (19)	C_O(O) (20)	S(C) (21)	(U-B)(O) w (22)	V w (23)	V_O ΔV (24)	S(V) (25)	ϕ_r n (26)	ϕ (21) (27)	(28)	Photo. (29)
N2550										154					
N2550A										153					
N2551	13.1 13.22	13.25 2.70	13.54 13.51	C	.99 3.75	.85	C		2296 1.7	2447 151	C				
N2552	12.5 12.54		14.23							37					
N2562		14.22 2.85	13.26	C	1.04 3.75	.82	C		4963 4.0	4853 -110	B				
N2563		13.63 3.11	13.82	CL	.97 4.60	.79	CL /L	.62	4775 4.0	4664 -111	B				
N2565										-106					
N2573										-217					
N2573A										-216					
N2573B										-216					
N2578										-248					
N2591										171					
N2595										-110					
N2598										-110					
N2601										-279					
N2608	12.9 12.93	12.98 1.79	13.87 13.82	C	.75 1.88	.56	C		2119 1.0	2043 -76	B				
N2613	11.3 11.24	11.33 1.65	14.02 13.93	C	.68* 3.75	.26	C		1688 7.3	1415 -273	BC				
N2614										149					
N2623									5435 6.3	5345 -90	B				
N2629										149					
N2633	12.6 12.65	12.94 2.75	14.08 13.79	C	.95* 3.75	.78	C		2228 4.9	2382 154	C				
N2634										153					
N2634A										153					
N2636										152					
N2639	12.4 12.96	12.91 1.90	13.05 13.10	BC	.88 1.88	.71	C		3314 1.8	3351 37	B				
N2642	12.7 12.73		13.87	C*	.95* 1.88	.76	C		4439 2.2	4219 -220	C				
N2646		13.56 2.57	12.60	C	1.00 3.75	.86	C		3546 1.7	3697 151	C				
N2649										-44					
N2650										136					
N2654	12.9 12.92	13.05 7.01	14.39 14.26	BCH	.97 8.13	.78	CH		1360 2.4	1448 88	B				
N2655	11.6 11.44	11.22 6.93	13.61 13.83	BCGH	.86 13.75	.74	BCGH		1299 2.4	1471 172	B				
N2672	12.6 12.76	13.21 3.34	13.20 12.75	CL	1.00 8.30	.87	CL /L	.45*	4223 1.0	4100 -123	B				
N2673		14.38 2.01	13.57	C	.78 1.88	.65	C		3792 2.4	3669 -123	B				
N2681	11.3 11.56	11.34 19.02	13.13 13.35	ABCFG H	.79 20.63	.69	ABCGH		709 13.8	751 42	BC				CP
N2683	10.8 10.80	10.74 4.33	13.78 13.84	CFG	.90 6.25	.69	CG		338 8.8	287 -51	ABCD				AB
N2685	12.5 12.18	12.35 10.87	14.09 13.92	BCGH	.86 12.50	.75	CGH		877 10.3	957 80	BD				P
N2692										46					
N2693	12.9 13.07	13.42 6.58	13.06 12.71	BCH*	1.04 6.87	.91	CH*		4956 4.0	4998 42	B				
N2694		15.27 3.98	14.51	BC*	1.03 1.88	.89	C*		5123 1.8	5165 42	B				
N2698										-217					

NGC (IC, A)	Coordinates					Classification			Diameters			
	RA (1950) Dec 100 P	100 P	L^I B^I	L^II B^II	SGL SGB	Rev. type (S) DDO (T,L)	Yerkes (1) Yerkes (2)	Hu-San Ho	log D w	log R w	log D(0)	S (D,R)
(1)	(2)	(3)	(4)	(5)	(6)	(7)	(8)	(9)	(10)	(11)	(12)	(13)
N2701	8 55.5	53 59	130.93	163.99	45.6	.SXT5*.W060	I *AF*		1.32	.18	1.25	AKQ
	7.3	-23	41.44	40.24	-15.6	S 5 3			3.16	3.16		
N2708	8 53.6	-3 9	199.62	231.53	97.7	.S....*H030			1.32	.44	1.15	A
	5.0	-23	26.94	25.68	-57.7				.48	.48		
N2712	8 56.2	45 7	142.78	175.64	50.6	.SBR3*.W100	S *FG		1.38	.22	1.30	AKW
	6.7	-23	42.36	41.01	-23.1	S 4 1			3.74	3.74		
N2713	8 54.8	3 8	193.72	225.65	88.1	.SBT2..W100	BS *G		1.54	.37	1.39	AKMW
	5.2	-23	30.53	29.19	-54.5	S 3 3			8.81	8.81		
N2715	9 2.0	78 16	101.54	134.74	33.7	.SXT5..W060	S AF		1.67	.45	1.49	AHKMXQ
	12.6	-23	33.95	33.34	5.7	S 5 K 3		S5	10.23	10.23		
N2716	8 55.0	3 17	193.60	225.53	87.9	RLBR+..W100	D *G *		.93	.05	.91	ABMW
	5.2	-23	30.65	29.31	-54.3				3.21	3.21		
N2719	8 57.1	35 55	155.21	187.79	56.5				1.18	.49	.98	AB
	6.3	-23	42.08	40.63	-30.6				1.54	1.54		
N2719A	8 57.1	35 55	155.21	187.79	56.5				1.04	.25	.94	B
	6.3	-23	42.08	40.63	-30.6				.59	.59		
N2722	8 57.0	-3 32	200.51	232.40	99.0	.E...$.H030						
	5.0	-23	27.43	26.18	-57.1							
N2723	8 57.7	3 23	193.89	225.81	88.4	.L.....W						
	5.2	-23	31.28	29.94	-53.7							
N2726	9 1.1	60 10	122.69	155.87	43.0				1.15	.29	1.03	A
	7.9	-23	40.85	39.79	-9.9				.73	.73		
N2732	9 7.3	79 24	100.20	133.40	33.3	.L...../W060	D K		1.19	.57	.96	KMQ
	13.3	-24	33.61	33.03	6.8	S *			3.29	3.29		
N2742	9 3.7	60 41	121.91	155.11	43.0	.SAS5*.W060	S AF		1.44	.28	1.33	AKMQ
	7.9	-24	41.01	39.96	-9.3	S 5 3	S AF		7.09	7.09		
N2742A	9 6.0	62 22	119.68	152.91	42.3							
	8.1	-24	40.76	39.75	-7.7							
N2744	9 1.8	18 40	177.62	209.72	71.4	.SBS.P.W100			1.15	.24	1.05	AW
	5.6	-23	38.90	37.44	-43.2				2.98	2.98		
N2748	9 8.2	76 41	103.02	136.24	34.8	.SA.4..W060	S *AF		1.39	.39	1.24	AKMQ
	11.5	-24	35.02	34.37	4.5	S 5			6.66	6.66		
N2749	9 2.5	18 31	177.88	209.97	71.7	.E.3...W100	E4 K		.96	.10	.92	AKW
	5.6	-23	39.00	37.54	-43.2	E 2			2.60	2.60		
N2752	9 2.9	18 31	177.92	210.01	71.8		S *G *		1.40	.66	1.13	A
	5.6	-23	39.09	37.63	-43.2				1.08	1.08		
N2763	9 4.5	-15 17	212.12	244.01	121.3	.SBR6P.W100	S AF	S5	1.33	.03	1.31	AKXW
	4.7	-24	21.92	20.86	-58.3	S 6 7*			4.97	4.97		
N2764	9 5.4	21 39	174.34	206.50	69.4	E *			1.13	.31	1.01	AK
	5.7	-24	40.71	39.23	-40.5				1.66	1.66		
N2768	9 7.8	60 16	122.24	155.46	43.6	.E+6.*.W060	E5 K *		1.55	.41	1.38	AKLQ
	7.8	-24	41.62	40.56	-9.4	E 5	D K		5.72	5.72		
N2770	9 6.5	33 20	159.06	191.56	60.1	.SAS5*.W060			1.57	.50	1.38	ABHQ
	6.1	-24	43.67	42.20	-31.5				5.59	5.59		
N2775	9 7.7	7 15	191.37	223.26	85.4	.SAR2..W100	DS *GK	S 1	1.45	.11	1.41	AKLW
	5.3	-24	35.36	34.00	-49.5	S 0			6.76	5.85		
N2776	9 8.9	45 11	142.56	175.46	52.6	.SXT5..W100	S F		1.48	.04	1.47	AKNW
	6.6	-24	44.60	43.25	-21.8	S 5 3			8.19	8.19		
N2777	9 8.1	7 25	191.25	223.14	85.3				.97	.25	.87	AL
	5.3	-24	35.53	34.16	-49.3				.99	.99		
N2781	9 9.1	-14 36	212.31	244.17	120.2	.LXR+..W100			1.35	.35	1.21	AFKW
	4.7	-24	23.22	22.15	-57.1	S 4 4	D K		4.95	4.95		
N2782	9 10.9	40 19	149.41	182.16	56.0	.SXT1P.W100	SDP*G		1.33	.09	1.30	AHW
	6.4	-24	45.09	43.68	-25.5	S 3 NT			4.82	4.82		
N2784	9 10.1	-23 58	220.03	251.97	137.4	.LAS0*.W100	D K		1.54	.41	1.37	DEKNW
	4.5	-24	17.27	16.35	-56.7	E 8	D K		9.22	9.22		
N2787	9 14.9	69 25	110.75	144.04	39.2	.LBR+..W060	B K		1.38	.16	1.31	HKQ
	9.0	-25	38.88	38.05	-1.3	S 0P *	B K		2.56	2.56		
N2788	9 8.3	-67 44	251.69	284.34	192.7	.S...*/S030			1.19	.74	.89	I
	1.4	-24	-13.37	-13.52	-33.5				1.05	1.05		
N2793	9 13.7	34 39	157.48	190.04	60.5	.SBS9P.W100	I AF		1.09	.03	1.08	AKW
	6.1	-25	45.31	43.85	-29.6	S 5P	I PA *		2.13	2.13		
N2798	9 14.4	42 10	146.76	179.59	55.4	.SBS1P.W060			1.22	.33	1.09	ABKQ
	6.5	-25	45.74	44.35	-23.6	S NT+*			4.27	4.27		
N2799	9 14.6	42 10	146.76	179.59	55.4	.SBS9.$W060	S *FG*		1.13	.54	.91	ABQ
	6.5	-25	45.77	44.38	-23.6				2.50	2.50		
N2805	9 16.5	64 19	116.71	150.00	42.2	.SXT7..P200			1.76	.09	1.72	ABXZ
	8.2	-25	41.16	40.21	-5.4			S6	7.65	7.65		
N2811	9 13.9	-16 6	214.37	246.22	123.1	.SBT1..P200		S 1	1.38	.45	1.20	AFKZ
	4.7	-25	23.14	22.12	-56.1	S 4 4	SD GK		7.30	7.30		
N2814	9 17.3	64 28	116.48	149.77	42.2	.I.0..$P200			1.04	.52	.83	ABZ
	8.2	-25	41.18	40.24	-5.3				3.54	3.54		
N2815	9 14.1	-23 24	220.24	252.16	136.2	.SBR3*.W100			1.49	.47	1.31	DEKW
	4.5	-25	18.32	17.42	-55.9	S 3P 5*	S G		7.59	7.59		
N2820	9 17.9	64 27	116.47	149.76	42.3	.SBS5P/P200			1.57	.79	1.25	ABXZ
	8.1	-25	41.25	40.31	-5.2			S6	7.05	7.05		
N2820A	9 17.6	64 25	116.52	149.81	42.3							
	8.1	-25	41.23	40.28	-5.3							
N2822	9 13.4	-69 26	253.29	285.97	193.6	.E...$.S030			1.07	.30	.95	I
	1.2	-25	-14.20	-14.31	-31.9				.18	.18		

NGC (IC, A) (14)	Magnitudes				Colors				Velocities			Radio			
	m_H m_c (15)	B(O) w (16)	B'(O) m'_c (17)	S(B) (18)	(B-V)(O) w (19)	C_o(O) (20)	S(C) (21)	(U-B)(O) w (22)	V w (23)	V_o ΔV (24)	S(V) (25)	ϕ_r n (26)	ϕ(21) (27)	(28)	Photo. (29)
N2701	12.5 12.71		13.70							55					
N2708										-218					
N2712	12.7 12.68	12.93 8.36	14.12 13.87	BCH	.69 8.13	.53	CH		1840 .3	1849 9	B				
N2713	12.7 12.43	13.17 1.11	14.86 14.12	C	.95 3.75		C			-194					
N2715	12.1 11.97	12.32 4.99	14.46 14.11	CGH	.58 7.50	.39	CGH		1158 1.7	1329 171	C				
N2716		13.63 2.52	12.92	C	.85 3.75	.71	C		3537 4.0	3344 -194	B				
N2719									3113 2.5	3073 -39	E				
N2719A									3250 2.5	3210 -39	E				
N2722										-219					
N2723				L*			L* /L	*	3725 2.4	3532 -193	B				
N2726										86					
N2732	13.0 13.26	13.20 2.64	12.74 12.80	C	.96 3.75	.82	C		2121 1.2	2297 176	C				
N2742	12.5 12.53	12.41 1.69	13.80 13.92	F						89					
N2742A										97					
N2744		14.19 1.14	14.18	C	.45 1.88	.31	C		3450 4.0	3324 -126	B				
N2748	12.4 12.68	12.66 1.83	13.55 13.57	C	.76 1.88	.58	C		1489 2.4	1653 164	C				
N2749	13.1 13.31	13.73 1.76	13.07 12.65	C	1.00 1.88	.87	C		4203 6.3	4076 -127	B				
N2752										-127					
N2763	12.7 12.73	12.91 1.20	14.20 14.02	G	.63 1.88		G			-256					
N2764	13.3									-111					
N2768	12.0 11.80	11.48 10.58	13.12 13.44	BCFH	.94* 8.13	.85	CH		1408 .3	1495 87	B				
N2770										-53					
N2775	11.5 11.73	11.53 10.22	13.32 13.52	CFH	.89 10.00	.76	CH		1135 1.8	958 -177	B				KP
N2776	12.2 12.07	12.25 7.11	14.29 14.11	CH	.57 8.13	.46	CH		2673 2.4	2682 9	C				K
N2777										-176					
N2781	12.7 12.64		13.43							-254					
N2782	12.4 12.47	12.66 6.38	13.85 13.66	CH	.64 8.13	.52	CH		2530 71.5	2514 -16	BDJ				
N2784	11.8 11.77	11.52 0.51	13.11 13.36	L	1.09 0.90	.88	L /L	.62	708 1.0	431 -277	C				
N2787	12.1 12.09	12.00 7.40	13.24 13.33	BCF	1.00 5.63	.90	C		621 7.8	753 131	BC				
N2788										-280					
N2793	12.9 13.35		13.44							-46					K
N2798	12.9 13.20	13.29 3.13	13.48 13.39	BC	.69 3.75	.54	C		1708 1.8	1702 -6	B				
N2799										-6					
N2805		11.95 1.41	15.29	G	.52 2.50	.40	G		1916 2.2	2023 107	C				
N2811	12.5 12.76	12.69 1.69	13.38 13.45	C	.73 1.88	.49	C		2514 1.8	2256 -258	B				P
N2814									1672 1.8	1780 108	E				
N2815	12.9 12.77		14.01							-275					
N2820		13.50 1.22	14.49	G	.51 2.50	.31	G		1691 4.0	1799 108	E				
N2820A									1497 2.3	1605 108	E				
N2822										-276					

NGC (IC, A) (1)	RA (1950) 100 P (2)	Dec 100 P (3)	L^I / B^I (4)	L^II / B^II (5)	SGL / SGB (6)	Rev. type (S) / DDO (T,L) (7)	Yerkes (1) / Yerkes (2) (8)	Hu-San / Ho (9)	log D w (10)	log R w (11)	log D(O) (12)	S (D,R) (13)
N2825	9 16.4	33 57	158.56	191.10	61.5	.S...*.W			.93	.66	.66	AR
	6.1	-25	45.79	44.32	-29.8				1.73	1.73		
N2826	9 16.4	33 50	158.73	191.26	61.6				1.05	.79	.74	AR
	6.1	-25	45.78	44.31	-29.8				1.60	1.60		
N2830	9 16.8	33 58	158.55	191.09	61.6	.S...*.W			1.08	.60	.84	ABR
	6.1	-25	45.88	44.41	-29.7				2.33	2.33		
N2831	9 16.7	33 59	158.53	191.06	61.5	.E.1...W			.90	.00	.90	AB
	6.1	-25	45.86	44.39	-29.7				.84	.84		
N2832	9 16.8	33 59	158.53	191.06	61.6	.E.2...W			1.02	.00	1.02	AB
	6.1	-25	45.88	44.41	-29.7	E T	ED *K		1.14	1.14		
N2835	9 15.7	-22 8	219.51	251.41	133.9	.SBT5..P200			1.78	.17	1.71	DEFGKNP
	4.5	-25	19.45	18.53	-55.7	S P	S A		25.08	25.08		TZ
N2836	9 13.1	-69 8	253.05	285.72	193.4	.S....*S030			1.33	.17	1.27	I
	1.6	-25	-14.01	-14.12	-32.2				1.28	1.28		
N2841	9 18.6	51 12	133.81	166.93	50.2	.SAR3*.P200	S K	S 3	1.87	.37	1.72	AKLRSVX
	6.9	-25	45.39	44.15	-16.0	S 2 1		S3	23.96	23.96		Z
N2844	9 18.6	40 22	149.34	182.11	57.3	.SAR1*.W100	SDP*G		1.05	.29	.94	AKW
	6.3	-25	46.56	45.15	-24.5	S 0			3.40	3.40		
N2848	9 17.8	-16 18	215.20	247.03	123.6	.SXS5*.W100			1.47	.19	1.40	AGKQ
	4.7	-25	23.72	22.71	-55.2	S 6 7*	S AF		4.60	4.60		
N2852	9 20.1	40 21	149.36	182.14	57.5	.SXR1$.W100			.73	.20	.65	W
	6.3	-25	46.85	45.43	-24.4				.28	.28		
N2853	9 20.2	40 23	149.31	182.09	57.5	.LB..*.W100			1.00	.32	.87	A
	6.3	-25	46.87	45.45	-24.3				.54	.54		
N2855	9 19.1	-11 41	211.53	243.32	115.7	RSATO..P200		S RO	1.33	.06	1.30	AFKZ
	4.8	-25	26.95	25.87	-54.3	E 1	D K		5.99	5.99		
N2859	9 21.3	34 44	157.58	190.15	61.8	RLBR+..P200	B K	LB2	1.53	.08	1.50	AHKZ
	6.1	-25	46.88	45.41	-28.5	SBO			8.34	8.34		
N2865	9 21.2	-22 58	221.08	252.96	135.2	.E.3+..W100			1.06	.14	1.00	DEKW
	4.5	-25	19.81	18.92	-54.3	E 4	ED K		3.95	3.95		
N2872	9 23.1	11 39	188.69	220.54	83.4	.E...$.			1.05	.08	1.02	AB
	5.4	-25	40.77	39.39	-43.9				1.21	1.21		
N2874	9 23.2	11 39	188.70	220.56	83.4	.SX..*.P048			1.44	.56	1.22	AB
	5.4	-25	40.80	39.41	-43.8				2.30	2.30		
N2880	9 25.7	62 44	118.11	151.43	44.0	.LB.-..W060	E2 K		1.13	.25	1.03	AKQ
	7.8	-26	42.74	41.76	-6.1	E 3			3.32	3.32		
N2884	9 24.0	-11 20	212.04	243.86	115.5	.S..0$.W060			1.21	.24	1.11	FQ
	4.8	-26	28.10	27.03	-53.0				2.02	2.02		
N2888	9 24.2	-27 48	225.22	257.15	143.1	.E.1+..W100			.63	.05	.61	W
	4.4	-26	16.91	16.11	-53.0				1.14	1.14		
N2889	9 24.8	-11 25	212.32	244.07	115.7	.SXT5..W060			1.25	.02	1.24	AFKQ
	4.8	-26	28.19	27.13	-52.9	S 4 T -*2*	S F		3.42	3.42		
N2892	9 28.9	67 51	111.78	145.12	41.2							
	8.5	-26	40.73	39.89	-1.8							
N2902	9 28.5	-14 30	215.60	247.36	121.0	.LAS0*.W100			.93	.05	.90	KW
	4.8	-26	26.84	25.84	-52.4	E 0			1.41	1.41		
N2903	9 29.3	21 44	176.62	208.69	74.2	.SXT4..P200	S F	S 5	2.06	.31	1.93	AHKLSUX
	5.7	-26	46.00	44.54	-36.4	S 4 2		S5	26.32	26.32		YZ
N2907	9 29.3	-16 32	217.42	249.19	124.3	.SAS1$/W100			1.12	.23	1.03	KW
	4.7	-26	25.61	24.64	-52.4	S 2	EDP*K		3.09	3.09		
N2911	9 31.0	10 22	191.39	223.17	86.3	.LAS.P*W100	E P*		.99	.14	.93	AKW
	5.4	-26	41.91	40.54	-43.0	E 2P			3.14	3.14		
N2914	9 31.3	10 20	191.48	223.26	86.4	.SBS2..W100			1.07	.19	.99	W
	5.4	-26	41.95	40.59	-42.9				.89	.89		
N2915	9 26.5	-76 25	259.18	291.97	198.1	.SA.2*.S030			1.17	.22	1.08	I
	-.6	-26	-18.41	-18.36	-26.1				1.01	1.01		
N2916	9 32.0	21 56	176.61	208.68	74.5	.S.....R020			1.28	.14	1.23	AH
	5.7	-26	46.67	45.21	-35.8				1.97	1.97		
N2919	9 32.3	10 30	191.44	223.21	86.4	.SXR3*.W100			1.26	.33	1.12	AW
	5.4	-26	42.25	40.89	-42.6				2.01	2.01		
N2924	9 32.8	-16 11	217.77	249.52	123.9				1.02	.00	1.02	K
	4.7	-26	26.46	25.50	-51.6	E 0			.33	.33		
N2935	9 34.5	-20 54	221.81	253.60	131.5	PSXS3..W100			1.45	.08	1.42	KW
	4.6	-26	23.46	22.59	-51.3	SX2 1	BS *G		4.55	4.55		
N2942	9 36.2	34 14	158.69	191.25	64.7	.SAS5*.W060	S AF		1.32	.03	1.30	CKQ
	6.0	-27	49.90	48.43	-26.8	S 3 3*			2.58	2.58		
N2944	9 36.2	32 32	161.30	193.78	66.1	.S.....R020			1.12	.33	.98	H
	6.0	-27	49.76	48.28	-28.0				.81	.81		
N2950	9 39.1	59 5	121.81	155.17	47.6	RLBR0..P200	B K	LB1+	1.27	.20	1.19	AKMZ
	7.3	-27	45.73	44.68	-8.0	S 0P			5.86	5.86		
N2955	9 38.3	36 7	155.78	188.43	63.6	PSAR3..W100	S FG		1.27	.24	1.18	CKW
	6.1	-27	50.41	48.95	-25.1	S 3 3			4.08	4.08		
N2957	9 41.8	73 13	105.14	138.48	38.6				1.03	.26	.93	AH
	9.3	-27	38.72	38.02	3.0				.81	.81		
N2959	9 41.1	68 49	109.90	143.28	41.4	.L.....$R020			1.17	.06	1.14	AH
	8.4	-27	41.19	40.38	-.4				1.03	1.03		
N2961	9 41.3	68 50	109.88	143.26	41.4	.S.....*R020			1.15	.42	.98	H
	8.4	-27	41.20	40.40	-.4				.85	.85		
N2962	9 38.3	5 24	198.33	229.99	93.5	RLXT+..W100	D P*G		1.31	.18	1.24	AKW
	5.2	-27	40.96	39.68	-43.9	S 4 5			4.88	4.88		

NGC (IC, A) (14)	m_H / m_C (15)	B(O) / w (16)	B'(O) / m'_C (17)	S(B) (18)	(B-V)(O) / w (19)	C_o(O) (20)	S(C) (21)	(U-B)(O) / w (22)	V / w (23)	V_o / ΔV (24)	S(V) (25)	φ_r / n (26)	φ(21) (27)	(28)	Photo. (29)
N2825															
										−49					
N2826															
										−50					
N2830		15.36	14.30	L	.88		L	.24							
		1.11			1.80		/L			−49					
N2831		14.58	13.82	CL	1.00	.87	CL	.44	5155	5106	B				
		4.14			5.60		/L		2.4	−49					
N2832	12.9	13.31	13.15	CHL	.99	.83	CHL	.59	6946	6897	B				
	13.01	7.30	12.85		10.80		/L		4.0	−49					
N2835	12.0								909	636	C				E
	11.38		14.67						8.2	−273					
N2836															
										−281					
N2841	10.5	10.27	13.61	ACFG	.85	.68	ACG		631	671	ABC				ABCJ
	10.50	8.97	13.84		10.63				9.2	41					KMP
N2844	13.0	14.11	13.50	H	.80		H								
	13.63	4.48	13.02		6.25					−16					
N2848	12.8														
	12.55		14.24							−258					
N2852															
										−16					
N2853															
										−15					
N2855	12.4	12.63	13.87	CL	.93	.78	CL	.46	1908	1663	B				LP
	12.40	2.60	13.64		4.60		/L		4.0	−245					
N2859	12.2	11.96	14.20	ACF	.93	.83	AC		1694	1649	B				LP
	11.81	12.91	14.05		8.13*				1.0	−45					
N2865	12.6	12.81	12.55	C	.75*	.56	C		2714	2440	B				
	12.84	1.96	12.58		3.75				1.8	−274					
N2872									2960	2803	E				
									2.0	−157					
N2874									3600	3443	E				
									2.0	−157					
N2880	12.9	12.97	12.86	BC	.88	.77	C		1514	1614	B				
	13.07	2.19	12.96		1.88				4.0	100					
N2884															
										−244					
N2888	13.1														
	13.85		11.59							−283					
N2889	12.4														
	12.70		13.59							−244					
N2892															
										125					
N2902	13.1														
	13.43		12.67							−252					
N2903	10.3	9.67	14.06	ACDFG	.67*	.53	ACDG	−.04	616	507	BCF				ABP
	9.94	8.95	14.33		38.75		/D		9.9	−109					
N2907	12.9														
	13.36		13.20							−258					
N2911	13.1	13.82	13.21	CL	1.08	.95	CL	.63	3140	2978	B				
	13.38	3.44	12.77		4.60		/L		1.8	−162					
N2914		14.19	13.88	C	.93	.76	C		3370	3208	B				
		1.96			1.88				1.0	−162					
N2915															
										−260					
N2916															
										−108					
N2919															
										−161					
N2924	13.2														
	13.22		13.01							−257					
N2935	12.4														
	12.24		14.03							−268					
N2942	12.9	13.76	15.00	H	.57		H								
	12.81	4.50	14.05		6.25					−46					
N2944															
										−54					
N2950	12.1	12.08	12.72	BCF	.91	.81	BC		1393	1475	BC				P
	12.29	6.75	12.93		11.88				6.8	82					
N2955	13.1	13.50	14.09	H	.66		H								
	13.17	4.81	13.76		6.25					−36					
N2957															
										150					
N2959															
										130					
N2961															
										130					
N2962	12.9														
	12.72		13.66							−182					

NGC (IC, A) (1)	RA (1950) Dec 100 P (2)	Dec 100 P (3)	L^{I} B^{I} (4)	L^{II} B^{II} (5)	SGL SGB (6)	Rev. type (S) DDO (T,L) (7)	Yerkes (1) Yerkes (2) (8)	Hu-San Ho (9)	log D w (10)	log R w (11)	log D(O) (12)	S (D,R) (13)
N2964	9 40.0	32 5	162.14	194.61	67.1	.SXR4*.W060			1.38	.26	1.28	ACHKLRS
	5.9	-27	50.51	49.03	-27.7	S 5 N 3*	S F	S5	12.50	11.61		VXQ
N2967	9 39.5	0 34	203.75	235.37	99.8	.SAS5..L036			1.52	.05	1.50	AKM
	5.1	-27	38.49	37.28	-45.8	S 5 K 5*	S F		5.01	5.01		
N2968	9 40.3	32 10	162.02	194.49	67.0	.I.0...W060			1.20	.22	1.11	CHKLRSX
	5.9	-27	50.58	49.10	-27.6	P	D P*GK*	I0	6.61	5.92		Q
N2970	9 40.6	32 13	161.95	194.42	67.1	.E...$.L036			.70	.10	.66	HR
	5.9	-27	50.65	49.17	-27.5				1.25	1.25		
N2974	9 40.0	-3 29	207.90	239.52	105.4	.E.4...W060			1.24	.22	1.15	AHKQ
	5.0	-27	36.14	35.00	-47.1	S 0	DS K		4.18	4.18		
N2976	9 43.2	68 8	110.53	143.93	42.0	.SA.5P.P200	I A		1.64	.34	1.50	AHKLRXZ
	8.2	-27	41.73	40.91	-.8	S		S P	13.88	13.88		
N2977	9 38.8	75 6	103.39	136.70	37.3							
	10.0	-27	37.44	36.79	4.3			S.				
N2978	9 40.9	-9 33	213.69	245.33	114.1	.S...*.H030			.99	.00	.99	F
	4.9	-27	32.40	31.36	-48.6				.88	.88		
N2980	9 40.8	-9 23	213.53	245.16	113.9	.SB..*.H030			1.25	.25	1.15	F
	4.9	-27	32.49	31.45	-48.6				1.29	1.29		
N2983	9 41.3	-20 15	222.56	254.30	130.5	.LBT+..W100			1.27	.23	1.18	KW
	4.7	-27	25.04	24.18	-49.8	SB0	B K		2.63	2.63		
N2985	9 46.0	72 31	105.64	139.00	39.3	PSAT2..W060	S FG		1.55	.08	1.52	AHKLXQ
	9.0	-27	39.40	38.69	2.7	S 2 1	S GK	S4	8.12	7.02		
N2986	9 42.0	-21 3	223.30	255.05	131.7	.E.2...W100			1.07	.06	1.05	KW
	4.6	-27	24.58	23.73	-49.6	E 1	ED K		2.40	2.40		
N2989	9 43.1	-18 9	221.27	252.98	127.2				1.12	.13	1.07	K
	4.7	-27	26.84	25.95	-49.3	S 4 3			.94	.94		
N2990	9 43.6	5 57	198.66	230.28	93.7	.S..5.W060	I *A		1.14	.24	1.05	AKQ
	5.3	-27	42.37	41.09	-42.5	S *			2.44	2.44		
N2992	9 43.3	-14 6	218.05	249.71	121.1	.S..1P.W100			1.36	.38	1.21	W
	4.8	-27	29.73	28.78	-48.8	P T +	S P G *		2.79	2.79		
N2993	9 43.4	-14 8	218.10	249.76	121.1	.S...P.W100			1.08	.17	1.01	W
	4.8	-27	29.73	28.77	-48.8	P T +	S P G *		1.97	1.97		
N2997	9 43.5	-30 58	230.70	262.59	146.7	.SXT5..W100	S F		1.84	.09	1.80	FGTW
	4.4	-27	17.44	16.76	-48.2				11.66	11.66		
N2998	9 45.8	44 19	142.65	175.70	58.5	.SXT5..W100	S F		1.49	.32	1.36	ABCKW
	6.3	-27	51.20	49.85	-18.3	S 5 3			7.89	7.89		
N3001	9 44.1	-30 13	230.29	262.16	145.5							
	4.4	-27	18.10	17.41	-48.2							
N3003	9 45.6	33 39	159.80	192.35	66.7	.S..4.$W060	SI *A *		1.73	.63	1.48	ACHKLXQ
	5.9	-27	51.81	50.34	-25.8	SX5 6*		S6	10.11	10.11		
N3020	9 47.4	13 3	190.65	222.36	86.2				1.55	.34	1.41	ABC
	5.4	-28	46.70	45.33	-38.2				3.23	3.23		
N3021	9 48.0	33 47	159.63	192.18	67.0	.SAT4*.W100	S AF		1.17	.25	1.07	ACHKW
	5.9	-28	52.31	50.84	-25.3	S 3			4.63	4.63		
N3023	9 47.3	0 51	204.95	236.51	100.5	.S.....R020			1.28	.08	1.25	H
	5.1	-28	40.23	39.04	-43.9				1.05	1.05		
N3024	9 47.8	12 59	190.80	222.50	86.3				1.33	.62	1.08	ABC
	5.4	-28	46.76	45.39	-38.1				2.40	2.40		
N3027	9 51.3	72 26	105.41	138.78	39.7	.SBT7*.W060			1.63	.29	1.51	ACHXQ
	8.9	-28	39.76	39.06	2.9			S6	5.12	5.12		
N3031	9 51.5	69 18	108.68	142.09	41.8	.SAS2......	S K	S 3	2.38	.26	2.28	AHKLVXY
	8.3	-28	41.68	40.91	0.6	S 3 2	S GK	S3	18.97	18.97		
N3032	9 49.2	29 28	166.69	199.02	70.8	.LXR0..P200	SDP*G *	L 3	1.12	.09	1.08	KZ
	5.8	-28	52.15	50.66	-28.0	S 0	SD *G *		3.41	3.41		
N3034	9 51.9	69 56	107.97	141.38	41.4	.I.0../....	I A	I 0	1.95	.53	1.74	AHKLUXY
	8.4	-28	41.33	40.57	1.1	P	E7P*	I0	11.45	11.45		
N3038	9 49.2	-32 32	232.72	264.62	148.6							
	4.4	-28	17.03	16.39	-46.7							
N3039	9 49.9	2 22	203.82	235.36	99.0	.S.....R020			1.20	.29	1.08	AH
	5.2	-28	41.66	40.45	-42.7				1.07	1.07		
N3041	9 50.3	16 55	185.87	217.65	82.7	.SXT5..W060	S AF		1.49	.17	1.42	AKQ
	5.5	-28	48.97	47.56	-35.4	S 5 4*			3.96	3.96		
N3043	9 52.8	59 32	120.09	153.54	48.6				1.15	.42	.98	AK
	7.1	-28	47.09	46.07	-6.5	S 2*			1.72	1.72		
N3044	9 51.0	1 49	204.65	236.18	99.8	.SBS5$/W100	SI *A		1.69	.84	1.36	AEHKW
	5.2	-28	41.55	40.35	-42.6	S 5*	S *F *		10.91	10.91		
N3052	9 52.0	-18 24	223.19	254.85	127.8	.SXR5*.W060			1.27	.14	1.21	KQ
	4.7	-28	28.12	27.27	-47.2	S 5 3	S AF*		3.14	3.14		
N3054	9 52.1	-25 28	228.41	260.18	138.2	.SXR3..W100			1.52	.20	1.44	EFKPW
	4.6	-28	22.85	22.12	-47.1	S 3 4*			10.55	10.55		
N3055	9 52.7	4 31	202.00	233.53	96.7	.SXS5..W100	SB *AF		1.26	.21	1.18	AHKW
	5.2	-28	43.46	42.23	-41.1	S 5 3*			4.80	4.80		
N3056	9 52.3	-28 4	230.26	262.06	142.0	RLAS+*.W100			.95	.17	.88	W
	4.5	-28	20.89	20.20	-46.8				1.67	1.67		
N3059	9 49.5	-73 41	258.43	291.14	194.7	.SBT4..B060			1.46	.05	1.44	DEPI
	1.0	-28	-15.39	-15.36	-26.9				6.08	6.08		
N3061	9 51.3	76 6	101.80	135.12	37.2				1.30	.15	1.24	AX
	9.9	-28	37.42	36.80	5.6			S5	.18	.18		
N3065	9 57.7	72 25	105.03	138.42	40.0	.LAR0..P200	SDP*F *	L 2	1.08	.03	1.07	AHKZ
	8.7	-28	40.15	39.45	3.2	S 0	D K		4.32	4.32		

NGC (IC, A)	Magnitudes				Colors				Velocities			Radio			
	m_H m_c	B(O) w	B'(O) m'_c	S(B)	(B-V)(O) w	C_o(O)	S(C)	(U-B)(O) w	V w	V_o ΔV	S(V)	ϕ_r n	ϕ(21)		Photo.
(14)	(15)	(16)	(17)	(18)	(19)	(20)	(21)	(22)	(23)	(24)	(25)	(26)	(27)	(28)	(29)
N2964	11.9 12.30	12.37 9.82	13.51 13.44	CGH	.73 18.75	.59	CGH		134C 4.C	1284 −56	B				
N2967	12.4 12.08	12.22 0.99	14.46 14.32	F					2245 2.2	2044 −201	C				
N2968	12.8 12.96	13.25 4.04	13.54 13.25	GH	1.02 15.00		GH			−56					B
N2970										−55					
N2974	12.7 12.65	12.31 4.20	12.80 13.14	C	.97 5.63	.86	C		2013 4.0	1797 −216	B				
N2976	11.2 11.43	11.09 7.50	13.33 13.67	BCFG	.66 10.63	.51	BCG		42 11.1	169 127	C				C
N2977				G*						158					
N2978										−236					
N2980										−235					
N2983	12.8 12.77	12.91 3.44	13.50 13.36	C	.93 3.75	.77	C		2015 1.0	1750 −265	B				
N2985	11.8 11.64	11.51 5.59	13.85 13.98	CFG	.75 4.38	.63	CG		1277 4.0	1424 147	B				
N2986	12.2 12.51	12.74 3.18	12.68 12.45	C	.91 3.75	.76	C		2397 1.0	2130 −267	B				
N2989	13.1 13.43		13.52							−260					
N2990	13.0 13.46		13.40							−179					
N2992	13.0 13.00		13.74							−249					
N2993	13.0 13.51		13.30							−249					
N2997	11.0 10.64		14.38							−285					
N2998	12.8 12.62		14.16							8					
N3001	13.2									−284					
N3003	12.5 12.16	12.52 2.34	14.66 14.30	CG	.50 4.38	.32	CG		1476 2.8	1429 −47	B				B
N3020										−147					
N3021	12.7 13.23		13.27							−46					
N3023										−198					
N3024										−147					
N3027		12.64 1.25	14.93	G					1079 1.8	1226 147	C				
N3031	8.9 8.35	7.88 8.90	13.97 14.44	ACDEF GK	.95* 16.87	.80	ABCDE G/E	.50	−44 234.6	88 133	ABCKR				ABJL P
N3032	12.8 12.92	12.86 2.03	13.00 13.06	C	.74 1.88	.65	C		1568 .4	1500 −68	B				LP
N3034	9.4 9.68	9.57 10.65	12.96 13.07	BCEFG K	.87 15.00	.73	BCEG /E	.33	186 409.0	322 136	ABCR				BLP
N3038	12.9									−287					
N3039										−192					
N3041	12.7 12.43	12.55 3.93	14.39 14.27	H	.82* 6.25		H			−129					
N3043	13.2 13.66		13.30							86					
N3044	12.6 12.54		14.03							−194					
N3052	12.8 12.97		13.76							−259					
N3054	12.6 12.31		14.20							−275					
N3055	12.5 12.90	13.00 3.77	13.59 13.49	CF	.63 1.88	.49	C		1913 2.0	1730 −183	C				
N3056	12.8 13.28		12.37							−279					
N3059	12.2 12.11		14.00							−265					
N3061		13.76 1.30	14.70	G						163		.			
N3065	12.9 13.02	13.13 1.46	13.17 13.06	CF*	.94 1.88	.83	C		2051 3.3	2198 147	C				P

NGC (IC, A) (1)	RA (1950) Dec 100 P / 100 P (2)(3)		L^I B^I (4)	L^II B^II (5)	SGL SGB (6)	Rev. type (S) DDO (T, L) (7)	Yerkes (1) Yerkes (2) (8)	Hu-San Ho (9)	log D w (10)	log R w (11)	log D(0) (12)	S (D,R) (13)
N3066	9 57.8	72 22	105.07	138.46	40.1	PSXS4P.P200			1.00	.08	.97	AHZ
	8.7	-28	40.19	39.49	3.2				3.45	3.45		
N3067	9 55.4	32 37	161.71	194.21	69.1	.SXS2.$W100	I A *		1.38	.41	1.21	ACHKW
	5.9	-28	53.80	52.32	-24.9	S 4 5			4.69	4.69		
N3073	9 57.4	55 51	124.54	157.99	51.6	.E...P$RO20			.99	.00	.99	ABHL
	6.8	-28	49.33	48.24	-8.7				1.75	1.75		
N3077	9 59.4	68 58	108.46	141.90	42.6	.I.O.P.P200	E P	I 0	1.51	.13	1.45	AHKLMUX
	8.0	-28	42.45	41.67	0.8	E 2P	EDP	IO	12.38	12.38		Z
N3078	9 56.2	-26 41	230.03	261.79	139.8	.E.2+..W100			1.04	.12	.99	KW
	4.5	-28	22.51	21.82	-46.1	E 3			2.29	2.29		
N3079	9 58.6	55 57	124.31	157.77	51.7	.SBS9./W060	SI *FG		1.83	.70	1.55	ABHLUXQ
	6.8	-28	49.44	48.35	-8.5	S 3 NT- 3*		S5	14.39	14.39		
N3081	9 56.8	-22 33	227.23	258.92	133.9	RLXR+..W100		SX 1	1.25	.09	1.22	KW
	4.6	-28	25.76	25.01	-46.1	S 4 5*	D GK*		3.63	3.63		
N3087	9 57.0	-33 59	235.00	266.89	150.1				1.02	.19	.94	E
	4.4	-28	16.91	16.33	-44.8				.65	.65		
N3089	9 57.3	-28 4	231.17	262.96	141.8	.SXT3..W100			1.24	.11	1.19	W
	4.5	-28	21.59	20.92	-45.7				1.10	1.10		
N3091	9 57.8	-19 23	225.09	256.73	129.3	.E+3.*..W060			1.11	.11	1.06	KQ
	4.7	-28	28.31	27.50	-45.8	E 2	DE *K		1.10	1.10		
N3095	9 57.9	-31 18	233.43	265.27	146.3	.SXT5..B060			1.47	.22	1.38	DEP
	4.4	-28	19.14	18.53	-45.1				5.03	5.03		
N3098	9 59.5	24 58	174.72	206.78	76.4	.L..../W100	D K		1.24	.51	1.04	ACKW
	5.6	-28	53.55	52.08	-29.0	E 7			3.47	3.47		
N3100	9 58.4	-31 25	233.59	265.43	146.5	.LXSOP.B060			1.33	.28	1.22	P
	4.4	-28	19.12	18.51	-45.0				2.13	2.13		
N3109	10 0.8	-25 55	230.37	262.10	138.6	.I...9./L036		I 9	2.15	.66	1.88	FGKM
	4.6	-29	23.76	23.07	-45.1	I 8			11.02	11.02		
N3113	10 2.2	-28 12	232.17	263.94	141.8				1.51	.25	1.42	F
	4.5	-29	22.16	21.51	-44.6				1.83	1.83		
N3115	10 2.8	-7 28	216.33	247.79	113.1	.L..-./P200	D K	E+7	1.63	.48	1.44	AEFKLMR
	5.0	-29	37.79	36.80	-42.8	E 6			18.99	18.99		TYZ
N3124	10 4.2	-19 0	226.11	257.71	128.9	.SXT4..W100			1.44	.06	1.42	FGKW
	4.8	-29	29.59	28.80	-44.3	SX4 1*	S F		7.02	7.02		
N3125	10 4.2	-29 41	233.52	265.30	143.8							
	4.5	-29	21.25	20.64	-44.0							
N3136	10 4.5	-67 8	255.44	287.98	188.0	.E.4+*.S030			1.15	.19	1.07	DEI
	2.6	-29	-9.39	-9.45	-29.9				2.49	2.49		
N3136A	10 2.1	-67 13	255.29	287.84	188.2	.S...$.S030			1.30	.59	1.06	I
	2.5	-29	-9.60	-9.65	-30.1				.88	.88		
N3136B	10 9.9	-66 44	255.65	288.18	187.3	.E.5...S030			1.12	.24	1.02	I
	2.7	-29	-8.77	-8.81	-29.7				.94	.94		
N3143	10 7.6	-12 20	221.61	253.08	119.9	.SBS3..W100			.82	.15	.77	W
	4.9	-29	35.13	34.24	-42.7				.64	.64		
N3144	10 11.4	74 28	102.19	135.58	39.2	.S....$RO20			1.07	.23	.97	AH
	8.7	-29	39.46	38.83	5.3				1.00	1.00		
N3145	10 7.7	-12 10	221.49	252.96	119.7	.SBT4..W100		S 3	1.44	.29	1.32	EKNW
	4.9	-29	35.27	34.38	-42.7	S 4 1	S *F *		7.52	7.52		
N3147	10 12.8	73 39	102.86	136.28	39.9	.SAT4..W060	S FG	S 3	1.48	.04	1.46	AHKLSUQ
	8.5	-29	40.12	39.47	4.9	S 3 2*	S GK		11.77	9.58		
N3151	10 10.6	38 51	150.54	183.48	66.0				1.18	.05	1.16	C
	5.9	-29	56.65	55.23	-18.5				.32	.32		
N3152	10 10.7	39 5	150.12	183.07	65.9				1.10	.00	1.10	C
	5.9	-29	56.64	55.22	-18.4				.27	.27		
N3156	10 10.1	3 22	206.93	238.27	100.4	.L...*.W060			1.18	.33	1.04	AHKLQ
	5.2	-29	46.29	45.13	-37.6	E 5P -*			3.38	2.74		
N3158	10 10.9	39 0	150.29	183.23	66.0	.E.3.*.W100			.99	.07	.96	ACKMW
	5.9	-29	56.69	55.27	-18.4	E 2	E3 K		2.99	2.99		
N3159	10 11.0	38 54	150.43	183.37	66.1	.E.2...L...			1.17	.00	1.17	BC
	5.9	-29	56.72	55.30	-18.5				1.07	1.07		
N3161	10 11.0	38 54	150.43	183.37	66.1	.E.3...L...			1.11	.00	1.11	BC
	5.9	-29	56.72	55.30	-18.5				.96	.96		
N3162	10 10.7	22 59	179.15	211.04	79.9	.SXT4..W100	S F		1.40	.07	1.38	ACHKNSW
	5.6	-29	55.52	54.07	-28.1	S 5 3*	S F		10.95	10.95		
N3163	10 11.2	38 53	150.45	183.39	66.1	.E.1...L...			1.09	.00	1.09	ABC
	5.9	-29	56.76	55.34	-18.4				1.51	1.51		
N3165	10 10.9	3 37	206.79	238.13	100.2	.S....$			1.26	.21	1.17	ABL
	5.2	-29	46.60	45.44	-37.3				2.43	1.66		
N3166	10 11.2	3 40	206.83	238.16	100.2	.SXT0..W060	SD *G		1.59	.26	1.48	ABKLXQ
	5.2	-29	46.69	45.53	-37.3	S N +		S1	8.15	6.89		
N3169	10 11.7	3 43	206.88	238.21	100.2	.SAS1P.W060	S GK		1.59	.24	1.50	ABCLXQ
	5.2	-29	46.82	45.66	-37.1	S 3 NT		S1	7.44	7.44		
N3175	10 12.4	-28 38	234.40	266.12	142.1	.SXS1.$W100			1.55	.55	1.33	GW
	4.6	-29	23.16	22.57	-42.3				4.38	4.38		
N3177	10 13.9	21 22	182.27	214.05	81.9	.SAT3..W100	S G		1.07	.05	1.05	ACEKW
	5.5	-29	55.76	54.32	-28.3	S 4	S P		4.28	4.28		
N3182	10 15.9	58 28	119.11	152.71	51.4	.SAR1$.W060			1.02	.00	1.02	AC
	6.7	-30	50.18	49.18	-5.1				.33	.33		
N3183	10 17.8	74 26	101.83	135.24	39.6	.SB.3*.W			1.35	.23	1.26	ABHX
	8.6	-30	39.79	39.17	5.6			S4	2.58	2.58		

NGC (IC, A)	Magnitudes				Colors				Velocities			Radio			
	m_H / m_C	B(O) / w	B'(O) / m'_C	S(B)	(B-V)(O) / w	C_o(O)	S(C)	(U-B)(O) / w	V / w	V_o / ΔV	S(V)	ϕ_r / n	ϕ(21)		Photo.
(14)	(15)	(16)	(17)	(18)	(19)	(20)	(21)	(22)	(23)	(24)	(25)	(26)	(27)	(28)	(29)
N3066		13.45 / 1.91	13.04 / 1.88	C	.77 / 2.2	.65	C		2132 / 2.2	2279 / 147	C				
N3067	12.8 / 12.90	12.91 / 2.64	13.70 / 13.69	C	.62 / 3.75	.44	C		1506 / 4.0	1455 / -51	B				K
N3073										63					
N3077	11.4 / 11.44	11.12 / 7.55	13.11 / 13.43	CEFG	.76 / 10.63	.67	CEG /E	.10	-158 / 2.2	-26 / 132	C				LP
N3078	12.4 / 12.73	12.51 / 2.95	12.20 / 12.42	C	.83 / 3.75	.67	C		2481 / 4.0	2205 / -276	B				
N3079	11.9 / 11.89	11.43 / 1.20	13.87 / 14.33	G	.65 / 2.50	.54	G		1171 / 2.8	1240 / 69	C				B
N3081	12.8 / 12.70		13.49							-268					P
N3087	13.0									-287					
N3089	13.0 / 13.07		13.76							-278					
N3091	12.7 / 12.81		12.85							-260					
N3095	12.7 / 12.52		14.16							-283					
N3098	13.0 / 13.48	13.15 / 5.12	13.04 / 13.37	H	.89 / 6.25		H			-88					
N3100										-283					
N3109	11.2 / 10.57		14.71						403 / 101.2	130 / -274	CR				P
N3113										-278					
N3115	9.8 / 10.33	10.43 / 11.21	12.37 / 12.27	BCD	.96 / 35.63	.84	BCD /D	.50	646 / 72.7	422 / -225	ABD				ACJK / P
N3124	12.8 / 12.48		14.27							-258					
N3125	13.0									-280					
N3136	12.4 / 12.59		12.68							-277					
N3136A										-277					
N3136B										-277					
N3143										-239					
N3144										157					
N3145	12.5 / 12.53		13.87						3855 / 2.0	3617 / -238	C				P
N3147	11.9 / 11.88	11.52 / 7.84	13.56 / 13.92	BCF	.80 / 5.63	.68	C		2721 / 1.6	2875 / 154	B				P
N3151									7140 / 1.4	7124 / -16	D				
N3152									6471 / .5	6456 / -15	D				
N3156	13.1 / 13.19		13.13							-183					
N3158	12.7 / 12.98	13.55 / 8.31	13.09 / 12.52	BCH	.98 / 16.25	.84	BCH		7024 / 4.0	7009 / -15	B				
N3159									6950 / 2.2	6934 / -16	C				
N3161									6204 / 2.2	6188 / -16	C				
N3162	12.3 / 12.30		13.89						1456 / 2.4	1361 / -95	B				K
N3163									6245 / 2.1	6229 / -16	C				
N3165										-182					
N3166	11.6 / 11.56	11.44 / 4.44	13.58 / 13.70	ABCG	.90 / 16.87	.78	ABCG		1381 / 4.0	1200 / -181	B				
N3169	11.9 / 11.74	11.50 / 3.76	13.69 / 13.93	ACG	.85 / 8.75	.71	ACG		1298 / 6.0	1116 / -181	BC				B
N3175	12.1 / 12.24		13.58							-276					
N3177	12.8 / 13.31		13.25						1220 / 2.4	1118 / -102	B				
N3182										84					
N3183		12.97 / 1.15	13.96	G						158					

NGC (IC, A) (1)	RA (1950) 100 P (2)	Dec 100 P (3)	L^I B^I (4)	L^II B^II (5)	SGL SGB (6)	Rev. type (S) DDO (T, L) (7)	Yerkes (1) Yerkes (2) (8)	Hu-San Ho (9)	log D w (10)	log R w (11)	log D(0) (12)	S (D,R) (13)
N3184	10 15.2 41 40	6.0 −30	145.22 57.00	178.35 55.62	64.4 −16.1	.SXT6..W100 S 5 3	S AF S F	S5	1.79 17.26	.01 17.26	1.80	ACHKLVX YW
N3185	10 14.9 21 56	5.5 −30	181.44 56.15	213.23 54.71	81.5 −27.8	RSBR1..P200 SX4 5*	B F BD FG	SBS1 S1	1.31 8.43	.16 8.43	1.25	ACEHKMX Z
N3187	10 15.0 22 8	5.5 −30	181.11 56.23	212.91 54.79	81.3 −27.7	.SBS5P.P200 B P*A	S.		1.43 7.45	.35 7.45	1.29	ACHMXZ
N3190	10 15.4 22 5	5.5 −30	181.24 56.31	213.04 54.86	81.4 −27.7	.SAS1P/P200 S 3 NT 4*	S GK SDP K	S1	1.60 11.72	.47 11.72	1.41	ABCEHMX Z
N3193	10 15.7 22 9	5.5 −30	181.16 56.39	212.96 54.95	81.4 −27.6	.E.2..P200 E 0	E2 K E2 K	E	1.21 7.54	.07 7.54	1.18	ABCEHKM XZ
N3198	10 16.7 45 49	6.1 −30	137.85 56.09	171.21 54.80	61.2 −13.2	.SBT5..W060 S 5 3	S AF	S5	1.94 15.48	.36 15.48	1.80	ACHKLVX YQ
N3200	10 16.2 −17 44	4.8 −30	227.73 32.38	259.23 31.63	127.5 −41.4	.SAS2*$W060 S 3 3	S *F		1.56 4.49	.49 4.49	1.36	KQ
N3203	10 16.3 −26 27	4.6 −30	233.77 25.44	265.43 24.83	139.1 −41.6	.LAR+$/B060 E 8			1.39 3.67	.72 3.67	1.10	KP
N3206	10 18.5 57 11	6.6 −30	120.48 51.18	154.09 50.16	52.6 −5.7	.SBS6..W060			1.46 6.49	.15 6.49	1.40	ACHNQ
N3213	10 18.6 19 55	5.5 −30	185.37 56.31	217.02 54.89	84.0 −28.2	.S....*R020			1.12 1.11	.10 1.11	1.08	CH
N3214	10 19.8 57 18	6.6 −30	120.16 51.27	153.78 50.25	52.7 −5.4	.L....$R020			1.21 1.95	.31 1.95	1.08	ABC
N3220	10 20.4 57 17	6.6 −30	120.10 51.35	153.74 50.33	52.7 −5.4	.S....*R020			1.32 2.54	.52 2.54	1.11	ABCH
N3221	10 19.6 21 51	5.5 −30	182.18 57.17	213.93 55.73	82.2 −29.9				1.56 1.36	.72 1.36	1.07	A
N3222	10 19.9 20 8	5.5 −30	185.18 56.65	216.83 55.23	83.9 −27.8	.LB....W			1.03 2.00	.18 1.47	.95	ACHL
N3223	10 19.4 −34 0	4.5 −30	238.99 19.59	270.80 19.11	149.0 −40.2	.SAS3..W100			1.54 9.96	.23 9.96	1.45	DEGPW
N3226	10 20.7 20 9	5.5 −30	185.29 56.86	216.93 55.44	84.0 −27.6	.E+2.P*P200 E 2	E3 K *		1.19 6.59	.05 5.96	1.17	ABCHKLZ
N3227	10 20.7 20 7	5.5 −30	185.34 56.85	216.90 55.43	84.1 −27.7	.SXS1P.P200 S 3 NT	S P G *		1.57 9.37	.19 9.37	1.49	ABCHLZ
N3238	10 23.4 57 28	6.5 −30	119.49 51.57	153.15 50.57	52.8 −5.0	.S....*R020			1.21 .18	.38 .18	1.05	H
N3239	10 22.4 17 25	5.4 −30	190.15 56.20	221.64 54.82	86.9 −28.7	.SB.9..L036			1.62 3.42	.24 3.42	1.52	ACN
N3241	10 22.1 −32 13	4.5 −30	233.45 21.39	270.21 20.90	146.6 −39.9	.SAR2*.B060			1.15 1.72	.13 1.72	1.10	P
N3244	10 23.3 −39 35	4.4 −30	242.82 15.30	274.73 14.91	155.9 −38.5	.SA.5*.S030			1.25 1.15	.06 1.15	1.23	I
N3245	10 24.5 28 46	5.6 −30	169.68 59.71	201.90 58.22	76.5 −22.3	.LAR0*$W100 E 5	D GK	L 1	1.33 7.27	.29 6.38	1.22	ACHKLW
N3245A	10 24.2 28 54	5.6 −30	169.41 59.66	201.63 58.17	76.4 −22.3	.SBS3./W100			1.36 2.83	.78 2.83	1.05	W
N3250	10 24.3 −39 41	4.4 −30	243.05 15.31	274.96 14.93	156.0 −38.3	.E.4...S030			1.25 .82	.19 .82	1.17	I
N3250A	10 25.6 −39 49	4.4 −30	243.34 15.33	275.25 14.96	156.1 −38.0	.S...*/S030			1.23 .80	.77 .80	.93	I
N3250B	10 25.6 −40 10	4.4 −30	243.53 15.03	275.44 14.66	156.5 −37.9	.L...*.S030			1.39 1.38	.66 1.38	1.13	I
N3250C	10 25.7 −39 45	4.4 −30	243.32 15.39	275.23 15.02	156.0 −38.0	.L...*.S030			1.29 .87	.56 .87	1.07	I
N3250D	10 25.8 −39 33	4.4 −30	243.23 15.58	275.13 15.20	155.8 −38.0	.L...*/S030			1.17 1.01	.62 1.01	.92	I
N3250E	10 26.9 −39 50	4.4 −30	243.57 15.44	275.48 15.07	156.1 −37.7	.S..5*.S030			1.21 1.08	.13 1.08	1.16	I
N3252	10 30.5 74 2	8.1 −30	101.33 40.66	134.78 40.05	40.4 6.0	.S...*.			1.34 1.00	.36 1.00	1.20	A
N3254	10 26.5 29 45	5.6 −30	167.81 60.24	200.10 58.75	75.9 −21.4	.SAS4..P200 S 3 3	S FG S G		1.67 12.06	.49 12.06	1.48	ACHKLZ
N3256	10 25.7 −43 38	4.3 −30	245.37 12.06	277.36 11.74	160.8 −37.1	.P.....S030			1.43 3.38	.20 3.38	1.35	DEI
N3256A	10 23.6 −43 32	4.3 −30	244.98 11.95	276.98 11.62	160.8 −37.5	.S...$.S030			1.18 1.03	.36 1.03	1.03	I
N3256B	10 26.9 −44 8	4.3 −30	245.82 11.74	277.82 11.43	161.3 −36.8	.S...*.S030			1.23 1.11	.47 1.11	1.04	I
N3256C	10 26.9 −43 36	4.3 −30	245.54 12.20	277.53 11.88	160.7 −36.9	.SBT7..B060			1.14 2.66	.09 2.66	1.10	PI
N3257	10 26.5 −35 25	4.5 −31	241.10 19.18	272.91 18.75	150.6 −38.6	.LXS−*$B060			.85 1.17	.02 1.17	.84	PI
N3258	10 26.6 −35 20	4.5 −30	241.08 19.26	272.88 18.83	150.4 −38.6	.E.1...B060			1.01 2.67	.05 2.67	.99	EPI
N3258A	10 26.1 −35 13	4.5 −30	240.92 19.31	272.73 18.87	150.3 −38.7	.L...*.S030			1.11 .47	.65 .47	.85	I
N3258B	10 28.1 −35 18	4.5 −30	241.33 19.45	273.14 19.02	150.3 −38.3	.S...*.S030			1.06 .60	.39 .60	.90	I
N3258C	10 29.1 −34 57	4.5 −30	241.33 19.85	273.12 19.43	149.9 −38.1	.S...*.S030			1.16 .72	.15 .72	1.10	I

NGC (IC, A) (14)	m_H / m_c (15)	B(O) w (16)	B'(O) m'_c (17)	S(B) (18)	(B-V)(O) w (19)	C_o(O) (20)	S(C) (21)	(U-B)(O) w (22)	V w (23)	V_o ΔV (24)	S(V) (25)	φ_r n (26)	φ(21) (27)	(28)	Photo. (29)
N3184	11.8	10.59	14.28	BCFG	.64	.57	CG		418	418	BC				
	11.14	5.07	14.83		4.38				2.1	-1					
N3185	12.7	13.23	14.17	CFG	.81	.70	CG		1241	1142	B				P
	12.75	4.56	13.69		4.38				2.4	-99					
N3187		13.55	14.69	G	.51		G								
		1.32			2.50					-98					
N3190	12.1	12.20	13.94	CFG	.96	.81	CG		1354	1255	BC				
	12.06	3.93	13.80		4.38				6.5	-98					
N3193	12.6	12.37	12.96	CFGL	.91	.84	CGL	.54	1371	1273	B				
	12.55	3.67	13.14		6.20		/L		4.0	-98					
N3198	11.7	11.09	14.78	G	.55	.41	G		649	670	C				A
	11.04	1.41	14.73		2.50				2.1	21					
N3200	12.8														
	12.55		14.09							-251					
N3203	13.2														
	13.15		13.39							-271					
N3206										78					
N3213										-108					
N3214										79					
N3220										79					
N3221										-98					
N3222		13.93	13.42	C	.94	.80	C		5577	5471	B				
		1.86			1.88				6.3	-106					
N3223	12.1														
	11.99		13.98							-282					
N3226	12.8	12.77	13.36	C	.91	.83	C		1338	1232	B				A
	12.68	1.86	13.27		1.88				44.4	-106					
N3227	12.2	11.75	13.94	C	.87	.75	C		1111	1005	B				A
	11.91	1.98	14.10		1.88				25.0	-106					
N3238										80					
N3239		12.23	14.57	C	.50	.41	C		880	761	C				
		0.88			1.88				3.8	-119					
N3241	13.0														
	13.26		13.50							-279					
N3244										-287					
N3245	12.0	12.04	12.83	CL	.88	.79	CL	.45	1261	1198	B				P
	12.17	3.42	12.96		4.70		/L		11.1	-63					
N3245A										-63					
N3250	12.4														
	12.42		13.01							-287					
N3250A										-286					
N3250B										-287					
N3250C										-286					
N3250D										-286					
N3250E										-286					
N3252										157					
N3254	12.6	12.41	14.50	C	.69	.54	C		1228	1170	B				
	12.24	1.79	14.33		1.88				2.8	-58					
N3256	12.1	11.92	13.41	M*			M*	*	2828	2539	H				F
		0.86					/M		6.3	-289					
N3256A										-289					
N3256B										-289					
N3256C										-288					
N3257										-281					
N3258	13.0														
	13.14		12.78							-282					
N3258A										-282					
N3258B										-281					
N3258C										-280					

NGC (IC, A)	Coordinates					Classification			Diameters			
	RA (1950) Dec 100 P 100 P		L^I B^I	L^II B^II	SGL SGB	Rev. type (S) DDO (T, L)	Yerkes (1) Yerkes (2)	Hu-San Ho	log D w	log R w	log D(O)	S (D,R)
(1)	(2)	(3)	(4)	(5)	(6)	(7)	(8)	(9)	(10)	(11)	(12)	(13)
N3258D	10 29.6	−35 9	241.53	273.32	150.1	.S...*.S030			1.21	.27	1.10	I
	4.5	−30	19.74	19.32	−38.0				1.08	1.08		
N3258E	10 30.0	−34 45	241.39	273.17	149.6	.S...$.S030			1.23	.52	1.02	I
	4.5	−30	20.12	19.70	−38.0				.80	.80		
N3259	10 29.2	65 18	109.62	143.24	47.2	.SXT4*.W060	SD *G		1.29	.21	1.20	KNQ
	7.0	−30	47.04	46.24	0.5	I 9P 7*			4.82	4.82		
N3260	10 25.9	−35 18	240.93	272.74	150.4	.E.2.*.B060			.85	.06	.82	PI
	4.5	−30	19.21	18.78	−38.7				1.17	1.17		
N3261	10 26.8	−44 23	245.93	277.94	161.6	.SBT3..B060			1.54	.12	1.49	DEPI
	4.3	−30	11.51	11.21	−36.7				7.23	7.23		
N3262	10 27.1	−43 55	245.74	277.73	161.0	.LX.-*.B060			.87	.07	.84	PI
	4.3	−30	11.94	11.63	−36.8				1.80	1.80		
N3263	10 27.2	−43 53	245.74	277.73	161.0	.SBT6*/B060			1.52	.52	1.32	PI
	4.3	−30	11.98	11.67	−36.8				4.36	4.36		
N3265	10 28.4	29 3	169.30	201.52	76.8	.E....*			.96	.11	.92	ACHL
	5.6	−30	60.60	59.11	−21.4				1.77	1.33		
N3266	10 29.9	65 1	109.84	143.47	47.5	.LX.0.$W060			1.12	.16	1.06	NQ
	7.0	−31	47.29	46.48	0.4				2.05	2.05		
N3267	10 27.5	−35 3	241.08	272.88	150.0	.LXR0..B060			1.20	.25	1.10	PI
	4.5	−30	19.60	19.17	−38.4				2.88	2.88		
N3268	10 27.7	−35 04	241.13	272.93	150.1	.E.2..B060			1.06	.10	1.02	EPI
	4.5	−31	19.61	19.18	−38.4				3.08	3.08		
N3269	10 27.8	−34 57	241.08	272.88	149.9	.LAR+..B060			1.33	.34	1.20	PI
	4.5	−30	19.72	19.29	−38.4				2.86	2.86		
N3271	10 28.2	−35 6	241.24	273.04	150.1	.LBR0..B060			1.19	.36	1.05	EPI
	4.5	−30	19.63	19.20	−38.3				3.59	3.59		
N3273	10 28.2	−35 21	241.38	273.18	150.4	.LAR0..B060			1.19	.37	1.04	PI
	4.5	−30	19.42	18.99	−38.3				2.86	2.86		
N3274	10 29.6	27 56	171.62	203.75	77.9				1.34	.36	1.19	ACHK
	5.6	−30	60.72	59.24	−21.8	S 5 K	I P*		3.82	3.82		
N3275	10 28.6	−36 28	242.06	273.89	151.8	.SBR2..S030			1.36	.09	1.32	EI
	4.5	−30	18.50	18.10	−38.0				1.75	1.75		
N3277	10 30.2	28 46	169.96	202.15	77.3	.SAR2..W100	SD *G		1.18	.04	1.16	ACKLW
	5.6	−30	60.95	59.46	−21.2	S 2 3*	S P*K *		5.00	5.00		
N3281	10 29.7	−34 36	241.25	273.03	149.4	.SAS3$.S030			1.45	.30	1.33	EFI
	4.5	−30	20.22	19.79	−38.1				3.64	3.64		
N3281C	10 30.7	−34 39	241.46	273.24	149.4	.L...*.S030			1.11	.64	.85	I
	4.5	−30	20.28	19.86	−37.8				.47	.47		
N3281D	10 32.0	−34 8	241.43	273.19	148.7	.S..5*/S030			1.33	.82	1.00	I
	4.6	−31	20.86	20.44	−37.6				.63	.63		
N3285	10 31.3	−27 12	237.32	268.93	140.0	.SBS1P.B060			1.19	.16	1.12	KP
	4.7	−30	26.69	26.17	−38.2	S N +			1.94	1.94		
N3285A	10 30.6	−27 15	237.20	268.82	140.0	.SA..*..B060			1.01	.04	.99	P
	4.7	−31	26.57	26.04	−38.4				1.43	1.43		
N3285B	10 32.3	−27 24	237.65	269.26	140.2	.SXR3$.B060			1.15	.15	1.09	P
	4.7	−31	26.64	26.13	−38.0				1.72	1.72		
N3287	10 32.1	21 55	183.75	215.37	83.8	.SBS7..W100	BI *A		1.31	.31	1.18	ACW
	5.5	−31	59.95	58.52	−24.4	S K 7*	I A *		4.06	4.06		
N3288	10 33.1	58 49	116.51	150.24	52.6	.S...*.			1.09	.00	1.09	AC
	6.5	−31	51.75	50.80	−3.1				.91	.91		
N3289	10 31.9	−35 4	241.91	273.70	149.9	.SB.5$.S030			1.32	.73	1.02	I
	4.5	−31	20.05	19.64	−37.5				.63	.63		
N3294	10 33.4	37 35	151.61	184.62	69.9	.SAS5..W100	S AF		1.51	.29	1.39	ABCHKLW
	5.8	−31	61.28	59.84	−15.8	S 5 1	S AF*		10.51	10.51		
N3299	10 33.7	12 58	199.56	230.72	92.9	.SXS8..W100			1.38	.15	1.32	ACW
	5.3	−31	56.56	55.29	−28.3				2.82	2.82		
N3300	10 34.0	14 26	197.31	228.51	91.4	.LXR0*$W100			1.16	.31	1.03	AKW
	5.3	−31	57.36	56.06	−27.6	SB0			2.72	2.72		
N3301	10 34.3	22 8	183.65	215.26	83.9	PSBT0..W100	SDP*GK		1.51	.56	1.29	ACKW
	5.5	−31	60.50	59.07	−23.9	S 0	DSP GK		6.85	6.85		
N3304	10 34.7	37 43	151.23	184.27	70.0	.SBS1$.W100			1.24	.43	1.06	ACHW
	5.7	−31	61.50	60.07	−15.5				3.26	3.26		
N3306	10 34.5	12 53	199.88	231.02	93.0	.SBS9.$W100			1.06	.38	.91	CW
	5.3	−31	56.68	55.41	−28.2				2.26	2.26		
N3307	10 33.9	−27 16	237.91	269.51	140.1	.S...*.B060			.89	.33	.76	P
	4.7	−31	26.94	26.43	−37.7				1.21	1.21		
N3308	10 34.0	−27 11	237.88	269.48	139.9	.LXS-*.B060			1.09	.16	1.02	P
	4.7	−31	27.03	26.51	−37.6				1.58	1.58		
N3309	10 34.3	−27 16	237.99	269.59	140.1	.E.3...B060			1.03	.05	1.01	DEKP
	4.7	−31	26.99	26.48	−37.6	E 0			2.92	2.92		
N3310	10 35.7	53 46	122.84	156.59	56.8	.SXR4P.W060	S PG *		1.50	.14	1.45	HKMRUQ
	6.2	−31	55.13	54.07	−5.9	I 3	S P		11.52	11.52		
N3311	10 34.4	−27 17	238.02	269.62	140.1	.E.2...B060			1.15	.06	1.13	P
	4.7	−31	26.99	26.48	−37.5				1.72	1.72		
N3312	10 34.8	−27 20	238.14	269.73	140.1	.SAS3P$B060			1.48	.38	1.33	KP
	4.7	−31	26.99	26.49	−37.5	S N			4.94	4.94		
N3314	10 34.9	−27 25	238.21	269.80	140.2	.SBS0P.B060			1.18	.12	1.14	P
	4.7	−31	26.93	26.43	−37.4				1.78	1.78		
N3316	10 35.2	−27 21	238.23	269.83	140.2	.LBT0..B060			.83	.12	.79	P
	4.7	−31	27.02	26.52	−37.4				.56	.56		

NGC (IC, A) (14)	Magnitudes				Colors				Velocities			Radio			
	m_H m_C (15)	B(O) w (16)	B'(O) m'_C (17)	S(B) (18)	(B-V)(O) w (19)	C_O(O) (20)	S(C) (21)	(U-B)(O) w (22)	V w (23)	V_O ΔV (24)	S(V) (25)	ϕ_r n (26)	ϕ(21) (27)	(28)	Photo. (29)
N3258D										−281					
N3258E										−280					
N3259	12.9 / 13.02		13.76						1866 / 2.5	1984 / 118	C				
N3260										−282					
N3261	12.8 / 12.28		14.47							−289					
N3262										−288					
N3263										−288					
N3265										−61					
N3266										117					
N3267										−281					
N3268	13.0 / 13.07		12.91							−282					
N3269										−281					
N3271	12.9 / 13.06		13.00							−281					
N3273										−281					
N3274	13.0 / 13.12		13.81							−66					
N3275	12.8 / 12.64		13.98							−282					
N3277	12.6 / 12.90	12.60 / 3.04	13.14 / 13.44	C	.85 / 3.75	.76	C		1460 / 1.8	1399 / −61	B				
N3281	12.9 / 12.70		14.09							−280					
N3281C										−280					
N3281D										−279					
N3285	13.2 / 13.30		13.64							−268					
N3285A										−268					
N3285B										−268					
N3287	12.8 / 13.15		13.79							−94					
N3288										89					
N3289										−280					
N3294	11.6 / 11.90	12.35 / 2.67	14.04 / 13.59	A	.55 / 4.38	.42	A		1469 / 3.6	1453 / −17	C				
N3299										−135					
N3300	13.1 / 13.21		13.10							−128					
N3301	12.4 / 12.45	12.43 / 1.91	13.57 / 13.59	C	.89 / 1.88	.76	C		1333 / 1.8	1241 / −92	B				
N3304										−15					
N3306										−135					
N3307										−267					
N3308										−267					
N3309	12.7 / 12.89		12.68							−267					
N3310	10.9 / 11.39	11.20 / 3.83	13.14 / 13.33	BC	.38 / 3.75	.28	C		1026 / 16.5	1090 / 65	BC				
N3311										−267					
N3312	13.1 / 12.83		14.17						2533 / .7	2266 / −267	D				
N3314										−267					
N3316										3609 / .7	3342 / −267	D				

NGC (IC, A) (1)	RA (1950) 100 P (2)	Dec 100 P (3)	L^I B^I (4)	L^II B^II (5)	SGL SGB (6)	Rev. type (S) DDO (T, L) (7)	Yerkes (1) Yerkes (2) (8)	Hu-San Ho (9)	log D w (10)	log R w (11)	log D(0) (12)	S (D,R) (13)
N3318	10 35.1	-41 22	245.76	277.68	157.6	.SXT3..B060			1.34	.26	1.23	PI
	4.4	-31	14.89	14.58	-35.9				3.45	3.45		
N3318A	10 33.3	-41 29	245.51	277.44	157.8	.S...$.S030			1.27	.51	1.07	I
	4.4	-31	14.62	14.30	-36.2				1.18	1.18		
N3318B	10 35.5	-41 12	245.74	277.66	157.3	.SBS5..B060			1.15	.05	1.13	I
	4.4	-31	15.07	14.76	-35.9				.99	.99		
N3319	10 36.4	41 56	142.62	175.99	66.6	.SBT6..W100	B AF		1.79	.25	1.69	AHKNXW
	5.8	-31	60.73	59.37	-12.8	SX5 3		S6	13.15	13.15		
N3320	10 36.7	47 40	132.17	165.82	61.9	.S..6*.W060	S AF		1.31	.27	1.20	KQ
	6.0	-31	58.49	57.27	-9.4	S 5 6			2.15	2.15		
N3329	10 40.6	77 5	98.28	131.68	38.3	RSAR3*.W060	D GK	L 1	1.15	.23	1.06	AKQ
	8.4	-31	38.61	38.07	8.4	S *			3.37	3.37		
N3333	10 37.6	-35 47	243.37	275.15	150.6				1.10			F
	4.6	-31	20.00	19.63	-36.3				1.05			
N3338	10 39.5	14 0	199.26	230.35	92.5	.SAS5..W100	S F		1.75	.19	1.67	ACHKNXYW
	5.3	-31	58.30	57.02	-26.6	S 4 3		S5	13.04	13.04		
N3344	10 40.7	25 11	178.24	210.03	81.8	RSXR4..W060	S F		1.78	.04	1.76	ACHKLSXQ
	5.5	-31	62.70	61.24	-21.1	S 5 3		S5	14.81	13.55		
N3346	10 41.0	15 9	197.69	228.79	91.5	.SBT6..W100	SB *AF		1.44	.07	1.41	ACHKLW
	5.3	-31	59.18	57.89	-25.8	S 5 3			8.50	7.51		
N3347	10 40.5	-36 6	244.08	275.85	150.9	.SBS2..S030			1.63	.26	1.52	FI
	4.6	-31	20.01	19.66	-35.7				3.45	3.45		
N3347A	10 38.1	-36 10	243.66	275.45	151.1	.S...$/S030			1.30	.60	1.06	I
	4.6	-31	19.72	19.35	-36.2				.61	.61		
N3347B	10 39.6	-36 40	244.19	275.99	151.7	.S...$/S030			1.56	.78	1.24	I
	4.6	-31	19.43	19.07	-35.8				.86	.86		
N3347C	10 38.5	-36 2	243.66	275.45	150.9	.SA.6*.S030			1.43	.18	1.36	I
	4.6	-31	19.88	19.51	-36.1				.63	.63		
N3348	10 43.5	73 7	101.11	134.61	41.7	.E.0...W060	E1 K		1.02	.02	1.01	AKQ
	7.5	-31	41.95	41.34	6.2	E 1	E2 K		1.45	1.45		
N3351	10 41.3	11 58	202.95	233.95	94.8	.SBR3..P200	B FG	SBT3	1.80	.15	1.74	ACHKLSUXYZ
	5.3	-31	57.59	56.36	-27.1	SX3 3	B G	S4	18.85	17.76		
N3353	10 42.3	56 14	118.46	152.28	55.4				1.06	.16	1.00	ACK
	6.2	-31	54.36	53.37	-3.7	S *	I P A *		1.73	1.73		
N3357	10 41.7	14 20	199.22	230.28	92.4				.94	.00	.94	ACH
	5.3	-31	58.92	57.65	-26.0				1.23	1.23		
N3358	10 41.3	-36 7	244.24	276.01	150.9	PSAS0*.S030			1.48	.26	1.38	FI
	4.6	-31	20.07	19.72	-35.5				2.92	2.92		
N3359	10 43.4	63 30	109.84	143.57	49.6	.SBT5..P200	B P A	SBT5	1.71	.19	1.63	KXZ
	6.6	-31	49.40	48.59	0.7	SX5 3		S5	5.97	5.97		
N3364	10 44.9	72 42	101.33	134.85	42.1	.S.....W			1.23	.00	1.23	AX
	7.4	-31	42.34	41.73	6.1			S5	.84	.84		
N3367	10 44.0	14 1	200.32	231.32	93.0	.SBT5..W100	BS *AF	SBT5	1.36	.07	1.33	ACHKLRSVW
	5.3	-31	59.24	57.98	-25.6	S 5 1	S AF		14.12	11.23		
N3368	10 44.2	12 5	203.51	234.45	95.0	.SXT2..P200	S P*GK	S 1	1.73	.15	1.67	ACHKLSXYZ
	5.3	-31	58.24	57.03	-26.4	S 3P	S P G	S1	13.52	11.85		
N3370	10 44.5	17 32	194.23	225.38	89.6	.SAS5..W060	S F		1.50	.25	1.40	ACHKNQ
	5.3	-31	61.03	59.69	-24.0	S 5 5			6.95	6.95		
N3377	10 45.1	14 15	200.19	231.19	92.9	.E.5+..P200	E5 K	E 6	1.39	.24	1.30	ACHKLRSVZ
	5.3	-31	59.59	58.33	-25.3	E 5	E5 K		13.75	13.75		
N3377A	10 44.7	14 20	199.95	230.96	92.8	.SXS9..P200			1.37	.04	1.35	Z
	5.3	-31	59.55	58.28	-25.3				1.50	1.50		
N3379	10 45.2	12 51	202.54	233.49	94.3	.E+1...P200	E1 K		1.39	.07	1.36	ABCHKLRSVZ
	5.3	-31	58.87	57.64	-25.8	E 1	ED K		14.27	9.78		
N3380	10 45.4	28 52	170.41	202.57	79.0	.S.....			1.21	.24	1.12	AC
	5.5	-31	64.27	62.79	-18.3				1.15	1.15		
N3384	10 45.7	12 54	202.59	233.53	94.3	.LBS-*.P200	D PK *		1.57	.40	1.41	ABCHKLRSV
	5.3	-31	59.00	57.77	-25.7	E 7	D K		13.34	10.18		
N3389	10 45.8	12 48	202.77	233.71	94.4	.SAS5..P200	S A		1.36	.23	1.27	ABCHKLRSV
	5.3	-31	58.96	57.74	-25.7	S 5 K 5*	SI *A		11.37	8.74		
N3390	10 45.8	-31 17	242.64	274.29	144.9							
	4.7	-31	24.77	24.38	-35.0							
N3395	10 47.1	33 15	160.23	192.91	75.3	.SXT6P*P200	I A		1.33	.20	1.25	ABCHKQZ
	5.6	-31	64.63	63.15	-15.8	S 5 T	I A		8.86	8.86		
N3396	10 47.2	33 16	160.19	192.87	75.3	.IB.9P.P200	I A		1.42	.44	1.25	ABCHQZ
	5.6	-31	64.65	63.17	-15.7	P T -	I A		8.54	8.54		
N3398	10 48.5	55 41	118.19	152.07	56.3				1.17	.36	1.03	AC
	6.1	-31	55.37	54.39	-3.3				1.07	1.07		
N3400	10 48.0	28 44	170.82	202.96	79.5	.LB..$.W			1.23	.29	1.11	AC
	5.5	-31	64.83	63.35	-17.9				1.18	1.18		
N3403	10 50.1	73 57	99.95	133.45	41.3	.SA.4*.W060			1.40	.45	1.22	ANQ
	7.4	-31	41.53	40.95	7.1	S 4 5	SD G *		4.31	4.31		
N3404	10 47.8	-11 51	231.02	262.16	121.6	.L..../L036			1.35			L
	5.0	-31	41.65	40.97	-33.0				.80			
N3408	10 49.1	58 41	114.36	148.22	53.9	.S.....			1.11	.00	1.11	AC
	6.2	-31	53.36	52.46	-1.5				.96	.96		
N3412	10 48.3	13 41	201.96	232.87	93.8	.LBS0..W100	D P*GK		1.38	.29	1.26	ACKNW
	5.3	-31	59.95	58.72	-24.8	E 5	D P GK		7.56	7.56		
N3413	10 48.6	33 2	160.68	193.34	75.7	.L..../W100	D P*K		1.27	.41	1.10	ABCHMW
	5.6	-31	64.96	63.48	-15.6				5.95	5.95		

NGC (IC, A) (14)	Magnitudes				Colors				Velocities			Radio			
	m_H m_C (15)	B(O) w (16)	B'(O) m'_C (17)	S(B) (18)	(B-V)(O) w (19)	C_o(O) (20)	S(C) (21)	(U-B)(O) w (22)	V w (23)	V_o ΔV (24)	S(V) (25)	ϕ_r n (26)	ϕ(21) (27)	(28)	Photo. (29)
N3318	12.6														
	12.77		13.66							-285					
N3318A										-285					
N3318B										-285					
N3319	12.3	11.95	15.14	G	.46	.36	G		826	832	C				
	11.64	1.41	14.83		2.50				2.9	6					
N3320	12.9														
	13.09		13.83							35					
N3329	12.9														P
	13.34		13.33							171					
N3333										-279					
N3338	12.2	11.59	14.63	CG	.68*	.56	CG		1330	1202	C				
	11.61	1.22	14.65		4.38				1.9	-128					
N3344	11.9	10.69	14.23	CG	.57*	.50	CG		579	504	B				K
	11.19	3.28	14.73		4.38				.4	-75					
N3346	12.4														K
	12.34		14.13							-122					
N3347	12.8														
	12.18		14.52							-278					
N3347A										-279					
N3347B										-279					
N3347C										-279					
N3348	12.1	12.45	12.24	BF					2855	3010	B				
	12.49	2.41	12.28						1.8	155					
N3351	11.5	10.75	14.14	CDFG	.82*	.70	CDG	.12	780	643	BD				BKLP
	11.02	9.32	14.41		41.88		/D		1.8	-136					
N3353	13.0	13.47	13.21	E	.50		E	-.30							
	13.26	1.64	13.00		6.25		/E			78					
N3357										-126					
N3358	13.0														F
	12.57		14.16							-278					
N3359	12.2	11.31	14.20	CG	.61	.49	CG		1008	1120	C				P
	11.68	2.33	14.57		6.25				2.1	112					
N3364		13.65	14.54	G						153					
		1.45													
N3367	12.3	12.22	13.61	C	.59	.48	C		2879	2753	B				DLP
	12.42	3.31	13.81		3.75				1.0	-126					
N3368	10.4	10.32	13.41	CDG	.89	.77	CDG	.36	935	800	ABD				BP
	10.54	6.81	13.63		41.88		/D		9.2	-135					
N3370	12.4								1400	1290	C				
	12.34		14.03						2.2	-110					
N3377	11.6	11.75	12.94	AC	.89	.83	AC		718	593	B				P
	11.69	10.58	12.88		8.13				6.3	-125					
N3377A										-124					
N3379	10.8	10.83	12.37	CFL	.94*	.87	CL	.57	877	746	ABD				D
	11.04	5.97	12.58		3.70		/L		14.4	-131					
N3380										-56					
N3384	11.3	10.84	12.58	ACFL*	.95	.86	ACL	.48*	767	636	BD				D
	11.39	7.91	13.13		8.10		/L		13.4	-130					
N3389	12.6	12.41	13.45	CF	.54	.42	C		1334	1203	C				AD
	12.74	1.91	13.78		1.88				2.4	-131					
N3390	13.2														
										-270					
N3395	12.4	12.46	13.40	E	.31	.20	E	-.25	1656	1622	CE				DK
	12.73	2.78	13.67		6.25		/E		15.8	-34					
N3396	12.8	12.90	13.84	E	.41	.33	E	-.21	1645	1611	CE				DK
	12.72	2.78	13.66		6.25		/E		16.2	-34					
N3398										77					
N3400										-56					
N3403	12.9								1244	1403	C				
	13.00		13.79						2.1	159					
N3404										-224					B
N3408										91					
N3412	11.6	12.00	13.04	CF	.89	.80	C		861	735	B				
	11.82	2.97	12.86		3.75				1.8	-126					
N3413										-34					

NGC (IC, A) (1)	RA (1950) Dec 100 P (2)	100 P (3)	L^I B^I (4)	L^II B^II (5)	SGL SGB (6)	Rev. type (S) DDO (T, L) (7)	Yerkes (1) Yerkes (2) (8)	Hu-San Ho (9)	log D w (10)	log R w (11)	log D(O) (12)	S (D,R) (13)
N3414	10 48.6 28 15	5.5 −31	171.99 64.92	204.06 63.44	80.0 −18.0	.LBS..$.... SB0	B *K B P K		1.38 2.82	.24 2.82	1.28	ACK
N3415	10 48.9 43 59	5.8 −31	136.84 62.06	170.50 60.77	66.2 −9.7	E 4			1.16 .74	.14 .74	1.11	CK
N3418	10 48.7 28 22	5.5 −31	171.72 64.95	203.80 63.47	79.9 −18.0	.LBS+.$....			1.24 1.22	.28 1.22	1.13	AC
N3419	10 48.7 14 13	5.3 −31	201.16 60.32	232.08 59.07	93.3 −24.5	RLXR+..W100			1.07 3.26	.10 3.26	1.03	NW
N3419A	10 48.7 14 18	5.3 −31	201.01 60.36	231.94 59.11	93.3 −24.5	.SBS3*/W100			1.30 1.69	.78 1.69	.99	N
N3423	10 48.7 6 7	5.2 −31	213.36 55.44	244.17 54.39	101.6 −27.7	.SAS6..W100 S 5 3	S AF	S6	1.53 8.54	.05 8.54	1.51	ACHKXW
N3424	10 49.0 33 10	5.6 −31	160.35 65.03	193.03 63.56	75.6 −15.5	.SBS3*$W100			1.40 7.69	.58 6.00	1.17	ABCHMS
N3430	10 49.5 33 14	5.6 −31	160.17 65.13	192.86 63.66	75.6 −15.4	.SXT5..W100 S 5 3*	S AF S A		1.53 14.12	.24 12.57	1.43	ABCHKMS W
N3432	10 49.7 36 54	5.6 −31	151.62 64.59	184.74 63.16	72.4 −13.4	.SBS9./W060 S T	SI *A SI *A *	S6	1.79 12.71	.71 12.71	1.50	ACHKNXQ
N3433	10 49.4 10 26	5.2 −31	207.47 58.32	238.28 57.17	97.2 −25.9	.SAS5..W100 S 3 1*	S F S F		1.47 6.68	.04 6.68	1.45	AHKW
N3437	10 49.9 23 11	5.4 −31	183.72 64.25	215.22 62.82	84.8 −20.2	.SXT5*.W100 S 3	SI *AF		1.32 5.37	.48 5.37	1.13	ACKW
N3440	10 50.8 57 23	6.2 −31	115.65 54.44	149.55 53.51	55.1 −2.1	.SBS.$.W060			1.26 2.11	.55 2.11	1.04	ACQ
N3444	10 50.4 10 27	5.2 −31	207.72 58.53	238.51 57.38	97.3 −25.7	.S....*R020			1.13 .83	.32 .83	1.00	ACH
N3445	10 51.6 57 15	6.1 −31	115.69 54.61	149.59 53.68	55.3 −2.1	.SXS9..W060 S 5 KT	I A ISP*A *		1.19 2.94	.01 2.94	1.18	ACKQ
N3447	10 50.8 17 2	5.3 −31	196.58 62.15	227.59 60.84	90.8 −22.8	.SX.7P.L036			1.49 3.32	.24 3.32	1.39	AN
N3447A	10 50.8 17 2	5.3 −31	196.57 62.14	227.57 60.84	90.8 −22.8	.I..9.*L036						
N3448	10 51.7 54 34	6.0 −31	119.12 56.46	153.05 55.46	57.5 −3.5	.I.0...W060 S NT	I A * IPA *		1.52 4.48	.49 4.48	1.33	ACQ
N3449	10 50.6 −32 40	4.7 −31	244.34 24.02	276.00 23.67	146.6 −33.9							
N3450	10 45.6 −20 35	4.9 −31	236.48 34.04	267.86 33.49	131.9 −34.7	.S.....H030			1.36 1.49	.00 1.49	1.36	F
N3454	10 51.8 17 36	5.3 −31	195.73 62.62	226.74 61.30	90.4 −22.4	.SBS5$/W100	SI *AF*		1.32 4.34	.63 4.34	1.07	ABCW
N3455	10 51.8 17 33	5.3 −31	195.83 62.60	226.84 61.28	90.4 −22.4	PSXT3..W100 S 3 NT−	SI *AF		1.28 5.31	.21 5.31	1.20	ABCKW
N3456	10 51.7 −15 46	4.9 −31	234.87 38.90	266.08 38.31	126.4 −32.7	.S.....H030			1.30 2.45	.21 2.45	1.22	FG
N3458	10 53.0 57 22	6.1 −32	115.31 54.66	149.23 53.74	55.3 −1.8	.LX..*.W060 S *	D *K		1.01 1.94	.10 1.94	.96	AKQ
N3464	10 52.2 −20 49	4.9 −32	238.23 34.62	269.58 34.12	132.4 −33.2	S 3 4			1.47 1.52	.22 1.52	1.38	K
N3466	10 53.6 10 1	5.2 −32	209.30 58.88	240.03 57.76	98.1 −25.1				1.11 1.33	.16 1.33	1.05	ACH
N3470	10 55.7 59 46	6.2 −32	112.09 53.15	145.99 52.29	53.5 −.2				1.02 .78	.00 .78	1.03	AC
N3478	10 56.5 46 23	5.8 −32	130.97 62.05	164.87 60.85	64.9 −7.3	S 4 2			1.40 1.40	.35 1.40	1.26	K
N3485	10 57.6 15 6	5.3 −32	201.90 62.57	232.66 61.33	93.4 −22.2	.SBR3*.W060 SX4 3*	SB *AF		1.28 4.88	.09 4.88	1.25	ACHKQ
N3486	10 57.8 29 15	5.5 −32	169.89 67.00	202.06 65.52	80.1 −15.8	.SXR5..W100 S 5 3	S FG S G	S5	1.82 15.25	.11 15.25	1.77	ACHKNXW
N3488	10 58.4 57 56	6.1 −32	113.73 54.75	147.69 53.85	55.2 −.9	.S..5*.W			1.31 1.34	.17 1.34	1.24	AC
N3489	10 57.7 14 10	5.3 −32	203.68 62.13	234.40 60.92	94.4 −22.5	.LXT+..W100 E 6	D GK SD K		1.41 10.07	.30 10.07	1.29	ACHKLSW
N3495	10 58.6 3 53	5.2 −32	219.23 55.64	249.88 54.70	105.0 −26.2	.S..7*.W100 S 3 3*	S *AF		1.63 7.29	.56 7.29	1.40	AKW
N3499	11 0.2 56 29	6.0 −32	115.15 55.98	149.14 55.06	56.6 −1.5				.93 .59	.00 .59	.93	AC
N3504	11 0.5 28 15	5.4 −32	172.57 67.53	204.58 66.05	81.3 −15.7	RSXS2..P200 S 3 T −*	B P*FG* BDP*G *	SXS3	1.34 10.97	.18 9.48	1.27	ACHKLSU Z
N3506	11 0.6 11 21	5.2 −32	209.35 61.06	239.94 59.94	97.5 −23.0	.S..5..W100 S 5 K	S F		1.06 2.57	.04 2.57	1.04	ACKW
N3509	11 1.6 5 6	5.2 −32	218.70 56.09	249.27 56.09	104.0 −25.0	.S...P*						
N3510	11 1.0 29 9	5.4 −32	170.23 67.70	202.38 66.21	80.5 −15.2	.SBS9./W100 S T	I *A S *FG*		1.52 9.86	.68 9.86	1.24	ACHKNW
N3511	11 0.8 −22 50	4.9 −32	241.52 33.80	272.87 33.38	134.9 −31.4	.SAS5..W100 S 5 K 3*	S A S 5	S 5	1.67 17.23	.43 17.23	1.50	EFGHKNT W
N3512	11 1.3 28 18	5.4 −32	172.48 67.71	204.49 66.23	81.3 −15.6	.SXT5..W100 S 5 5	S F S P FG*		1.18 8.56	.06 7.93	1.16	AHKLSUW
N3513	11 1.1 −22 58	4.9 −32	241.67 33.72	273.02 33.29	135.1 −31.4	.SBT5..W100 SX5 K 3*	B AF		1.39 12.10	.10 12.10	1.35	EFGHKNT W

NGC (IC, A)	Magnitudes				Colors				Velocities			Radio			
	m_H m_C	B(O) w	B'(O) m'_C	S(B)	(B-V)(O) w	C_o(O)	S(C)	(U-B)(O) w	V w	V_o ΔV	S(V)	ϕ_r n	ϕ (21)		Photo.
(14)	(15)	(16)	(17)	(18)	(19)	(20)	(21)	(22)	(23)	(24)	(25)	(26)	(27)	(28)	(29)
N3414	12.2 12.20	12.23 10.78	13.32 13.29	ACF	1.07 6.25	.98	AC		1449 1.0	1391 −58	B				
N3415	13.1 12.98		13.27							20					
N3418										−57					
N3419									2982 2.4	2859 −123	C				
N3419A										−123					
N3423	11.9 11.86	11.85 1.15	14.09 14.10	G	.46 2.50		G			−158					
N3424										−34					
N3430	12.4 12.24	12.39 3.66	14.28 14.13	CE	.60 8.13	.47	CE /E	.03	1742 1.7	1709 −33	C				
N3432	12.2 12.15	11.94 1.25	14.18 14.39	G	.48 2.50	.38	G		609 2.2	594 −15	C				
N3433	12.9 12.49		14.43							−140					K
N3437	12.6 13.06		13.40							−82					
N3440										86					
N3444										−139					
N3445	12.9 13.16		13.80							85					
N3447									965 1.5	855 −110	D				
N3447A									1014 1.5	904 −110	D				
N3448	12.6 12.42		13.76							72					
N3449	13.2									−270					
N3450										−249					
N3454									1167 1.6	1060 −107	E				
N3455	13.1 13.13		13.82						1113 1.6	1006 −107	E				
N3456										−233					
N3458	13.0 13.26		12.80							86					
N3464	13.2 12.77		14.36							−246					
N3466										−140					
N3470										98					
N3478	13.2 13.04		14.08							34					
N3485	12.8 12.85		13.79							−116					
N3486	11.4 10.92	11.10 7.75	14.69 14.51	ACFG	.53 10.63	.43	ACG		1116 1.0	1067 −49	B				K
N3488										90					
N3489	11.3 11.59	11.24 3.30	12.38 12.73	C	.59 3.75	.51	C		690 2.6	570 −120	AB				K
N3495	12.7 12.59		14.33							−163					
N3499										84					
N3504	11.7 12.16	11.80 8.25	12.89 13.25	AC	.77 8.13	.64	AC		1526 8.0	1473 −53	BF				P
N3506	13.2 13.57		13.51							−131					
N3509									7600 1.0	7443 −157	F				
N3510	12.8 12.99	13.80 0.88	14.74 13.93	D	.45 18.75	.35	D /D	−.13	719 2.3	670 −49	C				
N3511	11.9 11.81		14.05							−248					P
N3512	12.8 13.08	13.12 5.10	13.66 13.62	AC	.66 1.88	.57	C		1502 1.9	1449 −53	C				
N3513	12.0 12.21		13.70							−248					

NGC (IC, A) (1)	RA (1950) 100 P (2)	Dec 100 P (3)	L^I B^I (4)	L^{II} B^{II} (5)	SGL SGB (6)	Rev. type (S) DDO (T,L) (7)	Yerkes (1) Yerkes (2) (8)	Hu-San Ho (9)	log D w (10)	log R w (11)	log D(0) (12)	S (D,R) (13)
N3515	11 2.0 / 5.4	28 30 / -32	171.97 / 67.87	204.01 / 66.39	81.2 / -15.3	.S....*R020			1.06 / .89	.19 / .33	.98	HL
N3516	11 3.4 / 6.9	72 50 / -32	99.67 / 42.98	133.24 / 42.41	42.7 / 7.3	RLBS0*.W060 / E	BD *K		1.06 / 3.65	.12 / 3.65	1.01	AKNQ
N3517	11 2.6 / 6.0	56 48 / -32	114.33 / 55.97	148.34 / 55.06	56.5 / -1.0				1.07 / .90	.00 / .90	1.07	AC
N3521	11 3.2 / 5.1	0 14 / -32	224.88 / 53.64	255.52 / 52.82	109.2 / -26.2	.SXT4..W100	S F / S 4 3	S 3 / S3	1.91 / 14.18	.33 / 14.18	1.78	ACHKVXW
N3547	11 7.3 / 5.2	11 0 / -32	212.11 / 62.11	242.52 / 61.03	98.5 / -21.6	.S..3*.W100 / S *	SI *AF / I P		1.17 / 2.79	.20 / 2.79	1.09	AKW
N3549	11 8.2 / 5.8	53 39 / -32	117.19 / 58.83	151.32 / 57.87	59.6 / -2.0	.SAS5*.W060 / S 3 4	S AF / S AF		1.47 / 7.06	.40 / 7.06	1.31	ACHKQ
N3556	11 8.7 / 5.9	55 57 / -32	114.19 / 57.16	148.29 / 56.26	57.6 / -.7	.SBS6./W100 / S 5 K	SI *A / IS *A	S 5 / S6	1.92 / 12.95	.59 / 12.95	1.69	ACKLXYW
N3557	11 7.5 / 4.7	-37 16 / -32	249.83 / 21.29	281.56 / 21.08	151.8 / -30.2	.E.3...W100			1.34 / .92	.19 / .92	1.26	I
N3557A	11 4.8 / 4.7	-36 56 / -32	249.16 / 21.39	280.89 / 21.16	151.4 / -30.8	.S...*.S030			1.35 / 1.30	.59 / 1.30	1.11	I
N3557B	11 7.3 / 4.7	-37 5 / -32	249.72 / 21.45	281.44 / 21.23	151.6 / -30.2	.E+5.*.B060			1.04 / 2.09	.26 / 2.09	.94	PI
N3564	11 8.2 / 4.7	-37 16 / -32	249.97 / 21.35	281.70 / 21.14	151.8 / -30.1	.L..../B060			1.14 / 2.38	.75 / 2.38	.84	PI
N3568	11 8.5 / 4.7	-37 11 / -32	250.00 / 21.45	281.72 / 21.24	151.7 / -30.0	.SBS5*.B060			1.36 / 3.54	.57 / 3.54	1.13	PI
N3571	11 8.9 / 5.0	-18 1 / -32	240.90 / 38.96	272.06 / 38.51	129.7 / -29.0	.S...$.H030 / S 0			1.48 / 1.78	.33 / 1.78	1.34	AK
N3577	11 11.0 / 5.7	48 38 / -32	123.92 / 62.65	158.13 / 61.56	64.2 / -4.1	.SBR1..W060	B G		1.08 / 1.56	.04 / 1.56	1.07	Q
N3583	11 11.4 / 5.7	48 39 / -32	123.80 / 62.69	158.01 / 61.60	64.2 / -4.0	.SBS3..W060 / S 5 3	S P FG / S P FG*		1.45 / 4.43	.16 / 4.43	1.38	CKQ
N3585	11 10.9 / 4.9	-26 29 / -32	245.85 / 31.50	277.26 / 31.18	139.4 / -29.4	.E+7...W060 / E 5	E6 K		1.23 / 5.10	.28 / 5.10	1.12	FKMQ
N3593	11 12.0 / 5.2	13 6 / -32	210.11 / 64.33	240.41 / 63.22	96.9 / -19.8	.SAS0*.W060 / S 3 5	S P G * / D GK		1.65 / 15.67	.46 / 12.86	1.47	ACHKRSV Q
N3596	11 12.4 / 5.2	15 4 / -32	206.51 / 65.58	236.86 / 64.41	95.0 / -18.9	.SXT5..W060 / S 5 K 3	S F / S F		1.48 / 3.82	.04 / 3.82	1.46	AKQ
N3599	11 12.8 / 5.3	18 23 / -32	199.56 / 67.41	230.08 / 66.14	91.8 / -17.5	.LA..*.W100			1.33 / .42	.45 / .42	1.15	C
N3605	11 14.2 / 5.3	18 18 / -32	200.17 / 67.66	230.63 / 66.40	92.1 / -17.2	.E.4+..W060 / E 3			.99 / 2.58	.17 / 2.24	.92	ABHKLQ
N3607	11 14.3 / 5.3	18 20 / -32	200.13 / 67.70	230.59 / 66.43	92.0 / -17.2	.LAS0*.W060 / E 1	DE *GK* / E K		1.26 / 6.54	.08 / 5.82	1.22	ABEHKLQ
N3608	11 14.4 / 5.3	18 26 / -32	199.93 / 67.77	230.39 / 66.50	91.9 / -17.1	.E.2...W060 / E 3	E3 *K / DE K		1.15 / 4.51	.11 / 4.07	1.10	ABEHKLQ
N3610	11 15.6 / 5.8	59 4 / -32	109.44 / 55.27	143.52 / 54.46	55.4 / 1.6	.E+5.*.W060 / E 2P	E5 K / E5 K		1.19 / 4.74	.16 / 4.74	1.13	ACHKMQ
N3611	11 14.9 / 5.2	4 50 / -32	223.69 / 59.05	253.99 / 58.20	105.4 / -22.0	.SAS1P.W100 / S 0	I P GK* / DS GK		1.27 / 4.87	.10 / 4.87	1.23	ACKW
N3613	11 15.7 / 5.8	58 17 / -32	110.22 / 55.91	144.33 / 55.09	56.1 / 1.2	.E+6...W100 / E 5	E6 K		1.31 / 5.84	.29 / 5.00	1.20	ACHKLQ
N3614	11 15.6 / 5.6	46 2 / -32	127.25 / 64.93	161.52 / 63.78	66.8 / -4.6	.SXR5..W060 / S 5 3	S AF / S F		1.57 / 5.11	.24 / 5.11	1.47	CKQ
N3614A	11 15.5 / 5.6	46 0 / -33	127.34 / 64.94	161.60 / 63.79	66.9 / -4.7	.SBS9..W060			.96 / .58	.00 / .58	.96	Q
N3619	11 16.5 / 5.8	58 2 / -32	110.33 / 56.18	144.45 / 55.35	56.3 / 1.2	RLAS+*.W060 / S N +*	DSP GK*		1.26 / 3.28	.06 / 2.65	1.24	AHLQ
N3621	11 15.9 / 4.9	-32 32 / -32	249.65 / 26.33	281.22 / 26.11	146.3 / -28.6	.SAS7..W100	SI *A		2.05 / 11.10	.17 / 11.10	1.98	GPW
N3623	11 16.3 / 5.2	13 23 / -32	211.12 / 65.33	241.29 / 64.23	97.0 / -18.7	.SXT1..W100 / S 3 N 3*	S G / S GK	S 1 / S1	1.91 / 25.41	.52 / 25.41	1.70	ABCHKLS VXYW
N3625	11 17.7 / 5.8	58 3 / -32	110.08 / 56.26	144.21 / 55.44	56.4 / 1.3	.SXS3*.W060	SB *F		1.25 / 4.85	.41 / 4.22	1.08	ACHLQ
N3626	11 17.5 / 5.3	18 38 / -33	200.41 / 68.51	230.78 / 67.24	92.1 / -16.4	RLAR+..W100 / S 2 N 3*	D GK / DS K		1.24 / 7.36	.18 / 7.36	1.17	ACEHKMW
N3627	11 17.6 / 5.2	13 17 / -32	211.79 / 65.51	241.91 / 64.42	97.3 / -18.4	.SXS3..W100 / S 4 NK 3*	S P FG / S A	S 3 / S4	1.89 / 21.58	.33 / 21.58	1.76	ABCELSV XYW
N3628	11 17.7 / 5.2	13 53 / -32	210.69 / 65.90	240.82 / 64.80	96.7 / -18.2	.S..3P/W100 / S 3 NT	S *G * / S *G *	S4	2.16 / 23.32	.72 / 23.32	1.87	ABCELSX YW
N3629	11 17.9 / 5.3	27 15 / -32	176.46 / 71.27	208.14 / 69.80	84.0 / -12.8	.SAS6*.W100 / S 5 NK 5*	S AF		1.38 / 5.20	.16 / 5.20	1.31	ABCKW
N3630	11 17.7 / 5.1	3 15 / -32	226.64 / 58.25	256.93 / 57.47	107.3 / -21.8	.L..../W060 / E 7	D K		1.25 / 4.79	.52 / 4.79	1.04	ACKNQ
N3631	11 18.3 / 5.7	53 28 / -32	115.21 / 59.96	149.48 / 59.03	60.5 / -.7	.SAS5..W060 / S 5 1	S F / S FG	S5	1.59 / 10.63	.07 / 10.63	1.56	ACHKNXY Q
N3633	11 17.9 / 5.1	3 51 / -32	226.01 / 58.76	256.28 / 57.96	106.7 / -21.6	.L....*/L036			1.08 / 1.26	.42 / 1.26	.91	N
N3636	11 17.9 / 5.1	-10 1 / -32	238.52 / 47.06	269.33 / 46.56	121.3 / -25.4	.E.0...W100			.81 / 1.80	.00 / 1.80	.81	AW
N3637	11 18.1 / 5.1	-9 2 / -32	238.55 / 47.13	269.36 / 46.63	121.2 / -25.3	RLBR0..W100 / SX0*	B K		1.05 / 3.83	.03 / 3.83	1.03	AEKW

NGC (IC, A) (14)	m$_H$ / m$_c$ (15)	B(O) / w (16)	B'(O) / m'$_c$ (17)	S(B) (18)	(B-V)(O) / w (19)	C$_o$(O) (20)	S(C) (21)	(U-B)(O) / w (22)	V / w (23)	V$_o$ / ΔV (24)	S(V) (25)	φ$_r$ / n (26)	φ(21) (27)	(28)	Photo. (29)
N3515															
										−51					
N3516	12.2	12.86	12.65	BCE	.79	.68	CE	−.09	2621	2777	BC				
	12.65	4.70	12.44		14.38		/E		6.4	156					
N3517															
										86					
N3521	10.3	9.82	13.41	ACEFG	.80	.67	ACEG	.21	790	614	AB				P
	10.30	6.94	13.89		16.87		/E		12.1	−175					
N3547	12.9														
	13.25		13.44							−129					
N3549	12.8														
	12.76		14.00							72					
N3556	11.0	10.90	14.04	BCEG	.63	.50	BCEG	.02	680	763	BCF				ABMP
	10.96	5.62	14.10		16.87		/E		7.1	83					
N3557	12.1	11.95	12.99	M	1.05		M	.62							
	12.07	3.14	13.11				/M			−270					
N3557A															
										−271					
N3557B															
										−270					
N3564															
										−270					
N3568															
										−270					
N3571	13.1														
	13.02		14.46							−232					
N3577															
										50					
N3583	12.2														
	12.20		13.84							50					
N3585	11.5	11.41	11.75	C	.96	.85	C		1491	1240	B				
	11.91	2.11	12.25		3.75				1.8	−251					
N3593	12.4	11.91	13.95	C	.76	.64	C		547	429	3				A
	12.04	1.98	14.08		1.88				1.8	−118					
N3596	12.2	12.07	14.06	F											
	12.09	0.79	14.08							−109					
N3599															
										−94					
N3605	13.1	13.71	13.05	CF	.94	.88	C		693	599	B				
	13.31	0.84	12.65		3.75				2.4	−94					
N3607	11.4	11.42	12.26	CF	.92	.85	C		934	840	BC				
	11.76	2.28	12.60		1.88				8.0	−93					
N3608	12.5	12.31	12.55	CF	.89	.82	C		1210	1117	B				
	12.61	2.05	12.85		1.88				4.0	−93					
N3610	11.7	12.14	12.53	BCF	.88	.80	C		1765	1864	B				
	12.03	3.47	12.42		3.75				4.0	99					
N3611	12.5	13.02	13.91	C	.57	.46	C		1754	1603	B				
	12.67	1.72	13.56		1.88				1.8	−151					
N3613	12.0	12.25	12.94	B					2054	2150	B				
	12.12	0.57	12.81						1.8	96					
N3614	12.9														
	12.42		14.51							39					
N3614A															
										39					
N3619	12.8	12.86	13.75	B					1649	1744	B				
	12.67	1.83	13.56						1.8	95					
N3621	10.6														
	10.12		14.76							−260					
N3623	10.5	10.51	13.70	BCEFG	.95*	.80	BCEG*	.49	755	640	ABDF				ABP
	10.53	5.62	13.72		15.00		/E		13.3	−115					
N3625															
										95					
N3626	11.8	12.11	12.65	ACF	.79	.70	AC		1452	1361	B				K
	12.13	8.62	12.67		6.25				1.0	−90					
N3627	9.9	9.89	13.43	BCEFG	.74	.59	BCEG	.12	706	591	ABD				AP
	10.09	7.98	13.63		18.75		/E		7.4	−114					
N3628	11.3	10.43	14.52	EFG	.81	.62	EG	.40	842	730	C				B
	10.59	2.06	14.68		8.75		/E		2.4	−112					
N3629	12.9														
	12.84		14.13							−50					
N3630	12.8														
	13.01		12.90							−156					
N3631	11.8	11.27	13.81	FG	.61	.52	G		1087	1162	C				K
	11.62	2.81	14.16		2.50				3.4	75					
N3633															
										−154					
N3636															
										−204					
N3637	12.8														
	13.01		12.90							−204					

NGC (IC, A) (1)	RA (1950) 100 P (2)	Dec 100 P (3)	L^I / B^I (4)	L^{II} / B^{II} (5)	SGL / SGB (6)	Rev. type (S) / DDO (T, L) (7)	Yerkes (1) / Yerkes (2) (8)	Hu-San / Ho (9)	log D w (10)	log R w (11)	log D(0) (12)	S (D,R) (13)
N3640	11 18.5	3 31	226.63	256.90	107.1	.E.3...W060	E4 K		1.25	.11	1.21	ACKNQ
	5.1	-32	58.59	57.80	-21.6	E 1	ED *K		4.44	4.44		
N3641	11 18.6	3 28	226.73	257.00	107.2	.E.1..$L036			.84	.02	.83	ACN
	5.1	-32	58.56	57.78	-21.6				.94	.94		
N3642	11 19.6	59 21	108.42	142.52	55.4	.SAR4*.W060	S FG*		1.64	.09	1.60	HKXQ
	5.8	-32	55.32	54.54	2.2	S 5 N - 1	S GK	S5	5.20	5.20		
N3643	11 19.0	3 13	227.17	257.44	107.4	.LB..$.L036						
	5.1	-32	58.42	57.65	-21.5							
N3646	11 19.2	20 27	196.38	226.87	90.5	PSAR4P$P200	S AF		1.55	.21	1.47	ACEKMXZ
	5.3	-32	69.69	68.37	-15.3	S 5 1	S P F	S5	11.17	11.17		
N3649	11 19.7	20 28	196.48	226.95	90.5	.SBS1..W100			.92	.19	.85	ACMW
	5.3	-32	69.80	68.49	-15.2				3.23	3.23		
N3650	11 19.7	20 59	195.11	225.64	90.0	.SA.3./L036			1.25	.73	.96	M
	5.3	-32	70.02	68.69	-15.0				1.59	1.59		
N3655	11 20.3	16 51	205.47	235.62	94.0	.SAS5*.W060	S AF		1.18	.16	1.12	AKQ
	5.2	-32	68.15	66.96	-16.5	S *	SIP*		2.57	2.57		
N3656	11 20.8	54 7	113.83	148.12	60.1	.E....*R020			1.06	.04	1.05	ACH
	5.6	-32	59.68	58.78	-.1				1.10	1.10		
N3657	11 21.1	53 11	114.91	149.23	60.9				.94	.03	.93	ACH
	5.6	-32	60.44	59.52	-.5				.93	.93		
N3658	11 21.3	38 49	141.45	175.42	73.7	.E....*R020			1.05	.09	1.01	ACH
	5.4	-32	69.80	68.45	-7.0				1.56	1.56		
N3659	11 21.1	18 5	202.90	233.09	92.9	.SBS9.$W060	I *A *		1.19	.31	1.07	ACEHKQ
	5.2	-32	68.97	67.74	-15.8	S *	I P		4.50	4.50		
N3662	11 21.3	-0 49	232.26	262.65	111.8	.S...*.H030			1.18	.23	1.09	ACF
	5.1	-32	55.44	54.78	-22.2				2.28	1.22		
N3664	11 21.7	3 35	227.79	257.99	107.3	.SBS9P.W100	I A		1.29	.02	1.28	KW
	5.1	-32	59.12	58.36	-20.8	SX 8*	I P*A*		2.33	2.33		
N3664A	11 21.8	3 30	227.93	258.13	107.4	.SB.9P$W100			.84	.09	.81	W
	5.1	-32	59.07	58.31	-20.8				1.49	1.49		
N3665	11 22.1	39 2	140.68	174.70	73.6	.LAS0..W100	DEP*K		1.22	.12	1.17	ACHKW
	5.4	-32	69.84	68.51	-6.8	E 2			5.08	5.08		
N3666	11 21.9	11 37	216.45	246.43	99.3	.SAT5*.W100	SI *AF		1.57	.54	1.36	ACEHKRV
	5.2	-32	65.19	64.19	-18.1	S 3 5	B *F *		15.98	15.98		W
N3669	11 22.6	57 59	109.18	143.36	56.8	.S....*.			1.43	.55	1.21	AC
	5.7	-33	56.68	55.88	1.9				1.63	1.63		
N3672	11 22.5	-9 32	239.68	270.43	121.0	.SAS5..W100	S A	S 5	1.61	.31	1.48	ACEGHKN
	5.1	-33	48.01	47.54	-24.1	S 4 3	S AF		13.87	13.87		W
N3673	11 22.8	-26 28	248.74	280.11	139.6	.SBT3..W100			1.46	.17	1.40	GKW
	4.9	-33	32.53	32.28	-26.7	SX3 3			5.54	5.54		
N3674	11 23.6	57 19	109.65	143.86	57.4	.L..../W060			1.19	.46	1.01	ACQ
	5.7	-33	57.31	56.50	1.7				1.91	1.91		
N3675	11 23.5	43 52	129.22	163.63	69.4	.SAS3..W060	S G		1.66	.31	1.54	ACHKLQ
	5.5	-33	67.38	66.20	-4.4	S 2 3			9.49	9.49		
N3677	11 23.6	47 16	122.90	157.36	66.4				1.28	.23	1.18	C
	5.5	-33	65.12	64.05	-2.9				.38	.38		
N3681	11 23.9	17 9	206.09	236.11	94.1	.L.....W060 → .SXR4..W100	S G		1.23	.04	1.21	ACHKLSW
	5.2	-33	69.04	67.85	-15.6	S N +	DS G		7.24	6.61		
N3682	11 24.8	66 52	101.45	135.29	48.9	.SAS0*$W060			1.13	.23	1.04	Q
	5.9	-33	49.10	48.48	6.1				.73	.73		
N3683	11 24.8	57 9	109.57	143.80	57.6	.SBS5.$W060	SI *AF*		1.25	.46	1.07	ACKQ
	5.6	-33	57.53	56.73	1.8	S *			4.31	4.31		
N3683A	11 27.0	57 23	108.87	143.11	57.6	.SBT5..W060			1.31	.11	1.27	Q
	5.6	-33	57.50	56.71	2.1				2.08	2.08		
N3684	11 24.5	17 18	205.97	235.97	94.0	.SAT4..W100	S F		1.35	.14	1.29	ACHKLSW
	5.2	-33	69.24	68.05	-15.4	S 5 N 5	S FG		9.16	8.47		
N3686	11 25.1	17 30	205.72	235.71	93.9	.SBS4..L036			1.47	.12	1.42	ACEHKLS
	5.2	-33	69.47	68.28	-15.2	S 5 NK- 3	S AF		8.50	7.61		
N3687	11 25.3	29 47	168.40	200.64	82.3				1.22	.00	1.22	ACK
	5.3	-33	72.99	71.50	-10.2	S 4 4*	S G		2.28	2.28		
N3689	11 25.5	25 56	181.47	212.72	85.9	.SXT5..W060	S AF		1.17	.12	1.12	ACKQ
	5.3	-33	72.76	71.31	-11.8	S 5 3*			2.86	2.86		
N3690	11 26.0	58 49	107.69	141.87	56.2	.S...P.W060	I A		1.18	.16	1.12	AHQ
	5.7	-33	56.21	55.45	2.7	S T	I P*A *		2.61	2.61		
N3691	11 25.5	17 11	206.62	236.57	94.2	.SB....			1.10	.14	1.05	ACHKLS
	5.2	-33	69.37	68.20	-15.2	S			4.56	4.56		
N3705	11 27.6	9 33	222.22	252.05	101.8	.SXR2..W100		S 3	1.64	.38	1.49	ABCEKW
	5.2	-33	64.68	63.80	-17.5	S 3 4	SD G		10.67	10.67		
N3706	11 27.3	-36 8	253.43	285.08	150.4	.E+4...S030			1.23	.20	1.15	I
	4.9	-33	23.73	23.62	-26.3				.56	.56		
N3717	11 29.0	-29 59	251.64	283.10	143.6	.SA.3*/W100			1.64	.59	1.40	FW
	4.9	-33	29.68	29.51	-25.6				6.05	3.69		
N3718	11 29.9	53 21	112.55	146.99	61.4	.SBS1P.W060	P F *	L P	1.76	.24	1.67	ACLXQ
	5.5	-33	61.09	60.22	0.7	S NT+	S P FG	L P	5.88	4.78		
N3719	11 29.7	1 6	233.65	263.80	110.5				1.24	.17	1.17	ABC
	5.1	-33	58.18	57.55	-19.6		S F		1.97	1.97		
N3720	11 29.8	1 5	233.70	263.86	110.5				.92	.01	.92	ABCEK
	5.1	-33	58.18	57.55	-19.6	E 0	S P*		1.90	1.90		
N3726	11 30.7	47 19	120.72	155.34	66.9	.SXR5..W100	S AF		1.76	.15	1.70	ACHKLXW
	5.4	-33	65.92	64.88	-1.8	S 5 K - 2	S F	S5	12.62	12.62		

NGC (IC, A)	m_H / m_C	B(O) / w	B'(O) / m'_C	S(B)	(B-V)(O) / w	C_0(O)	S(C)	(U-B)(O) / w	V / w	V_0 / ΔV	S(V)	ϕ_r n	ϕ(21)		Photo.
	(15)	(16)	(17)	(18)	(19)	(20)	(21)	(22)	(23)	(24)	(25)	(26)	(27)	(28)	(29)
N3640	11.6	11.82	12.61	C	.92	.84	C .		1354	1199	B				
	11.82	1.65	12.61		1.88				6.3	-155					
N3641										-155					
N3642	12.4	11.96	14.70	BG	.51	.41	G		1623	1725	B				
	11.83	2.76	14.57		2.50				4.0	102					
N3643										-156					
N3646	11.8	12.12	14.21	CG	.68	.53	CG		4279	4198	CF*				
	11.80	2.51	13.89		4.38				3.4	-81					
N3649										-81					
N3650										-79					
N3655	12.3									-97					
	12.93		13.22												
N3656										78					
N3657										74					
N3658										6					
N3659	12.9									-91					
	13.36		13.40												
N3662										-170					
N3664	12.9									-153					K
	13.01		14.10												
N3664A										-153					
N3665	12.3	12.11	12.70	BC	.95	.86	C		2002	2010	B				K
	12.44	3.08	13.03		1.88				4.0	8					
N3666	12.6									-119					
	12.54		14.03												
N3669										96					
N3672	11.8									2045	1845	C				P
	11.80		13.94						1.6	-200					
N3673	12.9									-246					
	12.56		14.25												
N3674										94					
N3675	11.8	11.11	13.50	B					696	727	BD				B
	11.64	1.96	14.03						7.3	31					
N3677										47					
N3681	12.8	12.70	13.49	C	.70	.63	C		1314	1220	B				
	12.94	2.90	13.73		3.75				2.4	-94					
N3682										135					
N3683	13.2									93					
	13.53		13.57												
N3683A										95					
N3684	12.6	12.63	13.82	C	.66	.56	C		1422	1329	B				
	12.65	1.11	13.84		1.88				1.8	-93					
N3686	12.3	12.24	14.03	C	.60	.50	C		1022	930	B				
	12.21	1.58	14.00		1.88				2.8	-92					
N3687	13.0									-35					
	13.03		13.87												
N3689	12.8									-53					
	13.17		13.51												
N3690	12.1									101					K
	12.73		13.07												
N3691	13.1									-93					
	13.53		13.47												
N3705	12.2									-125					P
	11.95		14.09												
N3706	12.7									-261					
	12.65		13.14												
N3717	12.6									-250					
	12.37		14.11												
N3718	12.4	11.72	14.76	FG	.74	.62	G		1050	1128	B				BLP
	11.62	3.31	14.66		2.50				1.0	78					
N3719										-158					
N3720	13.0									-158					
N3726	11.7	11.09	14.40	BFG*	.52	.42	BG*		948	998	B				AK
	11.24	1.97	14.48		2.50				1.8	50					

NGC (IC, A) (1)	RA (1950) Dec 100 P (2)	100 P (3)	L^I / B^I (4)	L^II / B^II (5)	SGL / SGB (6)	Rev. type (S) / DDO (T, L) (7)	Yerkes (1) / Yerkes (2) (8)	Hu-San / Ho (9)	log D / w (10)	log R / w (11)	log D(O) (12)	S (D,R) (13)
N3729	11 31.0	53 24	112.21	146.66	61.4	.SBR1P.W060			1.32	.18	1.24	ACKLXQ
	5.5	-33	61.14	60.28	0.9	P	D FG	S5	5.47	5.47		
N3732	11 31.7	-9 34	242.79	273.46	121.6	.SXS0*.W100			.97	.02	.96	ACEKW
	5.1	-33	48.96	48.56	-21.9	E 0	ISP*K *		3.47	3.47		
N3733	11 32.3	55 7	109.98	144.38	59.9	.S..5*.W060			1.47	.27	1.36	AC
	5.5	-33	59.81	58.99	1.8				.75	.75		
N3735	11 33.1	70 48	98.03	131.74	45.6	.SA.5*/W060	S F		1.59	.68	1.32	AHKQ
	5.9	-33	45.83	45.29	8.4	S 3 3*	S *G *		5.73	5.73		
N3737	11 32.9	55 14	109.72	144.12	59.8				.91	.00	.91	ABC
	5.5	-33	59.76	58.94	2.0				1.01	1.01		
N3738	11 33.1	54 48	110.12	144.55	60.3	.I..9..W060	I A *		1.29	.16	1.22	ACKMUXQ
	5.5	-33	60.14	59.32	1.8	P	I P*	I9	7.74	7.74		
N3755	11 33.9	36 41	143.85	177.97	76.8	.SXT5P.W100			1.40	.33	1.26	ACHW
	5.3	-33	73.00	71.63	-5.7				5.07	5.07		
N3756	11 34.1	54 34	110.13	144.57	60.5	.SXT4..W060	S AF		1.55	.29	1.44	ACKMUXQ
	5.5	-33	60.41	59.59	1.8	S 5 3	S AF	S5	11.07	11.07		
N3759	11 34.3	55 6	109.52	143.94	60.1				1.07	.00	1.07	AC
	5.5	-33	59.97	59.17	2.1				.73	.73		
N3759A	11 34.2	55 26	109.20	143.60	59.7	.S...*.						
	5.5	-33	59.68	58.88	2.2							
N3769	11 35.1	48 11	117.97	152.68	66.4	.SBR3*.W060	S *F		1.45	.53	1.24	ABCHKQ
	5.4	-33	65.73	64.75	-.7	S 3 N	SD *FG*		8.10	8.10		
N3769A	11 35.1	48 11	117.97	152.68	66.4	.SB.9P*W060			1.07	.32	.94	AC
	5.4	-33	65.73	64.75	-.7				.87	.87		
N3773	11 35.6	12 23	221.08	250.54	99.8	.LA..*.W100			.92	.03	.91	AEHKW
	5.2	-33	68.10	67.18	-14.7	E 0P	D P*K *		2.92	2.92		
N3780	11 36.7	56 33	107.51	141.89	58.9	.SAS5*.W060	S AF		1.46	.09	1.42	ACKNQ
	5.5	-33	58.89	58.13	3.0	S 5 3	S AF		7.75	7.75		
N3782	11 36.9	46 44	119.67	154.46	67.8	.SXS6*.W060	I A		1.20	.19	1.12	ACHKQ
	5.4	-33	67.05	66.03	-1.0	S 5P	I *A		4.90	4.90		
N3783	11 36.5	-37 28	255.78	287.45	151.9	.SBR1..S030			1.17	.10	1.13	I
	4.9	-33	23.00	22.94	-24.4				1.01	1.01		
N3786	11 37.1	32 11	158.48	191.59	81.2	.SXT1P.P200			1.26	.23	1.17	ABRVQZ
	5.3	-33	75.18	73.71	-6.9				9.91	9.91		
N3788	11 37.2	32 13	158.33	191.46	81.2	.SXT2P.P200			1.29	.49	1.09	ABRVQZ
	5.3	-33	75.19	73.72	-6.9				8.97	8.97		
N3799	11 37.6	15 36	215.50	244.82	96.8	.SB.1*.			1.08	.43	.90	A
	5.2	-33	70.70	69.67	-13.1				.64	.64		
N3800	11 37.6	15 37	215.46	244.78	96.8	.S..3..			1.36	.52	1.15	A
	5.2	-33	70.71	69.68	-13.1				1.03	1.03		
N3804	11 38.1	56 29	107.25	141.65	59.0	.SA.5..L036			1.32	.18	1.25	ACN
	5.4	-33	59.04	58.28	3.1				2.32	2.32		
N3810	11 38.4	11 45	223.58	252.94	100.6	.SAT5..W100	S F	S 5	1.63	.13	1.57	ACEHKXW
	5.2	-33	68.09	67.22	-14.2	S 5 1		S5	8.53	8.53		
N3813	11 38.7	36 49	141.85	176.20	77.0	.SAT3*.W060	S A		1.32	.32	1.19	ACHKQ
	5.3	-33	73.78	72.43	-4.8	S	S A *		5.83	5.83		
N3818	11 39.4	-5 53	243.19	273.60	118.3	.E.5...W060			1.02	.20	.94	ACEKQ
	5.1	-33	53.10	52.71	-19.2	E 2P *	B *K		2.97	2.97		
N3824	11 40.1	53 3	110.19	144.79	62.3				1.16	.22	1.07	AC
	5.4	-33	62.16	61.34	2.0				.45	.45		
N3829	11 40.8	53 0	110.04	144.66	62.4	.SB..*.			1.15	.14	1.09	AC
	5.4	-33	62.27	61.44	2.1				1.02	1.02		
N3835	11 41.4	60 23	103.31	137.53	55.6	.S....*			1.28	.39	1.12	ACH
	5.4	-33	55.73	55.07	5.1				2.32	2.32		
N3838	11 41.6	58 14	104.92	139.27	57.6				1.23	.40	1.07	AC
	5.4	-33	57.70	56.99	4.3				1.19	1.19		
N3846	11 41.8	55 55	106.87	141.34	59.7	.SA.5*.W060			1.18	.07	1.15	AC
	5.4	-33	59.78	59.03	3.4				.46	.46		
N3846A	11 42.0	55 18	107.40	141.90	60.3							
	5.4	-33	60.34	59.58	3.2							
N3850	11 42.0	56 10	106.60	141.06	59.5	.SBS5*.W060			1.40	.27	1.29	ACQ
	5.4	-33	59.57	58.83	3.5				1.69	1.69		
N3865	11 42.7	-8 56	246.29	276.83	121.6				1.26	.15	1.19	EK
	5.1	-33	50.59	50.28	-19.2	S 3 N	S F		1.85	1.85		
N3872	11 43.2	14 3	221.70	250.74	98.8	.E.5...W060			.97	.20	.89	ACEKSQ
	5.2	-33	70.58	69.67	-12.3	E 4	E4 K		4.04	4.04		
N3877	11 43.5	47 46	115.79	150.72	67.3	.SAS5*.W060	S AF		1.71	.61	1.46	ACHKQ
	5.3	-33	66.91	65.96	0.4	S 3 N	S AF		9.61	9.61		
N3885	11 44.3	-27 39	254.59	285.93	141.4	.SAS0..W100			1.22	.30	1.10	W
	5.0	-33	32.89	32.80	-22.1				2.41	2.41		
N3887	11 44.6	-16 35	250.66	281.57	129.7	.SBR4..W100	S F		1.45	.12	1.40	AGKMW
	5.1	-33	43.53	43.33	-20.3	S 5 K 4*			8.61	8.61		
N3888	11 45.0	56 15	105.79	140.27	59.6	.SXT5..W060	S F		1.15	.14	1.09	ACKQ
	5.3	-33	59.68	58.96	3.9	S 3 4*	S P F *		3.36	3.36		
N3892	11 45.5	-10 41	248.24	278.85	123.6	.LBT+..W060			1.30	.11	1.26	AKLQ
	5.1	-33	49.19	48.92	-18.9	SX0*	B K		3.01	2.12		
N3393	11 46.1	49 0	113.17	148.11	66.4	.SXT5*.L036			1.59	.18	1.52	ABCHKU
	5.3	-33	66.12	65.23	1.3	S 5 N 1*	S FG		9.28	9.28		
N3894	11 46.2	59 42	102.81	137.11	56.5	.E.4+..W060			1.16	.20	1.08	ABCHQ
	5.4	-33	56.61	55.95	5.4				3.44	3.44		

| NGC (IC, A) (14) | Magnitudes | | | | Colors | | | | Velocities | | | Radio | | | |
	m_H m_C (15)	B(O) w (16)	B'(O) m'_C (17)	S(B) (18)	(B-V)(O) w (19)	C_O(O) (20)	S(C) (21)	(U-B)(O) w (22)	V w (23)	V_o ΔV (24)	S(V) (25)	$φ_r$ n (26)	φ (21) (27)	(28)	Photo. (29)
N3729	13.0 12.91	12.26 1.52	13.20 13.85	FG	.62 2.50		G			78					
N3732	12.9 13.46		13.00							−195					
N3733										87					
N3735	12.6 12.60		13.94							153					
N3737										87					
N3738	12.2 12.36	12.20 1.71	13.04 13.20	FG*	.44 2.50		G			85					
N3755										2					
N3756	12.5 12.27	12.42 2.25	14.31 14.16	FG	.65 2.50		G			84					
N3759										87					
N3759A										89					
N3769	12.5 12.71		13.60						748 3.0	804 56	E				
N3769A									712 3.0	768 56	E				
N3773	13.0 13.34		12.63							−109					
N3780	12.6 12.37	12.47 2.71	14.31 14.21	F						94					
N3782	12.9 13.30		13.59							50					
N3783	12.8 13.08		13.42							−258					
N3786									2755 .9	2737 −18	E				D
N3788									2345 .9	2327 −18	E				D
N3799									3518 4.2	3424 −93	E				
N3800									3562 4.2	3469 −93	E				
N3804		12.72 0.89	13.71	F						94					
N3810	11.8 11.60	11.40 11.91	13.99 14.19	ACDFG	.61 29.38	.51	ACDG /D	−.08	988 4.7	878 −110	BC				JKP
N3813	12.6 12.88		13.52							5					
N3818	12.7 13.03	13.23 0.84	12.62 12.42	C	.89 1.88	.81	C		1498 2.4	1320 −178	B				
N3824										80					
N3829										80					
N3835										112					
N3838										103					
N3846		13.91 0.76	14.40	F						93					
N3846A										91					
N3850										94					
N3865	13.0 13.07		13.76							−187					
N3872	12.8 13.18	13.30 0.73	12.44 12.32	C	.95 1.88	.86	C		3109 1.8	3012 −97	B				
N3877	12.0 11.96		14.00							57					
N3885	12.9 13.13		13.37							−237					
N3887	11.6 11.86		13.60						1163 1.5	954 −209	C				
N3888	13.0 13.35	13.00 0.68	13.19 13.54	F						96					
N3892	12.9 12.70		13.69							−191					
N3893	11.0 11.28	11.10 4.49	13.44 13.62	BF					1001 8.2	1065 64	BC				
N3894										111					

NGC (IC, A)	RA (1950) Dec 100 P	L^I B^I	L^II B^II	SGL SGB	Rev. type (S) DDO (T, L)	Yerkes (1) Yerkes (2)	Hu-San Ho	log D w	log R w	log D(O)	S (D,R)
(1)	(2) (3)	(4)	(5)	(6)	(7)	(8)	(9)	(10)	(11)	(12)	(13)
N3895	11 46.4 59 42	102.77	137.07	56.5	.SBT1*.W060			1.13	.14	1.07	ABCQ
	5.3 -33	56.62	55.96	5.4				2.39	2.39		
N3896	11 46.4 48 58	113.12	148.06	66.4				.98	.06	.96	ABCHL
	5.3 -33	66.17	65.28	1.3				1.61	1.26		
N3898	11 46.7 56 22	105.27	139.76	59.6	.SAS2..P200	SD *K	S 1	1.67	.28	1.56	ACKUZ
	5.3 -33	59.68	58.96	4.2	S 2 3	S K		10.34	10.34		
N3900	11 46.6 27 17	178.74	209.88	86.5	.LAR+..W060	SD *G		1.33	.27	1.22	ACEHKQ
	5.2 -33	77.61	76.15	-6.9	S 4 5	SD G		5.61	5.61		
N3902	11 46.7 26 24	182.80	213.53	87.4				1.18	.13	1.13	ACH
	5.2 -33	77.52	76.08	-7.2				2.00	2.00		
N3904	11 46.7 -29 2	255.61	287.00	142.9	.E+2+*.W100	E3 K		1.12	.15	1.06	DW
	5.1 -33	31.69	31.63	-21.7				3.15	3.15		
N3905	11 46.5 -9 29	247.98	278.52	122.4	.S.....H030			1.30	.20	1.22	F
	5.1 -33	50.40	50.13	-18.4				1.39	1.39		
N3906	11 47.1 48 42	113.22	148.20	66.7	.S.....R020			1.27	.04	1.26	ACH
	5.3 -33	66.45	65.56	1.3				2.32	2.32		
N3912	11 47.5 26 46	181.26	212.12	87.1				1.14	.28	1.02	ACEHK
	5.2 -33	77.75	76.31	-6.9	S 4 5*	I P*		3.41	3.41		
N3913	11 47.8 55 37	105.62	140.18	60.3				1.43	.05	1.41	H
	5.3 -33	60.42	59.70	4.0				1.30	1.30		
N3916	11 48.2 55 25	105.69	140.26	60.6	.S....*R020			1.18	.46	1.00	ACH
	5.3 -33	60.63	59.90	4.0				1.99	1.99		
N3917	11 48.3 52 6	108.82	143.60	63.6	.SA.6*.W060	SI *AF		1.67	.57	1.44	ACHKYQ
	5.3 -33	63.61	62.81	2.8	S NK-	S AF		9.18	9.18		
N3921	11 48.5 55 22	105.65	140.23	60.6	.L...P.R020			1.34	.21	1.26	H
	5.3 -33	60.69	59.97	4.0				1.15	1.15		
N3923	11 48.5 -28 33	255.92	287.28	142.5	.E.4+..W100	E4 K		1.21	.21	1.30	DMW
	5.1 -33	32.26	32.20	-21.3				4.15	4.15		
N3928	11 49.2 48 58	112.14	147.14	66.6	.E.....R020			1.03	.00	1.03	ACH
	5.2 -33	66.41	65.54	1.7				1.50	1.50		
N3930	11 49.2 38 17	133.05	168.20	76.5	.SXS5..P048			1.53	.13	1.47	ABCH
	5.2 -33	74.66	73.42	-2.3				3.44	3.44		
N3931	11 48.6 52 17	108.53	143.31	63.5	.LA.-*.W060			.95	.12	.90	CQ
	5.3 -33	63.47	62.68	2.9				.77	.77		
N3936	11 49.9 -26 37	255.72	287.01	140.5	.S....*/H030			1.56	.86	1.22	EFK
	5.1 -33	34.21	34.15	-20.7	S 3 5			4.69	4.69		
N3938	11 50.2 44 24	118.60	153.88	70.9	.SAS5..W100	S FG		1.73	.05	1.71	ACHKLXW
	5.2 -33	70.32	69.32	0.2	S 5 1	S F	S5	12.19	10.85		
N3941	11 50.3 37 16	135.63	170.72	77.5	.LBSO..W060	B P*K *		1.38	.21	1.30	ACHKMQ
	5.2 -33	75.47	74.19	-2.5	E 3	D P K		5.96	5.96		
N3945	11 50.6 60 57	101.07	135.33	55.5	.LBT+..W060	B GK*		1.45	.20	1.37	ACHKQ
	5.3 -33	55.65	55.03	6.3	SB0			4.42	4.42		
N3949	11 51.1 48 8	112.53	147.63	67.5	.SAS4*.W060	SI *F		1.40	.24	1.31	ABCHKMQ
	5.2 -33	67.29	66.41	1.7	S 3 N	S *F *		9.57	9.57		
N3952	11 51.1 -3 43	246.45	276.59	116.9	P	I P A *		1.17	.31	1.04	ACK
	5.1 -33	56.21	55.89	-15.8				1.71	1.71		
N3953	11 51.2 52 37	107.41	142.21	63.3	.SBR4..W060	S F		1.77	.30	1.65	ACHKXYQ
	5.2 -33	63.35	62.58	3.4	S 4 1	S FG	S4	10.31	10.31		
N3955	11 51.5 -22 54	255.03	286.17	136.6	.I.0...W100			1.31	.51	1.10	DKQW
	5.1 -33	37.90	37.82	-19.8	S 3 5	SIP*		4.89	4.89		
N3956	11 51.6 -20 18	254.21	285.25	133.9	.SAS5*.W100			1.51	.49	1.31	AEKW
	5.1 -33	40.42	40.32	-19.4	S 6 7*	S F		6.63	6.63		
N3957	11 51.6 -19 17	253.86	284.86	132.8	.LA.+*/W100			1.40	.72	1.12	AEKW
	5.1 -33	41.41	41.29	-19.2	E 8	SD *K *		6.51	6.51		
N3958	11 52.0 58 38	102.28	136.69	57.7	.SBS1..W060	SD *G		1.12	.31	1.00	ACHQ
	5.2 -33	57.87	57.23	5.7				3.48	3.48		
N3962	11 52.2 -13 42	251.95	282.68	127.1	.E.1...W060			.98	.05	.96	AKQ
	5.1 -33	46.82	46.65	-17.9	E 2	E K		2.19	2.19		
N3963	11 52.4 58 46	102.10	136.50	57.6	.SXT4..W060	S AF		1.38	.03	1.37	ACHKQ
	5.2 -33	57.77	57.13	5.8	S 5 2			6.37	6.37		
N3972	11 53.2 55 35	104.23	138.85	60.7	.SAS4..W060	S AF		1.57	.53	1.36	ABCHQ
	5.2 -33	60.76	60.07	4.7				7.73	7.73		
N3975	11 53.3 60 48	100.62	134.90	55.8	.S....$R020			1.01	.07	.98	ABCH
	5.2 -33	55.90	55.29	6.6				1.55	1.55		
N3976	11 53.4 7 2	238.35	267.53	106.4	.SXS3..W060	S *G		1.59	.48	1.40	ABCHKQ
	5.1 -33	66.27	65.74	-12.2	S 3 3			8.14	8.14		
N3977	11 53.5 55 40	104.08	138.70	60.6	RSAT2*.W060			1.27	.11	1.22	HQ
	5.2 -33	60.70	60.01	4.8				2.10	2.10		
N3978	11 53.6 60 48	100.55	134.84	55.8	.S....*R020			1.11	.03	1.10	ABCH
	5.2 -33	55.91	55.31	6.6				2.00	2.00		
N3981	11 53.7 -19 37	254.61	285.62	133.3	.S...*.			1.61	.39	1.45	AEK
	5.1 -33	41.21	41.11	-18.8	S 3 T	S F		4.36	4.36		
N3982	11 53.9 55 24	104.19	138.82	60.9	.SXR3*.W060	S F		1.29	.06	1.27	ACHKQ
	5.2 -33	60.97	60.28	4.8	S 3 N	S P G *		4.72	4.72		
N3985	11 54.1 48 37	110.80	145.94	67.2	.SBS9*.W060	SIP*G *		1.13	.21	1.05	ACHKQ
	5.2 -33	67.12	66.27	2.4	S *	ISP		3.55	3.55		
N3986	11 54.2 32 18	153.35	187.27	82.4	.L..../W100			1.38	.64	1.13	ACNW
	5.2 -33	78.61	77.16	-3.5				4.57	4.57		
N3990	11 55.0 55 44	103.63	138.26	60.6	.L..-*/W060	D *K		1.01	.28	.90	ABCHQ
	5.2 -33	60.72	60.04	5.0				3.46	3.46		

NGC (IC, A)	m_H / m_C	B(O) w	B'(O) m'_C	S(B)	(B-V)(O) w	C_0(O)	S(C)	(U-B)(O) w	V w	V_0 ΔV	S(V)	ϕ_r n	ϕ(21)		Photo.
	(14)	(15)	(16)	(17)	(18)	(19)	(20)	(21)	(22)	(23)	(24)	(25)	(26)	(27)	(28)	(29)
N3895										109					
N3896										64					
N3898	12.0	11.60	14.14	BF	.90	.75	B		1038	1135	B				KP
	11.66	4.88	14.20		6.25				1.8	97					
N3900	12.7	12.63	13.47	C	.82	.73	C		1702	1666	B				
	12.62	2.70	13.46		3.75				4.0	-36					
N3902										-40					
N3904	11.9	12.43	12.42	C	1.01	.89	C		1613	1374	B				
	12.29	1.18	12.28		1.88				1.8	-239					
N3905										-186					
N3906										63					
N3912	13.0									-38					
N3913										94					
N3916				F*						93					
N3917	12.8									79					
	12.48		14.42						5930	6023	F				
N3921									4.0	93					
N3923	11.1	11.40	12.59	C	1.00	.88	C		1788	1551	B				
	11.36	1.98	12.55		1.88				2.4	-237					
N3928										65					
N3930										16					
N3931										80					
N3936	13.0									-232					
	13.17		13.96						874	919	C				K
N3938	11.6	11.02	14.26	FG	.53	.45	G		3.4	45					
	11.19	2.45	14.43		2.50				957	969	BC				
N3941	11.4	11.66	12.85	B					6.0	12					
	11.64	1.14	12.83						1220	1337	B				
N3945	12.1	11.91	13.45	B					1.8	117					
	11.98	2.04	13.52						681	743	B				
N3949	11.6	11.66	12.90	BF	.46	.35	B		.4	62					
	12.09	1.82	13.33		6.25										
N3952	13.0									-164					
	13.19		13.13						953	1041	BC				
N3953	11.5	11.11	14.05	BCFG	.72	.59	CG		5.6	82					
	11.25	6.62	14.19		4.38										
N3955	12.8									-222					
	12.98		13.22												
N3956	12.6									-216					
	12.63		13.92												
N3957	12.9									-213					
	12.94		13.23												
N3958										108					
N3962	12.2	12.29	11.83	C	.97	.88	C		1794	1597	B				
	12.65	0.88	12.19		1.88				2.4	-196					
N3963	12.7									109					K
	12.52		14.11												
N3972		13.76	15.25	F						96					
		0.89													
N3975										118					
N3976	12.4									-121					
	12.27		14.01												
N3977										96					
N3978										118					
N3981	12.7									-213					
	12.57		14.56												
N3982	11.8	12.45	13.49	F						95					
	12.26	1.57	13.30												
N3985	12.9									66					
	13.38		13.37												
N3986										-9					
N3990		13.85	13.09	BE	.86	.77	E	.39	720	817	C				
		2.79			6.25		/E		4.9	97					

NGC (IC, A) (1)	RA (1950) Dec 100 P 100 P (2) (3)		L^I B^I (4)	L^II B^II (5)	SGL SGB (6)	Rev. type (S) DDO (T, L) (7)	Yerkes (1) Yerkes (2) (8)	Hu-San Ho (9)	log D w (10)	log R w (11)	log D(O) (12)	S (D,R) (13)
N3991	11 55.0	32 38	151.47	185.60	82.2	.I..9P/W100	I A		1.18	.49	.98	BCNW
	5.2	-33	78.64	77.21	-3.3				3.58	3.58		
N3992	11 55.0	53 39	105.32	140.10	62.6	.SBT4..P200	B F		1.84	.19	1.76	ACKLXYQ
	5.2	-33	62.64	61.93	4.3	SX4 1		S4	15.53	13.86		Z
N3993	11 55.1	25 31	189.00	218.79	88.9				1.35	.55	1.13	ABC
	5.1	-33	79.19	77.80	-5.7				2.47	2.47		
N3994	11 55.1	32 34	151.74	185.84	82.3	.SAR5P$W100	SI *AF		1.03	.24	.94	ABCNW
	5.2	-33	78.70	77.26	-3.2				3.46	3.46		
N3995	11 55.2	32 35	151.62	185.74	82.3	.SA.9P.W100	IS *AF		1.44	.40	1.28	ABCKNW
	5.2	-33	78.69	77.25	-3.3	S 5 T	ISP*A *		7.63	7.63		
N3997	11 55.3	25 33	188.89	218.68	88.9				1.30	.51	1.10	ABC
	5.1	-33	79.24	77.85	-5.7				2.30	2.30		
N3998	11 55.3	55 44	103.55	138.18	60.6	.LARO.$W060	D K		1.27	.11	1.23	ABCHKQ
	5.2	-33	60.74	60.06	5.1	E 2P *	D K		5.85	5.85		
N4008	11 55.7	28 28	173.09	204.71	86.1	.E.5...W100	E4 K		1.09	.25	.99	ACEKW
	5.1	-33	79.67	78.19	-4.6	S 0	D K		4.13	4.13		
N4010	11 56.1	47 31	111.41	146.69	68.4	.S.....R020			1.60	.76	1.29	ABCH
	5.2	-33	68.24	67.38	2.3				5.07	5.07		
N4013	11 56.0	44 13	116.34	151.86	71.4	.S..3./W100	S GK*		1.69	.71	1.41	ACHKLYW
	5.2	-33	71.06	70.10	1.1	S 3	S *GK*		11.61	10.35		
N4020	11 56.4	30 42	160.69	193.85	84.1	.S.....			1.34	.42	1.18	ACLS
	5.1	-33	79.53	78.05	-3.7				4.01	3.23		
N4024	11 56.0	-18 5	254.82	285.74	131.8	.LX.-..W060			1.09	.20	1.02	AEKQ
	5.1	-33	42.83	42.74	-17.9	E 2	DB *K *		3.80	3.80		
N4025	11 56.6	38 5	129.84	165.48	77.2	.SBS6..L036			1.29	.08	1.26	AC
	5.1	-33	75.89	74.68	-1.0				1.32	.94		
N4026	11 56.9	51 14	106.93	141.93	64.9	.L...../W060	D K		1.60	.62	1.36	ACKLQ
	5.2	-33	64.97	64.21	3.7	E 8	D K		7.21	6.12		
N4027	11 57.0	-18 59	255.42	286.38	132.8	.SBS8..W100	ISP*AF		1.41	.11	1.37	AEFKNPY
	5.1	-33	42.01	41.94	-17.9	S 5 T	SIP*AF*		12.84	12.84		W
N4030	11 57.8	-0 49	247.50	277.34	114.4	.SAS4..W060	S F		1.57	.14	1.51	ACFHKLM
	5.1	-33	59.51	59.24	-13.4	S 5 1			17.28	16.39		TQ
N4032	11 58.0	20 21	213.57	241.45	94.0				1.18	.03	1.17	ACK
	5.1	-33	77.46	76.39	-6.9	I 5*	I P G *		2.14	2.14		
N4033	11 58.0	-17 34	255.28	286.18	131.4	.E+6...W100			1.17	.40	1.01	AEKW
	5.1	-33	43.44	43.37	-17.4	E 5	D K		3.90	3.90		
N4035	11 58.5	-15 41	254.82	285.62	129.4	.S....*H030			1.18	.04	1.16	A
	5.1	-33	45.30	45.21	-16.9				.77	.77		
N4036	11 58.9	62 10	98.75	132.98	54.7	.L..-..W060	SD *K		1.50	.43	1.33	ACHKLXY
	5.1	-33	54.81	54.25	7.7	E 6		L	7.27	7.27		Q
N4037	11 58.8	13 41	231.83	260.01	100.4	.SBT3*$W060			1.34	.11	1.29	ACKQ
	5.1	-33	72.66	71.97	-8.9	SX 7*	S F		4.84	4.84		
N4038	11 59.3	-18 35	256.01	286.95	132.5	.IB.9P.W100	I P AF*		1.85	0.22	1.76	AEFYW
	5.1	-33	42.53	42.47	-17.3	S 5 T +	I P A *		11.30	11.30		
N4039	11 59.3	-18 35	256.01	286.95	132.5				-	-	-	-
	5.1	-33	42.53	42.47	-17.3							
N4041	11 59.7	62 25	98.47	132.69	54.5	.SAT4*.W060	S G		1.37	.03	1.36	ACHKLXW
	5.1	-33	54.60	54.05	7.9	S 5 K - 3		S5	7.73	6.84		
N4045	12 0.2	2 15	246.49	276.01	111.6	.SXR1..W060	S F		1.22	.10	1.18	ABEQ
	5.1	-33	62.59	62.27	-12.0	S PT -*			3.46	3.46		
N4047	12 0.2	48 55	108.13	143.39	67.3	RSAT3*.W060	SD *G		1.23	.05	1.20	ACKQ
	5.1	-33	67.30	66.51	3.4	S 4 5*	S P*		3.59	3.59		
N4050	12 0.4	-16 6	255.59	286.40	130.0	.SBR2..W100			1.45	.17	1.38	AFKW
	5.1	-33	45.00	44.93	-16.5	SX2 3*	SB *F		6.59	6.59		
N4051	12 0.6	44 48	113.25	148.90	71.2	.SXT4..W100	S F *		1.65	.14	1.60	ACHKLXY
	5.1	-33	70.99	70.09	2.1	S 5 K - 3	S F	S4	10.24	10.24		W
N4062	12 1.5	32 10	150.86	185.30	83.1	.SAS5..W100		S 3	1.57	.37	1.42	ACHKLSW
	5.1	-33	80.09	78.65	-2.1	S 3 3*	S AF		11.56	11.56		
N4064	12 1.6	18 43	221.64	249.07	95.8	.SBS1P*W100	SI *AF*		1.52	.40	1.35	AEKNW
	5.1	-33	77.00	76.08	-6.6	S 2 5	S *AF		7.98	7.98		
N4067	12 1.6	11 8	237.92	266.30	103.1	.E....$R020			1.19	.10	1.15	ACH
	5.1	-33	70.84	70.29	-9.0				1.28	1.28		
N4068	12 1.7	52 50	103.94	138.87	63.7	.S.....R020			1.61	.39	1.46	H
	5.1	-33	63.78	63.09	5.0				.31	.31		
N4073	12 1.9	2 11	247.41	276.91	111.8				1.20	.13	1.15	AK
	5.1	-33	62.68	62.38	-11.6	E 1			.60	.60		
N4079	12 2.3	-2 6	250.38	280.28	116.0	.S.....H030			1.20	.01	1.20	ACF
	5.1	-33	58.65	58.43	-12.7				2.34	1.29		
N4081	12 2.2	64 42	96.98	131.08	52.4	.S..1$.						
	5.1	-33	52.48	51.96	8.8							
N4085	12 2.8	50 38	105.45	140.60	65.8	.SXS5*$W060			1.44	.55	1.22	ABCHKMU
	5.1	-33	65.89	65.16	4.4	S 3 5*	IS *A	S5	10.68	10.68		XQ
N4088	12 3.0	50 49	105.21	140.34	65.7	.SXT4..W060	B *A *	SX 5	1.72	.39	1.56	ABCHKMU
	5.1	-33	65.73	65.01	4.5	S 5 K - 2*	S P A *	S5	14.79	14.79		XYQ
N4094	12 3.3	-14 16	255.98	286.69	128.3	.S.....H030			1.60	.45	1.42	AFK
	5.1	-33	46.95	46.88	-15.4	S 6 7	S AF		4.54	4.54		
N4096	12 3.5	47 45	108.09	143.54	68.6	.SXT5..W060	S AF		1.79	.56	1.57	ACHKLUX
	5.1	-33	68.59	67.80	3.5	S 5 K - 3*	S AF	S6	14.10	14.10		YQ
N4100	12 3.6	49 51	105.88	141.12	66.6	PSAT4..W060	S AF		1.66	.46	1.48	ACHKLYQ
	5.1	-33	66.66	65.93	4.2	S 3 N 2*	S P FG*		10.20	10.20		

NGC (IC, A)	Magnitudes				Colors				Velocities			Radio			
	m_H m_C	B(O) w	B'(O) m'_C	S(B)	(B-V)(O) w	C_O(O)	S(C)	(U-B)(O) w	V w	V_O ΔV	S(V)	ϕ_r n	ϕ(21)		Photo.
(14)	(15)	(16)	(17)	(18)	(19)	(20)	(21)	(22)	(23)	(24)	(25)	(26)	(27)	(28)	(29)
N3991		13.83	13.47	E	.37	.28	E	-.32*	3308	3301	DE				K
		2.60			12.50		/E		4.5	-7					
N3992	11.2	10.80	14.34	BEFG	.85	.74	EG	.39	1059	1147	B				K
	10.81	4.82	14.35		8.75		/E		1.0	88					
N3993									4831	4792	E				
									.9	-39					
N3994		13.68	13.12	E	.61	.47	E	-.12	3133	3126	E				
		2.28			12.50		/E		1.7	-7					
N3995	12.9	12.96	14.05	E	.23	.12	E	-.38	3362	3356	CE				K
	13.01	5.34	14.10		12.50		/E		5.6	-7					
N3997									4769	4730	E				
									.9	-39					
N3998	11.6	11.79	12.63	BDEF	.95	.87	BDE	.51	1080	1177	BC				
	11.89	13.17	12.73		50.00		/DE		9.7	97					
N4008	12.9	13.61	13.30	E	.91		E	.25							
	13.06	1.59	12.75		6.25		/E			-25					
N4010										62					
N4013	12.7														B
	12.43		14.17							47					
N4020										-15					
N4024	12.9														
	13.11		12.90							-207					
N4025										19					
N4026	12.0	12.13	13.62	B					878	956	B				K
	11.94	0.88	13.43						1.8	78					
N4027	11.6	11.90	13.44	E	.55	.44	E	-.06	1909	1701	DE				K
	12.09	2.78	13.63		6.25		/E		2.4	-209					
N4030	11.2	11.57	13.86	EF	.67	.56	E	-.03	1509	1361	C				
	11.39	2.56	13.68		6.25		/E		2.4	-149					
N4032	13.0									-61					
N4033	12.8														
	12.96		12.75							-204					
N4035										-199					
N4036	11.9	11.87	13.21	BEG	.92	.82	BEG	.57	1382	1507	B				
	11.92	4.89	13.26		15.00		/E		4.0	125					
N4037	12.8														
	12.74		13.93							-89					
N4038	11.0	11.17	14.71	BE*	.62	.53	BE*	-.21	1650	1443	BDE				K
	10.65	4.08	14.19		12.50		/E		17.7	-206					
N4039				E*			E*		1634	1427	BE				K
									15.9	-206					
N4041	12.0	11.93	13.47	EG	.59		EG	-.06							
	12.17	3.57	13.71		8.75		/E			126					
N4045	12.8	13.06	13.65	E	.84		E	.26							
	12.97	2.63	13.56		6.25		/E			-135					
N4047	12.8														
	12.94		13.68							69					
N4050	12.5														
	12.34		13.98							-199					
N4051	11.7	11.23	13.92	BEFG	.65	.55	EG	.10*	647	698	BJ				K
	11.47	7.72	14.16		15.00		/E		41.0	51					
N4062	12.1	12.17	14.01	E	.78		E	.07		-5					P
	12.10	2.10	13.94		6.25		/E								
N4064	12.8								1033	967	C				
	12.55		14.04						2.5	-66					
N4067										-98					
N4068										287					
N4073	13.2														
	12.98		13.47							-134					
N4079										-150					
N4081										136					
N4085	12.8	13.11	13.95	FG*	.60		G								
	12.94	1.27	13.78		2.50					78					
N4088	11.2	11.39	13.93	EFGD	.68	.54	EGD	.03	733	812	CD				P
	11.27	4.21	13.81		15.50		/DE		2.6	79					
N4094	13.0														
	12.82		14.66							-191					
N4096	12.2	11.31	13.90	FG	.45		G								
	11.81	1.81	14.40		2.50					66					
N4100	11.9	11.98	14.07	F											
	11.86	0.76	13.95							75					

NGC (IC, A) (1)	RA (1950) 100 P (2)	Dec 100 P (3)	L^I / B^I (4)	L^{II} / B^{II} (5)	SGL / SGB (6)	Rev. type (S) / DDO (T, L) (7)	Yerkes (1) / Yerkes (2) (8)	Hu-San Ho (9)	log D w (10)	log R w (11)	log D(O) (12)	S (D,R) (13)
N4102	12 3.8 / 5.1	52 59 / -33	103.15 / 63.75	138.10 / 63.08	63.6 / 5.3	.SXS3.$W060 / S 5 KT	S P G / DSP K *		1.39 / 6.81	.22 / 6.81	1.31	ACHKNQ
N4105	12 4.1 / 5.1	-29 30 / -33	260.09 / 32.04	291.46 / 32.09	143.9 / -18.0	.E.3...W100			1.13 / 5.45	.12 / 5.45	1.08	DEPW
N4106	12 4.2 / 5.1	-29 31 / -33	260.12 / 32.03	291.49 / 32.08	144.0 / -18.0	.LBS+..W100			1.13 / 4.51	.11 / 4.51	1.08	DEPW
N4108	12 4.3 / 5.0	67 26 / -33	95.60 / 49.87	129.56 / 49.40	49.8 / 9.9	.S...*.			1.21 / .74	.02 / .74	1.20	AC
N4108A	12 3.3 / 5.0	67 32 / -33	95.71 / 49.75	129.66 / 49.27	49.7 / 9.8	.S...*.						
N4108B	12 4.8 / 5.0	67 30 / -33	95.51 / 49.82	129.46 / 49.34	49.8 / 9.9	.S...P.P048						
N4109	12 4.5 / 5.1	43 15 / -33	113.74 / 72.69	149.70 / 71.77	72.9 / 2.2				1.02 / 1.15	.00 / 1.15	1.02	AB
N4111	12 4.5 / 5.1	43 21 / -33	113.57 / 72.60	149.52 / 71.69	72.8 / 2.2	.LAR+*/W100 / E 8	D K / D K	L 2 / L	1.53 / 12.86	.69 / 12.86	1.25	ABHKMUX / YW
N4114	12 4.7 / 5.1	-13 55 / -33	256.35 / 47.36	287.04 / 47.31	128.0 / -15.0	.S...$.H030			1.25 / 1.29	.25 / 1.29	1.15	F
N4116	12 5.1 / 5.1	2 58 / -33	248.50 / 63.68	277.87 / 63.41	111.3 / -10.6	.SBT8..W060 / SB5 5*	B AF / B *F *	/ S6	1.55 / 9.99	.23 / 9.99	1.46	ACEHKNX / Q
N4117	12 5.2 / 5.1	43 24 / -33	113.12 / 72.62	149.10 / 71.72	72.8 / 2.4				1.02 / 1.35	.18 / 1.35	.94	ABH
N4118	12 5.2 / 5.1	43 24 / -33	113.12 / 72.62	149.10 / 71.72	72.8 / 2.4							
N4120	12 5.5 / 5.0	69 52 / -33	94.64 / 47.52	128.47 / 47.07	47.5 / 10.7	.S.....			1.29 / 1.12	.46 / 1.12	1.11	AH
N4121	12 5.5 / 5.0	65 24 / -33	96.16 / 51.88	130.23 / 51.39	51.8 / 9.4	.E.2...W060			.78 / 1.82	.08 / 1.82	.74	ABCMQ
N4123	12 5.6 / 5.1	3 9 / -33	248.64 / 63.90	277.97 / 63.63	111.1 / -10.5	.SBR5..W060 / SB3 5	B AF / B *F *	/ S6	1.61 / 10.79	.12 / 10.79	1.56	ACEHKNX / Q
N4124	12 5.6 / 5.1	10 40 / -33	241.25 / 70.87	269.53 / 70.40	103.8 / -8.2	.LAR+..W100 / S 0*	D *FG / D G		1.52 / 10.20	.50 / 10.20	1.32	ADEHKSW
N4125	12 5.7 / 5.0	65 27 / -33	96.11 / 51.84	130.17 / 51.34	51.8 / 9.4	.E+6...W060 / E 5P	E5 K / E K		1.40 / 6.91	.26 / 6.91	1.30	ABCKMQ
N4128	12 6.1 / 5.0	69 3 / -33	94.82 / 48.33	128.69 / 47.87	48.3 / 10.5	.LA..*/W060 / S 0*	DB *K		1.30 / 6.48	.50 / 6.48	1.10	ABHKNQ
N4129	12 6.3 / 5.1	-8 45 / -33	255.17 / 52.49	285.54 / 52.40	122.9 / -13.5	.SBS2*/W100 / S *	/ DSP*G *		1.32 / 6.09	.60 / 6.09	1.08	ACEKW
N4135	12 6.6 / 5.1	44 17 / -33	111.04 / 71.95	146.98 / 71.09	72.0 / 2.9				1.00 / .66	.15 / .66	.95	H
N4136	12 6.7 / 5.1	30 12 / -33	160.26 / 81.80	193.68 / 80.32	85.3 / -1.7	.SXR5..L036 / S 5 N - 5	S F		1.58 / 6.13	.02 / 6.13	1.57	ACKN
N4137	12 6.3 / 5.1	44 22 / -33	110.82 / 71.89	146.75 / 71.04	72.0 / 2.9	.S.....			.96 / .30	.08 / .30	.93	H
N4138	12 7.0 / 5.1	43 58 / -33	111.29 / 72.27	147.28 / 71.40	72.4 / 2.9	.LAR+..W060 / E 4	SD *G / D K		1.20 / 3.44	.20 / 3.44	1.12	AHKYQ
N4142	12 7.1 / 5.0	53 24 / -33	101.79 / 63.50	136.74 / 62.86	63.4 / 5.9	.S....$R020			1.36 / .67	.21 / .67	1.28	CH
N4143	12 7.1 / 5.1	42 49 / -33	113.03 / 73.30	149.16 / 72.40	73.4 / 2.5	.LXS0..W100 / E 4	DB *K / DE K		1.20 / 4.44	.23 / 4.44	1.11	AHKYW
N4144	12 7.5 / 5.0	46 44 / -33	107.48 / 69.79	143.16 / 69.01	69.8 / 3.8	.SXS6$/W060 / S 3 5	SI *AF / S *FG*		1.71 / 7.80	.68 / 7.80	1.44	ACKYQ
N4145	12 7.5 / 5.1	40 10 / -33	117.81 / 75.62	154.25 / 74.62	76.0 / 1.7	.SXT7..... / S 5K 3	S F		1.73 / 10.35	.12 / 10.35	1.68	ABCKLU
N4146	12 7.6 / 5.1	26 42 / -33	185.48 / 82.19	214.97 / 80.76	88.7 / -2.7				1.18 / .77	.00 / .77	1.18	A
N4150	12 8.0 / 5.1	30 41 / -33	156.41 / 81.92	190.43 / 80.46	85.0 / -1.3	.LARO.$W100 / E 2	/ D GK	L 1	1.23 / 3.39	.16 / 3.39	1.17	ACKW
N4151	12 8.0 / 5.1	39 41 / -33	118.56 / 76.08	155.09 / 75.06	76.5 / 1.6	.SXT2*.W100 / P	S P GK / DSP G		1.52 / 7.86	.18 / 7.86	1.45	ABCLUW
N4152	12 8.1 / 5.1	16 19 / -33	233.32 / 76.10	260.39 / 75.42	98.6 / -5.9	.SXT5..W100 / S 5 N -*4*	S F / SD FG		1.27 / 5.71	.11 / 5.71	1.23	ACEKW
N4156	12 8.4 / 5.1	39 45 / -33	118.14 / 76.06	154.69 / 75.06	76.4 / 1.7	.SBT3..W100			1.14 / 6.06	.12 / 5.43	1.09	ABCLMUW
N4157	12 8.6 / 5.0	50 46 / -33	103.22 / 66.08	138.45 / 65.41	66.0 / 5.3	.SXS3$/W060 / S 4 3*	S FG / S F *		1.77 / 10.42	.66 / 10.42	1.51	ACHKYQ
N4158	12 8.6 / 5.1	20 27 / -33	221.42 / 79.39	247.83 / 78.45	94.7 / -4.5	.SAR3*.W100 / S 0	SD *FG		1.17 / 2.96	.05 / 2.96	1.15	ACKW
N4162	12 9.4 / 5.1	24 24 / -33	202.22 / 81.87	229.41 / 80.61	91.0 / -3.1	RSAT4..W100 / S 5 3	S F / S AF		1.33 / 4.96	.20 / 4.96	1.25	ACKW
N4163	12 9.5 / 5.1	36 28 / -33	126.41 / 78.82	163.21 / 77.66	79.6 / 0.9				1.16 / .91	.01 / .91	1.15	AH
N4165	12 9.7 / 5.1	13 31 / -33	240.05 / 73.87	267.59 / 73.36	101.4 / -6.4	.SXR1*$W060		S5	1.22 / 2.01	.23 / 2.01	1.13	ACXQ
N4168	12 9.8 / 5.1	13 29 / -33	240.18 / 73.85	267.73 / 73.35	101.5 / -6.4	.E.2...W060 / E 0	E2 K	E	1.13 / 5.23	.02 / 4.04	1.12	ACDEKSX / Q
N4178	12 10.2 / 5.1	11 9 / -33	243.83 / 71.78	271.84 / 71.37	103.7 / -7.0	.SBT8..W100 / SB5 3*	B AF / B AF	/ S6	1.69 / 13.85	.43 / 13.85	1.52	ACDEKNX / W
N4179	12 10.3 / 5.1	1 35 / -33	252.17 / 62.75	281.61 / 62.57	113.0 / -9.8	.L..../W060 / E 8	D K		1.39 / 6.14	.61 / 6.14	1.15	ACEKQ

NGC (IC, A)	Magnitudes				Colors				Velocities			Radio			
	m_H / m_c	B(O) w	B'(O) m'_c	S(B)	(B-V)(O) w	C_o(O)	S(C)	(U-B)(O) w	V w	V_o ΔV	S(V)	ϕ_r n	ϕ(21)		Photo.
(14)	(15)	(16)	(17)	(18)	(19)	(20)	(21)	(22)	(23)	(24)	(25)	(26)	(27)	(28)	(29)
N4102	12.1	12.67	13.91	BF					897	985	BC				
	12.33	3.42	13.57						6.4	89					
N4105	12.0	12.10	12.19	C	.98	.86	C		1895	1665	B				
	12.33	2.03	12.42		1.88				4.0	-230					
N4106	12.5	12.49	12.63	C	.97	.84	C		2178	1948	B				
	12.72	2.03	12.86		1.88				4.0	-230					
N4108										147					
N4108A										147					
N4108B										147					
N4109										46					
N4111	11.6	12.08	13.02	BG	.84	.74	G		794	841	ABC				KP
	11.86	2.59	12.80		2.50				50.3	47					
N4114										-189					
N4116	12.4	12.71	14.70	CG	.54	.45	CG		1304	1175	C				
	12.31	3.00	14.30		4.38				2.4	-129					
N4117										47					
N4118										47					
N4120										156					
N4121										139					
N4123	12.3	12.04	14.58	EG	.67		EG	-.05							
	11.89	3.97	14.43		15.00		/E			-128					
N4124	12.5	12.68	14.02	F											K
	12.32	1.27	13.66							-98					
N4125	11.3	11.36	12.55	B	.89	.81	B		1365	1504	BC				
	11.49	1.14	12.68		6.25				6.0	140					
N4128	12.9								2395	2548	C				
	12.95		13.19						2.4	153					
N4129	12.9														
	13.27		13.36							-171					
N4135										52					
N4136	12.1								445	434	B				
	11.76		14.35						4.0	-11					
N4137										52					
N4138	12.2	12.80	13.14	B					1039	1090	B				
	12.46	0.69	12.80						1.0	51					
N4142										92					
N4143	12.2	12.40	12.64	B					784	830	B				
	12.49	1.35	12.73						1.0	46					
N4144	12.4														
	12.29		14.18							63					
N4145	12.2														
	11.68		14.82							34					
N4146										-26					
N4150	12.6	12.83	13.37	C	.79	.72	C		244	236	B				P
	12.65	1.58	13.19		1.88				4.0	-8					
N4151	11.2	11.48	13.42	BE	.74*	.62	E	-.04*	957	989	ABCJ				K
	11.50	8.12	13.44		12.50		/E		260.6	32					
N4152	12.7	13.25	14.14	F											
	12.87	1.84	13.76							-72					
N4156		14.28	14.47	E	.76		E	.12*							
		2.29			12.50		/E			33					
N4157	12.0														
	11.80		14.09							81					
N4158	12.9														
	13.13		13.57							-54					
N4162	12.6								2546	2510	C				
	12.77		13.71						1.9	-36					
N4163										19					
N4165		14.72	15.11	G	.84		G								
		1.37			2.50					-83					
N4168	12.8	12.77	13.11	BEFG	.94		BEG	.39							
	12.77	7.71	13.11		15.00		/E			-83					
N4178	12.4	12.10	14.39	G	.50	.42	G		233	140	C				
	12.17	1.25	14.46		2.50				4.7	-93					
N4179	11.8	12.21	12.65	C	.91	.81	C		1279	1148	B				
	12.16	2.25	12.60		3.75				4.0	-131					

NGC (IC, A) (1)	RA (1950) 100 P / Dec 100 P (2,3)		L^I B^I (4)	L^{II} B^{II} (5)	SGL SGB (6)	Rev. type (S) DDO (T,L) (7)	Yerkes (1) Yerkes (2) (8)	Hu-San Ho (9)	log D w (10)	log R w (11)	log D(O) (12)	S (D,R) (13)
N4180	12 10.6	7 19	248.17	276.84	107.4				1.26	.21	1.18	AC
	5.1	-33	68.25	67.96	-8.1				1.26	1.26		
N4183	12 10.8	43 57	109.27	145.42	72.6	.SAS6$/W060	S *F *		1.69	.76	1.38	AKQ
	5.0	-33	72.58	71.75	3.5	S 6 7*			6.08	6.08		
N4186	12 11.6	15 1	238.97	266.04	100.1	.S....*R020			1.04	.13	.99	HLS
	5.1	-33	75.41	74.87	-5.5				2.44	1.91		
N4189	12 11.2	13 42	240.93	268.35	101.3	.SXT6$.W060	S AF	S5	1.34	.06	1.32	ACEHKSX
	5.1	-33	74.20	73.71	-6.0	S 5 3*			6.45	4.76		Q
N4190	12 11.1	36 54	123.74	160.74	79.3				1.16	.12	1.12	AHK
	5.0	-33	78.69	77.58	1.3	I			1.31	1.31		
N4192	12 11.3	15 11	238.40	265.45	99.9	.SXS2..W100	S FG	S4	1.91	.51	1.71	ABCEHKL
	5.1	-33	75.52	74.97	-5.5	S 3 T 2*	S G		24.41	24.41		SVXYW
N4193	12 11.3	13 27	241.41	268.88	101.6	.SXS5*$W060		S4	1.17	.22	1.08	ACHSVXQ
	5.1	-33	73.98	73.51	-6.1				4.12	3.88		
N4194	12 11.7	54 49	99.50	134.38	62.3	.LB..P.L036			1.13	.27	1.02	AC
	5.0	-33	62.34	61.75	7.0				.98	.98		
N4203	12 12.5	33 29	136.31	173.04	82.6	.LX.-*.W100	E3 K		1.33	.05	1.31	AKW
	5.0	-33	81.36	80.06	0.5	E P	D GK		4.93	4.93		
N4206	12 12.8	13 20	242.79	270.20	101.8	.SAS4..W100			1.65	.68	1.38	ABCHLRV
	5.1	-33	74.03	73.59	-5.8			S5	15.83	15.83		XW
N4210	12 12.8	66 16	94.69	128.74	51.2	.SBR3..W060	SB *F		1.25	.13	1.20	ACNQ
	4.8	-33	51.19	50.73	10.3				4.34	4.34		
N4212	12 13.1	14 11	241.69	268.88	101.0	.SAT4$.L036		S5	1.42	.21	1.34	ACDEFHK
	5.1	-33	74.83	74.36	-5.4	S 5 5	S F		11.12	11.12		LSX
N4214	12 13.1	36 36	123.04	160.30	79.7	.IXS9..P200	I A	I 9	1.84	.14	1.79	ACHKLSX
	5.0	-33	79.18	78.07	1.6	I 9 6	I A	I9	15.46	15.46		YZ
N4215	12 13.4	6 41	250.48	279.19	108.3	.LAR+*/W100		L 2	1.21	.48	1.02	ACEKW
	5.1	-33	67.86	67.63	-7.6	S 4 5*	D *K *		4.05	4.05		
N4216	12 13.4	13 25	243.15	270.50	101.8	.SXS3*.W100	S G	S 3	1.88	.67	1.61	ABCEHKL
	5.1	-33	74.17	73.73	-5.6	S 3 3		S3	28.39	28.39		RSVXYW
N4217	12 13.3	47 22	104.18	139.93	69.5	.S..3./W060	S *G *		1.70	.54	1.49	ABCHKYQ
	5.0	-33	69.55	68.85	5.0	S 3	S GK*		9.29	9.29		
N4218	12 13.5	48 25	103.16	138.77	68.5	.L....$R020			1.11	.20	1.03	ACHL
	5.0	-33	68.56	67.88	5.3				2.36	1.83		
N4219	12 13.8	-43 3	264.41	296.21	158.3	.SA.4*.S030			1.60	.47	1.41	I
	5.2	-33	18.92	19.09	-17.6				1.82	1.82		
N4219A	12 15.3	-43 14	264.72	296.52	158.5	.S....$.S030			1.14	.40	.98	I
	5.3	-33	18.77	18.94	-17.4				.98	.98		
N4220	12 13.7	48 10	103.29	138.94	68.7	.LAR+..W060	D *FG		1.47	.50	1.27	ACHKLQ
	5.0	-33	68.81	68.13	5.3	S 0*	SDP*FG*		8.07	8.07		
N4221	12 13.7	66 31	94.48	128.51	51.0	RLBR+..W060			1.27	.04	1.25	ANQ
	4.8	-33	50.96	50.50	10.5				3.97	3.97		
N4222	12 13.8	13 34	243.25	270.55	101.7	.S..7*/W100			1.52	.89	1.16	ABCHLRS
	5.1	-33	74.34	73.91	-5.5				15.63	14.54		VW
N4224	12 14.0	7 44	250.01	278.53	107.3	.SAS1*/W100		S1	1.39	.41	1.23	ACEKX
	5.1	-33	68.90	68.66	-7.1	S 0	DS *K *		3.73	3.73		
N4226	12 14.0	47 18	103.91	139.68	69.6	.S....$			1.12	.39	.97	ABCH
	5.0	-33	69.65	68.95	5.1				2.50	2.50		
N4231	12 14.5	47 46	103.27	138.99	69.1	.S....$			.98	.02	.97	ABCHL
	5.0	-33	69.23	68.55	5.3				2.34	1.90		
N4232	12 14.5	47 45	103.28	139.01	69.2	.S....$			1.11	.27	1.00	ABCHL
	5.0	-33	69.24	68.56	5.3				3.02	2.49		
N4233	12 14.6	7 54	250.26	278.74	107.2			L	1.31	.41	1.15	ACEKX
	5.1	-33	69.11	68.87	-6.9	E	D K *		2.35	2.35		
N4234	12 14.6	3 58	253.10	282.19	111.0	.I...$.			1.14	.03	1.13	ABCEK
	5.1	-33	65.33	65.17	-8.1	SB7 7	SI *A *		3.33	3.33		
N4235	12 14.6	7 28	250.62	279.18	107.6	.SAS1./W100	D *FG*	S1	1.60	.66	1.34	ABCDEKX
	5.1	-33	68.69	68.46	-7.1	S 0	D K		12.16	12.16		W
N4236	12 14.3	69 45	93.56	127.42	47.8	.SBS8..P200	BI *A		2.22	.46	2.04	ABHKLMR
	4.7	-33	47.78	47.35	11.4	SB7 7	BS A	S6	19.47	19.47		XY
N4237	12 14.7	15 36	240.58	267.26	99.8	.SXT4..W100		S 3	1.26	.18	1.19	ACDEHKW
	5.1	-33	76.27	75.77	-4.6	S	SD FG		6.50	6.50		
N4241	12 14.9	6 57	251.23	279.86	108.1				1.40	.33	1.26	ACX
	5.1	-33	68.22	68.01	-7.2			S1	1.55	1.55		
N4242	12 14.9	45 54	104.82	140.82	71.0	.SXS8..W060	I L*AF		1.64	.11	1.60	ACKNXYQ
	5.0	-33	71.03	70.31	4.8	S 6 7	SD *F	S6	9.77	9.77		
N4244	12 15.0	38 5	117.22	154.56	78.4	.SAS6*/P200	SI *AF	S 5	2.20	.91	1.84	ACHKLUX
	5.0	-33	78.16	77.16	2.4	S 6 7*	S *AF*	S6	25.63	25.63		YZ
N4245	12 15.2	29 53	158.46	192.49	86.2	.SBR0*.W100	B G		1.28	.12	1.23	AEHKW
	5.0	-33	83.65	82.18	-.1	SX4 5	B K		4.56	4.56		
N4246	12 15.3	7 28	251.08	279.62	107.6	.SAS5..W100			1.42	.22	1.33	ABCXW
	5.1	-33	68.75	68.53	-6.9			S5	5.78	5.78		
N4247	12 15.3	7 34	251.00	279.52	107.5	RSXS2P$W100			1.06	.16	1.00	BCW
	5.1	-33	68.84	68.62	-6.9				2.89	2.89		
N4248	12 15.3	47 42	102.97	138.72	69.3	.S.....R020			1.32	.52	1.11	ABCHLX
	5.0	-33	69.34	68.66	5.4			S.	4.22	4.22		
N4250	12 15.2	71 5	93.14	126.94	45.6	.LXR+..W060			1.38	.15	1.32	AQ
	4.7	-33	46.47	46.06	11.8				2.03	2.03		
N4251	12 15.7	28 27	171.38	202.94	87.6	.LB..$/W060			1.40	.45	1.22	ACDEHKN
	5.0	-33	84.06	82.57	-.4	E 7	D K		9.82	9.82		Q

NGC (IC, A) (14)	m_H / m_c (15)	B(O) w (16)	B'(O) m'_c (17)	S(B) (18)	(B-V)(O) w (19)	C_o(O) (20)	S(C) (21)	(U-B)(O) w (22)	V w (23)	V_o ΔV (24)	S(V) (25)	φ_r n (26)	φ(21) (27)	(28)	Photo. (29)
N4180										−108					
N4183	12.6 12.51		14.15							52					
N4186										−75					
N4189	13.0 12.89	12.96 2.14	14.25 14.18	FG	.78 2.50		G			−81					
N4190	13.2									21					
N4192	11.4 11.01	11.21 8.86	14.45 14.25	ACEFG	.85 15.00	.69	ACEG /E	.41	−124 6.3	−199 −75	B				B
N4193		13.53 0.86	13.67	G	.88 2.50		G			−82					
N4194									2585 4.3	2684 99	C				
N4203	12.0 12.02	11.80 3.35	13.04 13.26	C	.88 3.75	.82	C		1001 .4	1008 7	B				
N4206		13.00 1.27	14.59	G	.69 2.50		G			−82					B
N4210										145					
N4212	12.1 12.29	12.08 5.16	13.47 13.68	EFG	.67 8.75	.54	EG /E	.10	2125 2.4	2047 −78	C				B
N4214	10.7 10.40	10.38 5.66	14.07 14.09	BEFG	.45* 15.00	.39	BEG /E	−.27	290 415.7	311 21	ABCR				KP
N4215	12.8 13.04		12.83							−109					LP
N4216	11.3 11.19	11.17 8.11	13.96 13.98	ABDEF G	.93* 24.38	.75	BDEG /DE	.52	38 7.9	−43 −81	BC				BCP
N4217	11.9 11.81		13.95							69					
N4218										73					
N4219	12.7 12.43		14.22							−247					
N4219A										−247					
N4220	12.4 12.34	12.56 1.05	13.65 13.43	B					979 4.0	1051 72	B				BK
N4221										146					
N4222										−80					
N4224	13.0 12.96	13.21 1.15	14.05 13.80	G	1.11 2.50		G			−104					
N4226										69					
N4231										71					
N4232										71					
N4233	13.0 12.95	13.41 1.00	13.85 13.39	G	1.09 2.50		G			−103					
N4234	13.0 13.04	13.65 1.75	14.04 13.43	E	.63 6.25	.55	E /E	−.16	2143 2.0	2024 −119	D				
N4235	12.8 12.57	12.86 1.27	14.30 14.01	G	1.04 2.50		G			−105					
N4236	11.3 10.38	10.40 1.27	15.29 15.27	G	.41 2.50	.32	G			158	C*				
N4237	12.6 12.90	12.78 2.21	13.42 13.54	CF	.86 3.75		C			−71					P
N4241		13.32 1.15	14.36	G	1.05 2.50		G			−107					
N4242	11.8 11.67	11.96 2.98	14.65 14.36	FG	.53 2.50	.46	G		661 .8	724 63	D				
N4244	11.0 10.61	10.92 5.50	14.81 14.50	BCEFG	.51* 16.87	.38	BCEG /E	−.02	240 101.8	269 29	CR				ABLM P
N4245	12.3 12.51	12.57 5.18	13.46 13.40	BD	.89 28.13	.81	D /D	.37	890 2.4	882 −8	B				
N4246		13.60 1.35	14.94	G	.74 2.50		G			−104					
N4247										−104					
N4248				G*	.61 2.50		G			71					
N4250										163					
N4251	11.6 11.89	12.03 0.91	12.87 12.73	B					1014 1.8	1000 −14	B				

NGC (IC, A) (1)	RA (1950) 100 P (2)	Dec 100 P (3)	L^I B^I (4)	L^{II} B^{II} (5)	SGL SGB (6)	Rev. type (S) DDO (T, L) (7)	Yerkes (1) Yerkes (2) (8)	Hu-San Ho (9)	log D w (10)	log R w (11)	log D(0) (12)	S (D,R) (13)
N4252	12 15.9	5 51	252.64	281.44	109.2	.S.....*			1.26	.57	1.03	ACL
	5.1	-33	67.24	67.06	-7.2				1.97	1.28		
N4253	12 16.0	30 7	155.93	190.46	86.1				.97	.14	.91	AHLS
	5.0	-33	83.74	82.28	0.1				2.28	1.83		
N4254	12 16.3	14 42	243.60	270.43	100.8	.SAS5..P200	S F	S 5	1.72	.04	1.70	ACEFHKL
	5.1	-33	75.63	75.20	-4.5	S 5 1	S FG	S5	15.03	13.69		VXY
N4256	12 16.4	66 11	94.15	128.21	51.4	.SAS3*/W060	S GK		1.64	.75	1.34	ACKNQ
	4.8	-33	51.33	50.89	10.7	S 3*			7.72	7.72		
N4257	12 16.6	6 1	252.98	281.74	109.1	.S...*/L036			1.12	.54	.90	ACLN
	5.1	-33	67.44	67.27	-7.0				2.91	2.35		
N4258	12 16.5	47 35	102.52	138.31	69.4	.SXS4......	S G	S 3	2.27	.39	2.11	ABCHKLU
	4.9	-33	69.51	68.84	5.6	S 4PT -*	S G	S4	19.34	19.34		XY
N4259	12 16.8	5 39	253.35	282.16	109.5	.L.....W			1.04	.22	.95	ABCX
	5.1	-33	67.10	66.94	-7.1			L	.87	.87		
N4260	12 16.8	6 23	252.85	281.55	108.8	.SBS1..W100	B GK		1.38	.31	1.26	ACDEKNW
	5.1	-33	67.81	67.64	-6.9	SB2 5*	B G		10.01	10.01		
N4261	12 16.8	6 6	253.05	281.79	109.1	.E.2+..W100	E3 K		1.35	.09	1.31	ACEKLNW
	5.1	-33	67.53	67.37	-6.9	E 2	DE K		6.95	6.16		
N4262	12 17.0	15 9	243.49	270.13	100.4	.LBS-$.P200		LB2+	1.12	.03	1.11	ACDEHK
	5.1	-33	76.11	75.67	-4.2	E 1	B K		4.33	4.33		
N4264	12 17.0	6 7	253.16	281.90	109.1	.LBT+..W100			.92	.04	.90	ACLNW
	5.1	-33	67.56	67.40	-6.9				2.81	2.81		
N4266	12 17.1	5 50	253.41	282.19	109.3	.S..../W060			1.32	.74	1.02	ACLU
	5.1	-33	67.29	67.14	-7.0				3.88	3.11		
N4267	12 17.2	13 3	246.80	274.05	102.4	.LBS-$.W100			1.38	.06	1.35	ADEW
	5.1	-33	74.18	73.84	-4.8	E 2	D GK		5.10	5.10		
N4268	12 17.2	5 34	253.65	282.47	109.6	.L...*/W060			1.22	.50	1.02	ABCLUX
	5.1	-33	67.04	66.89	-7.0			L	4.20	3.57		
N4269	12 17.3	6 18	253.23	281.93	108.9	.L...*/L036			.85	.08	.82	AN
	5.1	-33	67.76	67.60	-6.8				1.31	1.31		
N4270	12 17.3	5 44	253.60	282.39	109.5	.L.....W060			1.24	.43	1.07	ABCDEKL
	5.1	-33	67.21	67.06	-6.9	S 0	D K	L	7.42	7.42		UX
N4273	12 17.4	5 37	253.74	282.55	109.6	.SBS5..W060	SB *F		1.33	.17	1.26	ABCDEKL
	5.1	-33	67.10	66.96	-6.9	S 5 KT 5*	SD FG	S5	8.31	8.31		UX
N4274	12 17.4	29 53	157.00	191.43	86.4	RSBR2..P200	SDP*G	S 1	1.73	.43	1.55	AEHKLSU
	5.0	-33	84.10	82.64	0.3	S 4 4	DS GK	S1	17.08	17.08		XYZ
N4277	12 17.6	5 37	253.86	282.67	109.6				.92	.01	.91	ABCLX
	5.1	-33	67.12	66.97	-6.9			S.	1.12	1.12		
N4278	12 17.7	29 34	159.76	193.67	86.7	.E.1+..P200	E1 K	E 1	1.28	.04	1.26	ABEHKLS
	5.0	-33	84.27	82.79	0.3	E 1	DE K	E	7.75	7.12		UX
N4281	12 17.8	5 40	253.95	282.75	109.6	.L..+*/W060			1.34	.37	1.20	ABCDEKL
	5.1	-33	67.18	67.03	-6.8	E 5	E6 K	L	8.50	8.50		UXY
N4283	12 17.9	29 35	159.47	193.45	86.7	.E.0...P200	E1 K		.94	.03	.93	ABEHKLS
	5.0	-33	84.30	82.83	0.4	E 0	E1 K	E	3.83	3.83		X
N4286	12 18.2	29 38	158.78	192.92	86.7	.SARO*.P200			1.14	.12	1.09	AHLSU
	5.0	-33	84.35	82.88	0.4				4.31	3.68		
N4288	12 18.2	46 34	102.54	138.53	70.5	.S.....R020			1.24	.10	1.20	ABH
	4.9	-33	70.56	69.89	5.5				2.68	2.68		
N4290	12 18.5	58 22	96.05	130.67	59.1	.SBT2*.W060	B F		1.33	.18	1.26	ABCKQ
	4.8	-33	59.08	58.58	8.9	SB3 N -*3			4.05	4.05		
N4291	12 18.1	75 40	91.97	125.55	42.0	.E.2+..L036	E3 K		.98	.08	.95	AKM
	4.4	-33	41.96	41.58	13.0	E 1	E4 K		1.94	1.94		
N4292	12 18.7	4 52	254.98	283.89	110.4	.S.....			1.20	.29	1.08	ABCL
	5.1	-33	66.46	66.34	-6.8				2.58	1.95		
N4293	12 18.7	18 40	237.65	262.85	97.1	RSBS0..W100	S *FG*	S 1	1.66	.40	1.50	ACDEHKW
	5.1	-33	79.43	78.83	-2.8	P	SDP G *		12.27	12.27		
N4294	12 18.7	11 47	249.54	277.06	103.7	.SBS6..L036			1.47	.39	1.32	ABCEKNX
	5.1	-33	73.11	72.84	-4.8	SX5 K *6*	SB A	S5	6.89	6.89		
N4298	12 19.0	14 53	245.77	272.36	100.8	.SAT5..W100	SI *AF		1.47	.27	1.36	ABCDEFH
	5.1	-33	76.05	75.67	-3.9	S KT+	SD AF	S5	11.04	11.04		KNX
N4299	12 19.2	11 47	249.94	277.44	103.8	.SB.7P$L036			1.21	.03	1.20	ABCKNX
	5.1	-33	73.15	72.89	-4.7	S K 7*		S6	4.16	4.16		
N4301	12 19.9	4 50	255.74	284.63	110.5	.SB.6*.W			1.13	.07	1.10	ACLUX
	5.1	-33	66.49	66.39	-6.6			S6	2.96	2.33		
N4302	12 19.2	14 53	245.95	272.53	100.8	.S..5*/W100	S F		1.73	.74	1.44	ABCHKNX
	5.1	-33	76.07	75.69	-3.8	S 5		S.	11.48	11.48		W
N4303	12 19.4	4 45	255.48	284.40	110.6	.SXT4..P200	S F	S 5	1.74	.04	1.73	ABCEFHK
	5.1	-33	66.38	66.28	-6.7	S 5 1	S F	S5	19.83	18.29		LUXYZ
N4304	12 19.6	-33 12	264.49	295.97	148.3	.S.....H030			1.27	.01	1.26	EG
	5.2	-33	28.83	29.00	-15.3				1.28	1.28		
N4305	12 19.5	13 1	248.78	275.93	102.6				1.32	.26	1.22	ABC
	5.1	-33	74.34	74.05	-4.3				2.34*	2.34		
N4306	12 19.5	13 4	248.72	275.85	102.6				1.09	.00	1.09	ABC
	5.1	-33	74.39	74.10	-4.3				1.57	1.57		
N4307	12 19.5	9 20	252.46	280.54	106.1				1.55	.67	1.28	BCEK
	5.1	-33	70.83	70.64	-5.4	S 2 4	SD G *		4.63	4.63		
N4309	12 19.7	7 25	254.03	282.49	108.0	.LXR+..W100			1.25	.31	1.13	BC
	5.1	-33	68.99	68.84	-5.9				1.22	1.22		
N4310	12 20.0	29 29	158.93	193.15	86.9				1.15	.23	1.05	AH
	5.0	-33	84.77	83.29	0.8				1.22	1.22		

NGC (IC, A) (14)	Magnitudes				Colors				Velocities			Radio			
	m_H / m_C (15)	B(O) / w (16)	B'(O) / m'_C (17)	S(B) (18)	(B-V)(O) / w (19)	C_o(O) (20)	S(C) (21)	(U-B)(O) / w (22)	V / w (23)	V_o / ΔV (24)	S(V) (25)	ϕ_r / n (26)	ϕ(21) (27)	(28)	Photo. (29)
N4252										-111					
N4253										-6					
N4254	10.5 / 10.60	10.52 / 13.09	13.76 / 13.84	ABEFG H	.58 / 22.50	.48	ABEGH /E	-.03	2471 / 7.0	2397 / -74	BC				AKP
N4256	13.0 / 12.73		/ 14.17						2583 / 1.6	2728 / 145	C				
N4257										-109					
N4258	10.2 / 9.47	9.19 / 6.23	14.48 / 14.76	BCEFG	.70 / 10.63	.57	CEG /E	.08	459 / 11.3	530 / 71	ABF				ABMP
N4259		14.71 / 3.52	14.15	AG	1.00 / 2.50		G			-111					
N4260	12.7 / 12.70		13.74						1935 / 1.6	1827 / -108	D				
N4261	11.7 / 11.72	11.84 / 8.42	13.13 / 13.01	ABF	.97 / 4.38	.89	A		2202 / 1.8	2093 / -109	B				
N4262	12.6 / 12.74	12.67 / 9.02	12.96 / 13.03	CFH	.96 / 10.00		CH			-71					LP
N4264		13.99 / 2.34	13.23	A						-109					
N4266										-110					B
N4267	12.6 / 12.33	12.17 / 10.77	13.66 / 13.82	BFH	.95 / 12.50	.88	H		1260 / 1.8	1180 / -80	B				
N4268		13.82 / 2.77	13.66	AG	1.10 / 2.50		G			-111					
N4269										-108					
N4270	12.8 / 12.96	13.26 / 4.94	13.30 / 13.00	ABG	.88 / 6.87	.77	AG		2347 / 4.0	2237 / -110	B				
N4273	12.2 / 12.53	12.51 / 5.88	13.55 / 13.57	ACG	.46* / 10.63	.34	ACG		2302 / 6.3	2192 / -111	B				
N4274	11.7 / 11.52	11.50 / 9.62	13.99 / 14.01	CDFG	.94 / 23.12	.78	CDG /D	.44	767 / .4	761 / -6	B				BP
N4277			G*		1.03 / 2.50		G			-110					
N4278	11.6 / 11.74	11.58 / 14.43	12.62 / 12.78	BDFG	.93 / 46.25	.88	BDG /D	.48	630 / 6.8	622 / -8	BE				P
N4281	12.2 / 12.34	12.41 / 3.79	13.10 / 13.03	ACG	.96 / 8.75	.85	ACG		2602 / 4.0	2492 / -110	B				
N4283	12.8 / 13.09	13.42 / 5.95	12.81 / 12.48	BDFG	.92 / 18.13	.86	BDG /D	.56	1085 / 2.9	1078 / -7	BE				
N4286										-7					
N4288										67					
N4290	12.7 / 12.75		13.74							116					
N4291	12.5 / 12.88	12.83 / 0.86	12.27 / 12.32	B					1815 / 5.4	1994 / 178	BC				
N4292										-113					
N4293	11.7 / 11.59	11.70 / 2.10	13.89 / 13.78	AF					750 / 1.8	695 / -55	C				P
N4294	13.0 / 12.89	12.67 / 2.63	13.96 / 14.18	FG	.54 / 2.50	.44	G		390 / 1.4	306 / -84	D				
N4298	12.5 / 12.46	12.34 / 0.93	13.88 / 14.00	G	.71 / 2.50		G			-71					
N4299	13.1 / 13.27	13.06 / 1.87	13.80 / 14.01	FG	.42 / 2.50	.36	G		187 / 2.4	103 / -84	D				
N4301		13.71 / 0.98	13.95	G	.44 / 2.50		G			-112					
N4302	13.2 / 12.68	12.76 / 1.12	14.65 / 14.57	G	.91 / 2.50		G			-71					
N4303	10.4 / 10.45	10.28 / 10.15	13.67 / 13.84	ACFG	.59 / 10.63	.50	ACG		1671 / .4	1559 / -113	B				ALP
N4304	12.4 / 12.69		13.73							-229					
N4305										-79					
N4306										-78					
N4307	13.0 / 12.87		14.01							-94					
N4309										-102					
N4310										-7					

NGC (IC, A) (1)	RA (1950) 100 P (2)	Dec 100 P (3)	L^I B^I (4)	L^II B^II (5)	SGL SGB (6)	Rev. type (S) DDO (T, L) (7)	Yerkes (1) Yerkes (2) (8)	Hu-San Ho (9)	log D w (10)	log R w (11)	log D(O) (12)	S (D,R) (13)
N4312	12 20.0	15 49	245.20	271.39	100.0	.S..0*.L036			1.53	.58	1.29	ABCHLSX
	5.1	−33	77.01	76.61	−3.4			S.	6.64	6.64		
N4313	12 20.1	12 4	250.36	277.76	103.6	.SA.2*/L036			1.56	.55	1.34	ABCN
	5.1	−33	73.49	73.24	−4.4				5.63	5.63		
N4314	12 20.0	30 10	152.18	187.75	86.3	.SBT1..P200	BP	SBS1P	1.57	.07	1.55	AEHKNZ
	5.0	−33	84.52	83.07	1.0	SB0	B K		12.43	10.21		
N4319	12 19.8	75 36	91.84	125.42	42.1	.SBT2*.L036	B G		1.42	.09	1.38	AMU
	4.4	−33	42.04	41.66	13.1				4.13	4.13		
N4321	12 20.4	16 6	245.11	271.15	99.7	.SXS4..P200	S FG	S 5	1.80	.03	1.79	ABCEHKL
	5.1	−33	77.30	76.90	−3.2	S 5 1	S FG	S5	16.27	14.86		SUXY
N4322	12 20.4	16 10	244.99	271.01	99.7	.L.....*W						
	5.1	−33	77.37	76.96	−3.2							
N4324	12 20.6	5 31	255.79	284.57	109.9	.LAR+..W100	SDP*GK		1.28	.34	1.15	ABCDEKW
	5.1	−33	67.19	67.10	−6.2	S 4 5*	D G		8.06	8.06		
N4326	12 20.6	6 21	255.31	283.95	109.1	.SXR2$.W100			1.30	.00	1.30	A
	5.1	−33	68.00	67.90	−6.0				.18	.18		
N4329	12 20.8	−12 15	261.75	292.30	127.3	.E.5...B060			1.27	.20	1.19	CP
	5.2	−33	49.68	49.76	−10.8				2.34	2.34		
N4332	12 20.5	66 8	93.50	127.57	51.5	.SBS1..W060			1.29	.24	1.19	AC
	4.7	−33	51.44	51.01	11.1				.85	.85		
N4333	12 20.8	6 19	255.46	284.10	109.1	.SBS2..W100			.97	.11	.92	AC
	5.1	−33	67.98	67.88	−5.9				.69	.69		
N4334	12 20.8	7 45	254.55	282.93	107.8	.LB..*.L036			1.33	.39	1.17	ACN
	5.1	−33	69.38	69.25	−5.5				3.12	3.12		
N4339	12 21.0	6 22	255.56	284.19	109.1	.E.0...W100	E1 K		1.15	.01	1.15	ACDEKW
	5.1	−33	68.04	67.94	−5.9	E 0	D K		4.27	4.27		
N4340	12 21.0	17 0	244.05	269.68	98.9	.LBR+..W060	B *K		1.49	.11	1.44	ABCEKLS
	5.1	−33	78.19	77.75	−2.8	SB0	B GK		9.79	9.79		Q
N4341	12 21.3	7 23	255.13	283.57	108.1	.S...*/L036	E4 K		1.03	.41	.86	CNX
	5.1	−33	69.05	68.93	−5.5			L	1.42	1.42		
N4342	12 21.1	7 22	255.01	283.45	108.2	.L..-./W100	E1 *K		1.00	.32	.88	ACDENXW
	5.1	−33	69.02	68.90	−5.6			E	5.21	5.21		
N4343	12 21.1	7 16	255.07	283.54	108.2	.SAT3*.W100	S GK		1.41	.63	1.16	ACKNXW
	5.1	−33	68.92	68.81	−5.6	S 0*	SD GK	S1	7.98	7.98		
N4344	12 21.1	17 49	242.43	267.68	98.1				1.18	.08	1.15	ABCH
	5.1	−33	78.94	78.47	−2.5				1.61	1.61		
N4346	12 21.0	47 16	100.64	136.59	70.0	.L..../W100	D K		1.36	.45	1.18	ACHKW
	4.9	−33	70.01	69.39	6.2	E 6	D K		5.27	5.27		
N4348	12 21.3	−3 10	259.74	289.60	118.4				1.47	.59	1.23	ACK
	5.1	−33	58.69	58.71	−8.4	S 3 4*			3.23	3.23		
N4350	12 21.4	16 58	244.55	270.14	99.0	.LA.../W060	D GK		1.37	.50	1.17	ABCEHKL
	5.1	−33	78.19	77.77	−2.7	E 7			9.87	9.87		SQ
N4351	12 21.5	12 29	251.09	278.31	103.3	.SAS2*.L036			1.25	.21	1.16	ACHN
	5.1	−33	73.99	73.75	−4.0				3.00	3.00		
N4352	12 21.5	11 29	252.09	279.59	104.2				1.29	.48	1.10	AC
	5.1	−33	73.03	72.82	−4.3				1.32	1.32		
N4353	12 21.6	8 5	254.88	283.18	107.5	.I...$.L036			1.09	.20	1.01	CN
	5.1	−33	69.75	69.62	−5.2				1.58	1.58		
N4359	12 21.7	31 47	136.67	174.90	84.8				1.53	.70	1.25	A
	5.0	−33	83.94	82.63	1.8				1.31	1.31		
N4361	12 22.0	−18 30	263.25	294.14	133.5	.S.....H030			1.35	.02	1.34	AU
	5.2	−33	43.51	43.64	−12.0				2.78	2.78		
N4363	12 21.3	75 13	91.77	125.37	42.5				1.10	.00	1.10	A
	4.3	−33	42.43	42.06	13.1				.66	.66		
N4365	12 22.0	7 36	255.47	283.85	108.0	.E.3...P200	E4 K		1.56	.16	1.49	ACDEKNZ
	5.1	−33	69.30	69.19	−5.3	E 2	E4 K		11.16	11.16		
N4369	12 22.1	39 39	108.12	145.79	77.3	RSAT1..W100	S P*AF*		1.14	.03	1.13	ACKQ
	4.9	−33	77.35	76.54	4.2	S 0	D G		3.63	3.63		
N4370	12 22.4	7 43	255.67	284.03	107.9	.SA.1./L036			1.12	.22	1.03	ACN
	5.1	−33	69.44	69.33	−5.2				2.33	2.33		
N4371	12 22.4	11 59	252.35	279.68	103.8	.LBR+..P200			1.39	.17	1.32	ACDEKXY
	5.1	−33	73.57	73.37	−3.9	SB0	B K	L	4.64	4.64		
N4373	12 22.7	−39 28	265.81	297.49	154.8	.E.3+..S030			1.26	.17	1.19	I
	5.3	−33	22.65	22.85	−15.6				.83	.83		
N4373A	12 22.8	−39 2	265.79	297.46	154.4	.S....*.S030			1.26	.58	1.03	I
	5.3	−33	23.08	23.29	−15.5				1.16	1.16		
N4373B	12 24.0	−38 51	266.03	297.69	154.2	.S..7*.S030			1.09	.04	1.08	I
	5.3	−33	23.28	23.49	−15.2				.91	.91		
N4374	12 22.6	13 10	251.30	278.26	102.7	.E+1...P200	E2P		1.41	.08	1.38	ABCDEHK
	5.1	−33	74.72	74.49	−3.5	E 1	E1 K	L	14.21	14.21		LNSXYZ
N4375	12 22.2	28 50	164.81	197.80	87.7	.S..1.*W			1.14	.04	1.12	AC
	5.0	−33	85.41	83.92	1.0				1.04	1.04		
N4377	12 22.7	15 2	249.07	275.37	100.9	.LA.-..W060	D K		1.10	.08	1.06	AEKQ
	5.1	−33	76.50	76.21	−3.0	E 1	D K		2.89	2.89		
N4378	12 22.8	5 12	257.34	286.14	110.4	RSAS1..W100	SD *GK	S 1	1.46	.04	1.44	ACDEKW
	5.1	−33	66.99	66.94	−5.8	S N +	S K		8.88	8.88		
N4379	12 22.8	15 53	247.91	273.86	100.1				1.08	.05	1.06	AEHK
	5.1	−33	77.31	76.98	−2.7	E 1	D K		1.90	1.90		
N4380	12 22.9	10 17	254.23	282.01	105.5	.SAT3*$W060			1.56	.27	1.45	ACDEKQ
	5.1	−33	71.96	71.81	−4.3	S N +	SD FG		7.73	7.73		

NGC (IC, A) (14)	m_H m_c (15)	B(O) w (16)	B'(O) m'_c (17)	S(B) (18)	(B-V)(O) w (19)	C_o(O) (20)	S(C) (21)	(U-B)(O) w (22)	V w (23)	V_o ΔV (24)	S(V) (25)	φ_r n (26)	φ(21) (27)	(28)	Photo. (29)
N4312		12.93	14.12	G	.82		G								B
		0.98			2.50					−66					
N4313															
										−82					
N4314	11.7	11.61	14.05	C	.85	.77	C		883	879	B				P
	11.52	3.48	13.96		3.75				1.4	−4					
N4319															
										178					
N4321	10.8	10.26	13.95	ABEFG	.70*	.62	ABEGH	−.01	1617	1552	B				AKP
	10.53	13.83	14.22	H	21.88		/E		1.8	−65					
N4322				B*			B*								
										−65					
N4324	12.5								1714	1605	B				
	12.62		13.06						4.0	−109					
N4326															
										−105					
N4329															
										−173					
N4332															
										146					
N4333															
										−105					
N4334															
										−100					
N4339	12.6	12.83	13.32	B	.90	.83	B		1278	1173	B				
	12.59	3.46	13.08		6.25				1.0	−105					
N4340	13.0	12.25	14.19	FH	.99		H								
	12.44	3.47	14.38		3.13					−61					
N4341		14.66	13.70	G	.97		G								
		0.76			2.50					−101					
N4342	12.8	13.91	13.05	G	.98	.90	G		714	613	B				
	13.26	0.88	12.40		2.50				4.0	−101					
N4343		13.66	14.20	G	1.02		G								
		0.93			2.50					−101					
N4344															
										−57					
N4346	12.4														
	12.49		13.13							72					
N4348	13.1														
	13.04		13.93							−142					
N4350	12.0	12.30	12.89	CFH	.90	.80	CH		1184	1123	B				
	12.24	3.40	12.83		4.38				2.8	−61					
N4351															
										−80					
N4352															
										−84					
N4353															
										−98					
N4359															
										5					
N4361															
										−192					
N4363															
										177					
N4365	11.0	11.18	13.37	BF	.95	.88	B		1183	1083	BC				
	10.95	5.39	13.14		6.25				12.3	−99					
N4369	12.4														
	12.84		13.23							39					
N4370															
										−99					
N4371	12.1	12.25	13.59	FG	1.01		G								
	12.05	1.56	13.39		2.50					−81					
N4373	12.2														
	12.27		12.91							−238					
N4373A															
										−237					
N4373B															
										−236					
N4374	10.9	10.82	12.41	ABCDE	.98	.92	ABCDE	.56	954	878	B				
	11.09	17.10	12.68	FGH	35.63		GH/DE		4.0	−76					
N4375															
										−8					
N4377	12.9	13.20	13.24	F											
	13.02	1.17	13.06							−68					
N4378	12.8														P
	12.34		14.28							−108					
N4379	13.0	12.77	12.81	C	.98		C								
	13.09	1.98	13.13		1.88					−66					
N4380	12.8														
	12.37		14.36							−88					

NGC (IC, A) (1)	RA (1950) Dec 100 P (2)	100 P (3)	L^I B^I (4)	L^{II} B^{II} (5)	SGL SGB (6)	Rev. type (S) DDO (T, L) (7)	Yerkes (1) Yerkes (2) (8)	Hu-San Ho (9)	log D w (10)	log R w (11)	log D(0) (12)	S (D,R) (13)
N4382	12 22.8	18 28	242.92	267.64	97.6	.LAS+P.P200	D GK		1.66	.15	1.60	ABCDEHK
	5.0	−33	79.70	79.23	−1.9	E P	D GK	L	20.59	20.59		LSUXYZ
N4383	12 23.0	16 45	246.68	272.22	99.3	.L....*			1.19	.27	1.09	ACDEHKL
	5.1	−33	78.14	77.77	−2.4	E P *	I P K *		5.77	5.77		S
N4385	12 23.1	0 50	259.34	288.76	114.6	.LBT+*.W060	B *FG		1.24	.18	1.17	ACEKQ
	5.1	−33	62.71	62.72	−6.9	SB2 4	BS G		3.91	3.91		
N4386	12 22.4	75 48	91.59	125.17	41.9	.E.6.*.L036			1.19	.35	1.05	AKMU
	4.3	−33	41.86	41.49	13.3	S 0*	D GK		4.18	4.18		
N4387	12 23.2	13 5	251.92	278.89	102.8	.E+3.*.L036			1.00	.22	.91	ACHLRS
	5.1	−33	74.68	74.47	−3.4				3.90	3.90		
N4388	12 23.3	12 56	252.17	279.18	103.0	.SB.5./L036			1.66	.66	1.39	ABCDEHK
	5.1	−33	74.55	74.34	−3.4	S 3 N	SD GK*	S.	18.74	16.22		LRSUX
N4389	12 23.1	45 58	100.51	136.74	71.3	.SBT.P.W060	BIP*AF		1.36	.26	1.25	ACHKLQ
	4.9	−33	71.36	70.74	6.2	SB6 7*	I P A *		6.12	6.12		
N4390	12 23.3	10 44	254.19	281.84	105.1				1.32	.17	1.26	AC
	5.1	−33	72.42	72.27	−4.1				1.38	1.38		
N4391	12 23.0	65 13	93.28	127.42	52.5	.SB..$.						
	4.6	−33	52.38	51.96	11.1							
N4394	12 23.4	18 29	243.61	268.23	97.7	RSBR3..P200	B G	SBT3	1.54	.06	1.51	ABCDEKL
	5.0	−33	79.77	79.32	−1.8	SB2 3	B G	S3	16.82	16.82		SUXZ
N4395	12 23.4	33 49	122.65	162.05	83.0	.SAS9*.W060	S A	S 9	2.09	.08	2.06	ACHKLRX
	5.0	−33	82.66	81.55	2.7	S 7 8	S A	S6	19.83	18.94		Q
N4396	12 23.5	15 57	248.53	274.40	100.1				1.53	.55	1.31	BCH
	5.1	−33	77.43	77.12	−2.5				2.15	2.15		
N4402	12 23.6	13 24	251.94	278.78	102.5	.S...*/P200			1.58	.57	1.35	ABCHLRU
	5.1	−33	75.01	74.80	−3.2			S.	13.68	13.68		XZ
N4405	12 23.6	16 27	247.82	273.45	99.6	.S....$R020			1.32	.23	1.23	ACH
	5.1	−33	77.92	77.58	−2.3				1.58	1.58		
N4406	12 23.7	13 13	252.22	279.13	102.7	.E+3...P200	E2 K	E 3	1.53	.16	1.47	ABCDEHK
	5.1	−33	74.84	74.63	−3.3	E 3	E2 K	E	16.24	13.72		LRSXYZ
N4410A	12 23.9	9 18	255.71	283.70	106.5				1.19	.31	1.07	AC
	5.1	−33	71.06	70.96	−4.3			S.	1.12	1.12		
N4410B	12 23.9	9 18	255.71	283.70	106.5							
	5.1	−33	71.06	70.96	−4.3			S.				
N4411A	12 24.0	9 9	255.88	283.91	106.6							
	5.1	−33	70.92	70.82	−4.4			S6				
N4411B	12 24.3	9 9	256.10	284.12	106.7							
	5.1	−33	70.94	70.84	−4.3			S6				
N4412	12 24.0	4 14	258.52	287.47	111.4	.SBR.P.W100	BS *A		1.11	.04	1.09	ACDEKW
	5.1	−33	66.10	66.08	−5.8	SX P	IS AF		5.60	5.60		
N4413	12 24.0	12 53	252.83	279.83	103.1	.SB.2*.L036			1.31	.15	1.25	ABCH
	5.1	−33	74.54	74.35	−3.3				2.51	2.51		
N4414	12 24.0	31 30	135.57	174.50	85.3	.SAT5$.W100	S FG		1.51	.24	1.41	ACKLSUY
	5.0	−33	84.49	83.19	2.2	S 5 NK 3*	SD F		10.21	10.21		W
N4417	12 24.3	9 52	255.62	283.46	106.0	.LBS.*.L036			1.41	.50	1.21	ACDEKNX
	5.1	−33	71.64	71.53	−4.1	E 7	D K	L	7.40	7.40		
N4419	12 24.4	15 19	250.37	276.45	100.8	.SBS1./W060	S G		1.44	.49	1.25	ACDEHKQ
	5.1	−33	76.90	76.63	−2.5	E P	SD GK		8.27	8.27		
N4420	12 24.4	2 46	259.36	288.51	112.8	.SBR4*.W100	SI *A		1.28	.32	1.15	ACEKLW
	5.1	−33	64.67	64.67	−6.1	S 5 K 5*	S F *		6.52	6.52		
N4421	12 24.5	15 44	249.90	275.79	100.4	.SB.1*.W			1.29	.09	1.25	ACH
	5.1	−33	77.31	77.02	−2.3				1.08	1.08		
N4424	12 24.6	9 42	255.96	283.84	106.2	.SBS1*.L036			1.49	.30	1.37	ACDEKNS
	5.1	−33	71.49	71.39	−4.1	S 3 N 5*	IS G	S.	10.22	7.32		X
N4425	12 24.7	13 1	253.32	280.25	103.0	.L...*/L036			1.38	.51	1.17	ABCHKLR
	5.1	−33	74.72	74.54	−3.1	S 2 5*		S.	9.04	9.04		SX
N4428	12 24.9	−7 54	262.51	292.76	123.2	.SXT5..P200			1.27	.34	1.13	ABCKZ
	5.2	−33	54.12	54.22	−8.8	S 5 K 5*			6.35	6.35		
N4429	12 24.9	11 23	254.95	282.38	104.6	.LAR+..P200	SDP*FG		1.57	.39	1.42	ACEKLSX
	5.1	−33	73.15	73.01	−3.5		D K	L	12.67	12.67		YZ
N4431	12 24.9	12 34	253.93	281.00	103.4	.L...$.W100			1.12	.11	1.08	ABC
	5.1	−33	74.29	74.13	−3.2				1.66	1.66		
N4433	12 25.0	−8 1	262.58	292.83	123.3	.SXS2..P200		S 3	1.28	.36	1.13	ABCEKZ
	5.2	−33	54.01	54.11	−8.8	S	S F		7.09	7.09		
N4435	12 25.2	13 21	253.44	280.24	102.7	.LBS0..W100	DB *K		1.21	.20	1.13	ABCDEHK
	5.1	−33	75.07	74.89	−2.9	E 4	DE K	L	7.10	7.10		XYW
N4436	12 25.2	12 36	254.16	281.21	103.4	.L.....W100			1.06	.44	.89	ABCW
	5.1	−33	74.35	74.19	−3.1				3.52	2.77		
N4438	12 25.3	13 17	253.60	280.41	102.8	.SASOP*W100	I P G *		1.85	.40	1.69	ABCDEHX
	5.1	−33	75.01	74.84	−2.9	S NT+	I GK	S1P	13.15	13.15		W
N4440	12 25.4	12 34	254.36	281.42	103.5	.SBT1..W100			1.25	.14	1.20	ABCW
	5.1	−33	74.33	74.17	−3.1				4.61	4.61		
N4441	12 25.1	65 5	92.95	127.10	52.7							
	4.6	−33	52.54	52.13	11.3							
N4442	12 25.6	10 5	256.47	284.23	105.9	.LBS0..W060	D *K		1.50	.42	1.33	ACDEKNX
	5.1	−33	71.92	71.83	−3.7	E 5P	D K	L	10.82	10.82		YQ
N4445	12 25.7	9 42	256.80	284.66	106.2	.SB.0*/L036			1.38	.74	1.09	ACNX
	5.1	−33	71.55	71.47	−3.8			S.	2.46	2.46		
N4448	12 25.8	28 54	161.21	195.30	87.9	.SBR2..W100	SD *G		1.54	.44	1.36	ACEKLSW
	5.0	−33	86.15	84.67	1.8	S 2 4	SD K		11.37	11.37		

NGC (IC, A) (14)	Magnitudes				Colors				Velocities			Radio			
	m_H m_c (15)	B(O) w (16)	B'(O) m'_c (17)	S(B) (18)	(B-V)(O) w (19)	C_o(O) (20)	S(C) (21)	(U-B)(O) w (22)	V w (23)	V_o ΔV (24)	S(V) (25)	ϕ_r n (26)	ϕ(21) (27)	(28)	Photo. (29)
N4382	10.5 10.52	10.43 6.49	13.17 13.26	ABFG	.88 8.75	.81	BG		765 11.6	712 -53	AB				
N4383	12.9 12.90		13.04							-60					
N4385	12.9 12.85		13.39							-125					
N4386	12.8 12.89		12.88						1811 2.4	1990 179	C				
N4387		13.42 7.41	12.71	AB	.92 6.25	.86	B		511 2.4	435 -76	B				
N4388	12.2 12.23	12.69 1.34	14.38 13.92	GH	.70 5.63		GH			-76					B
N4389	12.8 12.97		13.96							67					
N4390										-86					
N4391										144					
N4394	12.2 11.91	11.90 5.61	14.19 14.20	CFG	.84 6.25	.76	CG		772 .4	719 -53	B				KP
N4395	11.4 10.67	10.84 1.53	15.88 15.71	G	.53 2.50	.47	G			15	C*				DP
N4396										-63					
N4402		12.91 5.75	14.40	EGH	.83 11.88		EGH /E	.15		-74					B
N4405										-61					
N4406	10.9 10.92	10.75 17.04	12.84 13.01	ABDEF GH	.94 47.50	.89	ABDEG H/DE	.51	-292 9.9	-367 -75	BCD				P
N4410A				G*			G*			-91					
N4410B				G*			G*			-91					
N4411A				G*			G*			-92					
N4411B				G*			G*			-92					
N4412	12.8 13.25		13.44							-111					
N4413		13.04 0.97	14.03	F						-76					
N4414	11.1 11.59	11.21 5.18	13.00 13.38	AC	.73 8.13	.62	AC		715 1.0	720 5	B				B
N4417	12.3 12.39	12.43 4.98	13.17 13.13	AG	.89 2.50		G			-88					
N4419	12.2 12.48	12.23 2.10	13.17 13.42	C	1.00 3.75		C			-66					
N4420	12.5 12.94		13.38							-117					
N4421		12.35 2.54	13.34	CF*	.83 3.75	.74	C		1692 .2	1628 -64	B				
N4424	12.6 12.40	12.57 6.50	14.16 13.99	AG	.71 2.50		G			-89					
N4425	13.1 12.97	13.21 5.86	13.80 13.56	ACFG	.98 4.38	.87	CG		1883 4.0	1808 -75	B				
N4428	13.1 13.31		13.70							-156					
N4429	11.7 11.64	11.43 6.84	13.22 13.43	ACG	.98 4.38	.89	CG		1114 2.4	1032 -82	B				B
N4431										-77					
N4433	12.9 13.13		13.52							-156					P
N4435	11.8 12.19	12.03 13.38	12.37 12.53	ACEFG H	.92 18.13	.85	ACEGH /E	.49	869 1.0	796 -73	B				
N4436										-76					
N4438	11.9 11.24	11.30 12.00	14.49 14.43	ACEFG	.88 16.87	.78	ACEG /E	.41	-32 1.8	-105 -74	B				
N4440		13.09 3.90	13.78	CFH	.95 6.87		CH			-76					
N4441										144					
N4442	11.4 11.57	11.70 4.21	13.09 12.96	ACG	.94 4.38	.86	CG		580 1.0	493 -87	B				
N4445		14.04 3.96	14.18	AG	.84 2.50		G			-88					
N4448	11.9 12.07	12.29 1.35	13.83 13.61	C	.93 2.50	.77	C		693 2.4	687 -6	B				

NGC (IC, A) (1)	RA (1950) 100 P (2)	Dec 100 P (3)	L^I / B^I (4)	L^II / B^II (5)	SGL / SGB (6)	Rev. type (S) / DDO (T,L) (7)	Yerkes (1) / Yerkes (2) (8)	Hu-San / Ho (9)	log D w (10)	log R w (11)	log D(0) (12)	S (D,R) (13)
N4449	12 25.8	44 22	100.18	136.83	73.0	.IB.9..W100	I A	I 9	1.67	.19	1.59	ACHKLRX
	4.9	-33	73.03	72.41	6.2	I 5	I A	I9	14.49	14.49		YW
N4450	12 25.9	17 21	248.89	273.86	98.9	.SAS2..W100	S G	S 3	1.57	.15	1.51	ACDEKNV
	5.0	-33	78.94	78.62	-1.5	S 3 N	S G	S3	15.84	15.84		XYW
N4451	12 26.1	9 32	257.21	285.10	106.4	.S.....W			1.12	.14	1.06	AC
	5.1	-33	71.40	71.33	-3.8				.98	.98		
N4452	12 26.2	12 2	255.51	282.71	104.0	.S...$/W			1.31	.66	1.04	ACK
	5.1	-33	73.85	73.73	-3.0	S			2.58	2.58		
N4454	12 26.3	-1 40	261.76	291.45	117.2	RSBR0..W100	D *G		1.23	.09	1.20	ACEFKW
	5.1	-33	60.35	60.42	-6.8	S 4 4*			6.27	6.27		
N4455	12 26.2	23 6	230.63	251.59	93.4	.S..../			1.47	.54	1.26	ACEK
	5.0	-33	84.10	83.29	0.2	S 7 7*	I A		4.20	4.20		
N4457	12 26.4	3 51	260.13	289.11	111.9	RSXS0..W100	S G	S 1	1.35	.10	1.31	ACDKW
	5.1	-33	65.82	65.84	-5.3	SX0	SDP K		6.99	6.99		
N4458	12 26.4	13 31	254.38	281.07	102.6	.E.0+..W100			1.05	.05	1.03	ABCW
	5.1	-33	75.31	75.15	-2.5				3.15	3.15		
N4459	12 26.5	14 15	253.74	280.14	101.9	.LAR+..W100	E P*	L 3	1.28	.16	1.21	ADEHKYW
	5.1	-33	76.02	75.84	-2.3	E 2	E3 K		5.78	5.78		
N4460	12 26.4	45 8	99.29	135.78	72.3	.LBS+$/W060	D *FG*		1.46	.55	1.24	ACHKQ
	4.9	-33	72.30	71.70	6.5	E 8	DEP GK		7.01	7.01		
N4461	12 26.6	13 28	254.61	281.32	102.7	.LBS+*.W100	D GK		1.46	.43	1.29	ABCDEKW
	5.1	-33	75.27	75.12	-2.5	S 0	D K		9.66	9.66		
N4462	12 26.7	-22 54	265.26	296.35	138.2	.SBR2..W100			1.47	.41	1.30	EKW
	5.2	-33	39.23	39.41	-11.9	S 3 5*	S *G *		5.70	5.70		
N4464	12 26.8	8 26	258.36	286.50	107.5	.E.2...W			.95	.00	.95	ACL
	5.1	-33	70.36	70.32	-3.9				1.13	.78		
N4466	12 27.0	7 58	258.73	286.97	108.0	.S....$			1.17	.39	1.01	ABCL
	5.1	-33	69.91	69.89	-4.0				2.46	1.90		
N4467	12 27.0	8 16	258.59	286.76	107.7	.E.2...W			.97	.05	.94	ABC
	5.1	-33	70.20	70.17	-3.9				1.17	1.17		
N4468	12 27.0	14 19	254.15	280.51	101.9	.E.4..*R020			1.04	.13	.99	AH
	5.1	-33	76.12	75.95	-2.2				1.01	1.01		
N4469	12 27.0	9 2	258.18	286.17	107.0	.SBS0$/W100	DS *FG*		1.52	.49	1.33	ACDEKW
	5.1	-33	70.96	70.91	-3.7	S P	D G		9.69	9.69		
N4470	12 27.1	8 6	258.74	286.95	107.9	.S...P*L036			1.03	.08	1.00	ACLS
	5.1	-33	70.05	70.02	-3.9				2.54	2.54		
N4472	12 27.3	8 16	258.81	286.98	107.7	.E.2...P200	E2 K		1.68	.09	1.65	ABCDEKL
	5.1	-33	70.21	70.19	-3.8	E 4	E2 K	E	17.11	17.11		SXYZ
N4473	12 27.3	13 42	255.05	281.64	102.5	.E.5...W100	E4 K		1.39	.29	1.27	ACDEKYW
	5.1	-33	75.54	75.39	-2.3	E 4	E5 K		7.01	7.01		
N4474	12 27.4	14 21	254.51	280.84	101.9	.L.....W			1.24	.39	1.09	ADEHK
	5.1	-33	76.17	76.01	-2.1	E 6	D K		4.95	4.95		
N4476	12 27.5	12 37	256.18	283.15	103.6	.LAR-*.P200			1.02	.19	.95	ACKLSZ
	5.1	-33	74.49	74.38	-2.5	E 4			5.32	4.87		
N4477	12 27.6	13 55	255.13	281.63	102.3	.LBS0*$W100			1.47	.07	1.44	ADEHK
	5.1	-33	75.76	75.62	-2.2	SX0	BD K		6.15	6.15		
N4478	12 27.8	12 36	256.46	283.43	103.6	.E.2...P200			1.08	.06	1.05	ADEKLZ
	5.1	-33	74.49	74.39	-2.5	E 1	E2 *K		5.49	5.04		
N4479	12 27.8	13 51	255.39	281.90	102.4	.LBS0*$W100			1.05	.14	.99	ACHW
	5.1	-33	75.71	75.58	-2.1				1.76	1.76		
N4480	12 27.9	4 31	260.80	289.67	111.4		S *F		1.40	.24	1.30	ACLX
	5.1	-33	66.53	66.57	-4.7			S5	2.40	2.40		
N4483	12 28.2	9 17	258.94	286.86	106.8				1.12	.20	1.04	ACK
	5.1	-33	71.25	71.23	-3.3	SX0*			1.92	1.92		
N4485	12 28.2	41 58	100.55	137.92	75.4	.IBS9P.W100		S6	1.25	.20	1.17	ABCDHKL
	4.9	-33	75.47	74.83	6.0	I 6*	I A *		6.36	5.73		XW
N4486	12 28.3	12 40	256.85	283.79	103.6	.E.0+P.P200	E1 K	E 0 P	1.58	.03	1.57	ACDEHKL
	5.1	-33	74.58	74.49	-2.3	E 1	E1 K	E	15.35	14.46		SXYZ
N4486B	12 28.0	12 46	256.50	283.41	103.5	.E.0...P200						
	5.1	-33	74.66	74.56	-2.4							
N4487	12 28.3	-7 48	263.93	294.16	123.3	.SXT6..W100			1.60	.15	1.54	ACEFKTW
	5.2	-33	54.31	54.44	-7.9	S 5 4	S F		13.54	13.54		
N4488	12 28.3	8 38	259.34	287.41	107.4	.S....*			1.43	.37	1.28	ACL
	5.1	-33	70.62	70.61	-3.5				2.50	2.50		
N4490	12 28.3	41 55	100.52	137.91	75.5	.SBS7P.W100	I AF		1.73	.30	1.61	ABCHKLU
	4.9	-33	75.52	74.88	6.0	S 5 NT * 5	I A	S6	12.69	12.69		XYW
N4491	12 28.4	11 45	257.61	284.84	104.5				1.28	.36	1.13	AC
	5.1	-33	73.69	73.62	-2.6				1.28	1.28		
N4492	12 28.4	8 21	259.56	287.70	107.7	.S.....W			1.14	.05	1.12	ACL
	5.1	-33	70.34	70.34	-3.5				1.58	1.18		
N4494	12 28.9	26 3	208.19	228.60	90.8	.E.1+..P200	DE *K		1.34	.13	1.28	ACEHKMZ
	5.0	-33	86.54	85.31	1.6	E 1	E2 K		8.24	8.24		
N4496A	12 29.1	4 12	261.65	290.57	111.8	.SBT9..W060			1.56	.11	1.52	ABCDEKL
	5.1	-33	66.26	66.32	-4.5	SX5 5*	BS A	S6	10.13	9.35		XQ
N4496B	12 29.1	4 12	261.65	290.57	111.8	.I...$.	I *A		1.04	.10	1.00	BLX
	5.1	-33	66.26	66.32	-4.5		I A	S6	1.13	.69		
N4497	12 29.1	11 53	258.12	285.30	104.4				1.33	.34	1.19	AC
	5.1	-33	73.85	73.80	-2.4				1.40	1.40		
N4498	12 29.2	17 8	253.16	277.97	99.4				1.37	.27	1.26	AC
	5.0	-33	78.97	78.76	-.9				1.48	1.48		

NGC (IC, A) (14)	m_H / m_c (15)	B(O) w (16)	B'(O) m'_c (17)	S(B) (18)	(B-V)(O) w (19)	C_o(O) (20)	S(C) (21)	(U-B)(O) w (22)	V w (23)	V_o ΔV (24)	S(V) (25)	φ_r n (26)	φ(21) (27)	(28)	Photo. (29)
N4449	10.3 / 10.47	10.08 / 5.91	12.77 / 13.16	BDEFG	.38 / 24.38	.32	BDEG / /DE	-.25	207 / 107.8	269 / 62	ABDR				CJP
N4450	11.4 / 11.45	11.29 / 5.86	13.58 / 13.74	ABFG	.84 / 8.75	.72	BG		2048 / .4	1992 / -56	B				P
N4451	/ 6.27	13.57	13.61	AC	.80 / 1.88		C			-89					
N4452	13.2 / 13.25	13.33 / 0.71	13.27 / 13.19	C	1.10 / 1.88		C			-78					
N4454	12.8 / 12.87		13.56							-133					
N4455	13.0 / 12.83		13.82							-31					
N4457	11.7 / 12.00		13.29							-111					P
N4458		13.32 / 7.85	13.21	ABEFH	.86* / 12.50	.80	BEH* / /E	.34	383 / .2	311 / -72	B				
N4459	11.9 / 12.11	11.95 / 9.11	12.74 / 12.90	ACF	.86 / 1.88	.78	C		1111 / 1.8	1042 / -69	B				LP
N4460	12.5 / 12.47		13.36							65					
N4461	12.4 / 12.32	12.37 / 12.82	13.51 / 13.46	ACEFH	.90 / 14.38	.80	CEH / /E	.52	1887 / 6.3	1815 / -72	B				
N4462	13.0 / 12.80		14.04							-201					
N4464		13.77 / 1.79	13.21	B	.97 / 6.25	.90	B		1199 / 4.0	1106 / -93	B				
N4466										-94					
N4467		15.49 / 1.89	14.93	B	.93 / 6.25	.86	B		1474 / .1	1381 / -93	B				
N4468		14.21 / 4.88	13.90	H	.82 / 6.25		H			-68					
N4469	12.5 / 12.41		13.75							-90					
N4470										-94					
N4472	10.1 / 10.10	9.84 / 9.73	12.78 / 13.04	ABEFG	.95 / 20.00	.89	ABEG / /E	.60	948 / 7.2	855 / -93	ABD				
N4473	11.7 / 11.79	11.61 / 9.42	12.70 / 12.88	ACFH	.89 / 11.25	.81	ACH		2241 / 1.8	2171 / -70	B				
N4474	12.9 / 12.99	12.95 / 1.89	13.09 / 13.13	CF	.95 / 1.88	.86	C		1526 / 4.0	1459 / -68	B				
N4476	13.2 / 13.42	13.51 / 10.30	12.95 / 12.86	BEFH	.83 / 21.88		BEH / /E	.27		-75					
N4477	11.8 / 11.67	11.62 / 10.38	13.51 / 13.56	ACFH	.94 / 9.38	.87	ACH		1263 / 1.8	1194 / -69	B				
N4478	12.5 / 12.69	12.57 / 12.27	12.56 / 12.68	ACEFH	.92 / 18.75	.85	ACEH / /E	.34	1482 / 1.8	1407 / -75	B				
N4479		13.93 / 7.99	13.62	ACFH	.95 / 12.50	.88	ACH		822 / 1.0	753 / -69	B				
N4480		13.26 / 1.43	14.50	G	.73 / 2.50		G			-108					
N4483	13.3									-88					
N4485	12.9 / 12.90	12.60 / 4.47	13.19 / 13.49	BEG	.36 / 8.75	.30	EG / /E	-.23	795 / .7	848 / 53	E				A
N4486	10.7 / 10.78	10.30 / 20.02	12.89 / 13.37	ABDEF GH	.97 / 81.88	.90	ABDEG / H/DE	.53	1261 / 33.6	1187 / -74	ABCD				JP
N4486B				BCD*	1.03* / 15.63	.96	BCD / /D	.46	1486 / 4.0	1412 / -74	B				
N4487	12.0 / 11.82		14.26							-153					
N4488										-91					
N4490	10.5 / 10.92	10.29 / 6.63	13.08 / 13.71	ABEFG	.40* / 15.00	.30	ABEG* / /E	-.17	570 / 7.5	622 / 53	BDE				ABK
N4491		13.75 / 1.35	14.14	C	.92 / 1.88		C			-78					
N4492		13.40 / 1.98	13.69	C	.66 / 1.88	.55	C		1735 / .3	1643 / -92	B				
N4494	10.9 / 11.24	11.31 / 2.62	12.45 / 12.38	B	.93 / 6.25	.86	B		1321 / 3.9	1305 / -16	BC				
N4496A	12.0 / 11.99		14.33	G*	.61* / 2.50		G*			-108					
N4496B				G*			G*		1773 / 2.9	1665 / -108	D				
N4497										-77					
N4498										-55					

NGC (IC, A) (1)	RA (1950) 100 P (2)	Dec 100 P (3)	L^I / B^I (4)	L^{II} / B^{II} (5)	SGL / SGB (6)	Rev. type (S) / DDO (T,L) (7)	Yerkes (1) / Yerkes (2) (8)	Hu-San / Ho (9)	log D / w (10)	log R / w (11)	log D(O) (12)	S (D,R) (13)
N4500	12 29.1	58 14	93.40	128.08	59.6	.SBS1..W060			1.13	.28	1.01	ACQ
	4.7	-33	59.40	58.97	10.2				2.09	2.09		
N4501	12 29.5	14 42	256.27	282.36	101.7	.SAT3..W100	S FG		1.78	.26	1.68	ACDEHKL
	5.0	-33	76.63	76.51	-1.5	S 4 1	S G	S4	22.84	22.84		SUXYW
N4503	12 29.6	11 27	258.82	286.13	104.8	.LB.-*.W060	D *GK		1.36	.34	1.22	ACDEKYQ
	5.1	-33	73.45	73.41	-2.4	E 2*	D K		7.09	7.09		
N4504	12 29.7	-7 17	264.44	294.64	122.9	.SAS6..W100	S F		1.61	.19	1.53	ACEFKTW
	5.2	-33	54.85	55.00	-7.5	S 5 N 4*			14.26	14.26		
N4506	12 29.7	13 42	257.39	283.85	102.7				1.17	.23	1.08	AH
	5.1	-33	75.66	75.58	-1.7				.59	.59		
N4507	12 32.9	-39 38	267.95	299.64	155.3	.LXR+..S030			1.20	.07	1.18	I
	5.4	-33	22.60	22.86	-13.7				1.07	1.07		
N4509	12 30.7	32 22	117.95	160.49	84.8				1.07	.17	1.00	AC
	4.9	-33	84.71	83.65	3.8				.89	.89		
N4516	12 30.6	14 51	257.27	283.25	101.6				1.13	.13	1.08	AHLS
	5.0	-33	76.83	76.74	-1.2				3.51	2.88		
N4517	12 30.2	0 23	263.30	292.74	115.5	.SAS6*/W060	SI *AF		1.99	.83	1.65	ACEHKLU
	5.1	-33	62.50	62.61	-5.3	S 5	SI *F *	S5	20.83	20.83		XYQ
N4517A	12 29.9	0 38	263.08	292.49	115.3	.SBT8*.W060			1.54	.14	1.49	ELXQ
	5.1	-33	62.74	62.84	-5.3	S 9	S AF	S6	4.77	4.77		
N4519	12 31.0	8 56	261.22	289.19	107.3	.SBT7..W100	S AF		1.52	.13	1.46	ABCDEHK
	5.1	-33	71.01	71.05	-2.8	S 5 5	S AF	S5	13.33	13.33		NXW
N4520	12 31.1	-7 7	265.02	295.20	122.9	.S.....H030			1.63	.10	1.59	F
	5.2	-33	55.05	55.21	-7.1				2.11	2.11		
N4522	12 31.2	9 27	261.15	288.99	106.9				1.56	.57	1.33	ACDEK
	5.1	-33	71.53	71.57	-2.6	S 5P	S *AF*		6.50	6.50		
N4523	12 31.1	15 26	257.27	282.94	101.1	.SXS6$.L036			1.43	.02	1.42	AHN
	5.0	-33	77.43	77.33	-.9				2.85	2.85		
N4526	12 31.6	7 58	262.04	290.23	108.3	.LXS0*.W060	D G	L 3	1.73	.57	1.50	ACDEHKL
	5.1	-33	70.07	70.13	-2.9	E 7	D K		15.09	15.09		SYQ
N4527	12 31.6	2 56	263.50	292.60	113.2	.SXS4..W100	S G		1.77	.49	1.57	ACEHKLS
	5.1	-33	65.07	65.18	-4.3	S 4 N - 3	S G	S3	20.06	20.06		UXYW
N4528	12 31.5	11 35	260.37	287.60	104.8	.L.....			1.18	.32	1.05	A
	5.1	-33	73.65	73.66	-1.9				.77	.77		
N4531	12 31.7	13 21	259.51	286.10	103.1				1.37	.18	1.30	ACH
	5.0	-33	75.41	75.38	-1.4				1.79	1.79		
N4532	12 31.8	6 44	262.59	291.04	109.5	.IB.9..W100	I A *		1.39	.44	1.22	ACDEKXW
	5.1	-33	68.86	68.93	-3.2	I * 5*	I A *	I9	8.24	8.24		
N4533	12 31.8	2 36	263.70	292.85	113.5	.S....*R020			1.34	.52	1.13	HL
	5.1	-33	64.75	64.86	-4.3				1.92	1.15		
N4534	12 31.7	35 48	105.05	145.57	81.6	.S.....			1.21	.00	1.21	ABC
	4.9	-33	81.61	80.83	4.9				1.95	1.95		
N4535	12 31.8	8 28	262.00	290.08	107.8	.SXS5..W100	SB *AF		1.81	.16	1.75	ABCDEHK
	5.1	-33	70.58	70.63	-2.7	SX5 1*	S AF	S5	23.89	23.89		LNSXYW
N4536	12 31.9	2 28	263.78	292.95	113.6	.SXT4..W060	S F		1.88	.37	1.74	ACEHKLU
	5.1	-33	64.61	64.73	-4.3	S 5 T - 3*	S F	S5	18.42	18.42		XYQ
N4539	12 32.1	18 29	254.97	278.57	98.3				1.48	.50	1.28	ACX
	5.0	-33	80.46	80.27	0.2			S1	1.75	1.75		
N4540	12 32.3	15 50	258.24	283.64	100.8	.SXT6..W100	SI *AF		1.19	.11	1.15	ABCDEKN
	5.0	-33	77.88	77.80	-.5	I 7	I P A *		8.16	7.78		W
N4541	12 32.6	0 2	264.65	294.13	116.0	.S....$			1.16	.31	1.03	ACH
	5.1	-33	62.21	62.36	-4.8				1.91	1.91		
N4544	12 33.0	3 18	264.25	293.30	112.9				1.21	.34	1.07	H
	5.1	-33	65.47	65.60	-3.9				.94	.94		
N4545	12 32.4	63 47	91.83	126.08	54.1				1.37	.14	1.32	AC
	4.5	-33	53.91	53.52	11.8				.65	.65		
N4546	12 32.9	-3 31	265.35	295.22	119.5	.LBS-*.W100	D GK		1.33	.36	1.18	ACEFHKL
	5.1	-33	58.67	58.84	-5.7	E 6	E6 K		9.56	8.27		W
N4548	12 32.9	14 46	259.74	285.68	101.9	.SBT3..P200	B G	SBT3	1.68	.09	1.64	ACDEHKN
	5.0	-33	76.85	76.82	-.7	SB3 N	B G	S4	16.03	16.03		XYZ
N4550	12 32.9	12 30	261.12	288.02	104.0	.L...../L036			1.39	.57	1.16	ABDEHKM
	5.1	-33	74.61	74.63	-1.3	E 7	D K		9.03	9.03		Y
N4551	12 33.1	12 33	261.28	288.15	104.0	.E.3...L036			1.04	.15	.98	ABCHM
	5.1	-33	74.67	74.69	-1.3				3.37	3.37		
N4552	12 33.1	12 50	261.13	287.90	103.7	.E.0...L036	E1 K		1.30	.00	1.30	ADEHKMY
	5.0	-33	74.95	74.97	-1.2	E 0	E1 K		6.01	6.01		
N4553	12 33.4	-39 10	268.03	299.71	154.8	.LAR+..B060			1.15	.34	1.01	PI
	5.4	-33	23.07	23.33	-13.5				2.69	2.69		
N4555	12 33.2	26 48	203.56	221.71	90.3	.E....*R020			1.03	.03	1.01	ACH
	5.0	-33	87.75	86.44	2.8				1.14	1.14		
N4559	12 33.5	28 14	165.03	198.44	89.0	.SXT6..W100	S A		1.97	.38	1.82	ABCEHKL
	4.9	-33	87.96	86.47	3.2	S 5 4	S FG	S6	24.62	24.62		NSXYW
N4561	12 33.6	19 36	255.48	277.86	97.3	.SBT8..W100	SB *AF		1.18	.08	1.15	ACDEKW
	5.0	-33	81.63	81.44	0.8	S 5 K 6*			5.81	5.81		
N4562	12 33.2	26 7	217.31	232.04	91.0	.S...*.R020			1.42	.49	1.22	HL
	5.0	-33	87.39	86.25	2.6				2.13	2.13		
N4564	12 34.0	11 43	262.48	289.63	104.9	.E.6...W			1.29	.47	1.10	ACDEKLR
	5.1	-33	73.87	73.93	-1.3	E 6	D K	E	10.83	10.14		SVXY
N4565	12 33.9	26 16	216.91	230.74	90.9	.SAS3$/....	S GK	S 3	2.19	.86	1.84	ABCEHKL
	5.0	-33	87.60	86.45	2.8	S 3 1*	S GK	S4	29.99	29.99		SVXY

NGC (IC, A)	m_H m_c	B(O) w	B'(O) m'_c	S(B)	(B-V)(O) w	C_o(O)	S(C)	(U-B)(O) w	V w	V_o ΔV	S(V)	φ_r n	φ(21)		Photo.
	(14)	(15)	(16)	(17)	(18)	(19)	(20)	(21)	(22)	(23)	(24)	(25)	(26)	(27)	(28)	(29)
N4500										120					
N4501	10.9	10.49	13.63	ABDEF	.80*	.65	ABDEG	.33	2120	2056	B				A
	10.81	13.33	13.95	G	46.25		/DE		1.0	-65					
N4503	12.8														
	12.68		13.52							-78					
N4504	12.3														
	12.01		14.40							-150					
N4506										-69					
N4507	12.9														
	12.84		13.43							-232					
N4509										13					
N4516										-63					
N4517	11.6	11.43	14.42	G	.74	.60	G		1218	1095	C				B
	11.35	1.17	14.34		2.50				4.7	-122					
N4517A	13.0	12.89	15.08	G	.48		G								
	13.46	1.17	15.65		2.50					-121					
N4519	12.6	12.47	14.51	G	.54	.45	G		1213	1125	C				
	12.40	1.45	14.44		2.50				2.1	-88					
N4520										-149					
N4522	12.9														
	12.74		14.13							-85					
N4523										-60					
N4526	10.7	10.97	13.21	C	.94	.85	C		487	396	AB				BKP
	10.82	2.16	13.06		3.75				5.0	-91					
N4527	11.3	11.68	14.27	CG	.83	.67	CG		1727	1616	B				B
	11.30	2.32	13.89		4.38				1.8	-111					
N4528		12.98	12.92	C	1.00		C								
		1.94			1.88					-76					
N4531										-69					
N4532	12.1	12.59	13.38	G	.41		G								
	12.31	1.00	13.10		2.50					-96					
N4533										-112					
N4534										28					
N4535	11.1	10.90	14.39	AFG	.64	.52	AG		1943	1854	BC				
	10.81	5.73	14.30		6.87				27.0	-89					
N4536	11.2	11.21	14.60	AG	.60*	.45	AG		1927	1814	C				AB
	10.88	2.46	14.27		6.87				2.2	-113					
N4539		13.17	14.31	G	.86		G								
		1.12			2.50					-47					
N4540	12.9														
	13.23		13.67							-58					
N4541										-122					
N4544										-109					
N4545										141					
N4546	11.4	11.62	12.26	C	.98	.89	C		1014	879	B				
	11.83	1.65	12.47		1.88				6.3	-135					
N4548	11.9	11.19	14.08	CDEFG	.86	.77	CDEGH	.34	433	371	3				P
	11.47	15.25	14.36	H	39.38		/DE		4.0	-62					
N4550	12.7	12.73	13.27	AC	.92	.83	AC		350	279	B				
	12.72	3.11	13.26		6.25				4.0	-71					
N4551		13.27	12.91	AB	.93	.87	B		978	907	B				
		5.53			6.25				.1	-71					
N4552	11.3	11.30	12.49	ACFH	.97*	.91	ACH		265	195	BC				
	11.49	8.24	12.68		11.25				3.8	-70					
N4553										-231					
N4555										-10					
N4559	10.7	10.56	14.40	AEFG	.47	.36	AEG	-.06	856	852	C				A
	10.47	3.02	14.31		13.13		/E		2.4	-4					
N4561	12.9														
	13.30		13.74							-42					
N4562										-13					
N4564	12.1	12.24	12.48	CG	.98		CG								
	12.34	2.52	12.58		6.25					-74					
N4565	10.7	10.61	14.55	BDEFG	.92	.72	BDEG	.46	1183	1171	ABC				ABJL
	10.34	2.32	14.28	H	18.13		/DE		5.1	-12					MP

NGC (IC, A)	Coordinates					Classification		Hu-San	Diameters			
	RA (1950) Dec 100 P	100 P	L^I B^I	L^II B^II	SGL SGB	Rev. type (S) DDO (T, L)	Yerkes (1) Yerkes (2)	Ho	log D w	log R w	log D(O)	S (D,R)
(1)	(2)	(3)	(4)	(5)	(6)	(7)	(8)	(9)	(10)	(11)	(12)	(13)
N4567	12 34.0 11 32	262.55	289.76	105.1	.SAT4..P200	S F		1.39	.17	1.32	ABCDELR
	5.1 −33	73.69	73.75	−1.3	S 5 KT+	S AF	S5	17.02	17.02		SVXYQZ
N4568	12 34.1 11 31	262.65	289.86	105.1	.SAT4..P200	S AF		1.61	.37	1.46	ABDELRS
	5.1 −33	73.67	73.74	−1.3	S 5 KT+		S5	22.63	22.63		VXYQZ
N4569	12 34.3 13 26	261.96	288.47	103.2	.SXT2..P200	S P F * S 3	S 3	1.85	.33	1.72	ACDEHKM
	5.0 −33	75.58	75.62	−.7	S 4 N	S A	S4	23.92	23.92		VXZ
N4570	12 34.4 7 31	264.18	292.46	108.9	.L...../W100	D K		1.46	.57	1.23	ACDEHKW
	5.1 −33	69.70	69.82	−2.4	E 8	D K		9.33	9.33		
N4571	12 34.3 14 28	261.39	287.44	102.3	.SAR6*.L036			1.50	.04	1.48	ADEKNXY
	5.0 −33	76.61	76.62	−.4	S NK+	SD F	S6	7.61	7.61		
N4575	12 35.1 −40 16	268.43	300.13	156.0	.SBS4*.S030			1.29	.10	1.25	I
	5.4 −33	21.99	22.26	−13.3				1.21	1.21		
N4576	12 35.0 4 38	265.22	294.04	111.8			S5				
	5.1 −33	66.84	66.99	−3.0							
N4578	12 35.0 9 50	263.98	291.70	106.8	.LA..*.W	D G		1.42	.14	1.36	ABDEK
	5.1 −33	72.02	72.13	−1.6	S 0			5.45	5.45		
N4579	12 35.1 12 5	263.30	290.32	104.6	.SXT3..P200	SB *GK SB 3	SB 3	1.65	.08	1.62	ADEKMXZ
	5.0 −33	74.26	74.34	−.9	S 3 N	BS K	S3	11.88	11.88		
N4580	12 35.3 5 38	265.22	293.87	110.8	.SXT1P.W100		S 3	1.25	.10	1.22	ACDEKW
	5.1 −33	67.84	67.99	−2.7	S 4 N 5	S F		6.81	6.81		
N4584	12 35.8 13 23	263.43	289.94	103.4	.SBS2*.L036			1.09	.19	1.02	AHM
	5.0 −33	75.57	75.65	−.4				1.69	1.69		
N4586	12 35.9 4 35	265.79	294.63	111.9	.SAS0*/L036	D *F		1.55	.46	1.37	ACEKXQ
	5.1 −33	66.80	66.97	−2.8	S 4 5	DS G	S1	5.83	5.83		
N4589	12 35.6 74 28	90.57	124.22	43.4	.E.2...W060	E1 *K		1.14	.06	1.11	AKNQ
	3.9 −33	43.25	42.90	13.9	S 0	DE K		3.22	3.22		
N4592	12 36.7 −0 16	266.87	296.39	116.6	.SAS8*.W100			1.61	.55	1.39	ACEKNW
	5.1 −33	61.98	62.18	−3.9	S 3 4	SI *AF*		10.07	10.07		
N4593	12 37.0 −5 4	267.44	297.45	121.3	RSBT3..P200		SBT3	1.55	.11	1.51	ACEFKNT
	5.2 −33	57.18	57.40	−5.1	SB2 3	B G		14.43	12.96		Z
N4594	12 37.3 −11 21	267.94	298.43	127.4	.SAS1$/P200	SDP*K S 2	S 2	1.84	.44	1.66	ACFKLRV
	5.2 −33	50.90	51.15	−6.7	S 2	DS K	S1	23.36	23.36		XZ
N4595	12 37.3 15 34	264.07	289.49	101.4				1.22	.15	1.16	ACK
	5.0 −33	77.78	77.86	0.6	S 5 K 5*			2.27	2.27		
N4596	12 37.4 10 27	265.77	293.30	106.3	.LBR+..W100	B K		1.45	.21	1.36	ACDEKXW
	5.1 −33	72.68	72.83	−.8	SB0	B K	S1	7.27	7.27		
N4597	12 37.5 −5 32	267.70	297.75	121.7	.SBT9..W100			1.59	.32	1.46	ACEFKW
	5.2 −33	56.72	56.95	−5.1	SB5 K 5*	B AF		9.19	9.19		
N4601	12 38.2 −40 39	269.07	300.79	156.5	.LA..*.S030			1.24	.64	.98	I
	5.4 −33	21.62	21.90	−12.8				.81	.81		
N4602	12 38.0 −4 52	267.88	297.88	121.1	.SXT4..W100			1.51	.45	1.33	ACEFNTW
	5.2 −32	57.39	57.62	−4.9	S 5 NK 3*	S AF		12.72	12.72		
N4603	12 38.3 −40 42	269.10	300.81	156.5	.SAS5*.S030			1.55	.20	1.47	I
	5.4 −32	21.57	21.85	−12.8				1.71	1.71		
N4603A	12 36.9 −40 26	268.80	300.51	156.2	.S...*.S030			1.27	.50	1.07	I
	5.4 −33	21.83	22.11	−13.0				1.17	1.17		
N4603B	12 37.7 −40 28	268.87	300.68	156.3	.S...*.S030			1.20	.56	.98	I
	5.4 −33	21.80	22.08	−12.9				1.07	1.07		
N4603C	12 38.0 −40 29	269.03	300.74	156.3	.L..../S030			1.31	.94	.94	I
	5.4 −32	21.78	22.07	−12.8				.54	.54		
N4603D	12 39.5 −40 33	269.34	301.05	156.4	.S..5*.S030			1.20	.18	1.13	I
	5.4 −32	21.72	22.01	−12.6				1.07	1.07		
N4605	12 37.8 61 53	90.92	125.33	56.2	.SBS5P.W060	I A *		1.64	.45	1.46	ACHKLQ
	4.4 −33	55.83	55.47	12.0	S			9.24	9.24		
N4606	12 38.4 12 10	266.25	293.22	104.7	.SBS1..L036			1.38	.33	1.24	ABNX
	5.0 −32	74.41	74.57	−.1			S1	2.97	2.97		
N4607	12 38.7 12 10	266.53	293.50	104.8	.SBS.$/L036			1.56	.73	1.27	BCNX
	5.0 −32	74.42	74.58	0.0			S.	4.30	4.30		
N4608	12 38.7 10 26	266.84	294.38	106.4	.LBR0..W100	B K		1.34	.14	1.29	ADEKXW
	5.1 −32	72.68	72.86	−.5	SB0	B K	L	7.35	7.35		
N4612	12 39.0 7 35	267.46	295.72	109.2	RLX.0..P200	DB *K LB1	LB1	1.24	.09	1.21	AEKZ
	5.1 −32	69.84	70.04	−1.2	E P	D GK		5.58	5.58		
N4616	12 39.5 −40 22	269.34	301.04	156.2	.E.0.*.S030			.95	.00	.95	I
	5.4 −32	21.90	22.20	−12.5				.71	.71		
N4618	12 39.2 41 25	92.52	130.53	76.5	.SBT9..W100	I A		1.53	.09	1.50	ABCHKLX
	4.8 −32	76.29	75.84	7.8	S 5 KT	SIP*A *	S6	9.64	9.64		YW
N4619	12 39.4 35 20	94.63	136.87	82.4	.S.....			1.13	.12	1.08	AC
	4.9 −32	82.37	81.81	6.3				1.01	1.01		
N4621	12 39.5 11 55	267.29	294.35	105.1	.E.5...W100	E5 K		1.42	.22	1.33	ACDEKNY
	5.0 −32	74.18	74.36	0.1	E 3	E5 K		8.88	8.88		W
N4622	12 39.9 −40 28	269.42	301.13	156.3	.SAR1*.S030			1.21	.03	1.20	I
	5.5 −32	21.80	22.10	−12.5				.62	.62		
N4623	12 39.6 7 56	267.86	296.04	108.9				1.29	.41	1.13	ACK
	5.1 −32	70.20	70.41	−1.0	E 5*			2.50	2.50		
N4625	12 39.5 41 33	92.25	130.22	76.4	.SXT9P.W100			1.18	.03	1.17	ABHLXW
	4.8 −32	76.16	75.72	7.9			S6	4.72	4.09		
N4627	12 39.7 32 51	96.39	142.67	84.9	.E+..P.P200			1.29	.19	1.21	ABCHLXZ
	4.8 −32	84.84	84.19	5.8			S.	7.08	5.34		
N4630	12 40.0 4 14	268.41	297.31	112.5				1.27	.19	1.19	ACK
	5.1 −32	66.50	66.73	−1.9	P			2.41	2.41		

NGC (IC, A) (14)	m_H / m_C (15)	B(O) w (16)	B'(O) m'_C (17)	S(B) (18)	(B-V)(O) w (19)	C_0(O) (20)	S(C) (21)	(U-B)(O) w (22)	V w (23)	V_0 ΔV (24)	S(V) (25)	ϕ_r n (26)	ϕ(21) (27)	(28)	Photo. (29)
N4567	12.3	12.37	13.71	G	.77	.65	G		2253	2179	CE				BC
	12.42	0.91	13.76		2.50				4.5	−75					
N4568	12.2	11.98	13.97	G	.88	.73	G		2278	2204	CE				BC
	12.07	1.12	14.06		2.50				4.4	−75					
N4569	11.2	10.58	13.92	ACEFG	.74*	.59	ACEG	.30	960	893	B				LP
	10.86	7.85	14.20		15.00		/E		4.0	−67					
N4570	12.0	12.24	13.08	C	.95	.85	C		1730	1639	B				
	12.16	0.62	13.00		1.88				1.8	−91					
N4571	12.8	12.12	14.26	FG	.53		G								
	12.39	1.96	14.53		2.50					−62					
N4575										−232					
N4576				G*	.78		G								
					2.50					−102					
N4578	12.5	12.48	14.02	BC	.90	.82	BC		2282	2201	B				
	12.16	4.31	13.70		10.00				4.0	−81					
N4579	11.0	10.72	13.56	ABDEG	.85	.75	ABDEG	.34	1752	1680	B				P
	11.00	14.98	13.84		61.88		/DE		.4	−72					
N4580	12.8														P
	12.87		13.66							−98					
N4584										−66					
N4586	13.0	12.88	14.42	G	1.01		G								
	12.59	1.12	14.13		2.50					−102					
N4589	12.1	12.40	12.69	B					1825	2003	B				
	12.32	1.35	12.61						1.8	178					
N4592	12.4														
	12.45		14.14							−120					
N4593	12.1														P
	11.87		14.11							−137					
N4594	8.1	9.52	12.51	BEGK	.98	.82	BEG	.58	1160	1002	ABCD				BCJL
	9.32	8.78	12.31		21.25		/E		10.2	−159					P
N4595	13.1														
	13.24		13.78							−55					
N4596	12.2	11.88	13.42	G	.99		G								
	12.05	0.80	13.59		2.50					−77					
N4597	12.9														
	12.68		14.72							−139					
N4601										−231					
N4602	12.4														
	12.45		13.84							−136					
N4603	12.5														F
	12.21		14.30							−231					
N4603A										−231					
N4603B										−231					
N4603C										−231					
N4603D										−230					
N4605	10.9	11.09	13.13	E	.46	.32	E	−.11	140	276	C				
	11.36	1.86	13.40		6.25		/E		2.0	136					
N4606		13.10	14.04	G	.84		G								
		0.95			2.50					−69					
N4607				G*	.93		G								
					2.50					−69					
N4608	12.7	12.48	13.62	G	.96		G								K
	12.52	0.84	13.66		2.50					−76					
N4612	12.6														P
	12.59		13.33							−87					
N4616										−230					
N4618	11.5	11.60	13.79	EFG	.48	.42	EG	−.12	484	540	C				
	11.71	6.83	13.90		15.00		/E		2.2	56					
N4619										31					
N4621	11.4	11.28	12.67	ACF	1.00	.94	AC		414	345	B				
	11.49	3.26	12.88		6.25				.6	−69					
N4622										−230					F
N4623	13.2														
	13.03		13.37							−85					
N4625		13.22	13.81	EG	.60		EG	−.14							
		5.55			15.00		/E			57					
N4627		13.34	14.13	CDEG	.62		CDEG	.08							
		4.89			20.00		/DE			20					
N4630	13.1														
										−100					

NGC (IC, A) (1)	RA (1950) 100 P (2)	Dec 100 P (3)	L^I B^I (4)	L^II B^II (5)	SGL SGB (6)	Rev. type (S) DDO (T, L) (7)	Yerkes (1) Yerkes (2) (8)	Hu-San Ho (9)	log D w (10)	log R w (11)	log D(O) (12)	S (D,R) (13)
N4631	12 39.8	32 49	96.20	142.60	84.9	.SBS7./P200	SI *AF*	S 5	2.16	.74	1.87	ABCHKLU
	4.9	-32	84.88	84.23	5.8	S 5 K 5*		S6	27.67	27.67		XYZ
N4632	12 40.0	0 11	268.62	298.09	116.4	.SA.5..W100	S AF		1.46	.41	1.30	ACEHKW
	5.1	-32	62.45	62.70	-3.0	S 5 K 4	S AF		8.74	8.74		
N4633	12 40.0	14 38	267.32	293.23	102.5	.SBS7*/L036			1.42	.50	1.23	BNX
	5.0	-32	76.89	77.06	0.9			S6	3.10	3.10		
N4634	12 40.2	14 34	267.55	293.49	102.6	.S..7*.L036			1.42	.44	1.25	ABNX
	5.0	-32	76.83	77.00	1.0			S.	4.23	4.23		
N4635	12 40.2	20 12	265.91	286.93	97.1				1.35	.16	1.29	ACEK
	5.0	-32	82.46	82.52	2.5	N *	S A		3.55	3.55		
N4636	12 40.3	2 57	268.66	297.76	113.7	.E+0+..P200	E1 K	E+0	1.48	.09	1.45	ACEKMZ
	5.1	-32	65.22	65.46	-2.2	E 1	E1 K		7.82	7.82		
N4637	12 40.3	11 43	268.03	295.16	105.3							
	5.0	-32	73.98	74.18	0.2							
N4638	12 40.2	11 43	267.94	295.08	105.3	.L..-./L036	D G		1.13	.33	.99	ADEKLNS
	5.0	-32	73.98	74.18	0.2	E 5	D *K		5.87	5.35		
N4639	12 40.3	13 31	267.81	294.25	103.6	SX3 4*	S G	S4	1.30	.16	1.23	ADEKLSX
	5.0	-32	75.78	75.97	0.7				6.00	4.11		
N4642	12 40.7	-0 23	269.00	298.55	117.0	.S.....R020			1.34	.44	1.16	ACHL
	5.1	-32	61.89	62.15	-3.0				2.36	2.36		
N4643	12 40.8	2 15	268.98	298.19	114.4	.SBTO..P200	B K	SBRO	1.42	.15	1.36	ACEKNZ
	5.1	-32	64.52	64.77	-2.3	SB0	B K		8.38	8.38		
N4645	12 41.3	-41 29	269.71	301.45	157.4	.E.3+..S030			1.10	.18	1.03	I
	5.5	-32	20.79	21.09	-12.4				.65	.65		
N4645A	12 40.3	-41 5	269.51	301.24	157.0	.L...$.S030			1.46	.58	1.23	I
	5.5	-32	21.19	21.49	-12.5				1.10	1.10		
N4645B	12 40.8	-41 5	269.61	301.34	157.0	.L...$.S030			1.18	.57	.95	I
	5.5	-32	21.19	21.49	-12.4				.52	.52		
N4647	12 41.0	11 51	268.64	295.73	105.2	.SXT5..P200	SD *F		1.40	.09	1.36	ABDEKLX
	5.0	-32	74.12	74.34	0.4	S 5 K +	D F	S5	10.22	9.33		YZ
N4648	12 39.9	74 41	90.17	123.82	43.2	.E+3...W060			1.09	.06	1.07	AQ
	3.7	-32	43.04	42.70	14.2				1.32	1.32		
N4649	12 41.1	11 49	268.73	295.84	105.3	.E.2...P200	E2 K		1.53	.08	1.50	ABDEKLS
	5.0	-32	74.09	74.31	0.4	E 1	E2 K	E	13.71	12.82		XYZ
N4651	12 41.2	16 40	268.38	293.06	100.6	.SAT5..W100	S G		1.55	.17	1.48	ACDEKNX
	5.0	-32	78.94	79.12	1.8	S 5P 3*		S5	12.36	12.36		W
N4653	12 41.4	-0 18	269.37	298.91	116.9	.SXT6..W100			1.35	.05	1.33	ACHKLXW
	5.1	-32	61.98	62.24	-2.8	S 6 8		S5	5.32	5.32		
N4654	12 41.4	13 23	268.91	295.41	103.8	.SXT6..W100	BS *A		1.61	.24	1.52	ADEKLSX
	5.0	-32	75.65	75.87	0.9	S 5 K - 3	S A	S5	13.77	13.77		YW
N4656	12 41.6	32 26	92.14	140.21	85.4	.SBS9P.W060	I A	I 9	2.02	.65	1.76	ACHLVQ
	4.9	-32	85.29	84.72	6.0	S 5 T +	I A	I9	14.15	14.15		
N4657	12 41.7	32 29	91.82	139.78	85.3	.I...9..W060	I A		1.12	.29	1.00	H
	4.9	-32	85.24	84.67	6.1				.81	.81		
N4658	12 42.1	-9 49	269.80	300.19	126.2	.SBS4..W060			1.28	.32	1.15	ACEKQ
	5.2	-32	52.46	52.75	-5.2	S 5 K - 5	S FG*		4.09	4.09		
N4660	12 42.0	11 26	269.55	296.79	105.7	.E.6...L036	E 5		1.21	.31	1.09	AEKL
	5.0	-32	73.71	73.95	0.5		E6 K		2.79	2.79		
N4663	12 42.4	-9 54	269.92	300.32	126.3	.LBS0$.W060			.96	.07	.94	Q
	5.2	-32	52.37	52.67	-5.1				.58	.58		
N4665	12 42.6	3 19	270.03	299.09	113.5	.SBS0..W100	B K		1.50	.12	1.46	ACEKW
	5.1	-32	65.59	65.87	-1.5	SX0			7.15	7.15		
N4666	12 42.6	-0 12	270.01	299.54	116.9	.SX.5*.W100	S G		1.64	.57	1.41	ABCEHKL
	5.1	-32	62.08	62.36	-2.5	S 5 2*	S G	S5	13.58	13.58		XW
N4668	12 43.0	-0 17	270.23	299.77	117.0	.SBS7*.W100			1.12	.19	1.04	ABCHKLX
	5.1	-32	61.99	62.28	-2.4	P	I A *	I9	5.16	5.16		W
N4670	12 42.8	27 23	282.59	213.35	90.4	.SBS0P*P200	B P*K *		1.08	.17	1.01	AEKWZ
	4.9	-32	89.65	88.62	5.0	E P	D P*K *		6.49	6.49		
N4672	12 43.5	-41 27	270.15	301.89	157.5	.S.....*S030			1.17	.44	1.00	FI
	5.5	-32	20.82	21.14	-12.0				2.18	1.13		
N4673	12 43.2	27 20	292.82	215.64	90.4	.E.1+..W100			.78	.08	.75	AW
	4.9	-32	89.57	88.71	5.1				1.75	1.75		
N4674	12 43.4	-8 23	270.34	300.63	124.9	.S.....*H030			1.22	.47	1.04	ACF
	5.2	-32	53.89	54.19	-4.5				2.43	1.38		
N4676A	12 43.7	31 0	85.27	140.48	86.9	.L...P$M			1.34	.44	1.16	ABC
	4.9	-32	86.72	86.22	6.1				2.31	2.31		
N4676B	12 43.7	31 0	85.27	140.48	86.9	.SBS0P.M			1.10	.13	1.05	ABC
	4.9	-32	86.72	86.22	6.1				1.60	1.60		
N4677	12 44.2	-41 19	270.29	302.03	157.3	.L..../S030			1.27	.52	1.06	I
	5.5	-32	20.96	21.27	-11.8				.51	.51		
N4679	12 44.8	-39 18	270.43	302.11	155.4	.SA.5..S030			1.34	.30	1.22	I
	5.4	-33	22.97	23.29	-11.3				.93	.93		
N4682	12 44.7	-9 48	270.85	301.25	126.3	.SA.5..S030			1.40	.27	1.29	ACK
	5.2	-32	52.47	52.79	-4.5	S 6 7*			2.92	2.92		
N4683	12 44.9	-41 14	270.43	302.17	157.3	.L..-*.S030			1.12	.53	.91	I
	5.5	-32	21.04	21.36	-11.7				.94	.94		
N4684	12 44.7	-2 28	271.06	300.84	119.3	.LBR+..W100		L 1	1.34	.46	1.15	ACEKW
	5.1	-32	59.80	60.12	-2.6	S 0	E7 K *		5.84	5.84		
N4687	12 45.0	35 38	86.19	128.65	82.4				1.01	.06	.98	AC
	4.8	-32	82.07	81.72	7.5				.76	.76		

NGC (IC, A)	Magnitudes				Colors				Velocities			Radio			
	m_H / m_C	B(O) w	B'(O) m'_C	S(B)	(B-V)(O) w	$C_o(O)$	S(C)	(U-B)(O) w	V w	V_o ΔV	S(V)	ϕ_r n	ϕ(21)		Photo.
(14)	(15)	(16)	(17)	(18)	(19)	(20)	(21)	(22)	(23)	(24)	(25)	(26)	(27)	(28)	(29)
N4631	09.6	10.04	14.08	ACEFG	.54	.42	ACEG	-.08	626	646	GR				ABJL
	9.86	3.31	13.90		15.00		/E		24.2	20					P
N4632	12.1														
	12.38		13.62							-116					
N4633		13.88	14.72	G	.65		G			-57					
		1.30			2.50										
N4634		13.40	14.34	G	.78		G			-58					
		1.22			2.50										
N4635	13.0														
										-34					
N4636	10.8	11.01	12.95	B	.92	.85	B		883	778	BCD				P
	10.91	1.69	12.85		6.25				6.2	-105					
N4637															
										-69					
N4638	12.2	12.48	12.17	AC	.86*	.77	AC		1080	1010	B				
	12.68	3.72	12.37		6.25				.4	-69					
N4639	12.3	12.50	13.39	G	.71		G								
	12.63	0.88	13.52		2.50					-62					
N4642															
										-117					
N4643	11.6	11.64	13.18	D	.95	.85	D	.51	1432	1325	C				JKP
	11.83	4.15	13.37		18.75		/D		2.7	-107					
N4645	13.1														
	13.14		12.98							-231					
N4645A															
										-231					
N4645B															
										-230					
N4647	12.0	12.34	13.83	ACG*	.73*	.64	ACG*		1396	1328	CE				
	12.21	4.42	13.70		8.75				2.6	-68					
N4648															
										179					
N4649	10.6	10.30	12.54	ABCG*	1.00	.93	ABCG*		1269	1200	ABCDE				
	10.67	5.16	12.91		15.00				9.1	-68					
N4651	11.8	11.61	13.75	FG	.58		G								K
	11.80	2.75	13.94		2.50					-48					
N4653	13.1	13.08	14.47	G	.54		G								
	12.90	1.02	14.29		2.50					-116					
N4654	11.7	11.28	13.57	FG	.67		G								
	11.73	3.89	14.02		2.50					-62					
N4656	11.3	11.18	14.72	EFG	.33*	.24	EG	-.24	755	775	CJR				DP
	11.12	2.30	14.66		8.75		/E		29.8	20					
N4657															DP
										20					
N4658	12.4														
	12.86		13.35							-150					
N4660	12.3	12.30	12.44	AC	.99	.92	AC		1017	948	B				
	12.51	3.95	12.65		6.25				11.1	-69					
N4663															
										-150					
N4665	11.8								785	684	B				
	11.74		13.73						4.0	-102					
N4666	11.3	11.73	13.52	ACGD	.78	.62	ACGD	.23	1645	1530	C				B
	11.70	5.97	13.49		15.10		/D		2.7	-115					
N4668	13.0	13.84	13.73	G	.48		G								
	13.60	1.02	13.49		2.50					-115					
N4670	12.7	13.44	13.18	E	.39	.30	E	-.48	1210	1209	C				
	13.26	2.87	13.00		12.50		/E		2.0	-1					
N4672															
										-229					
N4673									6991	6990	C				
									2.0	-1					
N4674															
										-144					
N4676A									6500	6515	F				
									2.0	15					
N4676B									6605	6620	F				
									2.0	15					
N4677		13.99	14.03	M	1.04		M	.46							
		1.83					/M			-229					
N4679	12.9														
	13.00		13.84							-228					
N4682	13.1														
										-148					
N4683		14.34	13.63	M	1.11		M	.63							
		2.03					/M			-228					
N4684	12.2														P
	12.41		12.90							-122					
N4687															
										35					

NGC (IC, A) (1)	RA (1950) 100 P (2)	Dec 100 P (3)	L^I B^I (4)	L^II B^II (5)	SGL SGB (6)	Rev. type (S) DDO (T, L) (7)	Yerkes (1) Yerkes (2) (8)	Hu-San Ho (9)	log D w (10)	log R w (11)	log D(O) (12)	S (D,R) (13)
N4688	12 45.3 5.1	4 36 −32	271.75 66.86	300.62 67.18	112.5 −.5	.SBS6..P048 S 7	B AF		1.40 4.91	.03 4.91	1.39	ABCEK
N4689	12 45.2 5.0	14 1 −32	272.75 76.28	299.02 76.59	103.4 2.0	.SAT4..W100 S 4 3*	SD *F SD F	S5	1.48 10.04	.08 10.04	1.44	AEKLSXW
N4691	12 45.6 5.1	−3 4 −32	271.48 59.20	301.33 59.52	119.9 −2.5	RSBSOP.P200 S N +	B P* B F *	I 0	1.39 5.93	.13 5.93	1.34	AEKZ
N4692	12 45.5 4.9	27 29 −32	340.72 89.28	206.34 89.22	90.4 5.6				1.04 .59	.00 .59	1.04	A
N4694	12 45.7 5.0	11 15 −32	272.75 73.51	300.09 73.83	106.1 1.3	.LB..P.W100 E 5	I GK* D K		1.33 6.25	.39 6.25	1.17	ACEKW
N4696	12 46.1 5.5	−41 2 −32	270.68 21.24	302.41 21.56	157.1 −11.4	.E.1...S030			1.29 2.24	.04 .95	1.28	FI
N4696A	12 45.0 5.5	−41 12 −32	270.46 21.07	302.19 21.39	157.3 −11.7	.S...*.S030			1.24 .89	.55 .89	1.02	I
N4696B	12 45.5 5.5	−40 58 −32	270.56 21.30	302.29 21.63	157.0 −11.5	.L...*.S030			1.16 .71	.33 .71	1.02	I
N4696C	12 46.2 5.5	−40 32 −32	270.71 21.73	302.43 22.06	156.6 −11.3	.S...*/S030			1.29 1.21	.59 1.21	1.C6	I
N4696D	12 46.5 5.5	−41 26 −32	270.75 20.83	302.50 21.16	157.5 −11.4	.L...*/S030			1.13 .48	.58 .48	.90	I
N4696E	12 46.6 5.5	−40 39 −32	270.79 21.62	302.51 21.95	156.8 −11.3	.L.....S030			1.29 1.21	.59 1.21	1.06	I
N4697	12 46.0 5.2	−5 32 −32	271.55 56.73	301.63 57.06	122.3 −3.1	.E.6...P200 E 4	E6 G E6 K	E 5	1.58 9.80	.23 9.80	1.48	ACEHKLZ
N4698	12 45.8 5.1	8 45 −32	272.48 71.01	300.53 71.33	108.5 0.7	.SAS2..W100 S 2 3*	S K S K	S1	1.50 7.77	.34 7.77	1.36	ACEKXW
N4699	12 46.5 5.2	−8 24 −32	271.64 53.86	301.94 54.19	125.1 −3.7	.SXT3..W100 S 0	SD *K DS K	S 3	1.51 17.28	.15 17.28	1.44	ACEFKMP VW
N4700	12 46.5 5.2	−11 8 −32	271.52 51.13	302.02 51.46	127.7 −4.5	.SBS../W100 S *	SI *AF*		1.45 8.95	.69 7.29	1.17	ACEFKW
N4701	12 46.6 5.1	3 39 −32	272.48 65.90	301.51 66.24	113.5 −.5	.SAS6..W100 S N	S FG S G		1.30 4.38	.13 4.38	1.25	AEKW
N4703	12 46.8 5.2	−8 51 −32	271.74 53.41	302.08 53.75	125.6 −3.8	.S..5./L036			1.45 5.38	.70 3.71	1.17	ACFM
N4704	12 46.4 4.7	42 11 −32	87.00 75.52	124.86 75.20	76.1 9.3	.S....$R020			1.17 .85	.06 .85	1.15	ACH
N4705	12 46.9 5.2	−4 55 −32	271.99 57.33	302.01 57.67	121.8 −2.7	.S....$R020			1.47 1.01	.29 1.01	1.36	ACH
N4706	12 47.2 5.5	−40 59 −32	270.90 21.28	302.63 21.62	157.1 −11.2	.L..../S030			1.17 1.02	.44 1.02	.99	I
N4708	12 47.1 5.2	−10 49 −32	271.77 51.44	302.25 51.78	127.5 −4.2				1.09 2.59	.18 2.59	1.02	ABCF
N4709	12 47.3 5.5	−41 6 −32	270.92 21.16	302.65 21.50	157.2 −11.2	.E.1...S030			1.18 1.03	.04 1.03	1.16	I
N4710	12 47.1 5.0	15 26 −32	275.19 77.66	300.79 78.02	102.2 2.8	.LAR+$/W100 E 8	S P*G D *K *	L 3	1.56 10.78	.70 9.60	1.28	AEHKLSQ
N4712	12 47.2 4.9	25 44 −32	298.21 87.74	289.34 88.29	92.2 5.5	.SAS4..W100 S 7	S F * S AF	S5	1.41 10.75	.31 10.10	1.28	ABCEKLU XW
N4713	12 47.5 5.1	5 35 −32	273.27 67.82	302.00 68.18	111.7 0.2	.SXT7..W100 S 5 K 5	SB *AF S A		1.39 8.61	.18 8.61	1.32	ACEKNW
N4718	12 48.0 5.2	−5 0 −32	272.49 57.23	302.53 57.59	121.9 −2.5	.S....*R020			1.37 .42	.39 .42	1.21	AH
N4724	12 48.3 5.2	−14 4 −32	272.07 48.18	302.74 48.53	130.7 −4.8	.E...*.B			.94 .88	.00 .88	.94	AB
N4725	12 48.1 4.9	25 46 −32	303.01 87.67	295.94 88.35	92.2 5.7	.SXR2P.W100 SX3 1	BS *G SB GK	SX 3 S4	1.95 18.40	.15 18.40	1.89	ABCEKLU XYW
N4727	12 48.3 5.2	−14 4 −32	272.07 48.18	302.74 48.53	130.7 −4.8	.S...*.B			1.19 1.56	.10 1.56	1.15	AB
N4728	12 48.0 4.9	27 42 −32	359.24 88.77	158.61 89.63	90.3 6.2				.90 .84	.00 .84	.90	AB
N4731	12 48.4 5.2	−6 8 −32	272.59 56.11	302.73 56.47	123.0 −2.7	.SBS6..W060 SB5P 4*	BS AF		1.79 22.48	.28 19.08	1.68	ABCDEFH KPTQ
N4733	12 48.6 5.0	11 10 −32	275.22 73.38	302.65 73.77	106.4 2.0	.E.1...P048			1.13 1.12	.05 1.12	1.12	ABC
N4734	12 48.7 5.1	5 7 −32	273.98 67.34	302.80 67.72	112.2 0.4	.S..5*.L036			1.03 1.99	.06 1.99	1.00	ACN
N4736	12 48.6 4.7	41 23 −32	85.07 76.29	123.31 76.02	76.9 9.5	RSAR2..P200 S 2P 3*	S *G * DS G	S 3 S3	1.87 19.91	.10 19.91	1.83	ACHLRVX YZ
N4739	12 49.0 5.2	−8 8 −32	272.71 54.11	303.00 54.47	125.0 −3.1				1.05 .84	.00 .84	1.05	AC
N4742	12 49.2 5.2	−10 12 −32	272.64 52.04	303.08 52.40	127.0 −3.6	.E.4.*.W060 E 3	D K		1.13 5.34	.22 4.71	1.04	ACEFHKL Q
N4744	12 49.6 5.5	−40 46 −32	271.40 21.49	303.12 21.83	157.0 −10.7							
N4746	12 49.5 5.0	12 21 −32	276.41 74.54	303.47 74.95	105.3 2.5	.S....*			1.42 1.60	.51 1.60	1.21	AC
N4747	12 49.4 4.9	26 1 −32	312.52 87.69	306.74 88.61	92.1 6.1	.SBS5$/L036 P T −	SIP*F *	S5	1.56 7.69	.51 7.69	1.35	ABCELUX
N4749	12 48.3 3.7	71 53 −32	89.29 45.84	123.08 45.52	46.1 14.5	.S.....			1.34 1.00	.60 1.00	1.10	A

NGC (IC, A) (14)	Magnitudes				Colors				Velocities			Radio			
	m_H m_C (15)	B(O) w (16)	B'(O) m'_C (17)	S(B) (18)	(B-V)(O) w (19)	C_o(O) (20)	S(C) (21)	(U-B)(O) w (22)	V w (23)	V_o ΔV (24)	S(V) (25)	$φ_r$ n (26)	φ (21) (27)	(28)	Photo. (29)
N4688	13.0 12.73									-94					
N4689	12.0 11.98	11.87 0.95	13.81 13.92	G	.67 2.50		G			-56					
N4691	11.8 11.99	11.81 2.55	13.25 13.43·	E	.55 6.25		E /E	-.09		-124					LP
N4692				E*	.83 6.25	.68	E /E	.64	7911 2.0	7912 1	C				
N4694	12.6 12.64		13.23							-67					
N4696	12.2 12.10	12.38 3.06	13.52 13.24	M	1.06	.89	M /M	.64	2794 14.8	2567 -227	L				
N4696A										-228					
N4696B										-227					
N4696C										-226					
N4696D										-228					
N4696E										-226					
N4697	10.6 10.71	10.58 1.79	12.72 12.85	C	.89 1.88	.81	C		1308 2.4	1176 -132	B				P
N4698	12.2 12.23	11.81 10.83	13.35 13.77	CDG	.90* 49.37	.74	CDG* /D	.43	1032 4.0	955 -77	B				K
N4699	10.5 11.15	10.60 9.38	12.54 13.09	CD	.90 50.63	.77	CD /D	.37	1511 2.8	1369 -142	C				P
N4700	12.2 12.71		13.30							-151					
N4701	12.8 12.94		13.88							-97					
N4703										-143					
N4704										64					
N4705										-129					
N4706		14.11 2.00	13.80	M	1.07	.87	M /M	.53*	3511 6.6	3285 -226	L				
N4708										-150					
N4709		13.22 1.46	13.76	M	1.14	.95	M /M	.62	4500 11.1	4273 -227	L				
N4710	12.0 12.05	12.28 2.56	13.42 13.19	AC	.84 1.88		C			-49					BLP
N4712	12.9 12.84	13.73 1.39	14.87 13.98	G	.58 2.50		G			-5					
N4713	12.3 12.58	12.31 5.36	13.60 13.87	D	.44 18.75	.35	D /D	-.26	664 2.8	575 -89	C				
N4718										-129					
N4724										-160					
N4725	10.8 10.25	10.21 5.85	14.40 14.44	BFG	.85* 8.75	.74	BG		1114 2.4	1109 -5	B				AP
N4727										-160					
N4728									6522 2.0	6526 4	C				
N4731	12.2 11.63		14.72						1438 1.4	1305 -133	D				
N4733										-66					
N4734										-90					
N4736	9.0 9.44	8.91 7.96	12.75 13.28	BEFGK	.76 15.00	.67	BEG /E	.13	300 11.8	362 62	ABCF				ACLP
N4739										-139					
N4742	11.9 12.31	12.76 1.05	12.70 12.25	C	1.01 1.88	.93	C		1321 4.0	1175 -146	B				
N4744				M*			M*			-225					
N4746										-60					
N4747	12.7 12.59	13.22 1.25	14.71 14.08	G	.64 2.50		G			-3					
N4749										173					

NGC (IC, A) (1)	RA (1950) 100 P (2)	Dec 100 P (3)	L^I B^I (4)	L^{II} B^{II} (5)	SGL SGB (6)	Rev. type (S) DDO (T, L) (7)	Yerkes (1) Yerkes (2) (8)	Hu-San Ho (9)	log D w (10)	log R w (11)	log D(0) (12)	S (D,R) (13)
N4750	12 48.4	73 9	89.34	123.06	44.8	RSAT2..W060	SDP*FG	S 3	1.23	.06	1.21	AKMQ
	3.6	-32	44.57	44.25	14.6	S OP	DSP GK		4.69	4.69		
N4753	12 49.8	-0 55	273.76	303.41	118.1	.I.O...W100	E P	L P	1.66	.35	1.52	ACEFKUW
	5.1	-32	61.31	61.69	-1.0	S N +	D P G		12.99	12.99		
N4754	12 49.7	11 35	276.30	303.63	106.1	.LBR-*.W100	E T *	D K	1.50	.30	1.38	ABCEKMW
	5.0	-32	73.77	74.18	2.4	E T *	D K		10.05	10.05		
N4756	12 50.3	-15 8	272.72	303.46	131.9	.S....*R020			.98	.04	.96	AK
	5.3	-32	47.10	47.47	-4.6	E 2			.82	.82		
N4757	12 50.3	-10 2	273.09	303.53	126.9	.L..../W100			1.12	.66	.85	FLW
	5.2	-32	52.19	52.57	-3.3				2.60	1.97		
N4758	12 50.3	16 7	279.24	304.60	101.7	.S....*R020			1.47	.59	1.23	AH
	5.0	-32	78.25	78.72	3.7				1.27	1.27		
N4760	12 50.5	-10 13	273.16	303.60	127.1	.E.O..$W100			1.01	.01	1.00	AEFHKLW
	5.2	-32	52.01	52.38	-3.3	E 2	D K		3.87	3.87		
N4762	12 50.4	11 31	276.89	304.25	106.2	.LBRO$/W100	D GK	L 1	1.75	.87	1.41	ABCEHMW
	5.0	-32	73.68	74.11	2.5	S NT+*	D K		13.59	13.59		
N4763	12 50.6	-16 43	272.73	303.55	133.4				1.06	.09	1.02	AK
	5.3	-32	45.51	45.88	-4.9	S 0			1.44	1.44		
N4765	12 50.7	4 45	275.19	304.10	112.7				1.00	.16	.93	ACEKQ
	5.1	-32	66.94	67.35	0.8	S *	E4P*		2.65	2.65		
N4766	12 50.5	-10 6	273.17	303.61	127.0	.L..../W100			.97	.75	.67	FW
	5.2	-32	52.12	52.50	-3.2				1.64	1.64		
N4767	12 51.2	-39 27	271.77	303.46	155.7	.E.5...S030			1.17	.30	1.05	I
	5.5	-32	22.79	23.15	-10.2				.72	.72		
N4767A	12 50.3	-39 35	271.58	303.27	155.8	.S...$.S030			1.10	.54	.39	I
	5.5	-32	22.67	23.02	-10.4				.92	.92		
N4767B	12 52.0	-39 35	271.93	303.63	155.9	.SBS7.$S030			1.17	.05	1.15	I
	5.5	-32	22.65	23.01	-10.0				1.01	1.01		
N4771	12 50.8	1 33	274.66	304.03	115.8	.SA.7$/W100	SD *F		1.58	.67	1.31	ACEKW
	5.1	-32	63.75	64.15	-.1	S 3 5	S *G *		8.47	8.47		
N4772	12 51.0	2 27	274.93	304.18	114.9	.SAS1..W060			1.54	.38	1.38	AEKQ
	5.1	-32	64.64	65.05	0.2	S 0	S K		5.15	5.15		
N4773	12 51.0	-8 24	273.52	303.85	125.4				1.06	.02	1.05	AC
	5.2	-32	53.81	54.20	-2.7				.87	.87		
N4775	12 51.1	-6 21	273.77	303.94	123.4	.SAS7..W060	S A		1.31	.02	1.30	ACEFKNQ
	5.2	-32	55.86	56.25	-2.1	S 5 K - 5	S F		8.55	8.55		
N4777	12 51.4	-8 28	273.68	304.01	125.5				1.32	.29	1.21	A
	5.2	-32	53.74	54.13	-2.6				.97	.97		
N4780	12 51.5	-8 21	273.74	304.06	125.4	.S.....H030			1.30	.14	1.24	BCF
	5.2	-32	53.86	54.24	-2.5				2.68	2.68		
N4781	12 51.8	-10 16	273.67	304.13	127.3	.SBT7..W060	SI *A		1.52	.33	1.39	ABCEFGH
	5.2	-32	51.94	52.33	-3.0	S 5 K 4	SI *A		15.95	15.95		KLTQ
N4782	12 52.0	-12 19	273.56	304.15	129.2	.E+O.P.W100	D *K		.96	.00	.96	ABCDKW
	5.2	-33	49.89	50.28	-3.5	E O T -*	D *K		3.12	3.12		
N4783	12 52.0	-12 18	273.56	304.15	129.2	.E.O.P.W100	D K		.97	.01	.97	ABCDKW
	5.2	-33	49.91	50.29	-3.5	E O T -*	D K		3.14	3.14		
N4784	12 52.0	-10 21	273.74	304.20	127.3	.L..../W060			1.22	.74	.93	BFLQ
	5.2	-32	51.85	52.24	-3.0				3.55	2.92		
N4786	12 52.0	-6 35	274.14	304.33	123.7	.E.2.*.L036	D K		1.06	.14	1.00	ACDENK
	5.2	-32	55.61	56.01	-2.0	E 2P	D K		4.08	4.08		
N4789	12 51.9	27 20	349.86	27.23	90.9	.L...*.L036			1.08	.12	1.03	A
	4.9	-32	87.87	89.35	6.9				.64	.64		
N4789A	12 51.7	27 25	351.88	34.72	90.8	.I..9..L036						
	4.9	-33	87.93	89.40	6.9							
N4790	12 52.2	-9 58	273.86	304.30	127.0	.SBT5*$W060			1.22	.17	1.15	ACDEFGH
	5.2	-32	52.23	52.62	-2.8	S 5 K 5*	SI *AF		9.04	8.41		KLQ
N4792	12 52.4	-12 16	273.72	304.30	129.2	.L..../W100			.84	.18	.77	CW
	5.2	-32	49.93	50.32	-3.4				.82	.82		
N4793	12 52.3	29 13	35.08	101.39	89.1	.SXT5..W100		S 5	1.36	.26	1.26	ACEKNW
	4.8	-32	87.37	88.04	7.5	S 5 5	S P FG*		8.26	8.26		
N4794	12 52.6	-12 21	273.79	304.37	129.3	.SBT1..W100			1.35	.36	1.20	W
	5.2	-32	49.85	50.24	-3.3				1.25	1.25		
N4795	12 52.5	8 20	277.39	305.65	109.4				1.27	.14	1.22	AEK
	5.0	-32	70.46	70.92	2.2	S NT+*			2.45	2.45		
N4798	12 52.4	27 42	359.83	54.87	90.6	.E.2...W			1.04	.00	1.04	A
	4.9	-32	87.80	89.19	7.1				.59	.59		
N4800	12 52.4	46 48	84.75	121.25	71.7	.SAT3..W060		S 3	1.14	.12	1.09	ACKQ
	4.6	-32	70.83	70.59	11.3	S	DSP*K		3.68	3.68		
N4802	12 53.2	-11 47	274.07	304.63	128.8							
	5.2	-32	50.40	50.80	-3.1							
N4808	12 53.3	4 35	276.79	305.76	113.0	.SAS6*.W100	SI *AF		1.44	.35	1.30	ACEKNW
	5.1	-32	66.71	67.16	1.4	S 5 K 5	SI *AF*		9.22	9.22		
N4809	12 52.3	2 56	275.79	304.99	114.6	.I..9P.P200			1.28	.41	1.11	ABCLZ
	5.1	-33	65.10	65.52	0.7				5.14	4.51		
N4810	12 52.3	2 55	275.78	304.99	114.6	.I..9P.P200			.99	.18	.92	ABCLZ
	5.1	-33	65.05	65.50	0.7				3.42	2.98		
N4814	12 53.3	58 37	87.20	121.92	59.8	.SAS3..W060	S G		1.33	.10	1.30	ACKQ
	4.3	-32	59.05	58.77	13.4	S 3P 3*			4.25	4.25		
N4818	12 54.3	-8 15	274.92	305.25	125.5	.SXS2*.....			1.62	.46	1.43	ACDEFGK
	5.2	-32	53.91	54.33	-1.8	SX N +*	B *G *		9.97	9.97		

NGC (IC, A) (14)	m_H / m_C (15)	B(O) w (16)	B'(O) m'_C (17)	S(B) (18)	(B-V)(O) w (19)	C_o(O) (20)	S(C) (21)	(U-B)(O) w (22)	V w (23)	V_o ΔV (24)	S(V) (25)	ϕ_r n (26)	ϕ(21) (27)	(28)	Photo. (29)
N4750	12.2		13.34						1647	1823	C				P
	12.60								2.5	176					
N4753	10.5	11.00	13.29	CE	.93	.81	CE	.50	1364	1252	C				LP
	10.78	3.57	13.07		10.00		/E		1.2	-112					
N4754	12.0	11.77	13.41	C	.95	.86	C		1461	1398	B				
	11.88	1.43	13.52		1.88				1.8	-63					
N4756	13.3														
	13.37		12.91							-162					
N4757										-145					
N4758										-44					
N4760	12.5														
	12.78		12.52							-145					
N4762	11.8	11.53	13.27	CD	.83	.73	CD	.42	939	876	BCD				JKP
	11.72	1.56	13.46		11.25		/D		13.1	-63					
N4763	13.2														
										-166					
N4765	12.9														
										-90					
N4766										-145					
N4767	12.8														
	12.89		12.88							-222					
N4767A										-222					
N4767B										-221					
N4771	12.9														
	12.93		14.17							-102					
N4772	12.6														
	12.37		14.01							-99					
N4773										-139					
N4775	11.6								1684	1553	C				K
	12.23		13.47						3.8	-131					
N4777										-138					
N4780										-138					
N4781	11.7								895	751	C				E
	12.10		13.74						2.4	-144					
N4782	12.9								4009	3858	EK				
	13.11		12.65						11.6	-151					
N4783	12.7								4677	4527	EK				
	12.98		12.52						11.6	-151					
N4784										-145					
N4786	12.7														
	12.91		12.65							-131					
N4789		13.57	13.46	C	1.07	.91	C		8372	8377	C				
		0.67			1.88				3.8	5					
N4789A										5					
N4790	12.5														
	12.94		13.43							-143					
N4792										-151					
N4793	12.5	12.86	13.85	C	.67	.54	C				C*				P
	12.71	1.58	13.70		3.75					13					
N4794										-151					
N4795	13.1									-74					
N4798		14.56	14.50	C	1.06	.92	C		7673	7680	B				
		1.05			1.88				4.0	7					
N4800	12.0	12.62	12.81	B					746	832	B				P
	12.76	1.28	12.95						4.0	86					
N4802										-148					
N4808	12.5														
	12.64		13.88							-88					
N4809									950	854	E				
									.8	-96					
N4810									890	794	E				
									.8	-96					
N4814	12.3	13.16	14.35	B					2531	2661	B				
	12.47	1.14	13.66						2.4	131					
N4818	12.1														
	12.01		13.90							-136					

NGC (IC, A) (1)	Coordinates RA (1950) Dec 100 P (2)	100 P (3)	L^I B^I (4)	L^II B^II (5)	SGL SGB (6)	Classification Rev. type (S) DDO (T, L) (7)	Yerkes (1) Yerkes (2) (8)	Hu-San Ho (9)	Diameters log D w (10)	log R w (11)	log D(O) (12)	S (D,R) (13)
N4819	12 54.0 / 4.9	27 15 / -32	350.17 / 87.39	25.81 / 88.88	91.1 / 7.4				1.18 / 1.54	.24 / 1.54	1.08	AB
N4821	12 54.1 / 4.9	27 13 / -32	349.55 / 87.36	24.31 / 88.85	91.1 / 7.4							
N4825	12 54.5 / 5.2	-13 24 / -32	274.39 / 48.77	305.05 / 49.18	130.5 / -3.2	.LA.-..W100 E 2P	D K		1.10 / 4.86	.16 / 4.86	1.04	ADEKW
N4826	12 54.3 / 4.9	21 57 / -32	295.53 / 83.63	315.74 / 84.42	96.3 / 6.1	RSAT2..W060	S P FG	S 3 S3	1.87 / 18.75	.25 / 18.75	1.77	ACHKLSU XYQ
N4827	12 54.3 / 4.9	27 27 / -33	354.62 / 87.36	35.72 / 88.82	90.9 / 7.5	.E.....			1.04 / .59	.00 / .59	1.04	A
N4835	12 55.3 / 5.7	-45 59 / -32	272.27 / 16.23	304.14 / 16.60	162.4 / -10.7	.SXT4*.R074			1.48 / 4.32	.59 / 4.32	1.24	IO
N4835A	12 54.2 / 5.7	-46 7 / -32	272.06 / 16.11	303.94 / 16.47	162.5 / -11.0	.S...*/S030			1.45 / 1.07	1.00 / 1.07	1.05	I
N4839	12 55.0 / 4.8	27 45 / -32	1.24 / 87.22	48.20 / 88.62	90.7 / 7.7				1.30 / .94	.26 / .94	1.20	A
N4841A	12 55.2 / 4.8	28 45 / -32	20.72 / 87.01	77.97 / 88.08	89.7 / 8.0	.E.1...W			1.06 / 1.23	.00 / 1.23	1.06	AB
N4841B	12 55.2 / 4.8	28 45 / -32	20.72 / 87.01	77.97 / 88.08	89.7 / 8.0	.E.0...W			.98 / 1.03	.00 / 1.03	.98	AB
N4842	12 55.2 / 4.8	27 46 / -32	1.58 / 87.18	48.40 / 88.57	90.7 / 7.7							
N4845	12 55.5 / 5.1	1 51 / -32	277.38 / 63.94	306.76 / 64.40	115.8 / 1.2	.SAS2./W060 S 3 5	SD *FG S G *		1.63 / 9.89	.56 / 9.89	1.41	ACEHKQ
N4848	12 55.7 / 4.8	28 30 / -32	15.61 / 86.97	70.03 / 88.15	90.0 / 8.0				1.11 / .69	.49 / .69	.91	A
N4849	12 55.9 / 4.9	26 40 / -32	341.29 / 86.83	8.05 / 88.30	91.8 / 7.6				.96 / .96	.04 / .96	.94	AB
N4850	12 55.8 / 4.8	28 14 / -32	10.55 / 87.01	62.43 / 88.28	90.2 / 8.0	.L.....W			.90 / .42	.00 / .42	.90	A
N4853	12 56.2 / 4.8	27 53 / -32	3.70 / 86.96	50.26 / 88.33	90.6 / 8.0	.E.1...W			.90 / .42	.00 / .42	.90	A
N4856	12 56.7 / 5.3	-14 46 / -32	275.03 / 47.37	305.77 / 47.79	131.9 / -3.0	.SBS0..W060 SX0	B *K D K		1.59 / 8.65	.60 / 8.65	1.35	AEFMQ
N4858	12 56.5 / 4.8	28 23 / -32	12.79 / 86.83	64.14 / 88.07	90.1 / 8.2				.95 / .48	.00 / .48	.95	A
N4860	12 56.5 / 4.8	28 24 / -32	13.03 / 86.83	64.53 / 88.06	90.1 / 8.2	.E.2...W			1.00 / .54	.00 / .54	1.00	A
N4861	12 56.7 / 4.7	35 8 / -32	68.54 / 82.00	111.47 / 82.09	83.5 / 9.7	.SBS9*.W060 I 8	I *A I P A *		1.56 / 7.10	.46 / 7.10	1.38	ACKNQ
N4864	12 56.8 / 4.8	28 15 / -32	10.22 / 86.79	59.73 / 88.07	90.3 / 8.2	.E.1...W						
N4865	12 56.8 / 4.8	28 22 / -32	12.22 / 86.77	62.72 / 88.02	90.2 / 8.2	.E.6...W			1.00 / .54	.30 / .54	.88	A
N4866	12 57.0 / 5.0	14 27 / -32	284.97 / 76.30	311.59 / 76.92	103.8 / 4.9	.LAR+*/W100 S 2 5*	DS *K *	S 1	1.66 / 7.11	.71 / 7.11	1.38	ACEHK
N4867	12 56.9 / 4.8	28 16 / -32	10.46 / 86.76	59.88 / 88.04	90.3 / 8.2	.S..1..W						
N4868	12 56.8 / 4.7	37 35 / -32	73.86 / 79.69	114.33 / 79.69	81.0 / 10.2	S 4 3*			1.21 / 1.81	.02 / 1.41	1.20	ACK
N4869	12 57.0 / 4.8	28 11 / -32	8.95 / 86.75	57.39 / 88.06	90.3 / 8.2	.E.3...W						
N4872	12 57.2 / 4.8	28 14 / -32	9.65 / 86.71	58.15 / 88.00	90.3 / 8.3	.E.4...W			1.18 / .15	.00 / .15	1.18	A
N4874	12 57.2 / 4.8	28 14 / -32	9.65 / 86.71	58.15 / 88.00	90.3 / 8.3	.L.....W			.84 / .34	.00 / .34	.84	A
N4877	12 57.8 / 5.3	-15 1 / -32	275.39 / 47.10	306.15 / 47.53	132.2 / -2.8	.SAS2*.W060			1.31 / 1.86	.30 / 1.86	1.19	AQ
N4880	12 57.7 / 5.0	12 45 / -32	284.08 / 74.61	311.34 / 75.21	105.4 / 4.6	.L.....P048 S 0			1.39 / 3.92	.15 / 3.92	1.33	ABCK
N4881	12 57.5 / 4.8	28 31 / -32	14.22 / 86.59	64.23 / 87.82	90.0 / 8.4	.E.1...W			.90 / .42	.00 / .42	.90	A
N4886	12 57.6 / 4.8	28 15 / -32	9.73 / 86.62	57.57 / 87.92	90.3 / 8.4	.L.....W			.88 / .38	.00 / .38	.88	A
N4889	12 57.7 / 4.8	28 15 / -32	9.68 / 86.59	57.33 / 87.90	90.3 / 8.4	.E.4...L036 E 4	E4 K		1.18 / 2.67	.19 / 2.67	1.10	AKM
N4891	12 58.1 / 5.3	-13 9 / -32	275.75 / 48.95	306.40 / 49.39	130.4 / -2.3	N	S FG		1.38 / 2.16	.04 / 2.16	1.37	EK
N4895	12 57.8 / 4.8	28 29 / -32	13.45 / 86.53	62.63 / 87.77	90.1 / 8.5	.L.....W			1.18 / .77	.37 / .77	1.03	A
N4895A	12 57.7 / 4.8	28 26 / -32	12.75 / 86.56	61.79 / 87.81	90.1 / 8.4							
N4896	12 57.9 / 4.8	28 35 / -32	14.98 / 86.49	64.57 / 87.71	90.0 / 8.5	.L.....W						
N4898	12 57.9 / 4.8	28 13 / -32	9.03 / 86.55	56.04 / 87.87	90.4 / 8.4	.L.....W						
N4899	12 58.3 / 5.3	-13 41 / -32	275.75 / 48.41	306.43 / 48.85	131.0 / -2.4	.SXT5*.W100 S P	S A		1.41 / 7.76	.25 / 7.76	1.31	AEKUW
N4900	12 58.2 / 5.1	2 46 / -32	279.20 / 64.76	308.50 / 65.27	115.1 / 2.1	.SBT5..W100 S 5 K 5	BI *A I AF		1.31 / 11.69	.04 / 9.86	1.29	ACEHKNR VW

NGC (IC, A) (14)	m_H m_C (15)	B(O) w (16)	B'(O) m'_C (17)	S(B) (18)	(B-V)(O) w (19)	C_O(O) (20)	S(C) (21)	(U-B)(O) w (22)	V w (23)	V_O ΔV (24)	S(V) (25)	φ_r n (26)	φ(21) (27)	(28)	Photo. (29)
N4819									6696 2.0	6702 6	C				
N4821									6974 2.0	6980 6	C				
N4825	12.9 13.07		12.96							-153					
N4826	8.0 9.04	9.60 7.62	13.14 12.58	BEFGK /E	.86 15.00	.73	BEG /E	.28	368 12.1	352 -16	AB				ABP
N4827		14.35 0.71	14.29	C	.95 1.88	.81	C		7650 2.0	7657 7	C				
N4835	12.5 12.71		13.65							-229					H
N4835A										-230					
N4839									7446 2.0	7455 9	C				
N4841A				C*			C*			13					
N4841B				C*			C*			13					
N4842									7512 2.0	7521 9	C				
N4845	12.6 12.33		14.12							-97					
N4848									7209 2.1	7221 12	C				
N4849									5823 2.0	5828 5	C				
N4850		15.32 3.38	14.56	C	1.02 3.75	.90	C		5984 1.0	5995 11	B				
N4853		14.46 3.43	13.70	C	.90 3.75	.76	C		7550 4.0	7560 10	B				
N4856	11.4 11.75	11.68 3.68	13.17 13.24	C	.97 3.75	.83	C		1251 1.8	1095 -156	B				
N4858									9386 2.0	9398 12	C				
N4860		14.59 2.59	14.33	C	1.01* 3.75	.87	C		7862 8.3	7874 12	BC				
N4861	12.7 12.70	13.16 2.04	14.75 14.29	C	.57 3.75	.48	C		790 4.0	831 41	C*F				
N4864				C*			C*		6819 .6	6831 12	B				
N4865		14.73 4.80	13.87	CD /D	.95 22.50	.85	CD /D	.49	4643 4.0	4655 12	B				
N4866	12.1 11.97	12.36 1.43	13.95 13.56	C	.86 1.88	.75	C		1910 11.1	1864 -46	B				P
N4867				C*			C*		4815 1.0	4827 12	B				
N4868	13.1 13.15		13.84							51					
N4869				C*			C*		6703 1.0	6715 12	B				
N4872		14.65 2.72	15.24	BC	1.00 10.00	.86	BC		6910 .1	6922 12	B				
N4874		14.01 25.33	12.95	ABCDE H	1.02 61.88	.88	BCDEH /DE	.56	7171 11.1	7183 12	B				
N4877										-156					
N4880	13.1 12.70		14.09							-52					
N4881		14.85 5.34	14.09	CD /D	1.00* 20.63	.87	CD /D	.48	6691 4.0	6705 14	B				
N4886		15.05 2.01	14.14	C	.95 1.88	.82	C		6214 .4	6227 13	B				
N4889	12.6 12.67	13.17 18.74	13.41 12.91	ABCDH	1.05 36.87	.92	BCDH /D	.56	6443 7.5	6456 13	BC				
N4891	13.0									-149					
N4895		14.32 3.43	14.21	C	1.02 3.75	.85	C		8406 1.8	8420 14	B				
N4895A									6758 2.0	6771 13	C				
N4896				C*			C*		5820 .4	5834 14	B				
N4898				C*			C*		6935 4.0	6948 13	B				
N4899	12.7 12.70		13.94							-151					
N4900	11.8 12.24	12.17 4.28	13.36 13.43	CF	.66 1.88	.58	C		1054 2.8	962 -92	C				

NGC (IC, A) (1)	RA (1950) 100 P (2)	Dec 100 P (3)	L^I B^I (4)	L^II B^II (5)	SGL SGB (6)	Rev. type (S) DDO (T, L) (7)	Yerkes (1) Yerkes (2) (8)	Hu-San Ho (9)	log D w (10)	log R w (11)	log D(O) (12)	S (D,R) (13)
N4902	12 58.3	-14 15	275.67	306.39	131.5	.SBR3..W060	B AF		1.43	.04	1.41	AEFGKQ
	5.3	-32	47.85	48.29	-2.5	SB3 1	B F		8.19	8.19		
N4904	12 58.4	0 15	278.53	308.14	117.6	.SBS6..W100	BSP*AF		1.32	.17	1.25	AEKW
	5.1	-32	62.26	62.76	1.4	SX5 NK-	B F		5.71	5.71		
N4907	12 58.4	28 25	12.02	59.66	90.2	.S.....L			1.11	.17	1.05	A
	4.8	-32	86.41	87.68	8.6				.69	.69		
N4908	12 58.4	28 18	10.13	56.95	90.3	.E.4...W			.90	.00	.90	A
	4.8	-32	86.43	87.74	8.6				.42	.42		
N4911	12 58.6	28 3	6.07	50.56	90.6	.S..3..L			1.08	.04	1.07	ABC
	4.8	-32	86.42	87.78	8.5				1.55	1.55		
N4914	12 58.4	37 35	72.19	112.60	81.1				1.25	.24	1.15	ACK
	4.7	-32	79.59	79.63	10.6	E 2P *	ED *K		1.72	1.72		
N4915	12 58.8	-4 16	277.60	307.65	121.9	.E.0...W060			.96	.04	.94	ACEKQ
	5.2	-32	57.77	58.24	0.3	S 0	D K *		2.82	2.82		
N4921	12 59.3	28 9	7.42	51.81	90.5	.S..1..W			1.40	.04	1.38	A
	4.8	-32	86.26	87.60	8.7				1.08	1.08		
N4922	12 59.0	29 35	28.03	78.39	89.1				1.19	.26	1.09	AC
	4.8	-32	85.92	86.90	9.0				1.09	1.09		
N4924	12 59.6	-14 42	276.07	306.82	132.0	.E...$.H030			.95	.00	.95	A
	5.3	-32	47.37	47.82	-2.3				.48	.48		
N4926	12 59.5	27 53	3.37	45.40	90.8	.E.....W			1.00	.00	1.00	A
	4.8	-32	86.22	87.62	8.7				.54	.54		
N4926A	12 59.7	27 54	3.61	45.59	90.8							
	4.8	-32	86.18	87.57	8.7							
N4928	13 0.3	-7 49	277.51	307.84	125.5	.SAS4P.W100			1.09	.13	1.04	ACEFKW
	5.2	-32	54.20	54.68	-.3	S 7 K 7	S F *		5.53	4.47		
N4931	13 0.6	28 18	9.15	53.00	90.4	.E.4...W			1.23	.31	1.11	AC
	4.8	-32	85.95	87.28	9.0				.48	.48		
N4933A	13 1.2	-11 14	277.22	307.78	128.8	.S..OP.W100			1.06	.13	1.01	ABCW
	5.2	-32	50.78	51.25	-1.0	E PT -*	D *K		2.09	2.09		
N4933B	13 1.2	-11 14	277.22	307.78	128.8	.E...P.W100			.80	.03	.78	ABW
	5.2	-32	50.78	51.25	-1.0				1.30	1.30		
N4936	13 1.5	-30 15	274.78	306.19	147.2	.E.0...W100			1.03	.00	1.02	DWE
	5.5	-32	31.85	32.27	-6.0				3.43	3.43		
N4939	13 1.7	-10 5	277.63	308.13	127.7	.SAS4..W100			1.72	.27	1.61	ACEKW
	5.2	-32	51.90	52.39	-.6	N	S F		10.18	10.18		
N4941	13 1.6	-5 17	278.64	308.79	123.1	RSXR2*.W060		S 2	1.50	.27	1.39	ACEFGQ
	5.2	-32	56.67	57.17	0.7	S 3P	SD G		8.50	8.50		
N4942	13 1.7	-7 24	278.19	308.50	125.1	.SA.6..L036			1.30	.18	1.23	ACFN
	5.2	-32	54.57	55.06	0.1				3.66	3.66		
N4944	13 1.5	28 28	11.09	54.87	90.3				1.28	.42	1.11	A
	4.8	-32	85.73	87.03	9.3				.91	.91		
N4945	13 2.4	-49 13	273.28	305.25	165.9	.SBS6*$S030			2.22	.79	1.90	EI
	5.8	-32	12.93	13.32	-10.2				3.86	3.86		
N4945A	13 3.7	-49 24	273.48	305.45	166.1	.S...$/S030			1.32	.58	1.09	I
	5.8	-32	12.73	13.13	-10.1				.63	.63		
N4947	13 2.6	-35 4	274.57	306.13	152.0	.SBR2..S030			1.36	.26	1.26	I
	5.5	-32	27.03	27.45	-7.0				1.33	1.33		
N4947A	13 1.5	-34 58	274.33	305.89	151.8	.SB.7$.S030			1.19	.27	1.08	I
	5.5	-32	27.15	27.56	-7.1				.74	.74		
N4948	13 2.3	-7 41	278.38	308.72	125.5	.SBS7*.L036			1.29	.44	1.12	BCFN
	5.2	-32	54.27	54.77	0.2				4.37	4.37		
N4948A	13 2.5	-7 53	278.42	308.77	125.7	.SBS7*.L036			1.18	.18	1.10	BN
	5.2	-32	54.06	54.57	0.2				2.22	2.22		
N4951	13 2.5	-6 14	278.81	309.04	124.1	.SXT6*.W060			1.50	.42	1.33	ACEKLQ
	5.2	-32	55.70	56.21	0.7	S NK *	S G *		7.78	7.09		
N4952	13 2.7	29 24	21.79	67.38	89.4	.E.5...L			1.18	.22	1.09	A
	4.8	-32	85.24	86.38	9.7				.77	.77		
N4957	13 2.8	27 50	2.49	41.86	91.0	.E.3...W100	E3 K		.87	.11	.83	W
	4.8	-32	85.50	86.91	9.4				1.57	1.57		
N4958	13 3.1	-7 45	278.70	309.05	125.6	.LBR.$/W060	D K		1.46	.51	1.26	ACEFKNQ
	5.2	-32	54.17	54.68	0.4	E 6	D K		10.36	9.07		
N4961	13 3.4	28 0	4.55	44.49	90.9	.SBS6..W100	SI *F		1.20	.13	1.15	ACKW
	4.8	-32	85.36	86.76	9.6	S 5 5*			4.59	4.59		
N4965	13 4.5	-27 57	275.82	307.15	145.1	.S.....H030			1.51	.15	1.46	F
	5.5	-32	34.07	34.52	-4.7				2.43	2.43		
N4976	13 5.9	-49 14	273.86	305.83	166.0	.E.4...S030			1.45	.21	1.37	DEI
	5.9	-32	12.86	13.27	-9.7				4.26	4.26		
N4980	13 6.4	-28 23	276.27	307.62	145.7	.S.....H030			1.18	.26	1.08	F
	5.5	-32	33.60	34.06	-4.5				1.57	1.57		
N4981	13 6.1	-6 31	280.29	310.58	124.6	.SXR4..W060			1.38	.11	1.33	ACEFKLQ
	5.2	-32	55.28	55.83	1.4	S 5 4	S FG		8.78	8.01		
N4984	13 6.4	-15 15	278.37	309.18	133.0	RLXT+..W100	D GK		1.28	.12	1.23	ADEKW
	5.3	-32	46.63	47.14	-.9	S N +	D K		6.67	6.67		
N4995	13 7.0	-7 34	280.38	310.75	125.7	.SXT3..W100	S F		1.33	.18	1.26	ACEFKNW
	5.2	-32	54.21	54.76	1.4	S 3 N	S FG		9.37	8.31		
N4999	13 7.2	1 55	283.92	313.48	116.5	.SBR3..W060	B FG		1.37	.10	1.33	AEKQ
	5.1	-32	63.52	64.15	4.0	N *			5.44	5.44		
N5003	13 9.1	42 28	71.48	109.08	76.6	.S....$L036			1.44	.56	1.22	L
	4.5	-31	74.29	74.38	13.5				.89	.89		

| NGC (IC, A) | Magnitudes | | | | Colors | | | | Velocities | | | Radio | | | Photo. |
| | m_H / m_C | B(O) / w | B'(O) / m'_C | S(B) | (B-V)(O) / w | C_o(O) | S(C) | (U-B)(O) / w | V / w | V_o / ΔV | S(V) | ϕ_r / n | ϕ(21) | | Photo. |
(14)	(15)	(16)	(17)	(18)	(19)	(20)	(21)	(22)	(23)	(24)	(25)	(26)	(27)	(28)	(29)
N4902	11.6	11.86	13.65	C	.85*	.74	C		2758	2605	C				
	11.81	2.03	13.60		3.75				2.4	-153					
N4904	12.8	12.82	13.81	E	.66		E	-.05							
	12.92	2.78	13.91		6.25		/E			-101					
N4907		14.56	14.50	CD	.90	.73	CD	.40	5868	5882	C				
		8.58			37.50		/D		2.6	14					
N4908		14.87	14.11	C	1.04	.88	C		8838	8851	B				
		1.96			1.88				.4	13					
N4911		13.90	13.94	CD	.86*	.70	CD	.23	8006	8018	C				
		4.44			22.50		/D		2.4	12					
N4914	13.0														
	12.85		13.34							52					
N4915	12.9	13.30	12.74	C	.89	.79	C		3152	3034	B				
	13.14	2.66	12.58		3.75				6.3	-118					
N4921		13.58	15.22	CD	.92	.80	CD	.42	5459	5472	C				
		7.05			39.38		/D		2.7	13					
N4922									7357	7376	C				
									2.0	19					
N4924															
										-153					
N4926		14.40	14.14	C	1.10	.96	C		7661	7673	C				
		2.73			3.75				2.0	12					
N4926A									7175	7188	C				
									2.0	12					
N4928	12.9														
	13.39		13.33							-129					
N4931		14.79	15.03	C	1.04		C								
		1.28			1.88					15					
N4933A	12.8*														
										-140					
N4933B															
										-140					
N4936	12.6														
	12.81		12.65							-196					
N4939	12.2														
	11.70		14.49							-136					
N4941	12.4	12.17	13.86	C	.86	.72	C		846	727	B				P
	12.27	1.46	13.96		1.88				6.3	-119					
N4942															
										-127					
N4944									6993	7009	C				
									2.0	16					
N4945	9.2														F
	9.48		13.72							-230					
N4945A															
										-229					
N4947	12.6														
	12.70		13.69							-206					
N4947A															
										-207					
N4948															
										-127					
N4948A															
										-128					
N4951	12.7														
	12.68		14.07							-122					
N4952									5865	5886	C				
									1.8	21					
N4957		14.60	13.49	C	1.06		C								
		0.59			1.88					14					
N4958	11.6	11.73	12.72	C	.87	.76	C		1515	1388	B				
	11.84	2.91	12.83		3.75				1.8	-127					
N4961	13.2	14.24	14.68	C	.46	.36	C		2559	2574	C				
	13.39	0.94	13.83		1.88				2.0	15					
N4965															
										-188					
N4976	11.6	11.45	13.04	M	.97	.74	M	.36	1369	1141	LM				
	11.57	2.60	13.16				/M		12.1	-228					
N4980															
										-188					
N4981	12.2														
	12.34		13.73							-120					
N4984	11.9														K
	12.07		12.96							-150					
N4995	11.7	12.11	13.15	C	.84	.71	C		1835	1712	C				
	12.21	1.83	13.25		3.75				2.8	-123					
N4999	12.8														
	12.64		14.03							-88					
N5003															
										78					

NGC (IC, A) (1)	Coordinates RA (1950) Dec 100 P (2)	100 P (3)	L^I B^I (4)	L^II B^II (5)	SGL SGB (6)	Classification Rev. type (S) DDO (T, L) (7)	Yerkes (1) Yerkes (2) (8)	Hu-San Ho (9)	Diameters log D w (10)	log R w (11)	log D(O) (12)	S (D,R) (13)
N5005	13 8.5 / 4.6	37 19 / -31	61.85 / 78.96	101.72 / 79.27	81.8 / 12.5	.SXT4..W100 / S 2 3	S G / S GK	S 3 / S4	1.65 / 15.91	.35 / 15.91	1.51	ACKLRVX / YW
N5011	13 10.0 / 5.7	-42 50 / -31	275.28 / 19.16	307.08 / 19.60	159.9 / -7.5	.E+1...S030			1.07 / .87	.00 / .87	1.07	I
N5011A	13 9.4 / 5.7	-43 3 / -31	275.14 / 18.95	306.95 / 19.39	160.1 / -7.6	.S..5$.S030			1.27 / 1.18	.26 / 1.18	1.17	I
N5012	13 9.3 / 4.8	23 11 / -31	324.57 / 82.43	351.53 / 83.77	95.9 / 9.8	.SXT5..W100 / S 3 3	S F		1.42 / 5.78	.23 / 5.78	1.32	HKW
N5014	13 9.2 / 4.6	36 33 / -31	58.96 / 79.52	99.18 / 79.90	82.6 / 12.5	.S....$L036			1.30 / 1.31	.19 / .54	1.22	ACL
N5016	13 9.7 / 4.8	24 21 / -31	332.59 / 83.01	.92 / 84.43	94.8 / 10.1	.SXT5..W100 / S 3 4	S F		1.18 / 4.05	.13 / 4.05	1.13	ACKW
N5017	13 10.3 / 5.3	-16 30 / -31	279.45 / 45.26	310.33 / 45.80	134.5 / -.3	E 2			.95 / .75	.04 / .75	.94	AK
N5018	13 10.3 / 5.4	-19 15 / -31	278.88 / 42.54	309.89 / 43.07	137.1 / -1.1	.E.3.*.W060 / S 0	D K		1.13 / 3.43	.13 / 3.43	1.08	AEKQ
N5022	13 10.7 / 5.4	-19 15 / -31	279.00 / 42.53	310.02 / 43.05	137.1 / -1.0	.S..../W060			1.28 / .88	.79 / .88	.97	Q
N5023	13 10.0 / 4.5	44 18 / -31	73.36 / 72.53	110.39 / 72.58	74.7 / 13.9	.S.....R020			1.70 / 3.34	.88 / 3.34	1.34	ACH
N5026	13 11.3 / 5.8	-42 42 / -31	275.55 / 19.26	307.35 / 19.71	159.8 / -7.2	.SBS1..S030			1.24 / .56	.13 / .56	1.19	I
N5028	13 11.1 / 5.3	-12 47 / -31	280.60 / 48.90	311.31 / 49.46	131.0 / 0.9	.E.6...B060			.99 / 1.39	.29 / 1.39	.88	P
N5030	13 11.2 / 5.3	-16 14 / -31	279.81 / 45.49	310.69 / 46.04	134.3 / -.1	.LB...$B060			1.36 / .18	.55 / .18	1.14	Q
N5033	13 11.2 / 4.6	36 51 / -31	58.15 / 79.05	97.99 / 79.45	82.3 / 12.9	.SAS5..W100 / S 4 T 2*	S G / S G	S5	2.02 / 17.46	.27 / 17.46	1.91	AKLUXYW
N5035	13 12.1 / 5.3	-16 15 / -31	280.11 / 45.44	310.99 / 45.99	134.4 / 0.1	.LXR+..W060			1.11 / .71	.15 / .71	1.05	Q
N5037	13 12.4 / 5.3	-16 20 / -31	280.19 / 45.35	311.08 / 45.90	134.5 / 0.2	.SAS1..W060 / S 4 5			1.32 / 3.14	.44 / 3.14	1.14	AKQ
N5042	13 12.8 / 5.4	-23 43 / -31	278.77 / 38.04	309.97 / 38.56	141.6 / -1.8	.S...*.H030			1.51 / 1.83	.25 / 1.83	1.42	F
N5044	13 12.8 / 5.3	-16 8 / -31	280.37 / 45.53	311.25 / 46.09	134.3 / 0.3	.E.0...W060 / E 0	E1 K		1.20 / 4.13	.00 / 4.13	1.20	ADEKQ
N5046	13 13.0 / 5.3	-16 4 / -31	280.46 / 45.59	311.34 / 46.15	134.2 / 0.4	.E.2.$.W060			.68 / .37	.08 / .37	.65	Q
N5047	13 13.1 / 5.3	-16 14 / -31	280.45 / 45.42	311.34 / 45.98	134.4 / 0.4	.L..../W100			1.31 / 4.59	.65 / 4.59	1.05	AQW
N5049	13 13.3 / 5.3	-16 8 / -31	280.54 / 45.51	311.43 / 46.07	134.3 / 0.5	.L..../W100			1.14 / 3.25	.47 / 3.25	.95	AQW
N5054	13 14.3 / 5.3	-16 23 / -31	280.82 / 45.22	311.72 / 45.79	134.6 / 0.6	.SAS4..W100 / S 3 NT 3*	S F / S FG		1.66 / 8.78	.22 / 8.78	1.57	AEKW
N5055	13 13.5 / 4.5	42 17 / -31	68.51 / 74.13	106.04 / 74.30	76.9 / 14.2	.SAT4..W100 / S 4 3	S G	S 3 / S4	2.01 / 12.57	.25 / 12.57	1.92	AHKLUXY / W
N5061	13 15.3 / 5.5	-26 36 / -31	278.92 / 35.10	310.24 / 35.63	144.5 / -2.1	.E+0...W100 / E 2	E1 K		1.18 / 5.08	.05 / 5.08	1.16	DEKNQ
N5064	13 16.0 / 5.9	-47 39 / -31	275.76 / 14.25	307.69 / 14.70	164.9 / -7.7	.SA.3.*.S030			1.37 / .97	.40 / .97	1.21	I
N5068	13 16.2 / 5.4	-20 47 / -31	280.38 / 40.81	311.48 / 41.37	139.0 / -.2	.SXT6..P200 / SX5 6	BI *A / SX AF		1.80 / 18.43	.04 / 18.43	1.78	DEFKNTZ
N5074	13 16.2 / 4.7	31 44 / -31	30.67 / 81.65	70.87 / 82.67	87.7 / 13.0	P *			1.03 / 1.33	.00 / 1.33	1.03	ACK
N5077	13 16.9 / 5.3	-12 24 / -31	282.83 / 49.01	313.55 / 49.63	131.0 / 2.4	.E.3+..W100 / E 3	ED K		1.00 / 4.95	.10 / 4.95	.96	ABCDEKW
N5078	13 17.1 / 5.5	-27 9 / -31	279.30 / 34.50	310.64 / 35.03	145.1 / -1.8	.SAS1*/W100			1.47 / 3.26	.38 / 3.26	1.31	W
N5079	13 17.0 / 5.3	-12 27 / -31	282.85 / 48.96	313.57 / 49.58	131.0 / 2.4	.S...P.W100			1.16 / 4.11	.17 / 4.11	1.09	ABCW
N5082	13 18.0 / 5.8	-43 26 / -31	276.73 / 18.37	308.56 / 18.85	160.9 / -6.2	.S.....S030			1.28 / .52	.53 / .52	1.07	I
N5084	13 17.5 / 5.4	-21 34 / -31	280.60 / 39.98	311.73 / 40.55	139.8 / -.1	.L..../W100 / E 8*	D K		1.56 / 7.25	.65 / 7.25	1.30	DEKW
N5085	13 17.6 / 5.5	-24 9 / -31	280.05 / 37.44	311.28 / 37.99	142.3 / -.9	.SAS5..W100 / S 3 4	S F		1.50 / 11.22	.05 / 11.22	1.48	DEFKWT
N5087	13 17.7 / 5.4	-20 21 / -31	280.94 / 41.17	312.03 / 41.75	138.7 / 0.2	.LA.-..W100 / E 4	E5 K		1.11 / 6.33	.23 / 6.33	1.02	ADEFKW
N5088	13 17.7 / 5.3	-12 19 / -31	283.14 / 49.06	313.87 / 49.68	131.0 / 2.6	.SAS3*$W100 / S 5 K 3*			1.36 / 6.69	.48 / 6.69	1.17	ABCKW
N5090	13 18.3 / 5.8	-43 28 / -31	276.78 / 18.33	308.61 / 18.81	160.9 / -6.2	.E+2...S030			1.18 / 2.94	.02 / 2.94	1.17	DEI
N5090A	13 16.4 / 5.8	-43 24 / -31	276.43 / 18.45	308.26 / 18.92	160.8 / -6.5	.S...*.S030			1.11 / .47	.42 / .47	.94	I
N5090B	13 17.3 / 5.8	-43 36 / -31	276.57 / 18.23	308.40 / 18.70	161.0 / -6.4	.S....*.S030			1.28 / 1.19	.33 / 1.19	1.15	I
N5091	13 18.2 / 5.8	-43 28 / -31	276.76 / 18.34	308.59 / 18.82	160.9 / -6.2	.S..../S030			1.22 / 1.10	.78 / 1.10	.91	I
N5101	13 19.0 / 5.5	-27 11 / -31	279.80 / 34.39	311.14 / 34.94	145.3 / -1.4	RSBT0..P200 / SB0		SBS0	1.57 / 8.71	.08 / 7.29	1.53	DEKZ

NGC (IC, A) (14)	Magnitudes				Colors				Velocities			Radio			
	m_H m_c (15)	B(O) w (16)	B'(O) m_c' (17)	S(B) (18)	(B-V)(O) w (19)	C_o(O) (20)	S(C) (21)	(U-B)(O) w (22)	V w (23)	V_o ΔV (24)	S(V) (25)	ϕ_r n (26)	ϕ (21) (27)	(28)	Photo. (29)
N5005	11.3 11.44	10.85 9.56	13.14 13.73	ABCDE G	.84 33.00	.71	ACDEG /DE	.32	1021 8.7	1078 57	ABCF				BP
N5011	12.9 12.94		12.98							-216					
N5011A										-217					
N5012	12.6 12.60		13.94							0					
N5014										54					
N5016	12.8 13.17		13.51							5					
N5017	13.3 13.42		12.81							-151					
N5018	11.6 12.06	12.48 1.18	12.57 12.15	C	1.05 1.88	.94	C		2897 1.8	2738 -159	B				
N5022										-159					
N5023										85					
N5026										-215					
N5028										-138					
N5030										-149					
N5033	11.6 10.73	10.85 5.61	15.09 14.97	ACEFG	.58* 8.75	.46	ACEG /E	.12	899 10.4	956 57	BCD				B
N5035										-149					
N5037	13.1 13.20		13.64							-149					
N5042										-171					
N5044	12.2 12.24		12.98							-148					
N5046										-147					
N5047										-148					
N5049		14.03 2.43	13.52	C	.69 3.75	.57	C		2744 2.4	2597 -147	B				
N5054	11.9 11.63		14.22							-147					
N5055	10.5 10.09	9.52 6.51	13.81 14.38	BEFG	.74* 15.00	.63	BEG /E	.07	520 21.9	600 80	ABCF				ABP
N5061	11.7 11.98		12.52						2065 2.4	1888 -177	C				
N5064	13.1 13.10		13.84							-220					
N5068	11.6 11.05		14.69						570 2.1	410 -159	C				
N5074	13.2									40					
N5077	12.2 12.65	12.66 1.65	12.20 12.19	C	1.07 1.88	.97	C		2647 1.0	2515 -132	B				
N5078										-177					
N5079										-132					
N5082										-212					
N5084	12.4 12.30		13.49							-161					
N5085	12.3 12.07		14.21							-168					
N5087	12.4 12.76	12.49 0.99	12.33 12.60	C	1.03 1.88	.92	C		1832 .4	1675 -157	B				
N5088	13.2 13.25		13.79							-131					
N5090	12.9 12.77		13.31							-212					
N5090A										-213					
N5090B										-213					
N5091										-212					
N5101	12.5 11.93		14.32							-176					P

NGC (IC, A) (1)	RA (1950) 100 P (2)	Dec 100 P (3)	L^I B^I (4)	L^II B^II (5)	SGL SGB (6)	Rev. type (S) DDO (T, L) (7)	Yerkes (1) Yerkes (2) (8)	Hu-San Ho (9)	log D w (10)	log R w (11)	log D(0) (12)	S (D,R) (13)
N5102	13 19.1	-36 23	278.09	309.73	154.1	.LA.-..L036			1.86	.39	1.70	I
	5.7	-31	25.31	25.82	-4.1				1.79	1.79		
N5107	13 19.1	38 49	57.74	96.09	80.6	.SB.../W060	SI *AF		1.20	.36	1.06	A
	4.5	-31	76.54	76.97	14.8				.40	.40		
N5112	13 19.6	39 0	57.88	96.14	80.4	.SBT6..W060	S P *A		1.57	.14	1.51	ACKQ
	4.5	-31	76.33	76.76	14.9	S 5 K 3*	SXI A		5.85	5.85		
N5116	13 20.5	27 14	358.80	33.44	92.4	.SBS5*.W060	S *AF*		1.28	.41	1.12	ACKQ
	4.7	-31	81.55	83.00	13.1	S 2			4.50	4.50		
N5121	13 21.9	-37 25	278.52	310.19	155.3	.LA....S030			1.25	.07	1.22	I
	5.7	-31	24.20	24.72	-3.8				.82	.82		
N5121A	13 22.4	-37 6	278.68	310.34	155.0	.S...*.S030			1.18	.57	.95	I
	5.7	-31	24.50	25.02	-3.6				.52	.52		
N5127	13 21.4	31 49	28.13	67.05	87.8	.E.2.*.W			1.25	.05	1.23	AC
	4.6	-31	80.62	81.69	14.1				.53	.53		
N5128	13 22.4	-42 45	277.68	309.49	160.4	.L...P.....	E P*	E O P	2.05	.11	2.01	DEFXI
	5.8	-31	18.93	19.43	-5.3			E P	11.19	11.19		
N5134	13 22.6	-20 51	282.30	313.43	139.5	.SAS3.$W100			1.35	.27	1.25	DEFKW
	5.4	-31	40.46	41.07	1.2	S 4 5	DS *G		8.35	8.35		
N5135	13 22.9	-29 34	280.30	311.74	147.8	.SBS2..W100			1.40	.37	1.25	DEW
	5.6	-31	31.90	32.46	-1.3				3.60	3.60		
N5144	13 21.5	70 46	85.28	119.13	47.4	.S..7P$L036			1.04	.07	1.01	ALM
	2.9	-31	46.61	46.39	17.1				1.83	1.38		
N5147	13 23.7	2 22	292.97	322.83	117.2	.SBS8..W060	SI *AF		1.24	.09	1.20	ACEKNQ
	5.1	-31	62.79	63.63	8.1	S 5 K - 4	SI *A		6.49	6.49		
N5148	13 24.0	2 34	293.28	323.13	117.0		L*		1.08	.06	1.06	A
	5.1	-31	62.95	63.79	8.2				.64	.64		
N5150	13 24.9	-29 18	280.87	312.30	147.7							
	5.6	-31	32.08	32.65	-.8							
N5156	13 25.7	-48 39	277.25	309.22	166.3	.SBR2..S030			1.24	.02	1.24	DEI
	6.0	-31	13.01	13.51	-6.4				3.03	3.03		
N5161	13 26.3	-32 54	280.41	311.95	151.2	.S.....W			1.70	.44	1.53	DE
	5.7	-31	28.49	29.05	-1.6				3.40	3.40		
N5169	13 26.0	46 53	68.80	104.97	72.4	.SBT3*.W060			1.37	.39	1.21	ACHQ
	4.3	-31	69.02	69.20	17.0				3.64	3.64		
N5170	13 27.1	-17 42	284.62	315.65	136.8	.SAS5*/W100			1.91	.91	1.55	AGKW
	5.4	-31	43.30	43.96	3.2	S N +*	S GK		11.61	10.12		
N5172	13 26.9	17 19	316.81	345.91	102.7	.SXT4*.W060	S FG		1.42	.27	1.31	ACKQ
	4.9	-31	75.40	76.65	12.5	S 4 2			4.78	4.78		
N5173	13 26.3	46 51	68.63	104.80	72.5	.E.0.*.W060			1.00	.05	.98	ACHQ
	4.2	-31	69.03	69.21	17.0				1.59	1.59		
N5188	13 28.6	-34 32	280.58	312.18	152.9	.S...*.W						
	5.7	-30	26.79	27.36	-1.7							
N5193	13 29.1	-32 58	281.05	312.60	151.5	.E...$.W			1.00	.05	.98	DE
	5.7	-30	28.30	28.89	-1.1				1.39	1.39		
N5194	13 27.8	47 27	68.79	104.84	71.9	.SAS4P.....	S F	S 5	2.03	.19	1.95	BCEHKLU
	4.2	-31	68.38	68.56	17.3	S 5 T - 1	S FG	S5	15.41	15.41		XY
N5195	13 27.9	47 31	68.84	104.87	71.8	.I.0.P.....	IEP*	I 0	1.50	.10	1.45	BCDHXY
	4.2	-31	68.31	68.49	17.3	P T-	E P*F *	I0	4.04	4.04		
N5198	13 28.2	46 56	67.95	104.07	72.4	.E+1+*.W060	E2 K		1.03	.07	1.00	ACEHKQ
	4.2	-31	68.80	69.00	17.4	E 2	S K		3.39	3.39		
N5204	13 28.3	58 40	78.68	113.36	60.1	.SAS9..P200	IS *F	S 9	1.66	.21	1.58	ACKNXZ
	3.7	-31	58.05	57.99	17.9	I 9 7		S6	10.81	10.81		
N5216	13 30.4	62 58	80.72	115.05	55.6	.E.0.P.P200			.91	.04	.89	CZ
	3.4	-30	53.90	53.79	18.2				1.55	1.55		
N5218	13 30.5	63 2	80.74	115.07	55.5	.SBS.P.P200			1.20	.16	1.13	CZ
	3.4	-30	53.83	53.72	18.2				3.12	3.12		
N5229	13 32.1	48 9	68.02	103.88	71.2	.S....*R020			1.46	.64	1.21	H
	4.1	-30	67.42	67.62	18.1				1.35	1.35		
N5230	13 33.0	13 56	312.97	342.50	106.4	.SAS5..W060	S AF		1.32	.05	1.30	AKQ
	4.9	-30	71.87	73.07	13.2	S 5 2			3.84	3.84		
N5236	13 34.3	-29 37	283.14	314.61	148.6	.SXS5..W100	S FG	SX 4	2.02	.05	2.00	EFGLMUO
	5.6	-30	31.33	31.96	1.0				31.67	31.67		WS
N5247	13 35.3	-17 38	287.23	318.31	137.3	.SAS4..W060	S F		1.71	.06	1.68	AEFGHKL
	5.4	-30	42.87	43.59	5.0	S 4 2			17.50	17.50		UQ
N5248	13 35.1	9 8	306.18	335.95	111.3	.SXT4..P200	S F	S 5	1.77	.15	1.71	AKLMSXZ
	5.0	-30	67.65	68.74	12.6	S 5 1		S5	15.22	15.22		
N5253	13 37.1	-31 24	283.33	314.86	150.5	.IB.9P.W100	IDP*FG*		1.54	.40	1.38	DEFMSW
	5.7	-30	29.46	30.09	1.0				11.54	11.54		
N5254	13 36.9	-11 14	290.49	321.32	131.3	.S.....H030			1.56	.32	1.44	ACG
	5.3	-30	48.87	49.66	7.4				2.81	2.81		
N5257	13 37.3	1 6	298.53	328.79	119.4	.SXS3P.P200			1.22	.26	1.11	ACRZ
	5.1	-30	60.31	61.26	11.0				5.07	5.07		
N5258	13 37.4	1 5	298.56	328.82	119.4	.SAS3P*P200			1.19	.24	1.09	ABCRZ
	5.1	-30	60.29	61.24	11.0				4.99	4.99		
N5266	13 39.9	-47 56	279.77	311.74	166.3	.LA.-*.S030			1.30	.21	1.22	DEI
	6.2	-30	13.25	13.80	-3.9				3.37	3.37		
N5266A	13 37.3	-48 6	279.30	311.27	166.3	.SA.6*.S030			1.48	.15	1.42	I
	6.1	-30	13.18	13.72	-4.4				.78	.78		
N5273	13 39.9	35 55	37.46	74.39	84.1	.LAS0..P200	D GK	S S0	1.30	.06	1.28	ABCKZ
	4.4	-30	75.33	76.24	18.5	E 1P -*			6.09	6.09		

| NGC (IC, A) | Magnitudes | | | | Colors | | | | Velocities | | | Radio | | | |
| | m_H m_c | B(O) w | B'(O) m'_c | S(B) | (B-V)(O) w | C_o(O) | S(C) | (U-B)(O) w | V w | V_o ΔV | S(V) | ϕ_r n | ϕ(21) | | Photo. |
(14)	(15)	(16)	(17)	(18)	(19)	(20)	(21)	(22)	(23)	(24)	(25)	(26)	(27)	(28)	(29)
N5102	10.8								546	348	M				P
	10.55		13.79						1.0	−198					
N5107										70					
N5112	12.6	12.72	15.01	E	.47		E	−.26		71					
	12.21	1.59	14.50		6.25		/E								
N5116	12.9									25					
	13.25		13.54												
N5121	12.5									−198					
	12.49		13.33												
N5121A										−197					
N5127										44					
N5128	7.2	8.38	13.17	G	.98	.81	G		480	271	BFI				EP
	7.65	0.71	12.44		2.50				12.3	−209					
N5134	12.4									−155					
	12.63		13.57												
N5135	12.8									−179					
	12.80		13.79												
N5144										178					
N5147	12.1									−73					
	12.73		13.47												
N5148										−72					
N5150	13.1									−177					
N5156	12.9									−216					
	12.90		13.79												
N5161	12.5									−185					
	12.32		14.66												
N5169										104					
N5170	12.6									−141					
	12.08		14.57												
N5172	12.5									−11					
	12.55		13.84												
N5173		14.12	13.76	B					2404	2508	B				
		0.94							4.0	104					
N5188	12.7									−187					
N5193	12.6									−183					
	12.88		12.52												
N5194	10.1	9.03	13.52	BCDEG	.61	.51	BCDEG	−.04	445	552	ABDER				AKLP
	9.78	6.05	14.27	*	35.63		/DE		23.8	107					
N5195	11.1	10.94	12.93	BCDEG	.97*	.89	BCDEG	.48	527	634	ABDE				ALP
	11.26	7.58	13.25	*	28.13		/DE		12.3	108					
N5198	12.9	13.30	13.04	B					2499	2605	BC				
	13.04	0.99	12.78						5.1	106					
N5204	12.2	12.00	14.59	CG	.47	.40	CG				C*				
	12.03	3.23	14.62		4.38					145					
N5216										159					
N5218										159					
N5229										112					
N5230	12.9									−19					
	12.81		14.05												
N5236	8.0	8.22	12.96	CEF	.72*	.61	CE	−.10	506	335	ABRM				BHIP
	8.56	2.72	13.30		8.13		/E		67.1	−171					
N5247	11.9														K
	11.38		14.52							−135					
N5248	11.0	10.89	14.18	ACDEF	.66	.55	ACDEG	−.01	1181	1144	BCF				KP
	10.82	13.43	14.11	G	54.38		/DE		10.5	−37					
N5253	10.8	11.14	12.78	E	.44	.33	E	−.19	403	229	BIM				
	11.16	2.77	12.80		6.25		/E		66.1	−174					
N5254										−112					
N5257									6810	6744	E				D
									.3	−66					
N5258									6635	6569	E				D
									.3	−66					
N5266	12.8									−207					
	12.70		13.49												
N5266A										−209					
N5273	12.9	12.71	13.80	BE	.84	.77	E	.41	1022	1094	B				KLP
	12.67	4.69	13.76		6.25		/E		25.0	72					

NGC (IC, A) (1)	RA (1950) 100 P (2)	Dec 100 P (3)	L^I B^I (4)	L^II B^II (5)	SGL SGB (6)	Rev. type (S) DDO (T, L) (7)	Yerkes (1) Yerkes (2) (8)	Hu-San Ho (9)	log D w (10)	log R w (11)	log D(O) (12)	S (D,R) (13)
N5276	13 40.1	35 53	37.27	74.18	84.2	.SXS3..P200			.96	.33	.83	ABCZ
	4.4	−30	75.31	76.23	18.5				3.35	3.35		
N5278	13 39.8	55 55	73.84	108.71	63.0	.SAS.P*P200			1.07	.14	1.C1	ACRZ
	3.7	−30	59.99	60.06	19.5				2.90	2.90		
N5279	13 39.8	55 55	73.84	108.71	63.0	.SBS1P.P200			.70	.15	.64	RZ
	3.7	−30	59.99	60.06	19.5				1.92	1.17		
N5289	13 43.0	41 45	52.50	88.92	78.1	.S....*R020			1.39	.48	1.20	ACH
	4.3	−30	71.32	71.90	19.6				1.89	1.89		
N5290	13 43.2	41 58	52.90	89.28	77.8	.SB.$P/W100			1.47	.65	1.21	ACHW
	4.3	−30	71.14	71.71	19.7				5.39	5.39		
N5291	13 44.5	−30 8	285.48	316.99	149.9	.E...P$B060			.92	.15	.86	P
	5.7	−30	30.27	30.96	2.9				1.26	1.26		
N5293	13 44.3	16 34	325.17	355.59	104.3	.SAR5..W100			1.27	.12	1.22	AW
	4.8	−30	71.88	73.24	16.4				3.49	3.49		
N5296	13 43.7	44 5	57.07	93.19	75.6	.L...*.L036			.90	.38	.74	N
	4.2	−30	69.55	70.02	19.9				.98	.98		
N5297	13 44.3	44 5	56.84	92.94	75.6	.SXS3*.L036	S AF		1.65	.54	1.43	ACHKN
	4.2	−30	69.47	69.96	20.0	S 4 1			7.06	7.06		
N5298	13 45.4	−30 11	285.68	317.20	150.0	.SBT3..B060			1.12	.17	1.06	D
	5.7	−29	30.17	30.86	3.1				1.65	1.65		
N5300	13 45.7	4 11	305.38	335.71	116.9				1.57	.16	1.51	AEK
	5.0	−29	62.05	63.13	13.9	S 5 3	S A		4.16	4.16		
N5301	13 45.0	46 24	60.70	96.52	73.1	.SAS3*/L036			1.62	.67	1.35	ACEK
	4.1	−30	67.63	68.02	20.2	S 3 4*	S F *		4.36	4.36		
N5302	13 46.0	−30 30	285.80	317.33	150.1	.LBS+*.B060			1.21	.18	1.14	P
	5.7	−29	30.09	30.78	3.2				1.85	1.85		
N5304	13 47.1	−30 19	286.04	317.57	150.2	.E.4..B060						
	5.7	−29	29.94	30.64	3.4							
N5308	13 45.4	61 14	76.83	111.25	57.3	.L..-./W060	D K		1.39	.68	1.12	ACKNRQ
	3.3	−29	54.87	54.86	20.0	E 8	D K		8.10	8.10		
N5313	13 47.7	40 13	47.02	83.33	79.7				1.28	.20	1.20	ACK
	4.3	−29	71.65	72.36	20.4	S 3 3*	S AF		2.49	2.49		
N5320	13 48.3	41 35	50.12	86.31	78.3	.S....*R020			1.24	.17	1.17	AH
	4.2	−29	70.69	71.33	20.6				1.15	1.15		
N5322	13 47.6	60 26	75.81	110.27	58.2	.E.3+..W060	E4 K		1.41	.16	1.35	ACKNQ
	3.3	−29	55.48	55.50	20.3	E 2	E4 K		5.90	5.90		
N5324	13 49.4	−5 48	298.21	328.98	127.0	.SAT5*.W100			1.32	.02	1.31	ACFKW
	5.2	−29	52.78	53.73	12.0	S 5 4	S AF		6.28	6.28		
N5326	13 48.7	39 49	45.63	81.92	80.2				1.22	.39	1.07	ACK
	4.3	−29	71.73	72.48	20.6	S 2 5			2.25	2.25		
N5328	13 50.0	−28 14	287.46	318.94	148.5	.E.1.*.W100			.96	.06	.93	DEW
	5.7	−29	31.75	32.48	4.7				3.08	3.08		
N5334	13 50.4	−0 53	302.45	333.06	122.2	.SBT5*.W060			1.63	.17	1.56	AKQ
	5.1	−29	57.08	58.11	13.6	S 6 8	SX A		4.70	4.70		
N5347	13 51.1	33 43	26.30	62.11	86.7				1.23	.08	1.20	ACK
	4.4	−29	74.10	75.24	20.6	SX4 5			2.30	2.30		
N5348	13 51.8	5 29	309.64	340.12	116.0	.S....*R020			1.64	.73	1.35	H
	5.0	−29	62.33	63.49	15.7				.32	.32		
N5350	13 51.2	40 37	46.74	82.87	79.4	.SBR3..W060	B F		1.40	.16	1.33	ABCKQ
	4.2	−29	70.87	71.59	21.1	S 3 1	BS *F		5.00	5.00		
N5351	13 51.2	38 9	40.27	76.46	82.0	.SAR3*.W060	S AF		1.44	.30	1.32	ABCKQ
	4.3	−29	72.25	73.12	21.0	S 4 3			6.15	6.15		
N5353	13 51.3	40 31	46.46	82.59	79.5	.L..../W060			1.17	.34	1.03	ABCKQ
	4.2	−29	70.92	71.65	21.1	E 5	E7 K		3.60	3.60		
N5354	13 51.4	40 33	46.51	82.63	79.4	.L..../W060			.95	.07	.93	ABCQ
	4.2	−29	70.88	71.61	21.1				1.74	1.74		
N5356	13 52.5	5 34	310.05	340.55	116.0	.S....*R020			1.54	.56	1.31	ACH
	5.0	−29	62.30	63.47	15.9				2.18	2.18		
N5357	13 53.1	−30 6	287.54	319.09	150.5							
	5.7	−29	29.76	30.49	4.7							
N5360	13 53.1	5 16	309.93	340.44	116.3	.I.0...P200			1.33	.52	1.12	ABCHW
	5.0	−29	61.96	63.12	15.9				3.01	3.01		
N5362	13 52.8	41 30	48.29	84.30	78.4	.S....*R020			1.33	.32	1.20	ACHK
	4.2	−29	70.10	70.78	21.4	S 3 N			2.74	2.74		
N5363	13 53.6	5 29	310.41	340.94	116.1	.I.0..$W100	E7P	IO	1.40	.22	1.31	ACHKMXW
	5.0	−29	62.06	63.23	16.1	E P			5.92	5.92		
N5364	13 53.7	5 15	310.17	340.70	116.4	.SAT4P.P200	S FG	S 5	1.82	.19	1.74	ABCHKMU
	5.0	−29	61.86	63.02	16.1	S 4P 1		S5	19.50	19.50		XZ
N5365	13 54.8	−43 42	283.49	315.38	163.3	.LB.-..S030			1.28	.12	1.23	I
	6.1	−29	16.67	17.32	0.0				1.17	1.17		
N5365A	13 53.3	−43 45	283.21	315.09	163.2	.S...*/S030			1.34	.71	1.06	I
	6.1	−29	16.70	17.34	-.3				1.30	1.30		
N5365B	13 55.4	−43 44	283.59	315.48	163.3	.S...*/S030			1.21	.77	.90	I
	6.2	−29	16.61	17.25	0.1				1.08	1.08		
N5368	13 52.7	54 35	69.31	104.20	64.4							
	3.6	−29	60.25	60.44	21.3							
N5371	13 53.6	40 43	46.17	82.18	79.3	.SXT4..W100	S F		1.59	.09	1.55	ACKNYW
	4.2	−29	70.45	71.18	21.6	S 4 1	S FG		10.01	10.01		
N5374	13 55.0	6 20	312.11	342.67	115.4	.S....$R020			1.23	.14	1.17	ACH
	5.0	−29	62.56	63.76	16.7				1.67	1.67		

NGC (IC, A)	m_H / m_C	$B(O)$ / w	$B'(O)$ / m'_C	$S(B)$	$(B{-}V)(O)$ / w	$C_o(O)$	$S(C)$	$(U{-}B)(O)$ / w	V / w	V_o / ΔV	$S(V)$	ϕ_r / n	$\phi(21)$		Photo.
(14)	(15)	(16)	(17)	(18)	(19)	(20)	(21)	(22)	(23)	(24)	(25)	(26)	(27)	(28)	(29)
N5276															
										72					
N5278									7523	7665	E				D
									1.1	142					
N5279									7566	7708	E				D
									1.1	142					
N5289															
										96					
N5290															
										97					
N5291															
										−165					
N5293															
										0					
N5296															
										105					
N5297	13.0	12.72	14.61	F						105					
	12.52	3.85	14.41							105					
N5298															
										−164					
N5300	12.3														
	12.03		14.27							−47					
N5301	13.0		14.27						1702	1816	C				
	12.71		14.20						1.8	114					
N5302															
										−164					
N5304															
										−163					
N5308	12.8	12.70	12.99	BC	.92	.80	BC		2039	2199	BC				
	12.87	3.47	13.16		10.00				4.6	160					
N5313	13.0														
	13.07		13.76							94					
N5320															
										99					
N5322	11.6	11.45	12.89	BCEF	.89	.81	BCE	.48	1902	2061	B				
	11.60	8.17	13.04		16.25		/E		1.8	159					
N5324	12.6														
	12.63		13.92							−82					
N5326	13.1														
	13.40		13.44							93					
N5328	12.9	13.24	12.63	C	.86		C								
	13.16	1.79	12.55		1.88					−155					
N5334	12.5														
	12.00		14.54							−63					
N5347	13.2														
	13.18		13.92							72					
N5348															
										−37					
N5350	12.9														
	12.70		14.09							97					
N5351	13.0														
	12.77		14.11							88					
N5353	12.4	12.39	12.28	C	1.00	.90	C		2188	2285	B				
	12.74	1.11	12.63		1.88				2.4	97					
N5354		12.85	12.19	C	.92		C								
		0.81			1.88					97					
N5356															
										−36					
N5357	13.2														
										−158					
N5360															
										−37					
N5362	13.2														
	13.16		13.90							101					
N5363	11.1	11.46	12.75	ABCDG	1.00	.90	ABCDG	.54	1138	1103	BC				
	11.54	12.15	12.83		26.25		/D		7.2	−35					
N5364	11.8	11.31	14.75	ACFG	.70	.59	ACG		1393	1357	B				P
	11.18	6.95	14.62		8.75				.4	−36					
N5365	13.0														F
	12.80		13.69							−190					
N5365A															
										−192					
N5365B															
										−190					
N5368															
										144					
N5371	11.7	11.59	14.08	CF	.67	.56	C		2583	2682	BC				
	11.57	3.82	14.06		1.88				10.3	99					
N5374															
										−31					

NGC (IC, A)	RA (1950) 100 P	Dec 100 P	L^I B^I	L^II B^II	SGL SGB	Rev. type (S) DDO (T, L)	Yerkes (1) Yerkes (2)	Hu-San Ho	log D w	log R w	log D(0)	S (D,R)
(1)	(2)	(3)	(4)	(5)	(6)	(7)	(8)	(9)	(10)	(11)	(12)	(13)
N5376	13 53.6 3.3	59 45 -29	74.08 55.74	108.56 55.81	58.8 21.1	.SXR3.$W060 S 0*	S FG SD FG		1.26 3.28	.19 3.28	1.19	ACKQ
N5377	13 54.3 4.0	47 27 -29	59.36 65.81	94.86 66.23	72.0 21.8	RSBS1..W100 S OP	SD *GK DS *GK		1.60 4.37	.27 4.37	1.49	HLYW
N5378	13 54.6 4.3	38 1 -29	38.87 71.74	74.87 72.63	82.2 21.6	.S....*R020			1.23 1.32	.08 1.32	1.19	CH
N5379	13 53.9 3.3	59 59 -29	74.22 55.52	108.68 55.58	58.6 21.1	.SXR3.$W060			1.24 2.18	.40 2.18	1.08	ABCQ
N5380	13 54.8 4.3	37 51 -29	38.29 71.79	74.27 72.69	82.4 21.6	S 0			1.04 2.15	.00 1.70	1.04	ACHLK
N5383	13 55.0 4.2	42 5 -29	48.87 69.41	84.77 70.09	77.8 21.9	.SBT.P.W060 SB3 3	B P FG* B G	SBS3	1.54 8.84	.05 5.67	1.52	ACHKRQ
N5387	13 56.0 5.0	6 18 -29	312.50 62.38	343.08 63.59	115.4 16.9				1.34 1.63	.68 1.63	1.06	ACH
N5389	13 54.5 3.3	59 59 -29	74.10 55.48	108.56 55.55	58.6 21.2	.SXR0*$W060			1.40 3.65	.56 3.65	1.18	ACBQ
N5394	13 56.5 4.3	37 41 -29	37.32 71.57	73.21 72.49	82.6 22.0	.SBS3P.W100	S P F *		1.18 5.01	.13 4.24	1.13	ABCHLW
N5395	13 56.5 4.3	37 39 -29	37.23 71.58	73.11 72.51	82.6 22.0	.SAS3P.W100 S 4 T 1*	S AF		1.42 8.80	.24 8.80	1.32	ABCHKLW
N5396	13 56.6 4.5	29 21 -29	10.10 73.64	44.51 75.00	91.5 21.3	.S.....R020			1.34 .57	.31 .57	1.22	H
N5398	13 58.3 5.8	-32 50 -29	287.76 26.82	319.39 27.56	153.4 4.7	.S...$.W						
N5403	13 57.7 4.3	38 25 -29	39.04 71.01	74.89 71.90	81.8 22.2	.S.....R020			1.40 3.20	.37 3.20	1.25	ABCH
N5406	13 58.2 4.2	39 9 -29	40.79 70.57	76.62 71.42	81.0 22.4	S 4 2	BS FG		1.27 1.99	.13 1.99	1.21	ACK
N5419	14 0.7 5.9	-33 44 -28	287.96 25.80	319.62 26.55	154.5 4.8	.E.....W						
N5422	13 59.0 3.5	55 24 -29	68.71 59.07	103.48 59.27	63.4 22.2	.L..../W060 E 9	D GK D K		1.47 7.67	.65 7.67	1.21	ABCHKQ
N5426	14 0.8 5.2	-5 49 -28	302.33 51.49	333.26 52.52	127.9 14.7	.SAS5P.P200 S 5 T	S *FG	S5	1.45 10.96	.25 10.96	1.34	ABCEKNX QZ
N5427	14 0.8 5.2	-5 47 -28	302.35 51.52	333.28 52.55	127.9 14.7	.SAS5P.P200 S 5 T - 1	S FG	S5	1.39 11.97	.03 11.97	1.38	ABCEGKN XQZ
N5430	13 59.1 3.2	59 34 -29	72.85 55.56	107.32 55.65	58.9 21.8	.SBS3..W060 S 3 NT-	B P F IBP*		1.27 2.55	.31 2.55	1.15	ABCK
N5443	14 0.4 3.5	56 3 -28	69.10 58.43	103.81 58.62	62.7 22.3				1.35 1.94	.42 1.94	1.18	ABC
N5444	14 1.2 4.3	35 22 -28	29.40 71.61	64.86 72.69	85.1 22.8	E 1			1.09 1.31	.02 1.31	1.09	ACK
N5448	14 0.9 3.8	49 25 -28	60.52 63.61	95.73 64.01	69.9 22.8	RSXR1..W060 S 4 4	S P FG		1.52 7.59	.41 7.59	1.36	ACHKQ
N5457	14 1.4 3.5	54 35 -28	67.23 59.54	102.04 59.78	64.3 22.6	.SXT6...... S 5 1	S F S F	S 5 S5	2.39 19.51	.02 19.51	2.39	ACHKLVX Y
N5464	14 4.2 5.8	-29 46 -28	290.28 29.28	321.86 30.07	151.1 7.0							
N5468	14 4.0 5.2	-5 14 -28	303.90 51.61	334.87 52.68	127.6 15.6	.SXT6..W100 S 5 3	S A		1.41 13.09	.02 13.09	1.40	ABCEFKN TW
N5472	14 4.3 5.2	-5 14 -28	304.01 51.58	334.97 52.64	127.6 15.7	.SAR.$/W100			1.08 5.02	.52 5.02	.88	ABCFNW
N5473	14 3.0 3.5	55 8 -28	67.50 58.96	102.26 59.19	63.7 22.8	.LXS-*.W060 E 2	E2P* BD K		1.22 5.53	.20 5.53	1.14	ACHKNQ
N5474	14 3.2 3.6	53 54 -28	66.00 59.93	100.84 60.20	65.0 22.9	.SAS6P.P200 S 5 NT *	S P F S P G	S6	1.60 10.48	.03 10.48	1.59	ACHKMXY Z
N5475	14 3.5 3.4	55 59 -28	68.35 58.23	103.04 58.44	62.7 22.8				1.43 1.06	.70 1.06	1.15	AC
N5477	14 3.7 3.5	54 41 -28	66.82 59.26	101.60 59.51	64.1 22.9	.S..7*.L036			1.20 3.20	.13 3.20	1.15	AHN
N5480	14 2.4 3.7	50 57 -28	62.35 62.30	97.42 62.66	68.2 23.0	.SAS5*.W060 S 5 KT+ 2*	SD *F S F *		1.24 4.01	.11 4.01	1.19	ABCKQ
N5481	14 2.6 3.7	50 57 -28	62.30 62.28	97.36 62.64	68.2 23.0	.L.....W060			1.07 1.18	.01 1.18	1.07	ABC
N5483	14 7.4 6.2	-43 5 -28	285.96 16.55	317.86 17.25	163.6 2.3	.SAS5..S030			1.47 4.06	.04 4.06	1.45	DEI
N5484	14 5.1 3.5	55 16 -28	67.19 58.68	101.92 58.92	63.5 23.1	.E.0.*.L036						
N5485	14 5.5 3.5	55 14 -28	67.07 58.67	101.79 58.91	63.5 23.1	.LA..P.W060 S 0*	E1P E2P K		1.10 4.27	.09 4.27	1.06	ACHKNQ
N5486	14 5.7 3.4	55 20 -28	67.14 58.57	101.85 58.81	63.4 23.2	.S..9.$W060			1.35 2.73	.20 2.73	1.27	ACHQ
N5490	14 7.6 4.7	17 46 -28	337.51 68.04	9.11 69.50	104.2 22.1	.E.2+..L036			1.07 2.74	.11 2.74	1.02	ABCN
N5490C	14 7.7 4.7	17 51 -28	337.73 68.06	9.35 69.52	104.1 22.2	.SBS4..L036			1.04 1.19	.21 1.19	.95	N
N5493	14 8.9 5.2	-4 49 -28	305.93 51.35	336.95 52.45	127.6 16.9	.L...P/W100	E7 *K		1.05 3.81	.18 2.90	.98	ACFKW
N5494	14 9.5 5.8	-30 26 -28	291.22 28.24	322.84 29.05	152.1 7.8	.SAS5..W100			1.29 5.33	.05 5.33	1.27	EFGW

NGC (IC, A)	m_H / m_c	B(O) / w	B'(O) / m'_c	S(B)	(B-V)(O) / w	C_o(O)	S(C)	(U-B)(O) / w	V / w	V_o / ΔV	S(V)	ϕ_r / n	ϕ(21)	(28)	Photo.
	(15)	(16)	(17)	(18)	(19)	(20)	(21)	(22)	(23)	(24)	(25)	(26)	(27)	(28)	(29)
N5376	13.0 / 13.07		13.76							160					
N5377	12.8 / 12.23	12.43 / 3.14	14.62 / 14.42	C	.83 / 3.75	.70	C		1830 / 1.0	1953 / 123	B				
N5378										90					
N5379										160					
N5380	13.2 / 13.25		13.19							90					
N5383	12.7 / 12.45	12.14 / 1.53	14.48 / 14.79	E	.67* / 6.25	.57	E / /E	.07	2264 / 4.0	2369 / 105	F				CLP
N5387										-30					
N5389										161					
N5394		13.85 / 4.20	14.24	CE	.69 / 8.13	.55	CE / /E	.16	3558 / 1.0	3648 / 90	B				B
N5395	13.0 / 12.77	12.47 / 4.66	13.81 / 14.11	CE	.75 / 8.13		CE / /E	.09		90					B
N5396										60					
N5398	12.8									-162					
N5403										94					
N5406	13.0 / 13.05		13.84							97					
N5419	12.4									-163					
N5422	13.0 / 12.83		13.62							150					
N5426	12.8 / 12.67	12.91 / 5.31	14.35 / 14.11	CEG	.64* / 6.25	.49	CEG / /E	-.03	2492 / 2.7	2420 / -72	E				E
N5427	12.0 / 12.14	12.06 / 5.60	13.70 / 13.78	CEG	.65 / 12.50	.54	CEG / /E	-.09	2588 / 2.7	2516 / -72	E				E
N5430	12.8 / 13.08		13.52							162					
N5443										152					
N5444	13.1 / 13.04		13.18							85					
N5448	12.5 / 12.39	12.53 / 0.88	14.02 / 13.88	B					1970 / 4.0	2103 / 133	B				
N5457	9.0 / 8.27	8.58 / 5.07	15.22 / 14.91	CDEFG / K	.50 / 4.38	.44	CDEG / /DE	*	266 / 414.8	415 / 149	BDR				AP
N5464	13.1									-149					
N5468	12.4 / 12.38		14.07						2856 / 7.7	2789 / -67	C				
N5472										-67					
N5473	12.8 / 12.84	12.66 / 5.85	13.05 / 13.23	CE	.91 / 10.00	.81	CE / /E	.54	2044 / 6.8	2195 / 151	BC				
N5474	11.7 / 11.54	11.74 / 4.01	14.43 / 14.23	CEFG	.51 / 10.63	.44	CEG / /E	-.10	247 / 3.3	395 / 148	C				
N5475										154					
N5477										150					
N5480	12.6 / 12.90		13.59						1720 / .8	1859 / 138	E				
N5481									2025 / .8	2165 / 138	E				
N5483	12.4 / 12.20		14.19							-181					F
N5484										152					
N5485	12.9 / 13.02	12.80 / 2.39	12.84 / 13.06	BC	.91 / 1.88	.82	C		1985 / 4.0	2137 / 153	B				
N5486										153					
N5490										24					
N5490C										25					
N5493	12.4 / 12.85	12.66 / 2.88	12.25 / 12.44	C	.89 / 3.75	.79	C		2627 / 1.8	2566 / -61	B				
N5494	12.6 / 12.74		13.78							-147					

NGC (IC, A) (1)	RA (1950) 100 P (2)	Dec 100 P (3)	L^I B^I (4)	L^II B^II (5)	SGL SGB (6)	Rev. type (S) DDO (T,L) (7)	Yerkes (1) Yerkes (2) (8)	Hu-San Ho (9)	log D w (10)	log R w (11)	log D(0) (12)	S (D,R) (13)
N5496	14 9.0	-0 56	309.47	340.43	123.7	.S..7*/W060			1.64	.70	1.36	FKLQ
	5.1	-28	54.61	55.77	18.1	S 6 7*	SI *AF		8.98	8.98		
N5506	14 10.7	-2 58	308.16	339.17	125.9	.S...$.H030			1.44	.50	1.24	ABCL
	5.2	-28	52.67	53.81	17.9				3.70	3.70		
N5507	14 10.8	-2 55	308.24	339.25	125.8	.E...$.H030			1.23	.29	1.11	ABC
	5.2	-28	52.70	53.84	17.9				2.00	2.00		
N5523	14 12.6	25 34	359.01	32.17	96.0	.SAS6*.W100	S *F		1.60	.55	1.38	ACKW
	4.5	-28	69.77	71.23	24.4	S 3 4			7.61	7.61		
N5529	14 13.4	36 27	30.12	65.16	84.0	.S..5*/W060			1.75	.82	1.42	ACLUQ
	4.2	-27	68.92	70.00	25.3				9.35	9.35		
N5530	14 15.4	-43 9	287.36	319.28	164.3	.SA.4..S030			1.56	.29	1.44	DEFI
	6.3	-27	15.98	16.71	3.6				6.01	6.01		
N5533	14 14.1	35 35	27.69	62.63	85.0	.SAT2..P200	S GK		1.39	.20	1.31	ACKZ
	4.2	-27	69.04	70.15	25.4	S N +	S K *		5.76	5.76		
N5534	14 15.0	-7 11	306.01	337.16	130.4				1.14	.53	.93	BE
	5.3	-27	48.54	49.64	17.6	S T	I P A *		1.29	1.29		
N5544	14 15.0	36 48	30.76	65.78	83.7	RSBT0..P200			.93	.04	.92	CLRZ
	4.2	-27	68.51	69.57	25.6				3.28	1.65		
N5545	14 15.0	36 48	30.76	65.78	83.7	.SAS4*.P200			1.12	.49	.93	LRZ
	4.2	-27	68.51	69.57	25.6				4.74	4.74		
N5548	14 15.7	25 22	358.84	31.95	96.3	PSAS0..W100	S P G *		1.01	.02	1.00	ACW
	4.5	-27	69.04	70.50	25.1	S PNT+*			2.61	2.61		
N5556	14 17.6	-29 1	293.69	325.31	151.5	.SXT7..W100			1.50	.09	1.46	DEW
	5.8	-27	28.86	29.73	10.0				6.01	6.01		
N5557	14 16.4	36 43	30.31	65.27	83.8	.E.1...W060			1.04	.04	1.03	ACKLQ
	4.2	-27	68.27	69.34	25.9	E 1	E2 *K *		2.89	2.89		
N5560	14 17.6	4 13	318.15	349.26	119.1	.SBS3P.P200			1.53	.81	1.20	ACRV
	5.0	-27	57.35	58.64	21.5				7.51	7.51		
N5566	14 17.8	4 11	318.18	349.29	119.1	.SBR2..P200	B *GK*	SBR1	1.72	.49	1.52	ACKRV
	5.0	-27	57.29	58.58	21.6	S 4 NT 4*			10.53	10.53		
N5569	14 18.1	4 13	318.33	349.44	119.1	.SXT3*.P200			1.20	.10	1.16	ACLV
	5.0	-27	57.27	58.56	21.7				3.82	3.19		
N5574	14 18.4	3 28	317.52	348.64	119.9	.LB*-$/W100	D GK		1.09	.35	.95	ABCKNW
	5.0	-27	56.66	57.93	21.5				5.88	5.88		
N5576	14 18.5	3 30	317.60	348.72	119.9	.E+3...W100	E3 K		1.24	.19	1.16	ACKNW
	5.0	-27	56.67	57.94	21.6	E 2			5.27	5.27		
N5577	14 18.7	3 40	317.87	348.99	119.7	.SA.4..L036			1.53	.48	1.34	ACN
	5.0	-27	56.76	58.04	21.7				4.15	4.15		
N5584	14 19.8	-0 10	313.97	345.10	123.7	.SXT6..W100			1.51	.15	1.45	CKNW
	5.1	-27	53.64	54.87	20.9	S 5 3	S A		7.77	7.77		
N5585	14 18.0	56 57	66.53	101.03	61.4	.SXS7..P200	SI *FG		1.71	.18	1.64	ACKXZ
	3.2	-27	56.24	56.50	24.6	S 7		S6	8.62	8.62		
N5592	14 21.0	-28 27	294.73	326.36	151.3							
	5.8	-27	29.06	29.95	10.9							
N5595	14 21.5	-16 30	301.40	332.78	140.1	.SXT5..W100			1.27	.24	1.17	ABFKPVW
	5.5	-27	39.68	40.70	15.8	S 5 T	S A		11.10	11.10		
N5597	14 21.7	-16 33	301.42	332.81	140.2	.SXS6..W100			1.30	.10	1.27	AKPVW
	5.5	-27	39.62	40.64	15.8	S 3 N	S AF		7.73	7.73		
N5600	14 21.4	14 52	335.80	7.44	108.0	.S..5P.W060	S P F		1.04	.06	1.01	KQ
	4.8	-27	63.69	65.14	24.9	S 5 T*			2.30	2.30		
N5605	14 22.3	-12 57	303.96	335.28	136.7				1.23	.08	1.20	AK
	5.4	-27	42.67	43.74	17.3	S 5 1			1.95	1.95		
N5612	14 28.2	-78 11	275.41	308.14	196.4	.LA.-.$S030			1.09	.44	.91	EI
	11.5	-26	-17.04	-16.58	-10.6				1.25	1.25		
N5613	14 22.0	35 7	25.41	60.04	85.6	RLXR+..P200			.91	.06	.89	AZ
	4.2	-27	67.59	68.74	27.0				2.12	2.12		
N5614	14 22.0	35 5	25.33	59.95	85.6	.SAR2P.P200	S P*G	S 1	1.32	.07	1.29	Z
	4.2	-27	67.59	68.75	27.0	S NT			3.18	3.18		
N5631	14 25.1	56 48	65.05	99.50	61.4	.LAS0..W060	E2P		1.08	.03	1.07	ACKYQ
	3.1	-26	55.71	56.01	25.6	S 0			2.91	2.91		
N5633	14 25.6	46 22	49.45	84.33	72.9	RSAT3..W100	S P G		1.19	.15	1.13	ACKNW
	3.7	-26	62.46	63.14	27.2	S			5.86	5.86		
N5636	14 27.1	3 30	320.44	351.72	120.5	.LXR+..W060	B F		1.22	.12	1.17	ABCQ
	5.0	-26	55.23	56.54	23.6				2.82	2.82		
N5638	14 27.1	3 27	320.38	351.66	120.5	.E.1...W060	E2 K		1.13	.05	1.11	ABCKQ
	5.0	-26	55.19	56.51	23.6	E 1			3.42	3.42		
N5641	14 27.1	29 2	9.44	43.12	92.5				1.39	.30	1.27	K
	4.4	-26	66.99	68.37	27.9	SX2 2*			1.37	1.37		
N5643	14 29.4	-43 59	289.45	321.42	166.2	.SXT5..B060			1.60	.05	1.58	DEPI
	6.4	-26	14.23	15.00	5.5				7.76	7.76		
N5645	14 28.1	7 29	325.91	357.29	116.3	.SBS7..B060	BS *F		1.33	.19	1.25	ACKQ
	4.9	-26	57.85	59.22	24.9	S 5 NK 4*			4.79	4.79		
N5653	14 28.0	31 25	15.52	49.54	89.8	PSAT3..W100	SD *G		1.06	.07	1.03	ACKW
	4.3	-26	66.81	68.12	28.2	S N*			3.68	3.68		
N5660	14 28.1	49 50	54.81	89.54	69.0	.SXT5..W100	S AF		1.39	.06	1.37	ACHKYW
	3.5	-26	60.10	60.65	27.2	S 5 K 3			7.07	7.07		
N5665	14 29.9	8 18	327.62	359.06	115.6	.SBS9P*W060	S P F		1.16	.07	1.13	ACKQ
	4.9	-26	58.06	59.45	25.5	S 5 NT *			3.76	3.76		
N5668	14 30.9	4 40	323.07	354.43	119.5	.SAS7..P200	SI *F		1.50	.03	1.49	KNWZ
	5.0	-26	55.40	56.75	24.9	S 5 K 4			11.14	11.14		

NGC (IC, A) (14)	m_H / m_C (15)	B(O) w (16)	B'(O) / m'_C (17)	S(B) (18)	(B-V)(O) w (19)	C_o(O) (20)	S(C) (21)	(U-B)(O) w (22)	V w (23)	V_o ΔV (24)	S(V) (25)	φ_r n (26)	φ(21) (27)	(28)	Photo. (29)
N5496	12.8														
	12.74		14.28							−47					
N5506									2195	2142	E				B
									1.1	−53					
N5507									1884	1831	E				
									1.1	−52					
N5523	12.8														
	12.64		14.23							58					
N5529															B
										98					
N5530	12.3														
	12.14		14.08							−176					
N5533	12.9	12.98	14.22	BC	.89	.73	C		3781	3876	B				
	12.74	.2.64	13.98		1.88				2.8	95					
N5534	13.0														
	13.39		12.73							−65					
N5544									3165	3265	E				CD
									.4	100					
N5545									3175	3275	E				CD
									.4	100					
N5548	12.9	13.54	13.28	BC	.60	.48	C		4930	4990	B				
	13.36	1.93	13.10		1.88				4.0	60					
N5556	12.5														
	12.37		14.36							−137					
N5557	12.6	12.60	12.44	BC	.95	.86	C		3195	3296	B				
	12.81	2.10	12.65		1.88				2.8	101					
N5560		13.48	14.22	DE	.80		DE	.16							
		3.47			15.63		/DE			−19					
N5566	11.9	11.62	13.96	CDEL*	.89	.71	CDEL	.43	1601	1581	BD				LMP
	11.70	8.01	14.04		42.50		/DEL		2.0	−19					
N5569															
										−19					
N5574	13.1	13.58	13.02	CEL	.84	.74	CEL	.30	1716	1694	B				
	13.36	3.06	12.80		9.00		/EL		4.0	−21					
N5576	11.9	12.16	12.70	CDEL	.90	.82	CDEL	.43	1528	1507	B				
	12.11	7.72	12.65		19.30		/DEL		1.0	−21					
N5577															
										−20					
N5584	12.2														
	12.16		14.10							−34					
N5585	12.0	11.66	14.55	CG	.51	.42	CG		304	467	C				
	11.68	3.14	14.57		4.38				2.0	163					
N5592	13.1														
N5595	12.4									−132					
	12.84		13.43							−92					
N5597	12.6														
	12.79		13.83							−92					
N5600	12.4	13.42	13.21	E	.49		E	−.09							
	13.21	1.75	13.00		6.25		/E			25					
N5605	13.1														
	13.17		13.86							−79					
N5612	13.0														
	13.34		12.63							−218					
N5613															P
										99					
N5614	12.9	12.70	13.84	B					3872	3971	B				P
	12.79	1.96	13.93						1.8	99					
N5631	12.5	12.84	12.93	B					1979	2146	B				
	12.74	1.21	12.83						2.8	166					
N5633	12.8	13.07	13.46	CD	.61	.48	CD	−.03	2346	2484	BC				
	13.10	5.84	13.49		20.63		/D		6.8	138					
N5636															
										−14					
N5638	12.6	12.67	12.96	C	.86	.78	C		1677	1663	B				
	12.65	1.39	12.94		1.88				4.0	−14					
N5641	13.1														
	12.97		14.01							82					
N5643	11.4														F
	11.36		14.00							−169					
N5645	12.9	13.07	14.06	A											
	13.04	2.59	14.03							3					
N5653	12.9								3557	3648	C				
	13.39		13.28						2.9	91					
N5660	12.3	12.44	14.03	E	.47		E	−.17							K
	12.33	2.39	13.92		6.25		/E			150					
N5665	12.7														
	13.13		13.47							7					
N5668	12.4	12.31	14.45	C	.69	.60	C		1737	1732	BC				
	12.24	2.01	14.38		3.75				6.4	−6					

113

NGC (IC, A)	RA (1950) 100 P	Dec 100 P	L^I B^I	L^II B^II	SGL SGB	Rev. type (S) DDO (T, L)	Yerkes (1) Yerkes (2)	Hu-San Ho	log D w	log R w	log D(O)	S (D,R)
	(1)											
	(2)	(3)	(4)	(5)	(6)	(7)	(8)	(9)	(10)	(11)	(12)	(13)
N5669	14 30.3	10 8	330.45	1.97	113.6	.SXT6..W060	SB *AF		1.53	.17	1.47	ACKQ
	4.9	-26	59.15	60.57	26.0	S 5 5			5.60	5.60		
N5672	14 30.5	31 53	16.63	50.66	89.3	.S..3..W			1.03	.26	.93	AC
	4.3	-26	66.26	67.55	28.7				.81	.81		
N5673	14 29.8	50 10	55.00	89.69	68.6	.S.....W			1.38	.52	1.17	ACHL
	3.5	-26	59.68	60.22	27.4				3.54	3.54		
N5676	14 31.0	49 41	54.00	88.69	69.1	.SAT4..W060	S F		1.56	.29	1.44	ACHKLUY
	3.5	-26	59.82	60.38	27.7	S 5 K 3*			11.31	11.31		Q
N5678	14 30.7	58 8	65.69	100.02	59.8	.SXT3..W060	S P F		1.44	.28	1.33	ACHKLUQ
	2.9	-26	54.22	54.50	26.1	S 5P *3*			9.71	9.71		
N5682	14 32.8	48 53	52.36	87.05	69.9	.SBS3..W060			1.18	.49	.98	ABCHQ
	3.5	-26	60.05	60.65	28.1				4.55	4.55		
N5683	14 33.0	48 53	52.32	87.01	69.9	.SBS0.$W060			.88	.05	.86	ABCHQ
	3.5	-26	60.02	60.63	28.1				1.93	1.93		
N5687	14 33.3	54 42	60.93	95.39	63.4	.L..-.$W060	E4 K		1.14	.24	1.04	KQ
	3.2	-26	56.36	56.76	27.2	S 0*	ED *K		2.60	2.60		
N5689	14 33.7	48 57	52.30	86.97	69.8	.SBS0*.W060	SD *K		1.46	.58	1.23	ACHYQ
	3.5	-26	59.89	60.49	28.2	S N +*			5.48	5.48		
N5690	14 35.2	2 30	321.76	353.16	122.1	.S..5$/W060	SB *A		1.49	.53	1.28	AEKQ
	5.1	-26	53.11	54.44	25.3	S 3 4	S F *		5.58	5.58		
N5691	14 35.3	-0 11	318.82	350.19	125.0	.SXS.P.W100			1.18	.17	1.11	ACEHKW
	5.1	-26	51.14	52.43	24.6	S N *	SIP*		5.18	5.18		
N5693	14 34.6	48 45	51.81	86.47	70.0	.SBT7..W060	S F		1.22	.07	1.19	ACHQ
	3.5	-26	59.88	60.50	28.4				2.82	2.82		
N5701	14 36.7	5 34	325.95	357.43	119.0	RSBT0..W100	B K		1.55	.03	1.53	ACKMW
	5.0	-25	54.98	56.35	26.5	SX 2 2			7.59	7.59		
N5705	14 37.3	-0 31	319.05	350.46	125.5	.SB.7*.L036			1.40	.28	1.29	HN
	5.1	-25	50.55	51.85	24.9				2.54	2.54		
N5707	14 35.8	51 47	56.35	90.90	66.6	.S.....W			1.50	.62	1.25	C
	3.3	-26	57.94	58.46	28.1				.54	.54		
N5713	14 37.6	-0 5	319.60	351.01	125.1	.SXT4P.P200	SI *A		1.37	.03	1.35	ACEHKNZ
	5.1	-25	50.82	52.13	25.1	S 5 NK	SIP*		10.01	10.01		
N5716	14 38.3	-17 15	305.32	336.84	142.5	.SBT5.$W100			1.20	.14	1.14	AFW
	5.6	-25	36.99	38.08	19.2				3.03	3.03		
N5719	14 38.3	-0 5	319.81	351.22	125.1	.SXS2P.P200			1.44	.45	1.26	ACHNZ
	5.1	-25	50.71	52.01	25.3				7.88	7.88		
N5728	14 39.6	-17 3	305.78	337.31	142.4	.SXR1*.W100			1.39	.27	1.29	AFKW
	5.6	-25	36.99	38.09	19.6	SX2 3	D *FG		5.35	5.35		
N5733	14 40.2	-0 9	320.28	351.73	125.3	.S....$R020			1.18	.42	1.01	ACH
	5.1	-25	50.33	51.65	25.7				1.26	1.26		
N5739	14 40.6	42 3	38.55	73.10	77.5	.L...$.W			1.50	.10	1.46	C
	3.8	-25	62.07	62.98	30.3	S N +			.54	.54		
N5740	14 41.9	1 54	323.02	354.51	123.3	.SXT3..W060			1.45	.30	1.34	ACEHKLR
	5.1	-25	51.50	52.85	26.8	S 4 4	S F	S4	13.84	13.84		VXQ
N5746	14 42.3	2 10	323.44	354.94	123.1	.SXT3$/P200	S GK		1.86	.73	1.57	ACEHKLM
	5.1	-25	51.62	52.97	26.9	S 3 N -*	S GK	S3	26.66	26.66		RVXZ
N5750	14 43.6	-0 1	321.39	352.88	125.5	.SBR0..W100			1.38	.26	1.28	ACEKW
	5.1	-25	49.85	51.18	26.6	S 4 5	DS *G *		6.57	6.57		
N5756	14 44.9	-14 39	308.81	340.35	140.6	.S....$/H030			1.24	.27	1.13	ABFK
	5.5	-25	38.27	39.42	21.7	S 5P			4.10	3.05		
N5757	14 45.0	-18 53	305.88	337.47	144.8	RSBR3..W060			1.18	.07	1.15	AKQ
	5.6	-25	34.75	35.86	20.0	SB3 N *	B F		3.56	3.56		
N5768	14 49.6	-2 20	320.62	352.16	128.5	.SAT5*.W100			1.29	.18	1.21	AKW
	5.2	-24	47.13	48.45	27.3	I 9 7*	SI *AF		4.64	4.64		
N5772	14 49.8	40 48	34.90	69.23	78.7	.SAR3*.W060			1.15	.15	1.09	ACQ
	3.8	-24	60.84	61.83	32.2				1.19	1.19		
N5774	14 51.3	3 47	327.79	359.43	122.0	.SXT7..W060	S F		1.47	.03	1.46	ABCXQ
	5.0	-24	51.08	52.47	29.5			S5	3.83	3.83		
N5775	14 51.5	3 45	327.80	359.45	122.1	.SB.5$/W060	S *FG*		1.64	.65	1.38	ABCEKXQ
	5.0	-24	51.02	52.41	29.6	S 3*	S *F *	S4	8.03	8.03		
N5783	14 51.8	52 18	54.53	88.86	65.4	.S..5*.W						
	3.2	-24	55.64	56.20	30.4							
N5791	14 56.0	-19 4	308.34	340.00	146.2	.E+6.*.W060			1.15	.25	1.05	AKQ
	5.7	-24	33.13	34.28	22.2	S 0	ED *K		1.88	1.88		
N5792	14 55.8	-0 54	323.72	355.35	127.5	.SBT3..W100			1.78	.57	1.55	AKW
	5.1	-24	47.07	48.43	29.2	S 3PN -*	S F		8.73	7.02		
N5793	14 56.6	-16 30	310.30	341.95	143.7	.S..3*/W100			1.16	.43	.98	W
	5.6	-24	35.12	36.30	23.5				2.25	2.25		
N5796	14 56.6	-16 26	310.35	342.00	143.7	.E.0+..W100			1.04	.08	1.01	KW
	5.6	-24	35.17	36.35	23.5	E 0	E2 K		2.26	2.26		
N5806	14 57.5	2 5	327.40	359.09	124.4	.SXS3..W100	SD *G		1.40	.28	1.29	AEKLW
	5.1	-23	48.79	50.18	30.5	S 4 5*	SD G *		7.18	7.18		
N5811	14 57.9	1 50	327.22	358.91	124.7	.SBS9*.W100			.94	.00	.94	ALW
	5.1	-23	48.55	49.94	30.6				1.69	1.29		
N5812	14 58.2	-7 16	318.16	349.78	134.5	.E.0...W100			.96	.04	.94	AEK
	5.3	-23	42.04	43.33	27.6	E 1	E1 K		1.33	1.33		
N5813	14 58.7	1 54	327.50	359.20	124.7	.E.1+..W100	E2 K		1.30	.12	1.26	ABEKLW
	5.1	-23	48.45	49.84	30.8	E 1	DE GK		6.84	6.09		
N5820	14 57.2	54 5	56.35	90.58	63.1	.L..../W060			1.06	.29	.94	ACKQ
	3.0	-23	53.98	54.50	30.7	E 5 T -*	E7 K		2.39	2.39		

NGC (IC, A) (14)	Magnitudes				Colors				Velocities			Radio			
	m_H m_C (15)	B(O) w (16)	B'(O) m'_C (17)	S(B) (18)	(B-V)(O) w (19)	$C_o(O)$ (20)	S(C) (21)	(U-B)(O) w (22)	V w (23)	V_o ΔV (24)	S(V) (25)	ϕ_r n (26)	ϕ(21) (27)	(28)	Photo. (29)
N5669	12.5 12.27		14.31							15					
N5672		14.34 4.33	13.68	BC	.62 10.00	.45	BC		3701 2.4	3796 95	B				
N5673										151					
N5676	11.9 11.93	11.87 3.57	13.81 13.87	C	.70* 3.75	.56	C		2244 1.8	2395 151	C				
N5678	12.1 12.29		13.63						2300 2.4	2472 172	C				
N5682										150					
N5683										150					
N5687	12.7 12.92		12.86	C*	.85 1.88	.75	C		2119 1.8	2284 165	B				
N5689	12.6 12.70	13.17 0.94	14.01 13.54	C	.94 1.88	.80	C		2205 4.0	2355 150	B				
N5690	12.9 12.86	12.76 2.22	13.90 14.00	A						-10					
N5691	13.0 13.34		13.63							-20					
N5693										150					
N5701	12.8 12.09	12.16 1.98	14.55 14.48	AL*			L* /L	*		3					
N5705										-20					
N5707										159					
N5713	11.8 12.08	11.99 9.60	13.48 13.57	CEF	.63 14.38	.54	CE /E	.02	1948 5.7	1930 -18	BC				K
N5716										-81					
N5719										-17					
N5728	12.4 12.50	12.21 1.59	13.35 13.64	A	.77 4.38		A			-79					
N5733										-16					
N5739	13.1 12.47		14.51							135					
N5740	12.8 12.64	12.89 7.21	14.28 14.03	ACEG	.74* 8.75		CEG /E	.16		-6					
N5746	11.8 11.55	11.81 3.72	14.40 14.14	CEG	1.01 12.50	.79	CEG /E	.52	1831 9.0	1826 -5	BCD				BCLM
N5750	12.6 12.58		13.67							-12					
N5756	13.1 13.04		13.43							-66					
N5757	12.6 12.97	13.04 1.39	13.48 13.41	A	.94 4.38		A			-81					
N5768	12.9 13.02		13.81							-16					
N5772										137					
N5774		12.98 1.39	15.02	G	.63 2.50	.54	G		1525 .9	1534 9	E				
N5775	12.4 12.38	12.48 1.15	14.07 13.97	G	.83 2.50	.65	G		1565 .9	1574 9	E				
N5783										169					
N5791	13.0 13.02	12.89 1.86	12.88 13.01	A	.97 4.38		A			-72					
N5792	12.9 12.19		14.68							-5					
N5793										-63					
N5796	12.8 12.96		12.75							-62					
N5806	12.5 12.57	12.70 1.11	13.89 13.76	C	.72 1.88	.56	C		1301 2.4	1309 8	B				
N5811										8					
N5812	12.5 12.88	12.90 0.84	12.34 12.32	C	.98 1.88	.88	C		2066 4.0	2040 -27	B				
N5813	12.2 12.15	12.09 5.60	13.08 13.14	BC	.99 5.63	.90	C		1882 2.4	1891 9	B				
N5820	12.8 13.16	13.61 1.70	13.05 12.60	BC	1.12* 8.13	1.00	BC		3269 2.8	3445 176	B				

NGC (IC, A) (1)	Coordinates					Classification			Diameters			
	RA (1950) Dec 100 P (2)	100 P (3)	L^I B^I (4)	L^II B^II (5)	SGL SGB (6)	Rev. type (S) DDO (T,L) (7)	Yerkes (1) Yerkes (2) (8)	Hu-San Ho (9)	log D w (10)	log R w (11)	log D(O) (12)	S (D,R) (13)
N5829	15 0.5	23 32	0.16	33.01	99.4	.SAS5..L036			1.33			L
	4.4	-23	58.70	60.15	35.1				.77			
N5831	15 1.6	1 24	327.66	359.38	125.5	.E.3...W060	E3 K		1.00	.05	.98	AEKQ
	5.1	-23	47.57	48.97	31.3	E P	E3 K		2.08	2.08		
N5832	14 57.8	71 53	76.44	110.09	44.4	.SBT3.$W060			1.54	.25	1.44	AQ
	0.4	-23	42.13	42.14	24.3				2.53	2.53		
N5838	15 2.9	2 18	328.98	0.73	124.6	.LA.-..W060	D GK		1.54	.55	1.32	AEKLQ
	5.1	-23	47.92	49.32	31.9	S 0	D K		6.34	5.55		
N5839	15 2.9	1 49	328.44	0.18	125.2	.L.....W			.88	.00	.88	A
	5.1	-23	47.60	49.00	31.7				.38	.38		
N5845	15 3.5	1 49	328.58	0.33	125.2	.E.3...W			.84	.00	.84	A
	5.1	-23	47.49	48.89	31.9				.34	.34		
N5846	15 4.0	1 48	328.69	0.44	125.3	.E+0+..P200	E1 K		1.32	.04	1.30	ABEKLXZ
	5.1	-23	47.38	48.79	32.0	E 0	E2 K	E	7.20	7.20		
N5846A	15 4.0	1 48	328.69	0.44	125.3	.E.2+..P200			.39	.08	.36	Z
	5.1	-23	47.38	48.79	32.0				.56	.56		
N5850	15 4.6	1 44	328.76	0.51	125.4	.SBR3..P200	B G		1.51	.04	1.49	AEKLXZ
	5.1	-23	47.23	48.63	32.1	SB2 1	B G	S4	8.81	7.87		
N5854	15 5.3	2 45	330.07	1.86	124.3	.LBS+./W100	BD *GK		1.33	.55	1.11	AEKW
	5.0	-23	47.75	49.17	32.6	S 0*			5.85	5.85		
N5857	15 5.2	19 47	354.12	26.68	104.0	.SBS3..W060			1.02	.29	.91	AHLUQ
	4.5	-23	56.51	57.99	35.9				3.73	3.10		
N5858	15 6.1	-11 1	316.83	348.51	139.3	.E.6.*.W100			.89	.37	.74	W
	5.4	-23	37.94	39.21	27.9				1.58	1.58		
N5859	15 5.3	19 46	354.11	26.67	104.1	.SBS4..W060			1.38	.45	1.20	AHULQ
	4.5	-23	56.48	57.96	35.9				6.18	4.96		
N5861	15 6.4	-11 8	316.80	348.49	139.5	.SXT5..W100			1.44	.26	1.34	AFKW
	5.4	-23	37.80	39.07	27.9	S 5P 1*	S A		8.04	8.04		
N5864	15 7.0	3 14	331.03	2.84	123.9	.LBS0$/W100	BD *GK		1.32	.54	1.11	AEKW
	5.0	-22	47.73	49.15	33.1	E 7P			5.85	5.85		
N5866	15 5.1	55 57	57.91	92.03	60.7	.LA.+../P200	SDP*K	L 3	1.52	.39	1.36	ACHKLMR
	2.7	-23	52.01	52.49	31.2	E 6P	D P K		17.55	17.55		VYZ
N5866B	15 10.9	55 58	57.24	91.30	60.3	.S..5..W						
	2.7	-22	51.32	51.82	31.9							
N5874	15 6.4	54 57	56.37	90.50	61.7							
	2.8	-23	52.39	52.91	31.7							
N5875	15 7.7	52 43	53.01	87.16	64.1	.S..3..W			1.46	.34	1.32	AC
	3.0	-22	53.35	53.94	32.6				1.68	1.68		
N5876	15 8.0	54 42	55.83	89.94	61.9							
	2.8	-22	52.33	52.86	32.0							
N5878	15 11.0	-14 5	315.46	347.19	143.0	.SAS3..W100			1.53	.38	1.38	AFKW
	5.5	-22	34.84	36.09	27.7	S N +	SD G		7.66	7.66		
N5879	15 8.4	57 12	59.19	93.25	59.1	.SAT4*$W060	S G		1.63	.51	1.42	ACHKQ
	2.6	-22	50.95	51.40	31.2	S 3 4			6.53	6.53		
N5885	15 12.4	-9 53	319.25	350.98	138.9	.SXR5..W100			1.48	.04	1.46	AEFKTW
	5.4	-22	37.74	39.05	29.8	S 6 8*	S A		11.22	9.19		
N5889	15 11.6	41 31	34.26	68.26	77.0	.E.....			1.09	.19	1.01	ACH
	3.7	-22	56.68	57.69	36.1				1.67	1.67		
N5893	15 11.8	42 8	35.34	69.35	76.3				1.10	.11	1.05	ABCH
	3.6	-22	56.51	57.49	36.0				2.38	2.38		
N5898	15 15.2	-23 55	309.13	340.96	153.1	.E.0...W100			.88	.03	.87	DEKW
	5.9	-22	26.58	27.74	23.8	E 1P *	DE K		2.75	2.75		
N5899	15 13.2	42 14	35.40	69.40	76.1	.SXT5..W060	S F		1.41	.45	1.23	ACHQ
	3.6	-22	56.24	57.22	36.3	S 4 K 1*			5.17	5.17		
N5900	15 13.3	42 23	35.66	69.66	75.9	.S....*R020			1.32	.38	1.16	ACH
	3.6	-22	56.18	57.16	36.2				1.90	1.90		
N5903	15 15.6	-23 51	309.26	341.08	153.1	.E.2...W100			.98	.07	.95	DEKW
	5.9	-22	26.57	27.73	23.9	E 1	DE K		3.17	3.17		
N5905	15 14.1	55 42	56.51	90.55	60.4	.SBR3..W060	BS *F		1.56	.14	1.50	ACHKMQ
	2.7	-22	51.07	51.58	32.5	SX3 1*			9.40	9.40		
N5907	15 14.6	56 31	57.57	91.59	59.5	.SAS5*/P200	S G	S 5	2.07	.94	1.69	ABCHKLR
	2.6	-22	50.59	51.08	32.2	S 4 3*	S G *	S4	32.73	32.73		VXYZ
N5908	15 15.4	55 36	56.22	90.26	60.5	.SAS3*/W060	S G		1.45	.51	1.25	ACKMQ
	2.7	-22	50.96	51.48	32.7	S 2	S GK		7.66	7.66		
N5915	15 18.8	-12 55	318.12	349.90	142.8	.SBS2P.P200	ISP*		1.27	.12	1.22	KZ
	5.5	-21	34.45	35.74	29.9	S 4 T			4.14	4.14		
N5916	15 18.9	-12 59	318.09	349.87	142.9	.SBT1P.P200			1.45	.47	1.27	AFZ
	5.5	-21	34.38	35.67	29.9				5.53	5.53		
N5916A	15 18.5	-12 55	318.06	349.83	142.8	.SBS5P.P200			1.09	.48	.90	FZ
	5.5	-21	34.50	35.79	29.8				3.47	2.41		
N5921	15 19.5	5 15	336.16	8.14	122.6	.SBR4..W100	BS *FG		1.63	.08	1.59	AHKLUW
	5.0	-21	46.47	47.93	36.7	SX4 2	SX F		10.44	9.74		
N5929	15 24.3	41 50	33.98	67.83	76.0	.E.2...			1.03	.01	1.03	ABC
	3.6	-21	54.30	55.31	38.3				1.10	1.10		
N5930	15 24.4	41 51	34.01	67.85	76.0	.E.0...			1.09	.02	1.08	ABC
	3.6	-21	54.28	55.29	38.4				1.23	1.23		
N5936	15 27.6	13 9	347.73	20.03	113.3	.SBT3..W060	S AF		1.12	.07	1.09	ACKQ
	4.7	-20	48.90	50.38	40.4	S 5 1*	S F		3.58	3.58		
N5949	15 27.2	64 55	66.80	100.56	49.9	.SAR4.$P200	SI *AF		1.31	.32	1.19	KMZ
	1.4	-20	44.73	44.99	29.9	S			6.16	6.16		

NGC (IC, A) (14)	Magnitudes				Colors				Velocities			Radio			
	m_H m_C (15)	B(O) w (16)	B'(O) m'_C (17)	S(B) (18)	(B-V)(O) w (19)	C_o(O) (20)	S(C) (21)	(U-B)(O) w (22)	V w (23)	V_o ΔV (24)	S(V) (25)	$φ_r$ n (26)	φ(21) (27)	(28)	Photo. (29)
N5829										90					
N5831	12.7 12.94	13.05 2.97	12.69 12.58	BCE	.92 8.13	.83	CE /E	.60	1684 4.0	1693 9	B				
N5832										207					
N5838	12.1 12.07	12.14 5.15	13.43 13.36	BCE	.96 8.13	.85	CE /E	.68	1427 4.0	1441 14	B				
N5839		13.95 2.73	13.04	A						12					
N5845		13.51 2.77	12.45	A	.86 4.38		A			13					
N5846	11.6 11.67	11.76 1.60	13.00 12.91	AG*	.98 21.25	.89	AGE* /E*		1771 6.9	1784 13	BC				
N5846A		14.52 3.16	11.06	BC	.99 3.75	.90	C		2291 9.0	2304 13	BC				
N5850	12.9 12.33	12.25 12.22	14.44 14.52	CDEFG	.86 39.38	.75	CDEG /DE	.39	2372 6.0	2385 13	BC			JK
N5854	12.7 12.82	12.93 1.35	13.17 13.06	C	.85 1.88	.74	C		1626 2.4	1644 18	B				
N5857		14.29 0.77	13.53	C*	.71 1.88	.52	C*		4705 2.9	4785 81	BC			A
N5858															
N5859		13.57 1.88	14.31	C*	.85 3.75	.66	C*		4664 .4	4745 81	B			A
N5861	12.4 12.47		13.86							−34					
N5864	12.8 12.89		13.13							21					
N5866	11.5 11.59	11.19 5.48	12.73 13.13	BCE	.87 14.38	.78	BCE /E	.38	788 13.2	972 184	ABC			ABCL P
N5866B										187					
N5874										183					
N5375										183					
N5876										179					
N5878	12.9 12.61	12.60 1.43	14.19 14.20	C	.82 1.88	.62	C		2111 2.4	2070 −41	B				
N5879	12.1 12.08	12.32 7.42	14.16 13.92	BCE	.67 10.00	.51	CE /E	.07	876 2.4	1064 188	B				
N5885	12.4 12.17		14.21							−24					
N5889										154					
N5893										156					
N5898	12.6 13.08	12.91 2.85	11.95 12.12	AC	.88* 6.25	.74	AC		2304 .3	2231 −73	B				
N5899	12.4 12.73	12.79 1.87	13.63 13.57	BC	.77 1.88	.60	C		2549 4.0	2706 157	B				
N5900										158					
N5903	12.9 13.14	12.92 3.45	12.36 12.58	AC	.97* 6.25	.83	AC		2612 .4	2539 −73	B				
N5905	13.1 12.41		14.65							188					
N5907	11.8 11.32	11.40 3.66	14.59 14.51	CDEG	.81 20.00	.63	CDEG /DE	.29	535 4.2	725 190	BC			BMP
N5908	13.0 12.96		13.90							189					
N5915	12.5 12.71		13.55							−30					
N5916										−30					
N5916A										−30					
N5921	12.5 11.91	11.65 5.57	14.34 14.60	BC	.78* 3.75	.68	C		1389 .4	1429 40	B			B
N5929										2520 4.7	2683 163	E			
N5930										2705 4.7	2868 164	E			
N5936	12.9 13.25	13.41 4.36	13.60 13.44	A						76					
N5949	12.9 13.07		13.71						380 1.2	589 209	C				

117

NGC (IC, A) (1)	RA (1950) Dec 100 P / 100 P (2)(3)	L^I B^I (4)	L^II B^II (5)	SGL SGB (6)	Rev. type (S) DDO (T, L) (7)	Yerkes (1) Yerkes (2) (8)	Hu-San Ho (9)	log D w (10)	log R w (11)	log D(O) (12)	S (D,R) (13)
N5951	15 31.4 / 4.6	351.11 / 48.95	23.52 / 50.44	110.8 / 41.6	.S....$			1.44 / 4.78	.52 / 2.60	1.23	ABCS
	15 10 / -20										
N5953	15 32.3 / 4.6	351.52 / 48.85	23.94 / 50.33	110.6 / 41.8	.E.....			.99 / 2.24	.00 / 1.05	.99	ABCS
	15 22 / -20										
N5954	15 32.3 / 4.6	351.52 / 48.85	23.94 / 50.33	110.6 / 41.8	.S..5..			1.17 / 1.84	.31 / 1.84	1.05	ABC
	15 22 / -20										
N5957	15 33.0 / 4.7	347.41 / 47.30	19.70 / 48.79	114.8 / 41.5	.SBR3*.L036			1.24 / 2.44	.02 / 2.44	1.24	AU
	12 13 / -20										
N5962	15 34.2 / 4.6	353.75 / 49.00	26.24 / 50.48	108.8 / 42.4	.SAR5..W100 / S 5 3	S F	S 5	1.38 / 7.80	.15 / 7.33	1.32	ABCKNW
	16 46 / -19										
N5964	15 35.1 / 4.9	340.29 / 43.76	12.40 / 45.24	122.8 / 40.7	.SBT7..W100			1.61 / 5.30	.11 / 5.30	1.56	AW
	6 8 / -19										
N5967	15 41.9 / 12.2	280.57 / -17.07	313.29 / -16.49	196.7 / -5.7	.SXR6*.S030			1.44 / 3.92	.24 / 3.92	1.35	DEI
	-75 31 / -18										
N5967A	15 40.5 / 12.3	280.42 / -17.10	313.14 / -16.52	196.7 / -5.8	.S....*.S030			1.22 / .55	.33 / .55	1.09	I
	-75 38 / -19										
N5968	15 36.9 / 6.2	308.80 / 18.50	340.77 / 19.66	161.9 / 24.1	.SXR2..W100			1.27 / 3.93	.01 / 3.93	1.27	FW
	-30 24 / -19										
N5970	15 36.1 / 4.7	348.07 / 46.68	20.38 / 48.17	114.8 / 42.3	.SBR5..W060 / S 5 4	SB *G / S G		1.39 / 5.60	.16 / 5.60	1.33	KNQ
	12 20 / -19										
N5976	15 35.8 / 2.1	59.56 / 46.64	93.37 / 47.09	54.8 / 33.4	.L.....			.95 / .09	.10 / .09	.91	A
	59 36 / -19										
N5981	15 36.9 / 2.0	59.40 / 46.54	93.21 / 46.99	54.7 / 33.6	.S..5$/W060	DS *G		1.43 / 7.70	.69 / 6.70	1.16	ABLVQ
	59 33 / -19										
N5982	15 37.6 / 2.0	59.32 / 46.47	93.12 / 46.92	54.7 / 33.6	.E.3...W060 / E 3P -*	E4 K		1.09 / 3.43	.09 / 2.80	1.05	ABKLQ
	59 32 / -19										
N5984	15 40.6 / 4.7	351.44 / 46.61	23.84 / 48.09	112.3 / 43.7	.SBT7*.W060 / S 3 4*	BS *F *		1.41 / 4.30	.51 / 4.30	1.21	AKQ
	14 22 / -19										
N5985	15 38.6 / 2.0	59.19 / 46.37	92.99 / 46.83	54.6 / 33.8	.SXR3..W060 / S 3 1	S FG		1.67 / 12.28	.24 / 12.28	1.58	ABKLVYQ
	59 30 / -19										
N6015	15 50.7 / 1.5	62.02 / 43.73	95.70 / 44.12	50.7 / 33.4	.SAS6..P200 / S 5 3	S AF	S6	1.71 / 7.93	.37 / 7.93	1.56	AKXYZ
	62 28 / -17										
N6027A	15 57.0 / 4.4	2.30 / 45.44	34.99 / 46.88	103.4 / 48.1	.L...P.P200						
	20 55 / -17										
N6027D	15 57.0 / 4.4	2.30 / 45.44	34.99 / 46.88	103.4 / 48.1	.S..1..P200						
	20 55 / -17										
N6041	16 2.4 / 4.5	358.85 / 43.19	31.43 / 44.65	108.1 / 49.2	.L.....W			1.04 / .59	.00 / .59	1.04	A
	17 49 / -16										
N6044	16 2.7 / 4.5	359.12 / 43.19	31.71 / 44.64	107.8 / 49.3	.E.0...W						
	18 0 / -16										
N6045	16 2.8 / 4.5	358.99 / 43.12	31.57 / 44.58	108.0 / 49.3	.S..3..W						
	17 53 / -16										
N6047	16 2.9 / 4.5	358.96 / 43.09	31.54 / 44.55	108.1 / 49.4	.E.0...W						
	17 51 / -16										
N6052	16 3.1 / 4.4	2.64 / 44.02	35.32 / 45.45	103.7 / 49.5	.IB.9P.W100	I A *		1.04 / 2.25	.08 / 2.25	1.00	AKW
	20 41 / -16										
N6055	16 3.3 / 4.5	359.51 / 43.15	32.11 / 44.60	107.4 / 49.5	.LB....W						
	18 15 / -16										
N6056	16 3.4 / 4.5	359.27 / 43.05	31.86 / 44.51	107.8 / 49.5							
	18 3 / -16										
N6061	16 4.0 / 4.5	359.74 / 43.03	32.35 / 44.49	107.3 / 49.6							
	18 22 / -16										
N6068	15 58.1 / -4.8	80.00 / 34.53	113.32 / 34.45	35.6 / 23.3	.S..4.*W			1.15 / .73	.25 / .73	1.05	A
	79 6 / -17										
N6068A	15 57.4 / -4.8	80.02 / 34.55	113.34 / 34.48	35.6 / 23.3	.L....*W						
	79 6 / -17										
N6070	16 7.4 / 5.1	340.29 / 34.12	12.46 / 35.59	133.3 / 46.6	.SAS6..W100 / S 5 1	S F		1.52 / 15.25	.26 / 15.25	1.41	ABEKLRVW
	0 50 / -15										
N6106	16 16.3 / 4.9	348.67 / 35.69	20.99 / 37.17	124.8 / 50.9	.SAS5..W100 / S 4 4*	S F / S *F *		1.36 / 5.23	.23 / 5.23	1.27	AKW
	7 31 / -14										
N6118	16 19.3 / 5.2	339.29 / 29.97	11.46 / 31.44	139.2 / 48.1	.SAS6..W100 / S 3 3	S F		1.62 / 9.30	.34 / 9.30	1.48	AFKW
	-2 11 / -14										
N6140	16 19.0 / .7	64.03 / 39.68	97.54 / 40.01	45.5 / 33.9	.SAS5..P048						
	65 29 / -14										
N6143	16 20.6 / 2.2	50.88 / 42.47	84.42 / 43.12	55.1 / 40.9	.SXT4*.W060			.91 / 1.24	.09 / 1.24	.88	Q
	55 12 / -14										
N6166	16 26.9 / 3.4	29.70 / 42.60	62.94 / 43.70	73.0 / 50.2	.E...P.W			1.00 / 1.08	.17 / 1.08	.93	AB
	39 40 / -13										
N6166A	16 26.9 / 3.4	29.70 / 42.60	62.94 / 43.70	73.0 / 50.2							
	39 40 / -13										
N6166B	16 26.9 / 3.4	29.70 / 42.60	62.94 / 43.70	73.0 / 50.2							
	39 40 / -13										
N6166C	16 26.9 / 3.4	29.70 / 42.60	62.94 / 43.70	73.0 / 50.2							
	39 40 / -13										
N6181	16 30.1 / 4.4	4.52 / 37.80	37.16 / 39.22	104.8 / 55.8	.SXT5..W100 / S 5 1	S F	S 5	1.36 / 6.30	.32 / 6.30	1.23	AEKLW
	19 56 / -12										
N6196	16 35.5 / 3.6	25.30 / 40.58	58.40 / 41.75	76.9 / 53.2	.E.5.*.L036						
	36 12 / -12										
N6207	16 41.3 / 3.5	26.46 / 39.53	59.55 / 40.68	74.9 / 54.0	.SAS5..P200 / S 5 3*	SIP*FG*		1.43 / 7.07	.33 / 7.07	1.30	AKLZ
	36 56 / -11										

NGC (IC, A) (14)	m_H / m_C (15)	$B(O)$ / w (16)	$B'(O)$ / m'_C (17)	$S(B)$ (18)	$(B-V)(O)$ / w (19)	$C_0(O)$ (20)	$S(C)$ (21)	$(U-B)(O)$ / w (22)	V / w (23)	V_0 / ΔV (24)	$S(V)$ (25)	ϕ_r / n (26)	$\phi(21)$ (27)	(28)	Photo. (29)
N5951										87					
N5953									2100	2188	E				
									9.2	88					
N5954									2140	2228	E				
									9.2	88					
N5957										78					
N5962	12.5	12.38	13.67	BCF	.66	.54	C		1993	2088	B				LP
	12.57	4.21	13.86		1.88				1.8	95					
N5964										57					
N5967	12.9														
	12.77		14.21							−201					
N5967A										−201					
N5968										−79					
N5970	12.4	12.40	13.79	BCF	.74	.61	C		2055	2136	BC				
	12.47	1.81	13.86		1.88				5.2	81					
N5976		16.01	15.30	C	1.03		C			205					
		1.72			1.88										
N5981		14.06	14.55	BC	.89		C			206					B
		3.43			1.88										
N5982	12.5	12.63	12.62	BCEF	.93	.82	BCE	.53	2866	3072	BC				
	12.69	4.98	12.68		14.38		/E		101.7	206					
N5984	13.0									92					
	13.21		13.95												
N5985	12.2	12.11	14.70	BE	.83	.66	E	.23	2467	2673	B				
	11.77	4.93	14.36		6.25		/E		6.3	206					
N6015	12.1	11.76	14.30	BCEG	.60	.47	BCEG	.01	674	889	BC				
	11.83	8.35	14.37		16.87		/E		5.9	215					
N6027A				C*			C*		4033	4161	BC				
									6.8	128					
N6027D				C*			C*		4443	4570	BC				
									8.3	128					
N6041									10457	10578	BF				
									5.0	122					
N6044									9936	10059	B				
									4.0	123					
N6045									9912	10034	BF				
									5.0	122					
N6047									9470	9592	B				
									4.0	122					
N6052	13.0	13.64	13.38	E	.44		E	−.30		132					K
	13.26	1.69	13.00		6.25		/E								
N6055									11363	11487	FK				
									12.1	124					
N6056									11658	11781	F				
									1.0	123					
N6061									11169	11294	F				
									1.0	125					
N6068									3929	4153	E				
									1.9	224					
N6068A									4000	4224	E				
									1.9	224					
N6070	12.7	12.62	14.41	CE	.71	.56	CE	.18	2110	2175	BC				C
	12.50	4.02	14.29		8.13		/E		1.8	66					
N6106	12.9	12.99	14.03	A	.79		A			98					
	12.90	4.36	13.94		4.38										
N6118	12.3	12.84	14.98	A	.86		A			64					
	12.12	0.85	14.26		4.38										
N6140										228					
N6143										221					
N6166									8882	9082	K				
									1.0	200					
N6166A									9280	9480	K				
									1.0	200					
N6166B									7760	7960	K				
									1.0	200					
N6166C									9850	10050	K				
									1.0	200					
N6181	12.6	12.71	13.60	CF	.63	.46	C		2158	2309	B				P
	12.81	2.93	13.70		3.75				.2	151					
N6196										198					
N6207	12.3	12.26	13.45	BCEF	.55	.40	CE	−.21	869	1072	B				
	12.51	7.37	13.70		8.13		/E		6.3	203					

NGC (IC, A) (1)	RA (1950) 100 P (2)	Dec 100 P (3)	L^I B^I (4)	L^II B^II (5)	SGL SGB (6)	Rev. type (S) DDO (T, L) (7)	Yerkes (1) Yerkes (2) (8)	Hu-San Ho (9)	log D w (10)	log R w (11)	log D(O) (12)	S (D,R) (13)
N6211	16 40.6 1.8	57 54 -11	53.69 39.24	87.11 39.83	50.0 41.1	.E.1...W						
N6215	16 46.8 8.6	-58 55 -10	297.28 -10.22	329.77 -9.27	191.5 11.1	.SAS5..B060			1.28 4.48	.11 4.48	1.24	DPI
N6215A	16 48.3 8.6	-58 51 -10	297.45 -10.34	329.95 -9.38	191.6 11.3	.S...$.S030			1.16 1.00	.40 1.00	1.00	I
N6217	16 34.8 -4.9	78 18 -12	78.05 33.40	111.33 33.38	34.7 25.1	RSBT4..P200 S 5 K 2	S AF*		1.34 10.67	.11 9.83	1.29	AHLRVZ
N6221	16 48.5 8.7	-59 8 -10	297.24 -10.53	329.74 -9.58	191.8 11.1	.SBS5..R074			1.48 8.52	.15 8.52	1.42	DPIO
N6239	16 48.4 3.2	42 50 -10	34.20 38.77	67.39 39.78	65.4 52.0	.SBS3P$P200 S 3 T	BIP*AF		1.45 4.62	.35 4.62	1.31	AKZ
N6240	16 50.7 5.0	2 28 -9	348.44 25.74	20.75 27.23	138.0 57.2	.P.....W100			1.15 2.98	.27 2.98	1.04	AW
N6246	16 48.7 2.0	55 38 -10	50.60 38.46	83.97 39.13	51.1 43.5	.SBR..*P048						
N6246A	16 48.0 2.0	55 47 -10	50.81 38.54	84.18 39.20	51.0 43.3	.S....*P048						
N6296	17 6.2 5.0	4 0 -7	351.97 23.11	24.32 24.59	138.6 61.3	.SBS.*.L036			1.02 1.07	.00 .54	1.02	AL
N6300	17 12.3 9.4	-62 46 -6	295.89 -14.98	328.49 -14.05	196.1 9.2	.SBR3..B060			1.53 7.17	.12 7.17	1.49	DEPI
N6306	17 7.0 1.2	60 47 -7	56.69 35.51	89.99 36.03	44.2 41.0	.S....*.W						
N6307	17 7.1 1.2	60 49 -7	56.73 35.50	90.03 36.01	44.1 41.0	.E.4.*.W			1.08 .77	.30 .77	.96	AB
N6308	17 9.9 4.2	23 26 -7	12.26 30.28	44.94 31.63	95.5 64.6	.SXR5..L036			1.10 1.99	.02 1.99	1.09	AM
N6310	17 7.3 1.2	61 3 -7	57.01 35.45	90.31 35.96	43.9 40.8	.S.....W			1.32 .48	.40 .48	1.16	A
N6314	17 10.5 4.2	23 20 -7	12.21 30.11	44.88 31.46	95.7 64.7	.SA.1*/L036			.95 1.05	.30 1.05	.83	M
N6315	17 10.6 4.2	23 17 -7	12.16 30.07	44.83 31.43	95.8 64.8	.SB.4*.L036			.95 1.05	.20 1.05	.87	M
N6340	17 11.1 -1.7	72 22 -7	70.46 33.19	103.73 33.37	36.2 31.4	.SAS0..P200 S OP	DS *G		1.42 5.06	.06 5.06	1.40	KZ
N6359	17 17.4 1.0	61 50 -6	57.82 34.17	91.08 34.67	42.0 40.8	.LA.-..L036			.84 .89	.18 .89	.76	M
N6381	17 26.6 1.3	60 3 -5	55.62 33.14	88.83 33.69	41.9 42.9	.S...$.W						
N6384	17 29.9 4.8	7 6 -4	357.86 19.33	30.25 20.79	137.9 68.0	.SXR4..P200 S 3 1*	BS *GK S4	SX 3	1.77 10.39	.16 10.39	1.71	AKNXZ
N6412	17 30.8 -3.6	75 45 -4	74.05 31.20	107.25 31.28	33.1 28.9	.SAS5..P200 S 5 3	SB *AF	S5	1.35 11.09	.07 10.20	1.33	AHKLRUX Z
N6438	18 9.4 33.0	-85 26 1	275.01 -26.98	308.02 -26.53	206.5 -11.2	.E.....B060						
N6438A	18 9.9 33.0	-85 26 1	275.01 -26.99	308.02 -26.54	206.6 -11.2	.I.....B060						
N6478	17 48.3 2.4	51 10 -1	45.48 29.50	78.51 30.28	43.9 52.2	.S..5..W			1.24 4.00	.32 4.00	1.11	RV
N6482	17 49.8 4.2	23 5 -1	15.51 21.58	48.10 22.90	88.3 73.4	.E.2..$.... E 3P *	E2 *K E3 *K *		.99 .98	.08 .98	.96	AKL
N6493A	17 49.3 1.0	61 30 -1	57.37 30.39	90.50 30.90	37.7 42.8	.S..3*.W						
N6500	17 53.8 4.4	18 21 0	11.25 18.88	43.76 20.24	104.4 75.6	.L....$L036			1.24 .69			L
N6501	17 54.1 4.4	18 23 0	11.32 18.83	43.83 20.19	104.3 75.7	.L....$L036			1.30 .74			L
N6503	17 49.9 -1.0	70 10 -1	67.42 30.39	100.59 30.65	33.8 34.6	.SAS6..P200 S 3 5*	SI *AF S G *	S5	1.77 11.59	.49 11.59	1.57	AKLMXYZ
N6555	18 5.6 4.4	17 30 1	11.65 15.97	44.13 17.32	106.4 78.6	.SXT5..W060			1.25 6.27	.11 5.38	1.21	ABLRQ
N6570	18 8.9 4.6	14 4 1	8.79 13.79	41.22 15.17	124.4 79.3	.SBT9*.W060			1.09 1.70	.16 1.70	1.03	AQ
N6574	18 9.5 4.5	14 58 1	9.69 14.05	42.13 15.42	119.7 79.5	.SXT4*.W100 S *	S F		1.08 3.79	.09 3.16	1.04	AKLW
N6587	18 11.7 4.4	18 48 2	13.51 15.19	45.99 16.53	98.1 79.7	.LA.-*.L036			.88 .90	.26 .90	.78	AM
N6615	18 16.3 4.6	13 13 2	8.80 11.80	41.22 13.19	131.6 80.8	.SBS1*.L036			.88 .38	.00 .38	.88	A
N6621	18 13.5 -.5	68 18 2	65.33 28.26	98.42 28.57	31.9 37.0	.S...P*						
N6627	18 20.5 4.5	15 39 3	11.50 11.95	43.93 13.31	116.3 82.2	.SBS3..L036			.84 .34	.00 .34	.84	A
N6635	18 25.3 4.5	14 44 4	11.17 10.51	43.59 11.87	124.3 83.3	.L.....L036			.90 .42	.00 .42	.90	A
N6643	18 21.2 -2.9	74 33 3	72.45 28.05	105.54 28.18	29.9 30.9	.SAT5..P200 S 5 2	S AF	S 5 S5	1.57 10.05	.29 10.05	1.45	AHKLVXZ
N6651	18 24.7 -1.5	71 34 4	69.11 27.58	102.18 27.79	30.1 33.9	.S..3*.W						

| NGC (IC, A) (14) | Magnitudes | | | | Colors | | | | Velocities | | | Radio | | | Photo. |
	m_H / m_C (15)	B(O) w (16)	B'(O) m'_C (17)	S(B) (18)	(B-V)(O) w (19)	c_o(O) (20)	S(C) (21)	(U-B)(O) w (22)	V w (23)	V_o ΔV (24)	S(V) (25)	ϕ_r n (26)	ϕ(21) (27)	(28)	Photo. (29)
N6211										232					
N6215	11.2 12.06		12.95						1547 6.2	1410 −137	M				
N6215A										−136					
N6217	12.6 12.65	12.17 5.64	13.36 13.84	BCEF	.67 8.13	.53	CE /E	−.12	1385 12.8	1616 230	3C				
N6221	11.4 11.75		13.54						1418 1.0	1281 −137	M				FH
N6239	13.1 12.87	12.95 6.37	14.19 14.11	CD	.50* 30.00	.32	CD /D	−.25	964 2.4	1183 219	C				
N6240										107					
N6246										234					
N6246A										234					
N6296										125					
N6300	11.4 11.54		13.68							−141					F
N6306										244					
N6307										244					
N6308										190					
N6310										244					
N6314		14.45 2.51	13.34	C	.81 3.75	.57	C		6748 1.6	6939 190	C				
N6315										190					
N6340	12.8 12.39	12.21 3.52	13.95 14.13	C	.86 3.75	.73	C		2109 −.1	2351 242	B				
N6359		13.62 2.63	12.16	AC	.89 1.88	.75	C		2948 1.8	3196 248	B				
N6381										247					
N6384	12.7 11.76	11.54 5.88	14.78 15.00	ACEG	.80* 16.87	.60	ACEG /E	.33	1754 10.6	1907 154	BCD				P
N6412	12.8 12.71	12.62 2.42	13.96 14.05	CG	.55 4.38	.42	CG		1508 2.4	1751 243	C				
N6438										−205					
N6438A										−205					
N6478										6857 4.0	7114 258	B				
N6482	12.2 12.66		12.15	AC*	.94 6.25	.76	AC		3922 2.8	4137 215	B				
N6493A										259					
N6500										205					
N6501										205					
N6503	11.4 11.43	11.04 8.68	13.63 14.02	BCDEF G	.69 35.63	.54	BCDEG /DE	.04	26 8.4	279 253	CD				B
N6555										210					C
N6570										202					
N6574	12.7 13.28	12.89 12.88	12.83 13.22	ABCD	.84 18.90	.60	ABCD /D	.14	2368 6.6	2572 205	BC				
N6587										217					
N6615		14.09 0.78	13.18	A	.93 4.38		A			203					
N6621										6230 4.0	6490 260	F				
N6627		14.75 2.10	13.69	AC	1.03 6.25	.75	AC		5206 1.0	5419 213	B				
N6635		14.52 2.63	13.76	AC	1.00 6.25	.70	AC		5071 2.4	5284 213	C				
N6643	12.7 12.36	11.97 3.06	13.96 14.35	CG	.70 6.25	.52	CG		1538 5.2	1790 253	BC				LP
N6651										258					

NGC (IC, A) (1)	RA (1950) 100 P (2)	Dec 100 P (3)	L^I B^I (4)	L^II B^II (5)	SGL SGB (6)	Rev. type (S) DDO (T, L) (7)	Yerkes (1) Yerkes (2) (8)	Hu-San Ho (9)	log D w (10)	log R w (11)	log D(O) (12)	S (D,R) (13)
N6654	18 25.2	73 9	70.89	103.97	29.8	PSBS0..W060			1.35	.13	1.30	LQ
	-2.2	4	27.68	27.85	32.4				2.02	1.20		
N6654A	18 41.0	73 30	71.43	104.47	28.4	.S..5..W						
	-2.3	6	26.59	26.75	32.1							
N6658	18 31.9	22 50	19.32	51.80	61.0	.L..../W100			1.16	.64	.90	W
	4.2	5	12.60	13.86	81.3				2.26	2.26		
N6661	18 32.5	22 52	19.41	51.89	60.1	.SAS0..W100			1.12	.21	1.03	AMW
	4.2	5	12.49	13.75	81.3				4.07	4.07		
N6667	18 30.6	67 57	65.14	98.18	30.0	.S...*.W						
	-.3	4	26.64	26.95	37.6							
N6674	18 36.5	25 20	22.09	54.59	48.2	.SBR3..W100			1.48	.18	1.41	MW
	4.1	5	12.70	13.92	79.6				4.39	4.39		
N6684	18 44.1	-65 14	297.51	330.33	206.5	.LB.+..S030			1.41	.16	1.34	DEI
	9.9	6	-25.16	-24.20	9.1				3.89	3.89		
N6684A	18 47.1	-64 55	297.92	330.75	206.8	.S...$.S030			1.54	.30	1.42	I
	9.8	7	-25.40	-24.44	9.4				.37	.37		
N6690	18 35.4	70 29	68.02	101.06	29.2	.S..7$/W060			1.45	.47	1.26	LQ
	-1.1	5	26.59	26.83	35.1				3.33	3.33		
N6699	18 47.8	-57 23	306.01	338.73	206.7	.SXS..S030			1.20	.02	1.19	DI
	8.5	7	-23.77	-22.65	17.0				2.21	2.21		
N6702	18 45.5	45 39	42.30	75.03	30.0	.E.4...L036			.95	.19	.88	M
	2.9	7	18.93	19.79	60.0				1.05	1.05		
N6703	18 45.9	45 30	42.18	74.90	29.8	.L.....L036			1.18	.06	1.16	MR
	2.9	7	18.81	19.67	60.1				3.22	1.49		
N6707	18 51.3	-53 53	309.84	342.52	207.2	.S...*.						
	8.1	7	-23.33	-22.15	20.5							
N6710	18 48.6	26 47	24.62	57.10	32.2	.LAS+*.W						
	4.0	7	10.86	12.05	78.8							
N6721	18 56.5	-57 51	305.82	338.57	207.9	.E+0...S030			1.06	.00	1.06	I
	8.6	8	-25.01	-23.90	16.5				.85	.85		
N6744	19 5.0	-63 56	299.37	332.23	208.8	.SXR4..S074			2.16	.20	2.08	SIJ
	9.5	9	-27.14	-26.14	10.4				13.40	13.40		
N6753	19 7.2	-57 8	306.93	339.69	209.5	RSAR3..S074			1.35	.07	1.32	DEIJ
	8.4	10	-26.27	-25.14	17.2				5.84	5.84		
N6754	19 7.5	-50 44	313.87	346.54	210.0	.SBT3..B060			1.27	.34	1.13	PI
	7.7	10	-24.92	-23.68	23.5				3.16	3.16		
N6758	19 9.8	-56 24	307.81	340.57	209.9	.E.1...S030			1.07	.06	1.05	DEI
	8.3	10	-26.48	-25.33	17.9				2.47	2.47		
N6761	19 11.4	-50 45	314.01	346.69	210.6	.SBR3*.S030			1.27	.04	1.25	I
	7.7	10	-25.52	-24.28	23.5				.51	.51		
N6764	19 6.9	50 51	48.77	81.49	23.5	.S.....R020			1.40	.26	1.29	H
	2.5	10	17.53	18.24	54.7				1.24	1.24		
N6769	19 13.9	-60 35	303.27	336.10	210.1	.SXR3P.R074			1.34	.19	1.26	DIO
	8.9	11	-27.69	-26.63	13.7				5.00	5.00		
N6770	19 14.2	-60 36	303.26	336.09	210.1	.SXT3P.R074			1.36	.13	1.31	IO
	8.9	11	-27.73	-26.67	13.6				3.08	3.08		
N6771	19 14.4	-60 41	303.17	336.00	210.1	.LBR+$/R074			1.26	.66	.99	IO
	8.9	11	-27.77	-26.70	13.5				2.96	2.96		
N6776	19 20.7	-63 59	299.53	332.43	210.5	.E.2...S030			1.03	.04	1.02	DI
	9.4	11	-28.86	-27.86	10.2				1.70	1.70		
N6776A	19 20.4	-63 48	299.74	332.63	210.5	.S...*/S030			1.20	.75	.90	I
	9.4	11	-28.81	-27.81	10.4				1.06	1.06		
N6780	19 18.7	-55 53	308.64	341.40	211.2	.SXT5..B060			1.26	.09	1.23	PI
	8.2	11	-27.61	-26.45	18.3				3.12	3.12		
N6782	19 19.5	-60 2	303.99	336.83	210.9	RLB.+*.S030			1.27	.26	1.17	DI
	8.8	11	-28.31	-27.23	14.1				2.09	2.09		
N6796	19 20.6	61 2	59.47	92.28	22.7	.S..3*.W						
	1.3	11	19.63	20.09	44.3							
N6808	19 38.5	-70 46	291.75	324.76	211.2	.SAR1*.S030			1.12	.43	.95	EI
	10.9	14	-30.66	-29.82	3.2				1.53	1.53		
N6810	19 39.4	-58 47	305.69	338.57	213.6	.SA.1*.S030			1.46	.58	1.22	DEI
	8.5	14	-30.71	-29.60	15.0				4.00	4.00		
N6814	19 39.9	-10 25	357.15	29.37	232.3	.SXT4..P200	S FG	S 3	1.35	.04	1.34	AFHKLZ
	5.5	14	-17.46	-16.00	61.4	S 4 1			9.04	6.66		
N6821	19 41.7	-6 57	0.60	32.80	236.5	.SBS7*.W100			1.03	.07	1.00	AW
	5.4	14	-16.32	-14.87	64.4				2.23	2.23		
N6822	19 42.1	-14 53	353.12	25.38	229.8	.IBS9......	L	I9	2.22	.13	2.16	KX
	5.7	14	-19.86	-18.38	57.1	I 8	I F *		1.90	1.90		
N6824	19 42.6	55 59	55.95	88.63	16.9	.SAS3*.W060			1.10	.18	1.03	AHQ
	2.1	14	14.90	15.45	48.5				2.72	2.72		
N6835	19 51.8	-12 42	356.29	28.51	235.5	.SBS1$/W100			1.28	.74	.98	KNW
	5.6	16	-21.08	-19.61	58.1	E 8	DS *K		5.41	5.41		
N6836	19 51.9	-12 49	356.19	28.41	235.4	.SX.9..W100			.99	.05	.97	NW
	5.6	16	-21.15	-19.68	58.0				2.90	2.90		
N6850	19 59.6	-54 59	310.32	343.20	217.4	.S...*.S030			1.15	.50	.95	I
	7.9	17	-33.29	-32.10	18.0				.70	.70		
N6851	19 59.9	-48 25	318.25	350.91	219.6	.E+4.*.S030			1.03	.15	.97	DEI
	7.3	17	-32.87	-31.58	24.2				2.31	2.31		
N6851A	20 2.3	-48 8	318.53	351.29	220.1	.S..7*.S030			1.39	.30	1.26	I
	7.3	17	-33.24	-31.94	24.4				.60	.60		

NGC (IC, A) (14)	Magnitudes				Colors				Velocities			Radio			
	m_H m_C (15)	B(O) w (16)	B'(O) m'_C (17)	S(B) (18)	(B-V)(O) w (19)	C_O(O) (20)	S(C) (21)	(U-B)(O) w (22)	V w (23)	V_O ΔV (24)	S(V) (25)	ϕ_r n (26)	ϕ(21) (27)	(28)	Photo. (29)
N6654		12.80 1.98	13.99	C	.91 3.75	.76	C		1924 1.8	2180 256	C				
N6654A										257					
N6658		14.23 6.61	13.47	ACF	1.06 10.00	.76	AC		4270 4.0	4508 238	B				
N6661		13.41 4.47	13.30	ACF	1.02 10.00	.73	AC		4316 5.8	4554 238	BC				
N6667										264					
N6674		13.16 1.54	14.95	C	.91* 3.75	.61	C		3502 4.0	3748 246	B				
N6684	11.7 11.75		13.19						838 1.0	713 -125	M				F
N6684A										-123					
N6690										261					B
N6699	12.4 12.75		13.44							-89					
N6702		14.16 3.61	13.25	C	1.01 3.75	.81	C		4726 5.1	5003 277	BC				
N6703		12.81 1.89	13.35	C	.92 1.88	.74	C		2333 7.9	2609 277	BC				
N6707										-72					
N6710				C*	1.02* 3.75		C		4556 4.0	4810 254	B				
N6721	13.1 13.09		13.08							-89					
N6744	10.6 9.78		14.87						659 1.0	544 -115	M				FIL
N6753	11.7 12.10		13.39						3066 1.0	2983 -83	M				GL
N6754	13.1 13.27		13.66							-53					
N6758	12.7 12.84		12.78							-79					
N6761										-52					
N6764										284					
N6769	12.7 12.75	12.80 1.11	13.84 13.79	M	.79	.58	M /M	.22	3530 4.0	3432 -98	I				FH
N6770		13.14 0.96	14.43	M	.92	.72	M /M	.2 *	3630 4.0	3532 -98	I				FH
N6771		13.84 2.00	13.53	M	1.05	.86	M /M	.3 *	4120 4.0	4021 -99	I				FH
N6776	12.8 12.96		12.75							-113					
N6776A										-112					
N6780	13.2 13.16		14.00							-75					
N6782	12.8 12.79		13.33							-95					
N6796										282					
N6808	13.0 13.60		13.04							-141					
N6810	12.4 12.63		13.47						1823 1.0	1738 -85	M				
N6814	12.2 12.34	12.46 5.41	13.85 13.73	AC	.89 10.00	.68	AC		1437 6.3	1589 152	B				P
N6821										168					
N6822	11.0 9.97	9.49 1.39	15.03 15.51	G					-60 438.5	73 133	BCDR				
N6824		13.06 2.03	12.90	C	.83 1.88	.55	C		3386 11.1	3676 290	B				
N6835	13.0 13.51	13.67 2.70	13.31 13.15	A	.88 4.38		A			145					
N6836										145					
N6850										-64					
N6851	12.8 13.02	13.18 2.03	12.77 12.61	M	.94		M /M	.48		-30					
N6851A										-28					

NGC (IC, A) (1)	RA (1950) 100 P (2)	Dec 100 P (3)	L^I B^I (4)	L^II B^II (5)	SGL SGB (6)	Rev. type (S) DDO (T, L) (7)	Yerkes (1) Yerkes (2) (8)	Hu-San Ho (9)	log D w (10)	log R w (11)	log D(O) (12)	S (D,R) (13)
N6851B	20 2.3	−48 8	318.53	351.29	220.1	.S..../S030			1.22	1.00	.82	I
	7.3	17	−33.24	−31.94	24.4				.24	.24		
N6854	20 1.8	−54 32	310.88	343.75	217.9	.E.2...S030			1.11	.09	1.07	I
	7.8	17	−33.59	−32.39	18.3				.92	.92		
N6861	20 3.7	−48 31	318.10	350.87	220.2	.LA.-..S030			1.22	.30	1.09	DEI
	7.3	17	−33.51	−32.21	23.9				3.01	3.01		
N6861D	20 4.7	−48 23	318.28	351.05	220.4	.LA..*.S030			1.35	.57	1.12	I
	7.3	17	−33.66	−32.36	24.0				1.31	1.31		
N6861E	20 7.3	−48 48	317.83	350.61	220.7	.S....$.S030			1.08	.51	.87	I
	7.3	18	−34.13	−32.83	23.5				.89	.89		
N6861F	20 7.6	−48 26	318.27	351.05	220.9	.S...*/S030			1.21	.73	.92	I
	7.3	18	−34.15	−32.85	23.8				1.08	1.08		
N6868	20 6.3	−48 31	318.15	350.93	220.6	.E.2...S030			1.18	.09	1.15	DEI
	7.3	17	−33.94	−32.64	23.8				2.98	2.98		
N6870	20 6.5	−48 26	318.25	351.03	220.7	.SAR2..S030			1.31	.46	1.13	I
	7.3	17	−33.97	−32.67	23.9				.89	.89		
N6872	20 11.7	−70 55	291.17	324.26	213.8	.SBS3P.R074			1.60	.60	1.36	IO
	10.5	18	−33.34	−32.51	2.4				4.09	4.09		
N6875	20 9.6	−46 19	320.86	353.60	222.0	.E.6.*.S030			1.14	.33	1.01	DEI
	7.1	18	−34.29	−32.96	25.7				2.80	2.80		
N6875A	20 8.3	−46 19	320.83	353.57	221.8	.S...*/S030			1.42	.72	1.14	I
	7.1	18	−34.07	−32.74	25.7				1.45	1.45		
N6876	20 13.1	−71 1	291.02	324.12	213.8	.E.3...R074			1.13	.15	1.07	DEIO
	10.5	18	−33.43	−32.60	2.2				4.05	4.05		
N6877	20 13.4	−71 0	291.03	324.14	213.9	.E.6...R074			.91	.34	.77	IO
	10.5	18	−33.46	−32.63	2.3				1.66	1.66		
N6878	20 10.3	−44 41	322.84	355.55	222.8	.SAS3..B060			1.15	.13	1.10	PI
	7.0	18	−34.23	−32.88	27.1				2.71	2.71		
N6878A	20 10.0	−44 59	322.47	355.19	222.6	.SXT3..B060			1.24	.36	1.10	PI
	7.0	18	−34.21	−32.87	26.9				3.06	3.06		
N6880	20 14.3	−71 1	291.00	324.10	213.9	.LXS+*.R074			1.17	.56	.94	IO
	10.5	18	−33.52	−32.70	2.2				2.92	2.92		
N6887	20 13.4	−52 56	312.86	345.74	220.1	.SA.4*.S030			1.56	.42	1.39	DEI
	7.6	18	−35.27	−34.05	19.2				4.57	4.57		
N6890	20 14.8	−44 58	322.60	355.33	223.5	.SAT3..S074			1.07	.13	1.02	DEJ
	7.0	18	−35.06	−33.71	26.6				3.19	3.19		
N6893	20 17.2	−48 25	318.42	351.23	222.5	.LXS0..S074			1.26	.20	1.18	DEJ
	7.2	19	−35.73	−34.43	23.2				4.16	4.16		
N6902	20 21.2	−43 50	324.13	356.85	225.2	.SBR0*.S030			1.20	.10	1.16	FI
	6.9	19	−36.08	−34.71	27.2				1.72	.98		
N6902A	20 19.4	−44 27	323.34	356.06	224.6	.I....$S030			1.15	.11	1.11	I
	6.9	19	−35.82	−34.46	26.7				.70	.70		
N6902B	20 21.6	−44 2	323.89	356.62	225.2	.S....$S030			1.21	.02	1.20	I
	6.9	19	−36.17	−34.81	27.0				1.08	1.08		
N6906	20 21.1	6 18	17.75	49.81	276.5	.S.R3*.L036			1.18	.35	1.04	ARVW
	4.9	19	−18.43	−17.14	66.4				6.77	5.84		
N6907	20 22.1	−24 58	346.54	18.85	236.0	.SBS4..W100		SB *F *	1.43	.05	1.41	DEGKNW
	6.0	19	−32.30	−30.82	43.9	SX3 2*			9.68	8.94		
N6909	20 24.1	−47 12	320.00	352.80	224.2	.E.6...S030			1.11	.31	.98	DEI
	7.1	20	−36.83	−35.51	23.9				2.66	2.66		
N6915	20 25.1	−3 13	9.50	41.56	259.8	.SBR2*.L036			1.00	.00	1.00	A
	5.2	20	−24.13	−22.75	60.4				.55	.55		
N6921	20 26.4	25 33	34.84	66.98	325.6	.SAR0*.L036			.84	.56	.61	M
	4.3	20	−8.58	−7.57	66.0				.44	.44		
N6923	20 28.6	−31 1	340.01	12.45	233.6	.S....*.W						
	6.2	20	−35.36	−33.88	38.0							
N6925	20 31.2	−32 9	338.81	11.27	233.5	.SAS4..W100			1.59	.43	1.42	GW
	6.2	20	−36.16	−34.69	36.7				4.66	4.66		
N6927	20 30.2	9 43	22.06	54.09	286.3	.L.....W			.90	.00	.90	AL
	4.8	20	−18.46	−17.24	65.5				.79	.34		
N6927A	20 30.2	9 41	22.05	54.08	286.3	.E.7...W						
	4.8	20	−18.48	−17.25	65.5							
N6928	20 30.4	9 45	22.12	54.15	286.5	.SBS2..W100			1.22	.46	1.03	ALRW
	4.8	20	−18.49	−17.26	65.5				5.73	5.73		
N6930	20 30.5	9 41	22.07	54.10	286.3	.SBS..$W100			1.08	.49	.89	ALRW
	4.8	20	−18.54	−17.32	65.4				3.55	3.55		
N6935	20 34.7	−52 17	313.57	346.51	223.5	.SXR1..B060			1.19	.07	1.17	EPI
	7.4	21	−38.52	−37.28	18.6				3.21	3.21		
N6937	20 35.1	−52 20	313.50	346.45	223.6	.SXR2..B060			1.38	.05	1.36	PI
	7.4	21	−38.58	−37.34	18.5				3.23	3.23		
N6942	20 37.0	−54 30	310.71	343.70	222.8	.LB.-..S030			1.21	.16	1.15	EI
	7.5	21	−38.69	−37.50	16.4				1.82	1.82		
N6943	20 39.8	−68 55	292.80	325.97	216.8	.SXR6*.S030			1.58	.33	1.44	DEI
	9.6	21	−36.17	−35.30	3.3				4.68	4.68		
N6944	20 35.9	6 48	20.30	52.30	281.0	.L.....L036			1.04	.38	.88	M
	4.9	21	−21.25	−20.00	63.2				1.19	1.19		
N6944A	20 35.7	6 43	20.20	52.20	280.8	.SB.3..L036			1.04	.21	.95	M
	4.9	21	−21.26	−20.00	63.2				1.19	1.19		
N6946	20 33.9	59 58	63.12	95.71	10.7	.SXT6..W060	S AF	S5	2.02	.05	2.00	AHKLSVX
	2.1	21	11.29	11.66	42.0	S 5 1	S 5		22.62	20.83		YQ

NGC (IC, A) (14)	m_H / m_c (15)	B(O) w (16)	B'(O) / m'_c (17)	S(B) (18)	(B-V)(O) w (19)	C_o(O) (20)	S(C) (21)	(U-B)(O) w (22)	V w (23)	V_o ΔV (24)	S(V) (25)	ϕ_r n (26)	ϕ(21) (27)	(28)	Photo. (29)
N6851B										−28					
N6854	13.2									−61					
	13.12		13.21												
N6861	12.3	12.43	12.62	M	1.05		M	.53		−30					
	12.58	1.72	12.77				/M								
N6861D		13.56	13.90	M	1.00		M	.51		−29					
		1.61					/M								
N6861E										−31					
N6861F										−29					
N6868	12.1	12.31	12.80	M	1.02	.89	M	.59	2764	2734	LM				
	12.27	1.50	12.76				/M		13.8	−30					
N6870		13.41	13.80	M	.99		M	.6 *		−29					
		1.58					/M								
N6872										−140					FH
N6875	12.6	13.22	13.01	M	.99	.86	M	.45	3103	3085	L				
	12.82	1.96	12.61				/M		11.1	−18					
N6875A										−18					
N6876	12.7									−140					H
	12.79		12.88												
N6877										−140					H
N6878	13.1	14.16	14.40	M	.70		M	.21		−9					
	13.33	1.69	13.57				/M								
N6878A										−11					
N6880										−140					H
N6887	12.8									−52					
	12.53		14.22												
N6890	12.7									−10					
	13.30		13.14												
N6893	12.5	12.85	13.49	M	1.05		M	.6 *		−28					GL
	12.55	1.39	13.19				/M								
N6902	12.4									−4					
	12.67		13.21												
N6902A										−7					
N6902B										−5					
N6906										227					
N6907	12.1	12.18	13.92	A	.66*		A			93					
	12.13	1.07	13.87		4.38										
N6909	12.8	13.31	12.95	M	.90		M	.4 *		−21					
	13.01	2.01	12.65				/M								
N6915										192					
N6921		14.77	12.56	AC	.97*	.48	AC		4317	4595	B				
		2.40			6.25				6.3	278					
N6923	12.9									63					
N6925	12.1								2619	2677	M				
	12.10		13.89						1.0	58					
N6927		15.41	14.60	C	.99	.77	C		4277	4516	B				
		2.00			1.88				4.0	239					
N6927A									4419	4658	B				
									.2	239					
N6928		13.93	13.82	C	1.02	.69	C		4754	4993	B				B
		2.99			5.63				1.8	239					
N6930		14.28	13.42	C*	.89*	.56	C		4182	4421	B				
		1.65			1.88				1.8	239					
N6935	12.9									−47					
	13.04		13.58												
N6937										−47					
N6942	12.9									−58					
	12.89		13.33												
N6943	12.5									−129					F
	12.32		14.26												
N6944		14.53	13.67	CD	1.04	.82	CD	.65	4415	4644	BC				
		3.55			4.13		/D		7.6	230					
N6944A										230					
N6946	11.1	10.01	14.70	ACFG	.82	.56	ACG		80	371	BR				A
	10.30	3.66	14.99		8.75				15.1	291					

NGC (IC, A) (1)	Coordinates					Classification			Diameters			
	RA (1950) 100 P (2)	Dec 100 P (3)	L^I B^I (4)	L^II B^II (5)	SGL SGB (6)	Rev. type (S) DDO (T,L) (7)	Yerkes (1) Yerkes (2) (8)	Hu-San Ho (9)	log D w (10)	log R w (11)	log D(O) (12)	S (D,R) (13)
N6951	20 36.5 / 1.3	65 56 / 21	68.21 / 14.62	100.89 / 14.86	14.5 / 36.8	.SXT4..P200 / S 3P 2*	SBP*F *	SXS3 / S4	1.54 / 6.83	.10 / 6.83	1.50	KLXZ
N6954	20 41.5 / 5.0	3 1 / 22	17.68 / -24.48	49.65 / -23.19	274.9 / 60.4	.S..3..W			1.00 / .54	.00 / .54	1.00	A
N6958	20 45.4 / 6.4	-38 11 / 22	331.87 / -40.03	4.50 / -38.60	232.8 / 30.0	.E.1...S030			1.13 / .95	.04 / .95	1.11	I
N6962	20 44.7 / 5.1	0 8 / 22	15.43 / -26.68	47.39 / -25.36	270.7 / 58.3	.SXR2..W100			1.37 / 3.52	.08 / 3.52	1.34	AFW
N6963	20 44.8 / 5.1	0 20 / 22	15.64 / -26.60	47.60 / -25.28	271.1 / 58.4	.E.0...W						
N6964	20 44.8 / 5.1	0 7 / 22	15.43 / -26.71	47.39 / -25.39	270.7 / 58.3	.E.4...W			.95 / .48	.05 / .48	.94	A
N6970	20 48.6 / 7.0	-48 59 / 22	317.69 / -40.91	350.61 / -39.62	227.2 / 20.5	.SBT1..S030			.97 / 2.00	.06 / 2.00	.95	DEI
N6982	20 53.8 / 7.2	-52 3 / 23	313.53 / -41.46	346.54 / -40.22	226.4 / 17.4	.S...*.S030			1.02 / .63	.45 / .63	.84	I
N6984	20 54.3 / 7.2	-52 4 / 23	313.49 / -41.53	346.51 / -40.30	226.4 / 17.3	.SBR5..B060			1.22 / 2.95	.18 / 2.95	1.15	PI
N7007	21 1.9 / 7.2	-52 45 / 24	312.36 / -42.58	345.42 / -41.36	227.1 / 16.1	.LA.-*.S030			1.06 / 2.36	.22 / 2.36	.97	DEI
N7013	21 1.4 / 4.2	29 42 / 24	43.08 / -11.98	75.13 / -11.14	328.5 / 57.3	.SAR0..W100			1.17 / 3.06	.36 / 3.06	1.02	AW
N7014	21 4.5 / 6.8	-47 24 / 24	319.56 / -43.67	352.50 / -42.36	230.5 / 20.4	.E.0...S030			1.04 / .84	.00 / .84	1.04	I
N7020	21 7.3 / 8.3	-64 15 / 24	297.28 / -40.26	330.53 / -39.30	221.4 / 6.1	RLAR+..B060			1.47 / 4.05	.29 / 4.05	1.35	PI
N7029	21 8.4 / 6.9	-49 30 / 24	316.56 / -44.08	349.58 / -42.80	229.9 / 18.3	.E+6.*.S074			1.12 / 2.89	.29 / 2.89	1.00	EIJ
N7038	21 11.7 / 6.7	-47 26 / 25	319.34 / -44.88	352.32 / -43.57	231.6 / 19.7	.SAS5*.S030			1.46 / 3.60	.22 / 3.60	1.37	DEI
N7041	21 13.0 / 6.8	-48 35 / 25	317.69 / -44.95	350.71 / -43.66	231.1 / 18.6	.LX.-..S030			1.38 / 1.36	.46 / 1.36	1.19	I
N7046	21 12.5 / 5.1	2 38 / 25	22.17 / -31.13	53.97 / -29.90	280.3 / 53.2	.S.....R020			1.31 / 2.05	.20 / 2.05	1.23	AH
N7049	21 15.6 / 6.8	-48 47 / 25	317.32 / -45.35	350.36 / -44.06	231.3 / 18.2	.LAS0..S030			1.26 / 1.17	.12 / 1.17	1.22	I
N7059	21 23.6 / 7.6	-60 14 / 26	301.40 / -43.48	334.69 / -42.44	225.3 / 8.3	.SXT5..S074			1.50 / 2.83	.40 / 2.83	1.34	J
N7064	21 25.5 / 7.0	-53 0 / 26	310.95 / -46.00	344.15 / -44.81	230.0 / 13.9	.SBS5$/S074			1.56 / 5.93	.86 / 5.93	1.22	DEJ
N7065	21 24.1 / 5.3	-7 14 / 26	13.90 / -38.89	45.69 / -37.56	268.8 / 46.1	.SBR1*.L036			.90 / .98	.00 / .98	.90	M
N7065A	21 24.3 / 5.3	-7 16 / 26	13.90 / -38.95	45.68 / -37.62	268.8 / 46.0	.SBR3$.L036			1.14 / 1.38	.07 / 1.38	1.12	M
N7070	21 27.3 / 6.4	-43 19 / 26	324.87 / -48.03	357.79 / -46.66	236.6 / 21.2	.SAS6..S074			1.32 / 4.99	.11 / 4.99	1.28	FIJ
N7070A	21 27.6 / 6.4	-43 1 / 26	325.31 / -48.11	358.22 / -46.73	236.8 / 21.4	.I.0...S074			1.09 / 2.15	.24 / 2.15	.99	IJ
N7072	21 27.4 / 6.4	-43 22 / 26	324.80 / -48.04	357.71 / -46.67	236.6 / 21.2	.SXS7*$S074			.90 / 1.63	.09 / 1.63	.86	IJ
N7072A	21 27.4 / 6.4	-43 26 / 26	324.70 / -48.04	357.62 / -46.67	236.5 / 21.1	.SAS5*.S074			.91 / 1.55	.16 / 1.55	.84	IJ
N7079	21 29.3 / 6.5	-44 18 / 26	323.35 / -48.29	356.31 / -46.93	236.2 / 20.3	.LBS0..S074			1.25 / 2.11	.23 / 2.11	1.16	J
N7083	21 31.8 / 7.9	-64 7 / 27	296.01 / -42.75	329.36 / -41.82	223.7 / 4.6	.SAS4..B060			1.60 / 6.35	.21 / 6.35	1.52	DEPI
N7090	21 32.9 / 7.0	-54 47 / 27	308.03 / -46.53	341.30 / -45.37	229.7 / 11.8	.SB.5$/S074			1.82 / 8.10	.76 / 8.10	1.52	DEO
N7096	21 37.4 / 7.8	-64 8 / 27	295.60 / -43.29	328.98 / -42.36	224.2 / 4.2	.SAS1..S030			1.31 / .90	.07 / .90	1.29	I
N7097	21 37.1 / 6.3	-42 46 / 27	325.42 / -49.87	358.37 / -48.49	238.4 / 20.5	.E.5...S074			1.15 / 1.86	.25 / 1.86	1.05	J
N7097A	21 37.4 / 6.3	-42 42 / 27	325.52 / -49.93	358.46 / -48.55	238.5 / 20.5	.E.5.*.S074			.81 / 1.19	.30 / 1.19	.69	J
N7098	21 41.9 / 10.0	-75 21 / 27	282.99 / -37.45	316.30 / -36.80	217.3 / -4.6	RSXT1..R074			1.52 / 2.94	.22 / 2.94	1.44	O
N7102	21 37.2 / 5.0	6 4 / 27	29.82 / -33.97	61.46 / -32.87	288.7 / 48.6	.SBT3.$W100			1.19 / 1.81	.08 / 1.81	1.15	AW
N7107	21 39.2 / 6.4	-45 2 / 27	321.86 / -49.92	354.90 / -48.58	237.1 / 18.5	.SBS8..S030			1.27 / 1.17	.04 / 1.17	1.25	I
N7119A	21 43.1 / 6.5	-46 45 / 28	319.03 / -50.26	352.15 / -48.95	236.4 / 16.8	.SAT5*.S074			1.02 / 1.57	.30 / 1.57	.90	J
N7119B	21 43.1 / 6.5	-46 45 / 28	319.03 / -50.26	352.15 / -48.95	236.4 / 16.8	.S...$.S074			.83 / .88	.37 / .88	.68	J
N7124	21 44.8 / 6.6	-50 48 / 28	312.84 / -49.48	346.10 / -48.25	233.8 / 13.7	.SBT4..S074			1.43 / 5.07	.33 / 5.07	1.30	DEJ
N7125	21 45.6 / 7.3	-60 56 / 28	298.92 / -45.63	332.33 / -44.64	227.0 / 6.0	.SXT5..S074			1.53 / 3.30	.21 / 3.30	1.44	IJ
N7126	21 45.7 / 7.3	-60 50 / 28	299.04 / -45.69	332.45 / -44.70	227.0 / 6.1	.SAT5..S074			1.34 / 2.45	.35 / 2.45	1.20	IJ

NGC (IC, A) (14)	m_H / m_C (15)	B(O) w (16)	B'(O) m'_C (17)	S(B) (18)	(B-V)(O) w (19)	C_o(O) (20)	S(C) (21)	(U-B)(O) w (22)	V w (23)	V_o ΔV (24)	S(V) (25)	ϕ_r n (26)	ϕ(21) (27)	(28)	Photo. (29)
N6951	12.4	12.41	14.60	ACG	.95	.72	ACG		1364	1647	C				P
	12.08	3.77	14.27		10.63				1.6	283					
N6954		14.16	13.90	C	.89	.71	C		4011	4228	B				
		1.98			1.88				1.0	217					
N6958	12.5								2757	2784	M				
	12.61		12.85						1.0	27					
N6962		13.10	14.49	C	.95*	.76	C		4183	4390	B				
		2.03			3.75				1.8	207					
N6963				C*	.93*	.76	C		4351	4558	B				
					3.75				4.0	207					
N6964		14.22	13.61	CD	1.03	.87	CD	.64	3832	4039	B				
		4.61			7.88		/D		1.0	207					
N6970	12.7									-29					
	13.44		12.88												
N6982										-45					
N6984	13.1									-45					
	13.29		13.73												
N7007	12.9									-48					
	13.19		12.73												
N7013		13.10	12.94	A	.97		A			287					
		2.04			4.38										
N7014	13.2									-21					
	13.17		13.11												
N7020	13.1									-106					F
	12.66		14.15												
N7029	12.3								2890	2858	M				
	12.64		12.38						1.0	-32					
N7038	12.5									-21					
	12.44		14.03												
N7041	12.2								1935	1908	M				
	12.34		13.03						1.0	-27					
N7046										216					
N7049	11.8								2181	2153	M				
	12.04		12.83						1.0	-28					
N7059	13.1									-87					
	12.85		14.24												
N7064	12.7									-51					
	12.91		13.70												
N7065										176					
N7065A										176					
N7070	12.6									0					
	12.74		13.88												
N7070A										1					
N7072										-1					
N7072A										-1					
N7079	12.3									-6					GL
	12.47		12.96												
N7083	12.6									-107					
	12.14		14.43												
N7090	11.8								790	730	M				
	11.74		14.03						6.2	-60					
N7096	13.1									-107					
	12.87		14.01												
N7097	12.6									1					
	12.77		12.71												
N7097A										2					
N7098										-159					H
N7102										225					
N7107	13.1									-11					
	13.15		14.14												
N7119A	13.1*									-20					
N7119B	*									-20					
N7124	12.9									-41					GL
	12.79		14.03												
N7125	13.2									-92					
	12.65		14.59												
N7126	13.2									-92					
	13.23		13.92												

NGC (IC, A) (1)	RA (1950) 100 P (2)	Dec 100 P (3)	L^I / B^I (4)	L^II / B^II (5)	SGL / SGB (6)	Rev. type (S) / DDO (T,L) (7)	Yerkes (1) / Yerkes (2) (8)	Hu-San / Ho (9)	log D w (10)	log R w (11)	log D(O) (12)	S (D,R) (13)
N7135	21 46.8	−35 7	337.44	10.06	245.7	.LA.−.P.S074			1.32	.26	1.21	J
	6.0	28	−52.12	−50.65	24.6				2.22	2.22		
N7137	21 45.9	21 56	44.69	76.43	313.0	.SXT5..P200	S F		1.16	.04	1.14	AKZ
	4.6	28	−24.55	−23.74	48.7	S *			4.36	4.36		
N7141	21 48.8	−55 48	305.41	338.80	230.8	.S...*/						
	6.9	28	−48.27	−47.15	9.6							
N7144	21 49.5	−48 29	315.96	349.19	236.0	.E.0...S074			1.25	.00	1.25	IJ
	6.5	28	−50.88	−49.61	14.8				2.37	2.37		
N7145	21 50.1	−48 7	316.48	349.70	236.3	.E.0...S074			1.16	.00	1.16	IJ
	6.5	28	−51.07	−49.80	15.0				2.08	2.08		
N7154	21 52.4	−35 3	337.58	10.21	246.6				1.10	.25	1.00	F
	5.9	28	−53.26	−51.79	23.8				1.05	1.05		
N7155	21 52.9	−49 46	313.76	347.05	235.5	.LBR...S030			1.09	.23	1.00	EI
	6.5	28	−51.03	−49.79	13.5				1.54	1.54		
N7156	21 52.0	2 42	29.51	61.03	285.7	.SXT6*.W060			1.17	.02	1.16	ALUQ
	5.1	28	−38.96	−37.85	44.0				3.57	2.94		
N7162	21 56.7	−43 33	323.28	356.37	240.5	.SAS5..S074			1.39	.42	1.22	IJ
	6.2	29	−53.27	−51.92	17.4				2.80	2.80		
N7162A	21 57.7	−43 23	323.49	356.58	240.8	.SXS9..S074			1.38	.02	1.38	IJ
	6.2	29	−53.49	−52.13	17.4				2.76	2.76		
N7163	21 56.4	−32 8	342.55	15.02	249.6	.S...*.H030			1.25	.25	1.15	F
	5.8	29	−53.97	−52.49	25.1				1.29	1.29		
N7166	21 57.6	−43 39	323.06	356.16	240.6	.LA.−..S074			1.24	.47	1.05	DEIJ
	6.2	29	−53.41	−52.06	17.2				4.31	4.31		
N7168	21 58.9	−52 0	309.90	343.29	234.5	.E.3...S074			1.05	.10	1.00	DEIJ
	6.6	29	−51.13	−49.95	11.3				3.85	3.85		
N7171	21 58.3	−13 31	11.82	43.44	267.5	.SBT3..P200	S F		1.38	.22	1.29	AFHKNZ
	5.4	29	−49.28	−47.92	35.7	S 4 3			8.53	8.53		
N7172	21 59.1	−32 7	342.64	15.12	250.0	.S...*/H030			1.36	.25	1.26	F
	5.8	29	−54.54	−53.06	24.7				1.49	1.49		
N7174	21 59.2	−32 15	342.42	14.90	249.9	.S...*/H030			1.16	.68	.89	F
	5.8	29	−54.57	−53.09	24.6				1.14	1.14		
N7177	21 58.3	17 29	43.75	75.36	306.6	.SXR3..P200	S P G		1.40	.18	1.33	AEKLRUZ
	4.8	29	−29.81	−28.97	45.6	S 2 3			11.33	10.24		
N7179	22 1.2	−64 18	293.49	326.98	226.0	.L..+*.S030			1.21	.49	1.01	I
	7.4	29	−45.39	−44.51	2.4				1.08	1.08		
N7180	21 59.5	−20 48	1.37	33.23	260.3	.L...*.H030			1.10	.30	.99	FHL
	5.5	29	−52.39	−50.95	31.5				2.40	.71		
N7184	21 59.9	−21 4	1.00	32.87	260.1	.SBR5..W100	SD G		1.73	.56	1.51	FHKLW
	5.6	29	−52.57	−51.12	31.2	S 4 4			12.15	12.15		
N7191	22 3.3	−64 53	292.63	326.13	225.7	.S....*.S030			1.28	.38	1.13	I
	7.4	29	−45.23	−44.37	1.8				.52	.52		
N7192	22 3.2	−64 33	293.02	326.52	225.9	.E.0...S030			1.14	.00	1.14	DI
	7.4	29	−45.42	−44.55	2.0				2.01	2.01		
N7196	22 2.6	−50 22	311.99	345.37	236.1	.E.3...S030			1.03	.13	.98	DEI
	6.4	29	−52.29	−51.07	12.0				2.33	2.33		
N7199	22 4.9	−64 57	292.41	325.92	225.8	.E.3..$S030			.99	.07	.96	I
	7.4	29	−45.33	−44.47	1.6				.76	.76		
N7200	22 4.1	−50 15	312.02	345.41	236.4	.E+4+*.S030			.98	.28	.86	I
	6.4	29	−52.55	−51.34	11.9				.75	.75		
N7205	22 5.1	−57 40	301.34	334.86	231.0	.SAS4..S074			1.58	.31	1.46	DEJ
	6.8	29	−49.40	−48.36	6.7				6.09	6.09		
N7205A	22 4.1	−57 41	301.42	334.93	230.9	.SXS7*.S074			.99	.08	.96	J
	6.8	29	−49.28	−48.24	6.8				1.52	1.52		
N7213	22 6.2	−47 25	316.25	349.57	238.8	.SAS1..R074			1.16	.02	1.15	EI
	6.3	29	−53.87	−52.59	13.6				1.62	1.62		
N7214	22 6.3	−28 3	350.01	22.22	254.6	.S.....H030			1.25	.15	1.19	F
	5.7	29	−55.65	−54.16	25.9				1.29	1.29		
N7217	22 5.6	31 7	54.70	86.50	325.7	RSAR2..P200	SDP*GK	S 3	1.47	.08	1.44	AKLRVXYZ
	4.5	29	−20.29	−19.70	43.5	S 2 3*		S3	12.72	12.72		
N7218	22 7.5	−16 54	8.48	40.11	265.4	.SBT6..W060	S A		1.37	.31	1.25	AKPQ
	5.4	29	−52.74	−51.35	32.0	S 5 6			6.85	6.85		
N7219	22 9.7	−65 5	291.82	325.35	226.0	RSAROP.B060			1.24	.19	1.16	P
	7.3	30	−45.65	−44.80	1.2				1.91	1.91		
N7232	22 12.6	−46 5	317.82	351.15	240.5	.SBT1*.B060			1.36	.61	1.11	EPI
	6.2	30	−55.33	−54.04	13.6				2.19	2.19		
N7232A	22 10.6	−46 2	318.10	351.40	240.3	.SBT2./S074			1.31	.79	.99	PIJ
	6.2	30	−55.02	−53.72	13.9				4.59	4.59		
N7232B	22 12.9	−45 56	318.04	351.36	240.7	.SBS9..B060			1.26	.10	1.23	PI
	6.2	30	−55.43	−54.13	13.7				2.22	2.22		
N7233	22 12.7	−46 6	317.78	351.11	240.5	.SXS0..B060			1.20	.25	1.10	PI
	6.2	30	−55.35	−54.05	13.6				2.28	1.72		
N7236	22 12.3	13 36	43.68	75.14	301.8	.L.....*W						
	4.9	30	−34.95	−34.11	41.8							
N7237	22 12.3	13 35	43.67	75.12	301.8	.L.....*W						
	4.9	30	−34.96	−34.12	41.8							
N7240	22 13.4	37 2	59.69	91.58	333.2	.L.....W			.84	.00	.84	A
	4.4	30	−16.39	−15.93	40.9				.34	.34		
N7242	22 13.5	37 3	59.72	91.61	333.2	.E.3...W			.82	.09	.78	ABR
	4.4	30	−16.39	−15.92	40.9				1.75	1.75		

NGC (IC, A)	m_H / m_C	B(O) w	B'(O) m'_C	S(B)	(B-V)(O) w	C_0(O)	S(C)	(U-B)(O) w	V w	V_0 ΔV	S(V)	ϕ_r n	φ(21)		Photo.
(14)	(15)	(16)	(17)	(18)	(19)	(20)	(21)	(22)	(23)	(24)	(25)	(26)	(27)	(28)	(29)
N7135	13.0									40					G
	12.83		13.62												
N7137	13.1	13.44	13.88	CH	.70	.55	CH		1505	1774	C				
	13.29	6.91	13.73		11.88				1.8	268					
N7141										−67					
N7144	12.2								2113	2083	M				L
	12.15		13.14						1.0	−30					
N7145	12.7									−28					
	12.65		13.14												
N7154										39					
N7155	12.8									−37					
	13.06		12.80												
N7156										211					
N7162	13.1									−5					
	13.10		13.94												
N7162A										−5					
N7163										53					
N7166	12.6									−6					L
	12.84		12.83												
N7168	12.7									−49					
	12.91		12.65												
N7171	12.8	13.27	14.46	C	.78	.62	C		2632	2776	B				
	12.74	1.98	13.93		3.75				4.0	144					
N7172										53					
N7174										52					
N7177	12.1	12.09	13.43	ABCH	.82	.64	ABCH		1105	1360	B				
	12.29	10.47	13.63		22.50				1.8	255					
N7179										−110					
N7180										109					
N7184	12.0									107					B
	11.87		14.11												
N7191										−113					
N7192	12.9									−112					
	12.82		13.21												
N7196	12.3								3016	2975	M				
	12.69		12.28						6.2	−41					
N7199										−114					
N7200										−41					
N7205	11.7								1482	1404	M				GL
	11.70		13.74						1.0	−78					
N7205A										−78					
N7213	11.8	11.57	12.06	M	.86	.77	M	.36	1778	1751	LM				
	12.49	0.75	12.98				/M		21.0	−27					
N7214										72					
N7217	11.6	11.29	13.18	ABCGH	.93	.75	ABCGH		911	1192	B				ACP
	11.74	11.69	13.63		26.88				11.1	281					
N7218	12.7								1808	1933	C				
	12.89		13.83						2.4	125					
N7219										−115					
N7232	13.0									−21					
	13.21		13.50												
N7232A										−21					
N7232B										−21					
N7233										−21					
N7236									7857	8098	K				
									11.1	241					
N7237									7852	8093	K				
									11.1	241					
N7240		15.06	14.00	C	1.06	.81	C		5984	6271	B				
		2.51			3.75				1.8	287					
N7242		14.65	13.29	C	1.00	.75	C		5684	5971	B				
		1.96			1.88				1.0	287					

NGC (IC, A)	Coordinates					Classification			Diameters			
	RA (1950) Dec 100 P	100 P	L^I B^I	L^II B^II	SGL SGB	Rev. type (S) DDO (T, L)	Yerkes (1) Yerkes (2)	Hu-San Ho	log D w	log R w	log D(0)	S (D,R)
(1)	(2)	(3)	(4)	(5)	(6)	(7)	(8)	(9)	(10)	(11)	(12)	(13)
N7248	22 14.8	40 16	61.78	93.73	337.3	.LB.-*.L036			1.02	.35	.88	A
	4.3	30	-13.85	-13.44	39.9				.57	.57		
N7252	22 18.0	-24 56	356.48	28.44	259.1	RLARO*.W100	P *K *		1.09	.09	1.06	EW
	5.6	30	-57.63	-56.16	25.6	E T			2.61	2.61		
N7280	22 24.0	15 53	48.13	79.54	305.4	.L....$			1.32	.21	1.24	A
	4.9	30	-34.98	-34.23	39.3				.97	.97		
N7290	22 26.0	16 53	49.32	80.74	306.7	.SAR4..W100			1.13	.21	1.04	AW
	4.9	31	-34.48	-33.77	39.0				2.28	2.28		
N7298	22 28.2	-14 27	16.04	47.33	270.7	.SAS5*.W100			1.12	.04	1.10	AW
	5.3	31	-56.14	-54.82	28.9				2.29	2.29		
N7300	22 28.3	-14 17	16.33	47.61	270.8	.SXT3*.W100			1.25	.29	1.14	AKW
	5.3	31	-56.08	-54.77	28.9	S 4 2*			4.11	4.11		
N7302	22 29.7	-14 23	16.46	47.73	270.9	.LAS-*.W100			.98	.17	.91	AKW
	5.3	31	-56.42	-55.11	28.6	E 3			2.73	2.73		
N7307	22 30.9	-41 12	324.66	357.92	246.6	.SA.5*.S030			1.59	.70	1.31	FI
	5.9	31	-59.97	-58.59	14.0				3.27	3.27		
N7309	22 31.6	-10 37	22.59	53.73	275.0	.SXT4..L036			1.23	.04	1.21	AFHKLU
	5.3	31	-54.86	-53.63	29.8	S 5 3			6.36	5.59		
N7313	22 32.8	-26 23	355.00	26.97	259.8	.SBS.*.P200			1.32	.30		
	5.5	31	-61.19	-59.71	22.0							
N7314	22 33.0	-26 18	355.19	27.15	259.9	.SXT4..P200	S AF	S 5	1.59	.33	1.46	DEFGKMT
	5.5	31	-61.21	-59.74	22.0	S 5 K - 2			17.22	17.22		Z
N7317	22 33.6	33 41	61.49	93.23	328.1	.E.4.*.W			.82	.02	.81	ABLM
	4.6	31	-21.42	-21.00	37.4				1.88	1.88		
N7318A	22 33.7	33 42	61.51	93.26	328.2	.E.2.P.L036			.72	.00	.72	ABM
	4.6	31	-21.41	-20.99	37.3				1.20	1.20		
N7318B	22 33.7	33 42	61.51	93.26	328.2	.SBS5P.L036			1.26	.21	1.18	LMU
	4.6	31	-21.41	-20.99	37.3				3.91	3.28		
N7319	22 33.8	33 42	61.53	93.28	328.2	.SBS4P.L036			1.24	.10	1.20	ABLMU
	4.6	31	-21.42	-21.00	37.3				4.82	4.26		
N7320	22 33.8	33 41	61.53	93.27	328.1	.SAS4P.L036			1.32	.30	1.20	ABHLMU
	4.6	31	-21.44	-21.02	37.3				7.30	7.30		
N7320C	22 34.1	33 43	61.60	93.35	328.2	.SB.3..L036			.84	.08	.81	M
	4.6	31	-21.44	-21.02	37.3				.89	.89		
N7329	22 37.0	-66 44	287.33	320.97	226.6	.SBR3..B060			1.55	.19	1.48	PI
	7.0	31	-46.55	-45.80	-2.0				4.49	4.49		
N7331	22 34.8	34 10	61.98	93.73	328.7	.SAS4..L036	S GK	S 3	2.00	.50	1.80	ABHKLVX
	4.6	31	-21.13	-20.72	37.1	S 3 2		S4	15.98	15.98		
N7332	22 35.0	23 32	55.87	87.38	315.4	.L...P/P200	D K *	L 2 P	1.47	.55	1.25	ABKLZ
	4.8	31	-30.23	-29.67	37.4	E 7			8.66	8.66		
N7335	22 35.0	34 10	62.03	93.79	328.7	.S..1..W			1.06	.35	.92	ABL
	4.6	31	-21.14	-20.73	37.0				1.75	1.31		
N7337	22 35.2	34 5	62.03	93.78	328.6	.S....$L036			1.18	.18	1.10	L
	4.6	31	-21.23	-20.82	37.0				.63	.63		
N7339	22 35.4	23 31	55.95	87.46	315.3	.SXS4*$P200	SI *F		1.46	.61	1.22	ABLZ
	4.8	31	-30.30	-29.74	37.3				7.04	7.04		
N7343	22 36.4	33 48	62.09	93.83	328.2	.SBS3..W			1.07	.11	1.02	AL
	4.6	31	-21.61	-21.20	36.8				1.17	.64		
N7348	22 38.1	11 38	48.30	79.51	300.8	.S..6.$W			1.10	.18	1.02	A
	5.0	31	-40.44	-39.70	35.3				.33	.33		
N7361	22 39.5	-30 19	346.97	19.30	257.0	.S.R5*$W100			1.49	.57	1.26	DEW
	5.6	31	-63.08	-61.59	18.7				5.99	5.99		
N7363	22 40.9	33 44	62.95	94.67	328.0	.S....*			1.10	.12	1.06	AL
	4.6	31	-22.12	-21.73	35.8				1.25	.73		
N7368	22 42.7	-39 36	326.54	359.82	249.3	.S...*/H030			1.44	.82	1.11	F
	5.7	31	-62.57	-61.18	13.1				1.67	1.67		
N7371	22 43.4	-11 16	24.57	55.51	275.7	RSARO*.W060			1.27	.01	1.27	ABHKLQ
	5.3	32	-57.62	-56.42	26.9	S 3 5*	DS *G		5.69	5.69		
N7377	22 45.1	-22 35	4.31	35.82	264.8	.LAS+..W100			1.18	.10	1.15	DEKW
	5.4	32	-63.02	-61.59	21.5	E 1	D K		5.02	5.02		
N7385	22 47.4	11 21	50.53	81.66	301.0	.E.0...W			.95	.00	.95	A
	5.0	32	-42.01	-41.32	33.0				.48	.48		
N7386	22 47.6	11 26	50.65	81.78	301.1	.L.....W			.84	.00	.84	A
	5.0	32	-41.97	-41.28	32.9				.34	.34		
N7392	22 49.2	-20 53	8.56	39.85	266.9	.SAS4..W100	S P GK*	S 3	1.28	.27	1.17	KW
	5.4	32	-63.37	-61.98	21.5	S 3 3*			3.79	3.79		
N7393	22 49.0	-5 49	33.84	64.64	282.0	.SBT5P.W100			1.24	.30	1.12	AHLW
	5.2	32	-55.29	-54.25	27.7				4.19	3.56		
N7408	22 52.7	-63 58	288.17	321.95	229.8	.SB..*.						
	6.4	32	-49.72	-48.94	-1.8							
N7410	22 52.1	-39 56	324.58	358.02	250.0	.LBS+..W100			1.57	.48	1.38	FIW
	5.7	32	-64.19	-62.81	11.4				7.34	7.34		
N7412	22 53.0	-42 55	318.22	351.89	247.5	.SBS3..S030			1.53	.12	1.48	EFI
	5.7	32	-63.19	-61.89	9.7				5.13	5.13		
N7412A	22 54.0	-43 4	317.74	351.44	247.5	.S..../S030			1.51	1.08	1.08	I
	5.7	32	-63.29	-61.99	9.5				1.63	1.63		
N7416	22 53.1	-5 46	35.14	65.86	282.5	.SBR3..W060			1.45	.47	1.26	AHQ
	5.2	32	-56.00	-54.99	26.8				3.89	3.89		
N7418	22 53.8	-37 17	330.28	3.49	252.5	.SXT6..W100			1.50	.09	1.46	FGPIW
	5.6	32	-65.29	-63.87	12.5				8.49	7.74		

NGC (IC, A) (14)	m_H / m_c (15)	B(O) w (16)	B'(O) m'_c (17)	S(B) (18)	(B-V)(O) w (19)	C_o(O) (20)	S(C) (21)	(U-B)(O) w (22)	V w (23)	V_o ΔV (24)	S(V) (25)	φ_r n (26)	φ (21) (27)	(28)	Photo. (29)
N7248										289					
N7252	13.0 / 13.11	13.21 / 2.04	13.20 / 13.10	C	.78 / 1.88	.66	C		4733 / 2.4	4817 / 84	B				
N7280										244					
N7290										246					
N7298										130					
N7300	13.2 / 13.32		13.71							131					
N7302	13.1 / 13.43	13.46 / 1.98	12.70 / 12.67	C	.90 / 3.75	.79	C		2586 / 2.4	2716 / 130	B				
N7307	13.1 / 12.92		14.16							−1					
N7309	13.1 / 13.10		13.89							146					E
N7313										72					
N7314	11.9 / 11.88	11.85 / 2.93	13.89 / 13.92	C	.71 / 3.75	.57	C		1766 / 4.0	1839 / 73	B				P
N7317		15.16 / 3.16	13.95	C	.92 / 3.75	.70	C		6736 / 2.4	7013 / 277	B				
N7318A		14.93 / 5.27	13.22	C*	1.03 / 5.63	.81	C*		6689 / 11.3	6967 / 277	BCF				
N7318B		14.41 / 1.08	15.05	C*	.98 / 3.75	.73	C*		5727 / 10.3	6005 / 277	BC				
N7319		13.56 / 1.96	14.30	C	.73 / 1.88	.49	C		6657 / 4.0	6935 / 277	B				
N7320									795 / 1.0	1073 / 277	F				
N7320C										277					
N7329	13.0 / 12.43		14.52							−126					
N7331	11.2 / 10.72	10.56 / 4.62	14.30 / 14.46	CFGD*	.86 / 6.63	.63	CGD /D	.37	794 / 31.5	1072 / 278	ABCD				ABKM P
N7332	12.6 / 12.50	12.02 / 4.51	13.01 / 13.49	BCL	.90 / 12.70	.75	BCL /L	.36	1204 / 4.0	1463 / 259	B				P
N7335									6298 / 2.8	6576 / 278	B				
N7337										278					
N7339		13.27 / 3.45	14.06	BC	.90 / 8.13		BC			259					
N7343		14.43 / 2.77	14.27	CD	.81 / 4.13	.62	CD /D	.19	1216 / .3	1493 / 277	B				
N7348										227					
N7361	12.8 / 12.85		13.89							51					
N7363										275					
N7368										4					
N7371	12.9 / 12.77		13.81							139					
N7377	12.7 / 12.75	12.05 / 1.50	12.49 / 13.19	C	.92 / 3.75	.82	C		3416 / 2.4	3502 / 86	B				
N7385		14.09 / 1.89	13.58	C	1.02 / 1.88	.85	C		7829 / 2.4	8051 / 222	B				
N7386		14.56 / 2.04	13.50	C	1.06 / 1.88	.90	C		7198 / 2.4	7420 / 222	B				
N7392	12.6 / 12.93	12.81 / 1.58	13.40 / 13.52	C	.95 / 1.88	.80	C		2941 / 1.2	3034 / 93	C				P
N7393									3813 / 1.4	3972 / 159	C				
N7408										−116					
N7410	11.8 / 11.77	11.61 / 1.76	13.25 / 13.41	M	.92	.82	M /M	.49	1638 / 23.9	1637 / −1	L				
N7412	12.2 / 11.97	12.04 / 1.39	14.18 / 14.11	M	.55		M /M	.00		−16					
N7412A										−17					
N7416										158					
N7418	11.8 / 11.90	12.02 / 1.46	14.06 / 13.94	M	.61		M /M	−.03		12					F

NGC (IC, A) (1)	RA (1950) 100 P (2)	Dec 100 P (3)	L^I B^I (4)	L^{II} B^{II} (5)	SGL SGB (6)	Rev. type (S) DDO (T, L) (7)	Yerkes (1) Yerkes (2) (8)	Hu-San Ho (9)	log D w (10)	log R w (11)	log D(O) (12)	S (D,R) (13)
N7418A	22 53.9 5.6	−37 1 32	330.89 −65.38	4.07 −63.95	252.7 12.6	.SBS5*.S030			1.62 .41	.48 .41	1.43	I
N7421	22 54.1 5.6	−37 37 32	329.47 −65.26	2.72 −63.85	252.2 12.3	.SBT2..W100			1.28 7.74	.05 5.80	1.26	FGPIW
N7424	22 54.5 5.7	−41 20 32	321.21 −64.10	354.80 −62.76	249.0 10.3	.SXT6..S074			1.85 15.17	.03 15.17	1.84	FPTIJ
N7442	22 57.0 5.0	15 15 32	55.95 −39.99	87.10 −39.43	306.0 31.4	.S....*R020			1.09 1.96	.00 1.36	1.09	AHL
N7443	22 57.5 5.3	−13 4 32	25.55 −61.47	56.24 −60.29	275.5 23.0	.L....$H030			1.15 .73	.29 .73	1.03	A
N7444	22 57.5 5.3	−13 5 32	25.52 −61.48	56.21 −60.30	275.4 23.0	.L....$H030			1.08 .65	.20 .65	1.00	A
N7448	22 57.6 5.0	15 43 32	56.41 −39.67	87.57 −39.12	306.6 31.3	.SAT4..W100 S 5 KT- 3*	S P *FG		1.38 9.21	.32 9.21	1.25	AHKLUW
N7454	22 58.6 5.0	16 7 32	56.94 −39.45	88.11 −38.91	307.1 31.1	.E+4...W100			1.05 3.85	.15 3.22	.99	AHLW
N7456	22 59.3 5.6	−39 51 32	323.61 −65.51	357.17 −64.14	250.8 10.3	.SAS6*.S030			1.74 5.36	.57 5.36	1.51	FI
N7457	22 58.6 4.8	29 53 32	64.66 −27.27	96.22 −26.93	323.2 32.2	.LAT-.$P200 E P	D GK ED K	L 1	1.44 10.28	.29 10.28	1.33	AKLWZ
N7462	23 0.0 5.6	−41 6 32	320.73 −65.14	354.41 −63.81	249.8 9.5	.SBS5*$S030			1.54 3.59	.88 1.76	1.19	FI
N7463	22 59.4 5.0	15 42 32	56.89 −39.90	88.05 −39.36	306.6 30.9	.S....*R020			1.24 3.28	.47 3.28	1.05	ABHL
N7464	22 59.4 5.0	15 42 32	56.89 −39.90	88.05 −39.36	306.6 30.9	.L....$R020			.86 1.36	.01 1.02	.85	ABHL
N7465	22 59.5 5.0	15 41 32	56.91 −39.92	88.06 −39.38	306.6 30.8	.E....*R020			1.01 2.25	.22 1.68	.93	ABHL
N7469	23 0.7 5.0	8 36 32	52.16 −46.12	83.08 −45.46	298.7 29.2	PSXT1..W100 S N +*	SDP*G *		1.13 5.75	.16 5.75	1.07	ABKNW
N7479	23 2.4 5.0	12 3 32	55.24 −43.42	86.26 −42.84	302.6 29.5	.SBS5..P200 SB4 1	B F		1.58 15.73	.12 14.44	1.53	AHKLSVYZ
N7496	23 7.0 5.6	−43 42 32	313.84 −65.05	347.83 −63.80	248.1 7.1	.SBS3..S030			1.47 1.55	.11 1.55	1.43	I
N7496A	23 9.6 5.6	−43 3 33	314.57 −65.80	348.58 −64.54	248.9 7.0	.SBS5*$S030			1.43 .32	.35 .32	1.29	I
N7497	23 6.6 5.0	17 53 32	60.21 −38.81	91.38 −38.35	309.4 29.5	.SBS5..P048			1.75 7.01	.70 7.01	1.47	AHLS
N7499	23 7.9 5.1	7 18 32	53.33 −48.18	84.14 −47.55	297.7 27.1	.L.....W			.88 .38	.00 .38	.88	A
N7501	23 8.0 5.1	7 19 32	53.37 −48.18	84.18 −47.55	297.7 27.1	.E.3...W			.88 .38	.00 .38	.88	A
N7503	23 8.0 5.1	7 15 32	53.32 −48.23	84.13 −47.60	297.6 27.1	.E.1...W			.88 .38	.00 .38	.88	A
N7507	23 9.5 5.4	−28 49 33	351.37 −69.54	23.43 −68.05	261.7 13.7	.E.0...W100			1.05 2.63	.00 2.63	1.05	NW
N7513	23 10.5 5.4	−28 38 33	351.93 −69.75	23.95 −68.26	262.0 13.6	.SBT3*.L036						
N7531	23 12.1 5.6	−43 53 33	312.27 −65.72	346.38 −64.50	248.4 6.2	.SAR4..S074			1.58 3.07	.28 3.07	1.47	J
N7537	23 12.0 5.1	4 13 33	52.09 −51.33	82.74 −50.66	294.7 25.4	.SA.4..$W060	S *F		1.35 6.70	.57 6.70	1.13	ABHLUQ
N7541	23 12.2 5.1	4 15 33	52.18 −51.32	82.84 −50.67	294.7 25.3	.SB.4..$W060 S 5 3*	SI *A		1.49 11.14	.43 11.14	1.32	ABHKLUQ
N7552	23 13.5 5.5	−42 53 33	313.98 −66.49	348.07 −65.24	249.4 6.5	PSBS2..S074			1.46 5.50	.17 3.04	1.39	FIJ
N7562	23 13.4 5.1	6 25 33	54.39 −49.65	85.11 −49.04	297.1 25.6	.E.2+..W060			1.05 2.67	.19 2.67	.97	MQ
N7562A	23 13.5 5.1	6 23 33	54.40 −49.69	85.11 −49.08	297.1 25.6	.S...$/L036			1.23 1.54	.56 1.54	1.00	M
N7576	23 14.9 5.2	−5 1 33	43.46 −59.19	73.76 −58.34	285.3 21.9	.LAR+..W100			.94 3.23	.10 3.23	.90	AMW
N7582	23 15.8 5.5	−42 38 33	313.92 −66.98	348.06 −65.73	249.9 6.2	PSBS2..S074			1.58 6.39	.49 5.57	1.39	FIJ
N7585	23 15.4 5.2	−4 56 33	43.75 −59.21	74.04 −58.36	285.4 21.9	PLAS+P.W100 S N +	DSP*K *		1.21 5.21	.10 5.21	1.16	AKNW
N7587	23 15.4 5.1	9 23 33	57.29 −47.32	88.10 −46.78	300.4 25.8	.S....*			1.14 1.33	.56 .77	.92	AL
N7590	23 16.3 5.5	−42 31 33	314.04 −67.12	348.19 −65.87	250.0 6.2	.SAT4*.S074			1.40 5.55	.42 5.55	1.23	FIJ
N7592	23 15.9 5.2	−4 42 33	44.23 −59.11	74.51 −58.27	285.7 21.8	.S...P.L036			1.00 1.67	.14 1.67	.94	AN
N7599	23 16.7 5.5	−42 32 33	313.90 −67.17	348.06 −65.92	250.0 6.1	.SAS5..S074			1.61 6.20	.50 6.20	1.41	FIJ
N7600	23 16.3 5.2	−7 52 33	40.16 −61.56	70.36 −60.63	282.5 20.7	.L..-./W100 E 6			1.17 4.11	.38 4.11	1.02	HKW
N7601	23 16.3 5.1	8 57 33	57.26 −47.80	88.05 −47.27	300.0 25.5	.S....*			1.18 .63	.08 .63	1.14	L
N7606	23 16.5 5.2	−8 46 33	38.92 −62.24	69.09 −61.29	281.6 20.3	.SAS3..W100 S 4 1	S FG		1.70 14.45	.39 14.45	1.54	AEFHKLW

NGC (IC, A) (14)	Magnitudes				Colors				Velocities			Radio			
	m_H m_C (15)	B(O) w (16)	B'(O) m'_C (17)	S(B) (18)	(B-V)(O) w (19)	C_o(O) (20)	S(C) (21)	(U-B)(O) w (22)	V w (23)	V_o ΔV (24)	S(V) (25)	$φ_r$ n (26)	φ(21) (27)	(28)	Photo. (29)
N7418A										13					
N7421	12.8 12.78	12.86 2.03	13.90 13.82	M	.72		M /M	.12		10					F
N7424	12.0 11.13	11.46 0.52	15.40 15.07	M	.54		M /M	-.05		-9					F
N7442										230					
N7443										125					
N7444										125					
N7448	11.8 12.33	12.23 6.45	13.17 13.27	ABC	.55 14.38	.38	ABC		2419 .2	2650 231	B				
N7454										232					
N7456	12.5 12.16		14.45							-3					
N7457	12.3 12.18	12.27 10.03	13.61 13.52	ABCH	.91 21.88	.77	ABCH		525 .2	788 263	B				LP
N7462	12.7 12.96		13.65							-9					
N7463										230					
N7464										230					
N7465										230					
N7469	13.0 13.33	13.06 3.94	13.10 13.37	AC	.67 1.88	.51	C		4807 14.4	5015 208	BCF				
N7479	11.9 11.74	11.93 4.61	14.32 14.13	ACD	.79* 8.25	.66	CD /D	.23	2441 9.3	2659 218	BCF				AK
N7496	12.2 12.11	12.08 1.58	13.97 14.00	M	.50	.39	M /M	-.03	1470 19.0	1446 -24	L				F
N7496A										-22					
N7497										233					
N7499		15.01 2.01	14.10	C	1.06 1.88	.85	C		11916 4.0	12116 200	B				
N7501		15.18 2.01	14.27	C	1.15 1.88	.93	C		12714 4.0	12914 200	B				
N7503		14.98 2.93	14.07	C	1.07 3.75	.85	C		13229 2.4	13429 200	B				
N7507	12.0 12.36	11.87 3.22	11.86 12.35	C	.88 3.75	.81	C		1637 1.8	1684 47	B				
N7513										47					
N7531	12.5 12.18	12.00 1.43	14.09 14.27	M	.73		M /M	-.03		-27					G
N7537		14.13 1.43	14.47	C	.63 1.88		C			187					B
N7541	12.8 12.69	12.80 3.98	14.14 14.03	AC	.76 1.88	.59	C		2672 1.0	2859 187	B				
N7552	11.6 11.83	11.44 2.49	13.13 13.52	M	.66	.53	M /M	.03*	1662 25.0	1639 -23	L				G
N7562		13.24 5.36	12.83	C	1.07 7.50	.96	C		3806 2.3	4000 194	C				
N7562A										194					
N7576		14.07 1.69	13.31	C	.82 1.88	.71	C		3572 5.9	3723 151	BD				
N7582	11.8 11.97	11.84 2.49	13.53 13.66	M	.80	.62	M /M	.20	1451 31.0	1428 -23	L				GL
N7585	12.8 12.79	12.74 1.89	13.28 13.33	C	.92 1.88	.81	C		3352 3.7	3502 151	BC				
N7587										203					
N7590	11.9 12.41	12.18 3.25	13.07 13.30	M	.64	.49	M /M	.01	1382 8.1	1360 -22	LM				G
N7592										7289 1.6	7440 151	D				
N7599	12.0 12.10	12.25 2.38	14.04 13.89	M	.61		M /M	-.07		-22					G
N7600	13.1 13.24	13.22 0.99	13.01 13.03	C	.92 1.88	.80	C		3391 2.8	3529 138	B				
N7601										201					
N7606	11.9 11.67	11.83 1.96	14.27 14.11	C	.80 3.75	.62	C		2341 1.8	2475 134	B				

NGC (IC, A) (1)	RA (1950) Dec 100 P (2)	100 P (3)	L^I B^I (4)	L^{II} B^{II} (5)	SGL SGB (6)	Rev. type (S) DDO (T, L) (7)	Yerkes (1) Yerkes (2) (8)	Hu-San Ho (9)	log D w (10)	log R w (11)	log D(O) (12)	S (D,R) (13)
N7611	23 17.1 7 47	5.1 33	56.66 −48.93	87.39 −48.38	298.8 25.0	.L.....W			1.06 2.13	.43 2.13	.89	AR
N7615	23 17.4 8 7	5.1 33	57.01 −48.66	87.75 −48.12	299.2 25.1				.95 1.81	.25 1.81	.85	AR
N7617	23 17.6 7 54	5.1 33	56.91 −48.89	87.64 −48.34	299.0 24.9	.L.....W			.88 .38	.00 .38	.88	A
N7619	23 17.8 7 55	5.1 33	56.99 −48.90	87.72 −48.35	299.0 24.9	.E.3...W E 1	E4 K DE *K *		1.07 1.68	.04 1.68	1.06	AEK
N7623	23 18.0 8 8	5.1 33	57.22 −48.73	87.95 −48.19	299.3 24.9	.E.4...W	E4 K		.70 1.16	.00 .42	.70	AR
N7625	23 18.0 16 57	5.0 33	62.84 −40.86	93.91 −40.47	308.8 26.7	.SAT1P.W100 E P	I P G *		1.11 5.02	.08 5.02	1.08	AKNW
N7626	23 18.2 7 56	5.1 33	57.13 −48.93	87.86 −48.39	299.0 24.8	.E.1...W E 2P *	E1 *K *		1.04 3.09	.05 1.87	1.02	AEKR
N7631	23 18.9 7 55	5.1 33	57.36 −49.02	88.08 −48.48	299.1 24.6	.S.....*			1.25 2.80	.40 2.80	1.09	AR
N7632	23 19.4 −42 46	5.5 33	312.68 −67.45	346.92 −66.22	250.0 5.6				1.01 .91			F
N7640	23 19.7 40 35	4.8 33	73.45 −19.04	105.24 −18.93	335.4 27.7	.SBS5..P200 SX4 3*	B *F	SBS5 S6	2.04 14.82	1.76 14.82	1.76	AHKLXZ
N7671	23 24.8 12 12	5.0 33	62.13 −45.86	92.97 −45.45	304.0 24.2	.L.....L036			1.00 1.67	.23 1.67	.91	AM
N7672	23 25.0 12 7	5.0 33	62.15 −45.96	92.98 −45.54	303.9 24.1	.SAR3..L036			1.09 1.91	.11 1.91	1.04	AM
N7678	23 26.1 22 9	5.0 33	67.71 −36.82	98.92 −36.55	314.9 25.5	.SXT5..W060 S 5 1	S AF		1.30 5.83	.11 5.83	1.26	AHKNQ
N7679	23 26.2 3 15	5.1 33	56.26 −53.99	86.68 −53.43	294.7 21.7	.LB..P*W060 S N +			1.08 4.20	.20 4.20	1.00	AKNQ
N7682	23 26.5 3 16	5.1 33	56.38 −54.01	86.81 −53.45	294.7 21.6	.SBR3*.L036			1.11 1.32	.12 1.32	1.06	N
N7685	23 27.9 3 38	5.1 33	57.20 −53.86	87.63 −53.32	295.2 21.4	.S...*.L036			1.16 1.08	.18 1.08	1.09	AN
N7689	23 29.9 −54 22	5.5 33	291.38 −60.25	325.78 −59.40	240.4 −1.2	.SXT6..S074			1.44 5.71	.18 5.71	1.37	PIJ
N7690	23 30.2 −51 58	5.5 33	294.16 −62.25	328.66 −61.34	242.6 −.2	.SAR3*$S074			1.38 1.52	.37 1.52	1.23	IJ
N7702	23 32.7 −56 17	5.5 33	288.70 −58.84	323.05 −58.05	238.9 −2.4	RLAR+..S074			1.27 2.14	.24 2.14	1.17	J
N7713	23 33.8 −38 13	5.3 33	319.39 −72.24	353.74 −70.91	255.4 5.1	.SB.6*$S030			1.60 3.85	.37 3.85	1.45	FI
N7713A	23 34.5 −37 53	5.3 33	320.11 −72.52	354.43 −71.19	255.7 5.1	.SA.6*$S030			1.28 1.19	.09 1.19	1.24	I
N7714	23 33.7 1 53	5.1 33	57.98 −56.09	88.23 −55.56	293.8 19.5	.SBS3P*P200			1.19 5.58	.12 5.58	1.14	ABNZ
N7715	23 33.8 1 53	5.1 33	58.02 −56.10	88.27 −55.58	293.8 19.5	.I..9P/P200			1.30 5.40	.67 5.40	1.04	ABNZ
N7716	23 33.9 0 1	5.1 33	56.42 −57.75	86.56 −57.19	291.9 19.0	.SXR3*.W100 S 3 3*	S *G		1.18 4.74	.06 4.74	1.15	AEKW
N7721	23 36.2 −6 48	5.1 33	50.00 −63.84	79.69 −63.12	285.3 16.4	.SAS5..W060 S 5 3	S AF		1.54 9.94	.38 9.94	1.39	ABEGKLQ
N7723	23 36.4 −13 14	5.2 33	39.87 −68.85	69.26 −67.91	279.0 14.2	.SBR3..P200 S 3 N	SB F		1.45 9.00	.15 8.23	1.39	AFKLZ
N7727	23 37.3 −12 34	5.2 33	41.57 −68.52	70.94 −67.61	279.7 14.2	.SXS1P.W100 S NT−*	S P		1.58 5.70	.16 5.70	1.51	APW
N7741	23 41.4 25 48	5.0 33	73.23 −34.50	104.51 −34.37	319.3 22.5	.SBS6..P200 SB5 3	B AF	SBS5 S6	1.56 8.85	.14 8.85	1.50	AHKXZ
N7742	23 41.8 10 29	5.1 33	66.83 −49.06	97.46 −48.76	303.2 19.7	.SAR3..P200 E OP	S P GK*		1.17 4.35	.00 4.35	1.17	AKZ
N7743	23 41.8 9 39	5.1 33	66.37 −49.84	96.96 −49.53	302.3 19.5	RLBS+..P200 S 0*	B GK	SBS1	1.39 7.72	.08 7.72	1.36	AKNZ
N7744	23 42.4 −43 12	5.3 33	304.09 −70.34	339.11 −69.24	251.5 1.6	.LX.−*.S030			1.15 1.58	.12 1.58	1.10	EI
N7752	23 44.5 29 11	5.0 33	75.11 −31.43	106.51 −31.35	323.1 22.2	.P.....L036			.91 1.31	.08 .96	.88	ABL
N7753	23 44.6 29 12	5.0 33	75.14 −31.41	106.54 −31.34	323.1 22.2	.SXT3..L036			1.52 5.77	.21 4.77	1.43	ABLU
N7755	23 45.3 −30 48	5.2 33	342.65 −77.17	15.46 −75.69	263.1 5.8	.S..5..H030			1.54 2.63	.08 2.63	1.51	FG
N7757	23 46.2 3 54	5.1 33	64.54 −55.59	94.75 −55.23	296.7 17.1	.SAR5..L036			1.41 2.22	.03 2.22	1.40	AB
N7764	23 48.4 −41 1	5.2 33	306.29 −72.69	341.54 −71.55	253.9 1.4	.IBS9..B060			1.17 2.77	.20 2.77	1.09	PI
N7764A	23 50.8 −40 59	5.2 33	305.25 −73.03	340.63 −71.90	254.1 1.0	.S...P.S074			1.14 2.26	.21 2.26	1.06	IJ
N7769	23 48.5 19 52	5.1 33	73.14 −40.65	104.17 −40.52	313.3 20.0	RSAT3..W060 S 5 NT	S F		1.19 6.72	.03 6.72	1.18	ABHKMQ
N7770	23 48.8 19 48	5.1 33	73.20 −40.72	104.23 −40.59	313.3 19.9	.S..3.*L			.90 1.34	.02 1.34	.89	ABH
N7771	23 48.9 19 50	5.1 33	73.24 −40.71	104.27 −40.58	313.3 19.9	.SBS1..W060	B *F		1.32 6.88	.44 6.88	1.15	ABHMQ

NGC (IC, A) (14)	m_H m_c (15)	B(O) w (16)	B'(O) m'_c (17)	S(B) (18)	(B-V)(O) w (19)	c_o(O) (20)	S(C) (21)	(U-B)(O) w (22)	V w (23)	V_o ΔV (24)	S(V) (25)	$φ_r$ n (26)	φ(21) (27)	(28)	Photo. (29)
N7611		13.89	13.08	CL	.94	.80	CL	.66	3383	3580	B				
		6.49			7.40		/L		2.4	197					
N7615										198					
N7617		15.06	14.15	CL	.96	.84	CL	.54*	4072	4269	B				
		3.58			5.50		/L		.4	197					
N7619	12.8	12.78	12.77	ACDL	1.03	.92	ACDL	.61	3757	3954	B				
	12.89	16.98	12.88		25.10		/DL		4.0	197					
N7623		14.17	12.36	CDL	1.04	.91	CDL	.55	3463	3661	B				
		9.48			11.40		/DL		2.4	198					
N7625	12.9	13.45	13.59	C	.73	.61	C		1784	2009	BC				
	13.23	1.28	13.37		1.88				2.8	225					
N7626	12.8	12.90	12.74	ACDL	1.00	.90	ACDL	.56	3357	3554	B				
	12.94	17.99	12.78		23.20		/DL		4.0	197					
N7631										197					
N7632										−25					
N7640	12.5	11.75	15.29	CG	.56*	.31	CG		423	692	C				BP
	11.54	3.43	15.08		4.38				5.2	269					
N7671		13.89	13.13	C	.92	.78	C		4129	4336	C				
		1.98			1.88				1.2	207					
N7672										207					
N7678	12.9	12.68	13.67	C	.71	.56	C		3446	3680	B				
	12.93	1.89	13.92		3.75				2.4	234					
N7679	13.1	13.47	13.16	AC	.57	.43	C		5154	5330	BC				
	13.27	4.73	12.96		1.88				11.9	176					
N7682		14.32	14.36	C	.97		C			176					
		3.25			3.75					176					
N7685										177					
N7689	12.3									−82					G
	12.40		13.94												
N7690	13.0									−72					
	13.00		13.84												
N7702	13.1									−92					GP
	12.98		13.52						6486	6394	M				
									*						
N7713	11.8									−9					
	11.92		13.91												
N7713A										−8					
N7714									2833	3000	C				
									3.4	167					
N7715									2795	2962	C				
									2.2	167					
N7716	13.0	13.28	13.77	ACH	.75*	.64	CH		2546	2706	B				
	13.17	7.05	13.66		8.13				.4	160					
N7721	12.4									132					
	12.34		14.03												
N7723	12.1	12.07	13.76	AC	.70	.57	AC		1973	2077	C				
	12.13	4.62	13.82		10.00				6.3	104					
N7727	12.0	11.66	13.95	AC	.86*	.75	AC		1846	1953	BC				
	11.75	4.36	14.04		10.00				13.8	107					
N7741	12.6	12.26	14.50	CGH	.65*	.53	CGH		729	964	B				LP
	12.24	5.61	14.48		14.38				4.0	235					
N7742	12.7	12.37	12.91	C	.72	.63	C		1678	1870	BC				
	12.98	3.43	13.52		3.75				10.6	192					
N7743	12.8	12.50	13.99	AC	.99	.90	C		1802	1992	B				P
	12.46	4.79	13.95		1.88				2.4	190					
N7744	12.8									−36					
	12.89		13.13												
N7752									4868	5108	D				
									.9	240					
N7753									4845	5085	D				
									2.8	240					
N7755	12.5									20					
	12.11		14.40												
N7757										167					
N7764	12.8									−29					
	12.97		13.16												
N7764A										−30					G
N7769	12.9			C*	.71*	.57	C		4349	4565	C				
	13.04		13.68		3.75				1.7	216					
N7770		14.52	13.71	C	.60	.46	C		4338	4554	C				
		2.01			1.88				1.6	216					
N7771		13.39	13.83	C	.85	.64	C		4282	4498	CD				
		1.50			1.88				3.3	216					

135

NGC (IC, A)	Coordinates					Classification			Diameters			
	RA (1950) Dec 100 P	100 P	L^I B^I	L^{II} B^{II}	SGL SGB	Rev. type (S) DDO (T,L)	Yerkes (1) Yerkes (2)	Hu-San Ho	log D w	log R w	log D(0)	S (D,R)
(1)	(2)	(3)	(4)	(5)	(6)	(7)	(8)	(9)	(10)	(11)	(12)	(13)
N7779	23 50.9	7 35	68.62	99.02	300.8	.S....*			1.14	.10	1.10	AL
	5.1	33	−52.54	−52.29	16.9				1.32	.69		
N7782	23 51.4	7 42	68.87	99.27	300.9	.SAS3..W060			1.38	.28	1.26	AKLQ
	5.1	33	−52.48	−52.23	16.8	S 3 N			5.47	5.47		
N7785	23 52.8	5 38	68.30	98.55	298.9	.E.5+..W100	D K		1.16	.27	1.05	AKNW
	5.1	33	−54.55	−54.28	15.9	E 5*			4.83	4.83		
N7793	23 55.3	−32 51	330.33	4.58	262.0	.SAS8..W100	SI *AF		1.92	.16	1.85	EFGMPIW
	5.2	33	−78.61	−77.19	3.1				16.62	16.62		
N7796	23 56.5	−55 44	283.23	317.87	240.7	.E.2...S030			1.11	.07	1.09	I
	5.2	33	−60.80	−60.13	−5.2				.94	.94		
N7814	0 0.7	15 51	75.61	106.41	309.7	.SAS2*.P200	SDP*K		1.73	.46	1.55	AHKLMZ
	5.1	33	−45.26	−45.19	16.4	S 2			12.88	12.88		
N7817	0 1.4	20 28	77.20	108.22	314.5	.SA.4..L036			1.55	.60	1.31	AHL
	5.1	33	−40.79	−40.77	17.1				2.63	2.63		
NGC (IC, A)	RA (1950) Dec 100 P	100 P	L^I B^I	L^{II} B^{II}	SGL SGB	Rev. type (S) DDO (T,L)	Yerkes (1) Yerkes (2)	Hu-San Ho	log D w	log R w	log D(0)	S (D,R)

NGC (IC, A)	m_H m_c	B(O) w	B'(O) m'_c	S(B)	(B-V)(O) w	C_o(O)	S(C)	(U-B)(O) w	V w	V_o ΔV	S(V)	ϕ_r n	ϕ(21)		Photo.
(14)	(15)	(16)	(17)	(18)	(19)	(20)	(21)	(22)	(23)	(24)	(25)	(26)	(27)	(28)	(29)
N7779										177					
N7782	13.1	13.33	14.37	A						177					
	12.97	2.63	14.01												
N7785	12.9	13.22	13.16	AC	1.04	.93	C		3846	4015	B				
	12.97	4.70	12.91		1.88				2.4	169					
N7793	9.7	10.43	14.42	AC	.72	.65	AC		192	197	BC				FL
	9.93	1.42	13.92		6.25				1.8	6					
N7796	12.9								3511	3413	M				
	12.90		13.04						1.0	−98					
N7814	12.4	11.71	14.20	AC	.97*	.78	AC		1047	1245	B				AB
	11.90	4.48	14.39		1.88				4.0	198					
N7817										210					B

NGC (IC, A)	RA (1950) 100 P	Dec 100 P	L^I B^I	L^{II} B^{II}	SGL SGB	Rev. type (S) DDO (T, L)	Yerkes (1) Yerkes (2)	Hu-San Ho	log D w	log R w	log D(0)	S (D,R)
(1)	(2)	(3)	(4)	(5)	(6)	(7)	(8)	(9)	(10)	(11)	(12)	(13)
I0010	0 17.6 5.4	59 2 33	86.74 -3.09	118.96 -3.32	355.1 17.9	.IB.9.$P200			1.60 1.09	.15 1.09	1.54	L
I0079	1 6.4 4.9	-16 13 32	116.89 -77.23	143.72 -78.12	282.6 -7.5	.E.1..*						
I0127	1 27.3 5.0	-7 14 31	119.42 -66.92	149.00 -67.88	292.7 -10.2	.L...$/H030			1.36 1.49	.63 1.49	1.10	F
I0167	1 48.3 5.5	21 38 30	109.52 -38.14	140.81 -38.91	322.1 -6.6	.S.....			1.60 1.09			L
I0239	2 33.5 6.2	38 45 26	112.48 -18.64	144.36 -19.49	341.9 -8.7	.SXT6..P200		S5	1.62 6.21	.03 6.21	1.61	HXZ
I0342	3 41.9 9.7	67 57 19	105.61 11.28	138.16 10.58	11.3 0.4	.SXT6..P200						
I0343	3 37.9 4.5	-18 36 19	176.84 -48.88	209.42 -50.34	286.4 -43.5	.SB..*.H030			1.10 1.05			F
I0346	3 39.5 4.5	-18 25 19	176.79 -48.46	209.37 -49.92	286.7 -43.9	.S...*/H030			1.36 1.49	.48 1.49	1.16	F
I0356	4 2.5 10.4	69 41 16	105.84 13.82	138.45 13.11	13.8 0.4							
I0391	4 49.8 15.2	78 6 10	101.22 21.66	134.05 21.06	21.3 5.3	.SAS5..L036			1.04 1.19	.04 1.19	1.02	M
I0398	4 55.8 4.8	-7 49 9	174.36 -27.18	206.76 -28.66	309.3 -60.4	.SBS5.$W100			1.09 1.94	.44 1.94	.91	FW
I0449	6 40.0 11.6	71 25 -5	110.70 25.98	143.59 25.16	26.4 -2.9							
I0451	6 46.6 13.0	74 34 -6	107.30 26.92	140.24 26.18	27.0 0.2							
I0467	7 19.3 17.0	80 1 -11	101.21 28.87	134.25 28.27	28.6 5.7	.SXS5*.W060			1.53 3.45	.38 3.45	1.38	MQ
I0469	7 42.5 30.0	85 23 -14	95.02 28.83	128.10 28.38	28.4 11.1	.S...*.W						
I0492	8 2.6 6.1	26 18 -17	163.45 28.56	195.81 27.07	49.7 -44.8	.SBR..$L036						
I0511	8 35.6 11.0	73 41 -21	107.38 34.36	140.54 33.61	34.4 0.9	.L....$W060			1.22 .82	.48 .82	1.03	Q
I0520	8 48.4 10.8	73 41 -22	106.99 35.20	140.19 34.46	35.2 1.3	.SXT2.$W060	SD GK		1.19 .78	.05 .78	1.17	Q
I0529	9 13.4 10.3	73 57 -25	105.75 36.65	139.01 35.94	36.6 2.4			S5				
I0562	9 43.5 5.0	-3 44 -27	208.82 36.67	240.41 35.54	106.1 -46.4	.S.....R020			1.23 .97	.46 .97	1.05	H
I0610	10 23.6 5.5	20 29 -30	185.13 57.60	216.76 56.18	84.1 -26.9	.S.....R020			1.32 1.11	.60 1.11	1.08	H
I0694	11 26.0 5.7	58 49 -33	107.69 56.21	141.87 55.45	56.2 2.7	*T	IPA*					
I0749	11 56.0 5.2	43 1 -33	118.48 72.06	154.07 71.05	72.6 0.7	.S...*.	S 5 K - 5*		1.33 1.27	.18 1.27	1.26	K
I0750	11 56.3 5.2	43 0 -33	118.36 72.10	153.97 71.10	72.6 0.7	.S 2 N *	I P*		1.31 1.23	.36 1.23	1.16	K
I0751	11 56.3 5.2	42 51 -33	118.65 72.22	154.26 71.22	72.7 0.6							
I0757	12 0.9 5.1	62 56 -33	97.99 54.14	132.19 53.60	54.0 8.2							
I0764	12 7.6 5.2	-29 28 -33	260.97 32.20	292.34 32.28	144.0 -17.3	.SAS5.$W100			1.62 6.93	.39 6.93	1.46	DEW
I0773	12 15.4 5.1	6 25 -33	251.94 67.75	280.66 67.55	108.7 -7.2	.L...*.L036			1.08 1.26	.32 1.26	.95	N
I0775	12 16.3 5.1	13 10 -33	245.89 74.21	273.16 73.85	102.2 -5.0				.88 .10	.00 .10	.88	H
I0783	12 19.2 5.1	16 0 -33	244.07 77.10	270.26 76.68	99.7 -3.5	.L....*W						
I0783A	12 19.9 5.1	15 59 -33	244.80 77.15	270.93 76.74	99.8 -3.3	.L....*W						
I0794	12 25.6 5.1	12 22 -33	254.72 74.14	281.83 74.00	103.7 -3.1							
I0800	12 31.4 5.0	15 38 -33	257.42 77.64	282.97 77.55	100.9 -.8	.SBS6*.L036			1.16 2.61	.17 2.61	1.09	CHN
I0844	13 0.5 5.5	-30 15 -32	274.53 31.86	305.94 32.28	147.1 -6.2	.L..../W100			1.10 1.51	.54 1.51	.88	W
I0982	14 7.6 4.7	17 55 -28	337.85 68.11	9.48 69.58	104.1 22.1	.LA....L036			1.08 .63	.08 .63	1.04	N
I0983	14 7.7 4.7	17 57 -28	337.96 68.11	9.60 69.57	104.0 22.2	.SBR2..L036			1.62 1.26	.05 1.26	1.60	N
I1029	14 30.7 3.5	50 8 -26	54.77 59.59	89.45 60.13	68.6 27.6	.S...*.W			1.60 1.09	.71 1.09	1.32	L
I1067	14 50.5 5.0	3 32 -24	327.28 51.06	358.91 52.45	122.2 29.3	.SBS3..W060			1.41 1.03	.04 1.03	1.39	Q
I1091	15 5.6 5.4	-10 57 -23	316.77 38.07	348.45 39.34	139.2 27.8	.SBS3.$W100			.95 1.53	.25 1.53	.85	FW
I1099	15 5.8 2.7	56 41 -23	58.82 51.53	92.91 51.99	59.8 31.0							

NGC (IC, A)	m_H / m_c	B(O) w	B'(O) m'_c	S (B)	(B-V)(O) w	C_0(O)	S (C)	(U-B)(O) w	V w	V_0 ΔV	S (V)	ϕ_r n	ϕ (21)		Photo.
	(15)	(16)	(17)	(18)	(19)	(20)	(21)	(22)	(23)	(24)	(25)	(26)	(27)	(28)	(29)
I0010		13.33 1.58	15.77	C	.92* 1.88		C		−347 204.1	−92 255	RB*				
I0079									12567 1.6	12598 31	C				
I0127										51					
I0167										137					
I0239		12.14 1.25	14.88	G	.72 2.50		G			153					
I0342				AC*			AC*		52 426.7	239 187	BCR				
I0343										−104					
I0346										−105					
I0356				A*			A*			184					
I0391		13.28 1.05	13.12	C	.33 1.88	.16	C		1607 .7	1800 193	C				
I0398										−131					
I0449										152					
I0451										164					
I0467										182					
I0469										201					
I0492										−81					
I0511										151					
I0520	12.8 13.01		13.55							151					
I0529				G*						152					
I0562										−216					
I0610										−104					
I0694										101					
I0749	13.2 13.24		14.23							41					
I0750	13.0									41					
I0751										41					
I0757										129					
I0764	12.9 12.44		14.48							−228					
I0773										−109					
I0775				H*	1.00 6.25		H			−80					
I0783				B*			B*			−66					
I0783A				B*			B*			−66					
I0794				H*						−77					
I0800										−59					
I0844										−197					
I0982										25					
I0983										25					
I1029										152					B
I1067										7					
I1091										−34					
I1099										186					

NGC (IC, A) (1)	RA (1950) 100 P (2)	Dec 100 P (3)	L^I B^I (4)	L^{II} B^{II} (5)	SGL SGB (6)	Rev. type (S) DDO (T,L) (7)	Yerkes (1) Yerkes (2) (8)	Hu-San Ho (9)	log D w (10)	log R w (11)	log D(0) (12)	S (D,R) (13)
I1131	15 36.5	12 15	348.03	20.34	115.0	.L...*.L036						
	4.7	-19	46.56	48.04	42.4							
I1173	16 2.9	17 32	358.56	31.14	108.5							
	4.5	-16	42.95	44.41	49.4							
I1181A	16 3.3	17 42	358.82	31.40	108.3							
	4.5	-16	42.92	44.38	49.5							
I1181B	16 3.3	17 42	358.82	31.40	108.3							
	4.5	-16	42.92	44.38	49.5							
I1182	16 3.3	17 56	359.10	31.69	108.0	.P....*						
	4.5	-16	43.02	44.47	49.5							
I1183	16 3.3	17 54	359.06	31.64	108.0	.E.1...W						
	4.5	-16	43.00	44.46	49.5							
I1185	16 3.4	17 51	359.01	31.59	108.1	.S..1..W						
	4.5	-16	42.96	44.42	49.5							
I1186	16 3.5	17 28	358.55	31.12	108.7							
	4.5	-16	42.79	44.25	49.5							
I1194	16 4.3	17 55	359.20	31.79	108.0	.E.1...W						
	4.5	-16	42.79	44.24	49.7							
I1237	16 55.2	55 8	49.86	83.19	50.6	.SB.5*.W						
	2.1	-9	37.59	38.27	44.5							
I1248	17 10.7	59 56	55.60	88.88	44.3							
	1.4	-7	35.13	35.68	42.0							
I1302	19 29.0	35 39	36.59	69.05	7.1	.S..3..W						
	3.6	13	7.24	8.22	68.4							
I1303	19 29.5	35 45	36.73	69.18	6.9	.SA.5*.W100			1.07	.16	1.01	W
	3.6	13	7.20	8.17	68.3				2.03	2.03		
I1308	19 42.3	-14 51	353.18	25.43	229.9							
	5.7	14	-19.89	-18.41	57.1							
I1317	20 20.7	0 30	12.41	44.48	264.6	.LB....W						
	5.1	19	-21.34	-19.99	63.5							
I1417	21 57.7	-13 23	11.90	43.52	267.5	.S...*.W100			1.14	.63	.89	FHW
	5.4	29	-49.09	-47.73	35.8				2.48	2.48		
I1459	22 54.5	-36 41	331.60	4.75	253.1	.E.3+..R074						
	5.6	32	-65.58	-64.14	12.7							
I1460	22 54.5	4 25	46.72	77.61	293.6	.L.....W						
	5.1	32	-48.64	-47.86	29.6							
I1530	0 4.8	32 19	80.82	112.29	326.9	.S....*R020			1.34	.44	1.17	H
	5.2	33	-29.28	-29.35	18.3				1.15	1.15		
I1554	0 30.7	-32 32	297.08	339.55	264.7	.L....*.H030						
	4.9	33	-84.56	-83.52	-3.8							
I1559	0 34.3	23 43	87.56	118.68	319.4	.E.....L036						
	5.3	33	-38.52	-38.76	10.3							
I1563	0 36.6	-9 17	85.39	113.24	287.4	.I..9..L036						
	5.1	33	-71.51	-71.65	1.3							
I1613	1 2.5	1 52	100.00	129.87	299.9	.I..9..L036		I 9	2.05	.07	2.02	MX
	5.1	32	-60.02	-60.55	-1.8			I9	2.09	2.09		
I1727	1 44.7	27 5	106.53	137.96	327.0	.SBS9..P200			1.73	.32	1.60	HMSXZ
	5.6	30	-33.19	-33.90	-4.0			I9	12.65	10.47		
I1731	1 47.4	26 57	107.27	138.71	327.1	.S....*R020			1.15	.16	1.09	H
	5.6	30	-33.14	-33.86	-4.6				.85	.85		
I1738	1 48.7	-10 2	134.51	164.85	291.2	.SXR3..W060						
	4.9	30	-66.43	-67.66	-16.0							
I1783	2 7.8	-33 13	201.84	236.71	267.5							
	4.4	28	-70.85	-72.06	-24.0							
I1784	2 13.2	32 24	111.21	142.89	334.3							
	5.9	28	-26.12	-26.94	-7.8							
I1788	2 13.4	-31 26	196.09	230.47	269.6			S4				
	4.4	28	-69.92	-71.21	-25.1							
I1830	2 37.0	-27 39	186.56	219.94	274.2							
	4.4	26	-64.71	-66.11	-30.0							
I1856	2 46.2	-0 56	143.13	174.66	304.7							
	5.1	25	-50.06	-51.41	-27.5							
I1913	3 17.5	-32 39	198.02	231.50	267.9							
	4.0	22	-56.32	-57.60	-38.6							
I1933	3 24.3	-52 57	231.54	265.52	242.8	.SA.6*.S030			1.37	.23	1.28	I
	2.8	21	-51.00	-51.63	-34.9				1.35	1.35		
I1953	3 31.4	-21 39	180.53	213.26	282.2	.SBT7..W060			1.39	.07	1.36	DEFKQ
	4.4	20	-51.33	-52.78	-42.1	S 5 K 4*	SX F		7.49	6.00		
I1954	3 30.2	-52 5	229.72	263.65	243.4	.SBS3*.S030			1.49	.32	1.36	DEI
	2.9	20	-50.51	-51.18	-36.0				3.83	3.83		
I1970	3 34.8	-44 7	217.14	250.93	252.5	.S...*/S030			1.42	.80	1.10	I
	3.4	20	-52.00	-52.95	-39.6				1.44	1.44		
I2006	3 52.2	-36 8	204.18	237.54	261.5	.E.1...S030			1.11	.05	1.09	EI
	3.7	18	-49.28	-50.47	-45.0				1.65	1.65		
I2033	4 6.1	-53 48	229.67	263.30	238.2	.L....$S030						•
	2.4	16	-44.84	-45.52	-40.0							
I2035	4 7.6	-45 38	218.14	251.66	247.6	.L...*.S030						
	3.1	16	-46.03	-46.96	-44.3							
I2038	4 7.7	-56 7	232.71	266.34	235.6	.S....*.S030			1.16	.38	1.01	I
	2.2	16	-44.00	-44.62	-38.9				.72	.72		

140

NGC (IC, A) (14)	Magnitudes				Colors				Velocities			Radio			
	m_H / m_C (15)	B(O) w (16)	B'(O) m'_C (17)	S(B) (18)	(B-V)(O) w (19)	C_o(O) (20)	S(C) (21)	(U-B)(O) w (22)	V w (23)	V_o ΔV (24)	S(V) (25)	ϕ_r n (26)	ϕ (21) (27)	(28)	Photo. (29)
I1131										81					
I1173									10840 / 1.0	10962 / 121	F				
I1181A									10324 / 1.0	10446 / 122	F				
I1181B									10690 / 1.0	10812 / 122	F				
I1182									10245 / 1.0	10368 / 123	F				
I1183				BC*			C*		10038 / 1.8	10161 / 123	B				
I1185				C*			C*		10452 / .3	10575 / 123	B				
I1186									11012 / 1.0	11134 / 122	F				
I1194				C*			C*		11642 / 2.4	11766 / 124	B				
I1237										237					
I1248										245					
I1302				C*			C*		4575 / 4.0	4857 / 282	B				
I1303		15.40 / 2.16	15.14	A	.88 / 4.38		A			283					
I1308				C*			C*		-30 / 11.1	103 / 133	B				
I1317				C*			C*		3975 / 1.7	4181 / 206	C				
I1417										143					
I1459	11.3			M*			M* /M	*	1618 / 30.3	1632 / 14	LM				
I1460				C*			C*		7262 / 1.8	7458 / 196	B				
I1530										236					
I1554										-13					
I1559										198					
I1563										82					
I1613	10.4 / 9.83	11.02 / 1.79	15.81 / 14.62	CG	.60 / 4.38	.54	CG		-236 / 1211	-129 / 106	BR				LP
I1727		12.57 / 3.16	15.31	CG	.56 / 4.38	.44	CG		362 / 4.0	518 / 156	B				
I1731										154					
I1738										22					
I1783	13.1									-82					
I1784				G*	.91* / 2.50		G			150					
I1788	13.2									-80					
I1830									1474 / 2.7	1389 / -85	D				
I1856										6					
I1913										-133					
I1933	13.2 / 13.09		14.18							-188					
I1953	12.5 / 12.57		14.11							-109					
I1954	12.2 / 12.25		13.79							-190					F
I1970										-176					
I2006	12.8 / 12.84		12.98							-168					
I2033										-212					
I2035	12.6									-199					
I2038										-216					

NGC (IC, A) (1)	RA (1950) 100 P (2)	Dec 100 P (3)	L^I B^I (4)	L^II B^II (5)	SGL SGB (6)	Rev. type (S) DDO (T, L) (7)	Yerkes (1) Yerkes (2) (8)	Hu-San Ho (9)	log D w (10)	log R w (11)	log D(O) (12)	S (D,R) (13)
I2056	4 15.6 1.6	-60 20 15	237.80 -41.77	271.37 -42.26	230.6 -37.1	RLB.-P*S030			1.08 1.48	.07 1.48	1.05	EI
I2058	4 16.8 2.1	-56 3 14	232.17 -42.80	265.74 -43.42	234.7 -39.9	.S..7$/B060			1.48 3.35	.94 3.35	1.10	PI
I2082	4 28.0 2.3	-53 56 13	228.94 -41.65	262.42 -42.35	235.5 -42.5							
I2085	4 30.3 2.2	-54 32 13	229.65 -41.22	263.12 -41.90	234.6 -42.4	.S...*/S030			1.43 .32	.78 .32	1.12	I
I2163	6 14.4 4.3	-21 21 -2	196.19 -15.67	228.70 -16.97	263.8 -79.3	.SBT5P.W100 S T			1.43 4.01	.38 4.01	1.27	KPW
I2174	7 2.5 13.4	75 26 -9	106.43 28.02	139.41 27.30	28.0 1.1	RLB....L036			1.11 .66	.03 .66	1.10	M
I2179	7 10.8 9.7	65 3 -10	118.21 27.90	151.10 26.93	29.3 -9.2	.E.1+..W060			.90 .98	.14 .98	.84	M
I2200	7 27.0 1.2	-62 14 -12	240.99 -19.32	273.80 -19.74	201.9 -43.0	.S...*.S030			1.15 .99	.27 .99	1.04	I
I2200A	7 27.4 1.2	-62 10 -12	240.91 -19.32	273.72 -19.74	201.9 -43.1	.E....$S030			1.00 .62	.13 .62	.95	I
I2209	7 52.0 8.6	60 27 -16	123.80 32.36	156.74 31.28	34.9 -13.0	.SBT3*.W060			1.04 .64	.05 .64	1.02	Q
I2233	8 10.4 7.1	45 54 -18	141.38 34.38	174.11 33.05	42.3 -26.0	.L..../L036		S.	1.67 6.14	1.08 4.73	1.24	HLRX
I2363	8 22.9 5.8	19 37 -19	172.51 30.67	204.74 29.19	60.3 -48.4	.S..5.*W						
I2389	8 42.6 10.9	73 44 -21	107.12 34.80	140.30 34.06	34.8 1.1	.SBS..$W060			1.24 .83	.50 .83	1.04	Q
I2421	8 51.3 6.2	32 53 -22	158.96 40.45	191.45 38.98	57.4 -33.8	.S....*R020			1.38 .60	.00 .60	1.38	H
I2487	9 27.3 5.6	20 18 -26	178.34 45.12	210.37 43.65	75.2 -37.7	.S....*			1.35 .80			L
I2522	9 53.1 4.4	-32 54 -28	233.63 17.26	265.52 16.65	148.8 -45.8	.S.....			1.32 2.82	.01 2.82	1.31	FΓ
I2523	9 53.1 4.4	-32 59 -28	233.69 17.19	265.58 16.58	149.0 -45.8	.SB....			1.10 1.05	.18 1.05	1.03	T
I2537	10 1.7 4.6	-27 19 -29	231.49 22.79	263.24 22.12	140.6 -44.8	.SXT5..W100 S 6 8			1.39 6.63	.17 6.63	1.32	KPW
I2554	10 7.5 2.7	-66 48 -29	255.49 -8.95	288.03 -9.01	187.5 -29.9	.SBS5P*S030			1.49 1.58	.37 1.58	1.34	I
I2574	10 25.0 7.4	68 43 -30	106.58 44.33	140.13 43.59	44.3 2.4	.SXS9..P200		I 9 I9	2.10 6.38	.39 6.38	1.94	LXZ
I2584	10 27.6 4.5	-34 39 -30	240.88 19.95	272.67 19.51	149.5 -38.5	.L....*/S030			1.50 1.59	.37 1.59	1.35	I
I2587	10 28.7 4.5	-34 18 -30	240.89 20.37	272.67 19.93	149.1 -38.3	.LB.-*.S030			1.19 .22	.05 .22	1.17	I
I2604	10 46.6 5.6	33 3 -31	160.71 64.55	193.36 63.07	75.4 -16.0	.I....*R020			1.08 .76	.05 .76	1.06	H
I2627	11 7.5 4.9	-23 28 -32	243.52 33.92	274.86 33.54	135.8 -29.9	.SAS4*.W060 S 4 3*	S F		1.41 5.31	.02 5.31	1.40	FKQ
I2943	11 34.0 5.5	55 7 -33	109.57 59.94	143.99 59.13	60.0 2.0							
I2995	12 3.0 5.1	-27 39 -33	259.42 33.82	290.72 33.85	142.0 -18.0	.SBS5*.W100			1.50 8.42	.45 8.42	1.32	DEFW
I3044	12 10.3 5.1	14 15 -33	239.28 74.59	266.63 74.06	100.8 -6.1	.S....*R020			1.29 .91	.30 .91	1.18	CH
I3061	12 12.5 5.1	14 18 -33	241.00 74.87	268.19 74.38	100.9 -5.5			S.	1.27 .89	.44 .89	1.10	CHX
I3115	12 15.4 5.1	6 56 -33	251.56 68.24	280.19 68.04	108.2 -7.0			S5	1.46 .51	.06 .51	1.44	CX
I3136	12 16.4 5.1	6 28 -33	252.54 67.86	281.23 67.68	108.7 -6.9	.S..5*.L036			1.19 1.82	.51 1.82	.99	CN
I3155	12 17.3 5.1	6 18 -33	253.23 67.76	281.93 67.60	108.9 -6.8	.L....*.L036			.92 1.46	.34 1.46	.78	BN
I3253	12 21.1 5.3	-34 21 -33	264.96 27.72	296.49 27.90	149.5 -15.2	.S.....H030			1.45 2.57	.35 2.57	1.31	EF
I3258	12 21.2 5.1	12 44 -33	250.56 74.21	277.72 73.96	103.0 -4.0	.SB.9*.L036			1.10 1.60	.00 1.60	1.11	CN
I3259	12 21.3 5.1	7 28 -33	255.08 69.13	283.50 69.01	108.1 -5.5	.LB..*.L036		S5	1.12 .97	.12 .97	1.08	CNX
I3267	12 21.6 5.1	7 19 -33	255.38 69.00	283.82 68.89	108.2 -5.5	PSB.0*.L036		S5	1.07 1.52	.03 1.52	1.05	CNX
I3290	12 22.5 5.3	-39 30 -33	265.77 22.61	297.46 22.82	154.8 -15.6	.L..-*.S030			1.11 .94	.40 .94	.95	I
I3303	12 22.8 5.1	13 0 -33	251.66 74.58	278.67 74.35	102.9 -3.5							
I3322	12 23.3 5.1	7 50 -33	256.22 69.60	284.54 69.51	107.9 -4.9	.S..5*/L036			1.38 2.32	.75 2.32	1.08	CN
I3322A	12 23.1 5.1	7 30 -33	256.28 69.26	284.67 69.18	108.2 -5.0	.S..7*/L036			1.57 2.36	.88 2.36	1.21	N
I3330	12 23.5 5.0	31 7 -33	139.40 84.66	177.72 83.31	85.6 2.0	.S...*.W						

Magnitudes — columns (15)–(18); Colors — columns (19)–(22); Velocities — columns (23)–(25); Radio — columns (26)–(27)

NGC (IC, A) (14)	m_H / m_C (15)	B(O) / w (16)	$B'(O)$ / m'_C (17)	S(B) (18)	(B-V)(O) / w (19)	$C_o(O)$ (20)	S(C) (21)	(U-B)(O) / w (22)	V / w (23)	V_o / ΔV (24)	S(V) (25)	ϕ_r / n (26)	ϕ (21) (27)	(28)	Photo. (29)
I2056	12.3 / 12.66		12.60							−223					
I2058										−220					
I2082										−223					
I2085										−225					
I2163										−225					
I2174										165					
I2179										119					
I2200										−282					
I2200A										−282					
I2209										91					
I2233		13.45 / 1.00	14.39	G	.51 / 2.50		G			16					
I2363										−119					
I2389		14.06 / 2.03	14.00	C*	.67 / 1.88	.47	C*		2632 / 2.2	2783 / 151	C				
I2421										−55					
I2487										−116					
I2522	12.9 / 12.94		14.23							−286					
I2523										−287					
I2537	12.8 / 12.74		14.03							−276					
I2554										−278					
I2574		11.20 / 1.39	15.64	G	.46 / 2.50	.36	G		46 / 108.2	179 / 133	CR				P
I2584										−281					
I2587										−280					
I2604										−35					
I2627	12.8 / 12.53		14.22							−246					
I2943										87					
I2995	12.7 / 12.68		13.97							−227					
I3044										−80					
I3061				G*	.78 / 2.50		G			−78					
I3115		13.81 / 1.55	15.70	G	.70 / 2.50		G			−107					
I3136										−108					
I3155										−108					
I3253	12.3 / 12.56		13.80							−230					
I3258				H*						−79					
I3259		14.69 / 0.95	14.78	G	.76 / 2.50		G			−100					
I3267		14.71 / 0.84	14.70	G	.78 / 2.50		G			−101					
I3290										−238					
I3303				H*						−76					
I3322										−97					
I3322A										−99					
I3330										3					

NGC (IC, A) (1)	RA (1950) Dec 100 P 100 P (2) (3)	L^I B^I (4)	L^II B^II (5)	SGL SGB (6)	Rev. type (S) DDO (T, L) (7)	Yerkes (1) Yerkes (2) (8)	Hu-San Ho (9)	log D w (10)	log R w (11)	log D(0) (12)	S (D,R) (13)
I3370	12 25.0 -39 4	266.26	297.93	154.5	.E.2+..S030			1.20	.08	1.17	I
	5.3 -33	23.08	23.30	-15.1				1.07	1.07		
I3381	12 25.8 12 0	255.20	282.42	104.0							
	5.1 -33	73.80	73.67	-3.1							
I3392	12 26.1 15 16	252.17	278.17	100.9	.S....*R020			1.34	.32	1.21	CH
	5.1 -33	76.98	76.75	-2.1				1.56	1.56		
I3393	12 26.3 13 11	254.60	281.42	102.9							
	5.1 -33	74.98	74.83	-2.7							
I3418	12 27.2 11 41	256.63	283.92	104.4	.E.....						
	5.1 -33	73.56	73.47	-2.9							
I3442	12 29.4 14 23	256.46	282.70	102.0	.S....*R020			1.15	.00	1.15	H
	5.0 -33	76.32	76.21	-1.6				.43	.43		
I3457	12 29.4 12 56	257.65	284.46	103.4							
	5.1 -33	74.90	74.82	-2.0							
I3474	12 30.1 2 56	262.62	291.72	113.1	.S..5*/R020			1.40	.68	1.13	H
	5.1 -33	65.03	65.12	-4.7				1.24	1.24		
I3475	12 30.2 13 3	258.30	285.05	103.3	.E.....						
	5.1 -33	75.05	74.99	-1.8							
I3476	12 30.2 14 19	257.32	283.56	102.1	.S..9*.W			1.20	.13	1.15	HL
	5.0 -33	76.29	76.20	-1.4				1.12	.49		
I3478	12 30.3 14 28	257.29	283.45	102.0	.S....*			1.10	.03	1.09	HL
	5.0 -33	76.45	76.36	-1.4				1.35	1.35		
I3481	12 30.3 11 40	259.28	286.50	104.7	.E.3...W						
	5.1 -33	73.69	73.67	-2.2							
I3481A	12 30.5 11 40	259.45	286.67	104.7	.L.....W						
	5.1 -33	73.70	73.68	-2.1							
I3483	12 30.6 11 37	259.57	286.80	104.7	.S..5P.W						
	5.1 -33	73.66	73.64	-2.1							
I3522	12 32.1 15 28	258.33	283.95	101.1				1.15	.37	1.00	HN
	5.0 -33	77.51	77.44	-.7				1.54	1.54		
I3528	12 32.3 15 49	258.25	283.67	100.8	.SXR3..W100			.69	.00	.69	W
	5.0 -33	77.86	77.79	-.5				1.25	1.25		
I3546	12 33.3 26 29	210.72	226.72	90.6	.S....*R020			1.21	.38	1.05	H
	5.0 -33	87.62	86.39	2.7				.18	.18		
I3547	12 33.3 26 36	208.55	225.01	90.5	.E....$R020			1.12	.30	.99	H
	5.0 -33	87.70	86.44	2.8				.81	.81		
I3583	12 34.2 13 32	261.81	288.28	103.1	.IB.9..P200			1.28	.30	1.16	HZ
	5.0 -33	75.68	75.71	-.7				4.06	4.06		
I3598	12 34.9 28 28	155.38	193.18	88.8	.L....*R020			1.23	.51	1.03	H
	4.9 -33	88.18	86.71	3.6				.97	.97		
I3720	12 42.2 12 21	269.71	296.63	104.8	.E.....						
	5.0 -32	74.62	74.87	0.8							
I3804	12 46.4 35 36	84.11	126.70	82.5				1.50	.30	1.38	C
	4.8 -32	82.08	81.78	7.8				.54	.54		
I3806	12 46.6 15 10	274.53	300.27	102.4	.S....$R020			1.23	.41	1.07	H
	5.0 -32	77.40	77.75	2.6				.97	.97		
I3896	12 53.7 -50 3	271.79	303.77	166.4	.E.1...S030			1.09	.04	1.07	I
	5.7 -32	12.18	12.54	-11.8				.89	.89		
I3896A	12 52.6 -49 49	271.62	303.59	166.2	.SB.7*.S030			1.08	.13	1.03	I
	5.7 -32	12.42	12.78	-11.9				.89	.89		
I3900	12 53.2 27 32	356.03	41.58	90.8	.L.....W						
	4.9 -32	87.61	89.05	7.3							
I3917	12 54.4 22 16	297.00	316.75	96.0	.S....$R020			1.13	.40	.97	H
	4.9 -32	83.91	84.73	6.2				.42	.42		
I3946	12 56.4 28 5	7.36	56.07	90.4	.L.....W						
	4.8 -32	86.90	88.23	8.1							
I3949	12 56.6 28 7	7.95	56.57	90.4	.L.....						
	4.8 -32	86.85	88.17	8.1							
I3960A	12 56.7 28 8	8.20	56.79	90.4	.E.0...W						
	4.8 -32	86.82	88.14	8.2							
I4011	12 57.7 28 16	10.01	57.80	90.3							
	4.8 -32	86.59	87.88	8.4							
I4012	12 57.7 28 21	11.34	59.79	90.2	.E.0...W						
	4.8 -32	86.58	87.86	8.4							
I4021	12 57.8 28 19	10.73	58.73	90.3	.E.0...W						
	4.8 -32	86.56	87.85	8.4							
I4040	12 58.2 28 20	10.82	58.22	90.3	.S...P*						
	4.8 -32	86.47	87.76	8.5							
I4045	12 58.4 28 21	10.93	58.11	90.3	.E.2...W						
	4.8 -32	86.43	87.72	8.6							
I4051	12 58.4 28 17	9.87	56.56	90.3	.E.1...W						
	4.8 -32	86.44	87.74	8.5							
I4182	13 3.5 37 52	67.77	107.69	81.0	.S..9..W						
	4.6 -32	78.94	79.10	11.6							
I4209	13 8.0 -6 54	280.99	311.32	125.1	.S...*/H030			1.18			F
	5.2 -31	54.83	55.39	1.8				.78			
I4237	13 21.8 -20 53	282.05	313.18	139.5	.SBR3$.W100			1.21	.12	1.16	FW
	5.4 -31	40.47	41.07	1.0				2.30	2.30		
I4263	13 26.5 47 10	68.97	105.08	72.1	.S....*R020			1.38	.61	1.14	H
	4.2 -31	68.73	68.91	17.1				1.21	1.21		

NGC (IC, A) (14)	m_H / m_C (15)	B(O) w (16)	B'(O) m'_C (17)	S(B) (18)	(B-V)(O) w (19)	C_O(O) (20)	S(C) (21)	(U-B)(O) w (22)	V w (23)	V_O / ΔV (24)	S(V) (25)	φ_r n (26)	φ (21) (27)	(28)	Photo. (29)
I3370	12.4 12.44		12.98							−236					
I3381				H*						−79					
I3392										−65					
I3393				H*						−73					
I3418										−79					
I3442										−66					
I3457				H*						−72					
I3474										−112					
I3475		14.94 2.78		E*	.65* 12.50		E* /E	.13		−71					
I3476		13.68 4.52	14.12	H	.44 6.25		H			−66					
I3478										−65					
I3481									7086 1.6	7009 −77	B				
I3481A									7304 2.4	7228 −77	B				
I3483									108 6.3	31 −77	B				
I3522										−60					
I3528										−58					
I3546										−11					
I3547										−11					
I3583										−66					
I3598										−2					
I3720										−65					
I3804										36					
I3806										−50					
I3896	13.0 12.99	13.06 1.79	13.15 13.08	M	1.03		M /M	.90*		−235					
I3896A										−235					
I3900									7171 4.0	7178 6	B				
I3917										−15					
I3946				C*			C*		6101 1.8	6112 11	B				
I3949									7526 1.3	7537 11	C				
I3960A									6868 2.4	5879 11	B				
I4011				E*			E*			13					
I4012				C*			C*			13					
I4021				C*			C*		5789 1.8	5802 13	B				
I4040									7515 2.9	7528 13	C				
I4045				C*			C*		6527 .3	6541 13	B				
I4051				CD*			CD*		4932 .4	4945 13	B				
I4182										56					
I4209										−120					
I4237										−155					
I4263										106					

NGC (IC, A) (1)	RA (1950) 100 P (2)	Dec 100 P (3)	L^I B^I (4)	L^II B^II (5)	SGL SGB (6)	Rev. type (S) DDO (T, L) (7)	Yerkes (1) Yerkes (2) (8)	Hu-San Ho (9)	log D w (10)	log R w (11)	log D(O) (12)	S (D,R) (13)
I4278	13 28.3	47 29	68.64	104.67	71.8	.S.....R020			1.30	.53	1.09	H
	4.2	-30	68.31	68.50	17.4				1.08	1.08		
I4296	13 33.8	-33 43	281.95	313.54	152.5	.E.0.*.W						
	5.7	-30	27.36	27.97	-.4							
I4327	13 45.8	-29 59	285.84	317.36	149.8	.SAS5.$B060			1.09	.19	1.01	P
	5.7	-29	30.34	31.03	3.2				1.58	1.58		
I4329	13 46.2	-30 3	285.91	317.43	149.9	.L..-.$W100			1.30	.35	1.16	E
	5.7	-29	30.25	30.95	3.3				.85	.85		
I4351	13 54.9	-29 5	288.34	319.87	149.7	.SAS3*/W100			1.74	.77	1.43	DW
	5.7	-29	30.60	31.35	5.4				6.75	6.75		
I4444	14 28.5	-43 12	289.63	321.58	165.4	.SA.4*.S030			1.23	.07	1.21	DEI
	6.4	-26	15.01	15.79	5.8				2.99	2.99		
I4448	14 34.2	-78 36	275.51	308.25	197.0	.SBS9*.S030			1.05	.06	1.02	I
	12.0	-26	-17.55	-17.09	-10.5				.84	.84		
I4653	17 22.3	-60 52	298.20	330.79	196.4	.S.....						
	9.1	-5	-14.99	-14.03	11.4							
I4662	17 42.1	-64 39	295.83	328.51	199.9	.IB.9.B060			1.33	.22	1.24	DEPI
	9.8	-2	-18.77	-17.85	8.6				5.50	5.50		
I4662A	17 46.2	-64 58	295.72	328.42	200.4	.S...*.S030			1.16	.04	1.14	I
	9.9	-2	-19.30	-18.38	8.4				1.00	1.00		
I4710	18 23.5	-67 1	295.06	327.86	204.5	.SB.7*.S030			1.59	.15	1.53	DEI
	10.3	3	-23.56	-22.66	7.2				4.37	4.37		
I4713	18 24.7	-67 16	294.83	327.64	204.7	.SB.9$/S030			1.13	.53	.91	I
	10.4	4	-23.74	-22.84	6.9				.95	.95		
I4714	18 25.7	-66 42	295.46	328.26	204.7	.S....$S030			1.04	.15	.98	I
	10.3	4	-23.69	-22.77	7.5				.83	.83		
I4717	18 28.9	-58 0	304.60	337.28	204.1	.S...*/S030			1.15	.60	.91	I
	8.7	4	-21.52	-20.43	16.2				.21	.21		
I4719	18 29.0	-56 46	305.86	338.53	204.0	.S....*						
	8.5	4	-21.14	-20.03	17.4							
I4720	18 29.2	-58 26	304.17	336.86	204.2	.SB.5*$S030			1.31	.48	1.12	I
	8.7	4	-21.69	-20.61	15.8				1.25	1.25		
I4721	18 30.1	-58 32	304.10	336.80	204.4	.SBS6*.S030			1.58	.48	1.39	DEI
	8.7	4	-21.84	-20.75	15.7				4.22	4.22		
I4796	18 52.3	-54 17	309.46	342.15	207.3	.SA.0*$S030			1.08	.39	.92	I
	8.1	8	-23.58	-22.40	20.1				.63	.63		
I4797	18 52.3	-54 22	309.37	342.06	207.3	.E.5+..S030			1.20	.36	1.06	DEI
	8.1	8	-23.60	-22.43	20.0				3.04	3.04		
I4806	18 57.2	-57 36	306.11	338.86	208.0	.L...*.S030			1.42	.60	1.18	I
	8.5	8	-25.05	-23.93	16.8				1.43	1.43		
I4810	18 58.8	-56 14	307.64	340.37	208.3	.S....$						
	8.3	8	-24.95	-23.81	18.1							
I4820	19 4.5	-63 32	299.81	332.66	208.8	.S..5*.S030			1.25	.56	1.03	I
	9.4	9	-27.03	-26.02	10.8				.25	.25		
I4829	19 8.6	-56 38	307.52	340.28	209.7	.S...*.S030			1.15	.56	.92	I
	8.4	10	-26.36	-25.22	17.6				.99	.99		
I4832	19 9.8	-56 43	307.46	340.23	209.9	.S..5*.S030			1.30	.66	1.04	I
	8.4	10	-26.54	-25.40	17.6				1.23	1.23		
I4836	19 11.7	-60 17	303.56	336.38	209.8	.SBS6..S030			1.11	.02	1.10	I
	8.8	10	-27.38	-26.31	14.0				.93	.93		
I4837	19 11.3	-54 46	309.64	342.38	210.3	.SB.5*$S030			1.42	.32	1.29	DEI
	8.1	10	-26.37	-25.19	19.5				3.32	3.32		
I4837A	19 11.2	-54 13	310.24	342.97	210.3	.S...*/S030			1.59	.98	1.20	I
	8.1	10	-26.24	-25.06	20.0				1.29	1.29		
I4839	19 11.5	-54 43	309.70	342.44	210.3	.SBS3..S030			1.41	.28	1.29	I
	8.1	10	-26.39	-25.21	19.5				1.41	1.41		
I4840	19 11.7	-56 19	307.96	340.72	210.2	.S....*.S030			1.05	.23	.96	I
	8.3	10	-26.72	-25.57	17.9				.84	.84		
I4842	19 15.0	-60 44	303.13	335.96	210.2	.E.5.*.S030			1.13	.30	1.01	I
	8.9	11	-27.85	-26.78	13.5				.75	.75		
I4845	19 16.0	-60 31	303.39	336.22	210.4	.SBR..$S030			1.20	.03	1.19	I
	8.8	11	-27.94	-26.87	13.7				.76	.76		
I4852	19 22.0	-60 28	303.54	336.40	211.1	.SA.5*.S030			1.30	.15	1.24	I
	8.8	12	-28.67	-27.60	13.7				.88	.88		
I4889	19 41.3	-54 29	310.70	343.52	214.8	.E.5+..B060			1.17	.29	1.06	DEPI
	7.9	14	-30.62	-29.42	19.1				4.68	4.68		
I4892	19 44.1	-70 22	292.18	325.20	211.7	.S...$/S030			1.29	.57	1.06	I
	10.7	15	-31.15	-30.30	3.5				.60	.60		
I4943	20 2.9	-48 32	318.07	350.84	220.0	.E.0.*.S030			.90	.00	.90	I
	7.3	17	-33.38	-32.08	24.0				.65	.65		
I4960	20 10.1	-70 42	291.45	324.54	213.7	.L...*/S030			1.11	.54	.89	I
	10.5	18	-33.25	-32.42	2.6				.39	.39		
I4970	20 11.7	-70 55	291.17	324.26	213.8	.LA.-*.R074			.69	.39	.53	IO
	10.5	18	-33.34	-32.51	2.4				1.17	1.17		
I4972	20 12.5	-71 4	290.97	324.07	213.8	.S..4$/R074			.96	.65	.70	IO
	10.6	18	-33.37	-32.55	2.2				2.21	2.21		
I4981	20 14.5	-71 0	291.01	324.12	214.0	.I...P/R074			.93	.59	.69	IO
	10.5	18	-33.54	-32.72	2.2				1.69	1.69		
I5000	20 19.9	6 17	17.57	49.63	276.2	.SBR2..W100			1.20	.26	1.09	W
	4.9	19	-18.18	-16.89	66.7				2.37	2.37		

NGC (IC, A) (14)	m_H / m_C (15)	B(O) w (16)	B'(O) / m'_C (17)	S(B) (18)	(B-V)(O) w (19)	C_o(O) (20)	S(C) (21)	(U-B)(O) w (22)	V / w (23)	V_o / ΔV (24)	S(V) (25)	φ_r n (26)	φ(21) (27)	(28)	Photo (29)
I4278										108					
I4296	11.9								3881 / 1.0	3699 / −182	M				
I4327										−164					
I4329	12.8 / 12.79		13.33							−163					
I4351	12.8 / 12.44		14.28							−154					
I4444	12.2 / 12.64		13.38							−168					
I4448										−217					
I4653										−131					
I4662	11.7 / 11.99		12.93						375 / 51.0	237 / −138	M				
I4662A										−138					
I4710	12.8 / 12.34		14.73							−137					F
I4713										−138					
I4714										−135					
I4717										−97					
I4719										−92					
I4720										−99					
I4721	12.9 / 12.65		14.34							−99					
I4796										−74					
I4797	12.2 / 12.49		12.48						2685 / 1.0	2611 / −74	M				
I4806										−88					
I4810															
I4820										−81					
I4829										−114					
I4832										−81					
I4836										−81					
I4837	12.9 / 12.84		14.03							−97					
I4837A										−71					
I4839										−69					
I4840										−71					
I4842										−79					
I4845										−99					
I4852										−98					
I4889	12.5 / 12.69		12.68							−96					
I4892										−64					
I4943										−139					
I4960										−30					
I4970										−139					FH
I4972										−140					H
I4981										−140					
I5000										−140 / 226					H

147

NGC (IC, A) (1)	RA (1950) 100 P (2)	Dec 100 P (3)	L^I B^I (4)	L^II B^II (5)	SGL SGB (6)	Rev. type (S) DDO (T, L) (7)	Yerkes (1) Yerkes (2) (8)	Hu-San Ho (9)	log D w (10)	log R w (11)	log D(O) (12)	S (D,R) (13)
I5020	20 27.8	-33 42	336.75	9.25	231.8							
	6.3	20	-35.79	-34.33	35.7							
I5039	20 40.2	-30 3	341.91	14.32	236.9							
	6.1	21	-37.56	-36.08	37.5							
I5052	20 47.5	-69 25	291.94	325.14	217.1	.S..7*/S030			1.73	.92	1.37	DEI
	9.5	22	-36.66	-35.81	2.6				5.67	5.67		
I5063	20 48.2	-57 16	306.89	339.98	223.0	.LA.-*.S030			1.07	.12	1.02	EI
	7.7	22	-39.87	-38.74	13.2				1.46	1.46		
I5092	21 12.1	-64 41	296.51	329.77	221.6	.SBT5*.S030			1.42	.05	1.39	I
	8.3	25	-40.58	-39.64	5.4				1.43	1.43		
I5105	21 21.2	-40 50	328.64	1.44	237.4	.E.4...S030			1.14	.23	1.05	I
	6.4	26	-47.05	-45.64	23.9				.97	.97		
I5105A	21 22.6	-40 29	329.15	1.94	237.8	.S..5$.S030			1.32	.29	1.20	I
	6.3	26	-47.32	-45.91	24.0				1.26	1.26		
I5105B	21 22.9	-41 3	328.31	1.12	237.5	.S...*.S030			1.18	.54	.97	I
	6.3	26	-47.36	-45.96	23.5				1.03	1.03		
I5131	21 44.4	-35 7	337.42	10.04	245.3	.LB.-..S074			.99	.04	.97	J
	6.0	28	-51.62	-50.16	24.9				1.50	1.50		
I5135	21 45.3	-35 11	337.32	9.94	245.4	.P.....S074			1.01	.04	.99	J
	6.0	28	-51.81	-50.35	24.8				1.53	1.53		
I5152	21 59.6	-51 32	310.52	343.91	234.9	.IAS9..R074			1.62	.25	1.52	DEIO
	6.5	29	-51.41	-50.22	11.5				8.27	8.27		
I5156	22 0.4	-34 2	339.35	11.94	248.6							
	5.9	29	-54.89	-53.42	23.2							
I5168	22 6.0	-28 6	349.91	22.12	254.5	.S....$H030			1.25	.38	1.09	F
	5.7	29	-55.59	-54.10	26.0				1.29	1.29		
I5179	22 13.3	-37 6	333.65	6.49	247.8	.SB..*.H030			1.25	.38	1.09	F
	5.9	30	-57.39	-55.94	19.2				1.29	1.29		
I5181	22 10.3	-46 16	317.74	351.05	240.1	.LA.../S074			1.32	.59	1.08	DEPIJ
	6.2	30	-54.90	-53.60	13.8				6.91	6.91		
I5186	22 13.4	-37 5	333.68	6.51	247.9	.SAT4..S074			1.31	.30	1.19	J
	5.9	30	-57.41	-55.97	19.2				2.28	2.28		
I5201	22 18.3	-46 19	316.84	350.23	241.0	.SBT6..S074			1.92	.36	1.77	DEJ
	6.1	30	-56.18	-54.90	12.7				9.09	9.09		
I5240	22 39.0	-45 4	316.38	349.96	244.3	.SBR1..B060			1.39	.13	1.33	EI
	5.9	31	-60.00	-58.72	10.6				1.89	1.89		
I5264	22 54.1	-36 49	331.33	4.49	252.9	.S..../S030			1.33	.83	1.00	I
	5.6	32	-65.47	-64.04	12.7				.64	.64		
I5267	22 54.4	-43 43	316.38	350.13	246.9	.SAS0..S030			1.51	.10	1.47	EPI
	5.7	32	-63.06	-61.78	9.1				3.36	3.36		
I5267A	22 53.0	-43 41	316.70	350.42	246.8	.S..3*.S030			1.49	.54	1.27	I
	5.7	32	-62.85	-61.57	9.3				1.13	1.13		
I5267B	22 54.1	-44 2	315.82	349.58	246.6	.S...$/S030			1.21	.52	1.00	I
	5.7	32	-62.87	-61.60	8.9				1.08	1.08		
I5269	22 55.0	-36 18	332.45	5.56	253.5	.LA....S030			1.22	.39	1.07	I
	5.6	32	-65.76	-64.32	12.8				1.10	1.10		
I5269A	22 53.1	-36 39	331.83	4.96	252.9	.SB.9.$S030			1.18	.06	1.15	I
	5.6	32	-65.31	-63.88	13.0				.52	.52		
I5269B	22 53.9	-36 31	332.06	5.18	253.1	.S....*.S030			1.57	.64	1.32	I
	5.6	32	-65.50	-64.06	12.9				1.76	1.76		
I5269C	22 57.6	-35 38	333.77	6.84	254.3	.SBS..$S030			1.43	.25	1.33	I
	5.6	32	-66.42	-64.97	12.7				.32	.32		
I5270	22 55.2	-36 7	332.86	5.96	253.6	.S....*.S030			1.43	.68	1.15	I
	5.6	32	-65.84	-64.40	12.9				1.46	1.46		
I5271	22 55.3	-34 1	337.94	10.77	255.5	.S....$						
	5.5	32	-66.24	-64.77	13.9							
I5273	22 56.7	-37 58	328.32	1.64	252.2	.SBT5*.W100			1.44	.15	1.38	IW
	5.6	32	-65.66	-64.25	11.7				2.86	2.86		
I5283	23 0.8	8 37	52.20	83.13	298.7	.S...P.W100			.91	.38	.76	QW
	5.0	32	-46.12	-45.47	29.2				2.21	2.21		
I5284	23 4.3	18 50	60.15	91.37	310.4	.S....*W			1.12	.33	.98	H
	4.9	32	-37.72	-37.26	30.2				.81	.81		
I5325	23 26.0	-41 36	313.34	347.71	251.6	.SAS4*.S030			1.35	.00	1.35	I
	5.4	33	-69.12	-67.88	5.0				1.31	1.31		
I5328	23 30.5	-45 19	304.25	338.88	248.6	.E.5...S074			1.14	.21	1.06	EJ
	5.4	33	-67.34	-66.24	2.6				2.48	2.48		
I5328A	23 30.4	-45 19	304.29	338.91	248.6	.S...$/S074			.87	.46	.69	J
	5.4	33	-67.33	-66.23	2.7				1.30	1.30		
I5328B	23 31.2	-45 31	303.66	338.31	248.5	.SBS5*.S074			1.19	.60	.95	J
	5.4	33	-67.29	-65.20	2.5				1.96	1.96		
I5332	23 31.7	-36 22	325.47	359.44	256.9	.SAS7..W100			1.79	.12	1.74	FPTIW
	5.3	33	-72.74	-71.35	6.2				14.39	14.39		
I5342	23 36.1	26 44	72.19	103.52	320.2	.E.0...W						
	5.0	33	-33.26	-33.10	23.8							
I5381	0 0.6	15 40	75.51	106.31	309.6	.S....*R020			1.26	.43	1.08	H
	5.1	33	-45.43	-45.35	16.4				1.01	1.01		

NGC (IC, A) (14)	Magnitudes				Colors				Velocities			Radio			
	m_H m_c (15)	B(O) w (16)	B'(O) m'_c (17)	S(B) (18)	(B-V)(O) w (19)	C_o(O) (20)	S(C) (21)	(U-B)(O) w (22)	V w (23)	V_o ΔV (24)	S(V) (25)	ϕ_r n (26)	ϕ(21) (27)	(28)	Photo. (29)
I5020	13.1									50					
I5039	13.1									69					
I5052	12.3 12.47		14.01							−131					
I5063	13.0 13.16		13.00							−72					
I5092										−109					
I5105	13.0 13.04		12.98							13					
I5105A										15					
I5105B										12					
I5131										40					
I5135	13.1									40					G
I5152	12.3 11.91		14.25						78 10.2	31 −47	IM				H
I5156	13.2									43					
I5168										71					
I5179										24					
I5181	12.6 12.79		12.93							−22					
I5186	12.5 12.83		13.52							24					
I5201	12.8 11.72		15.31							−24					
I5240	12.6 12.49		13.88							−22					
I5264										14					
I5267	11.8 11.69	11.65 2.05	13.74 13.78	M	.92	.83	M /M	.47	1715 2.8	1695 −20	L				F
I5267A										−20					
I5267B										−22					
I5269	13.1 13.15		13.19							16					
I5269A										15					
I5269B										15					
I5269C										18					
I5270										17					
I5271	12.6									27					
I5273	12.0 12.17	11.89 1.76	13.53 13.81	M	.46		M /M	−.01		7					
I5283									4875 1.0	5083 208	F				
I5284										236					
I5325	12.5 12.48		13.92							−22					
I5328	12.7 12.82		12.81							−41					
I5328A										−41					
I5328B										−42					
I5332	11.9 11.38		14.82							1					F
I5342										240					
I5381										197					

149

NGC (IC, A)	RA (1950) 100 P	Dec 100 P	L^I B^I	L^{II} B^{II}	SGL SGB	Rev. type (S) DDO (T, L)	Yerkes (1) Yerkes (2)	Hu-San Ho	log D w	log R w	log D(O)	S (D,R)
	(2)	(3)	(4)	(5)	(6)	(7)	(8)	(9)	(10)	(11)	(12)	(13)
A0026	0 26.1	2 39	81.90	111.69	298.2	.S.1...W						
	5.1	33	-59.36	-59.44	7.1							
A0035	0 35.0	-34 1	283.74	326.58	263.5	.P.....W						
	4.9	33	-83.51	-82.73	-5.1							
A0045A	0 45.0	-20 42	94.80	115.03	277.0	.S...P*						
	5.0	33	-82.95	-83.24	-3.7							
A0045B	0 45.0	-20 42	94.80	115.03	277.0	.S...P*						
	5.C	33	-82.95	-83.24	-3.7							
A0046	0 46.0	-13 5	93.35	120.05	284.4							
	5.0	33	-75.34	-75.67	-1.9							
A0051	0 51.0	-73 6	269.07	302.80	224.9	.IBS9......			3.4*	.30	3.3*	*
	3.5	33	-44.61	-44.30	-14.8							
A0055	0 54.6	-4 16	97.51	126.55	293.4	.S..3.*						
	5.1	33	-66.36	-66.83	-1.6							
A0058	0 57.6	-33 58	243.38	287.81	264.7	.E...P.						
	4.7	32	-82.97	-83.18	-9.6							
A0103	1 2.6	-6 29	103.54	132.39	291.8	.SXT7..W100			1.56	.03	1.55	DEW
	5.1	32	-68.23	-68.84	-4.1	SX 8	SX F		6.50	6.50		
A0118	1 18.4	15 26	102.45	133.33	314.0	.SB.5.*						
	5.3	32	-45.97	-46.58	-1.8							
A0143	1 43.0	-43 51	236.89	273.06	255.8	.I..9..B						
	4.2	30	-69.80	-70.28	-19.7							
A0218A	2 18.5	39 9	109.50	141.34	340.9	.SAS3P.W060			1.36	.18	1.29	Q
	6.2	27	-19.47	-20.25	-5.9				2.20	2.20		
A0218B	2 18.5	39 9	109.50	141.34	340.9	.SBS1P.W060			1.20	.58	.96	Q
	6.2	27	-19.47	-20.25	-5.9				1.29	1.29		
A0235	2 34.6	34 12	114.84	146.64	337.9	.SB.1..W						
	6.1	26	-22.62	-23.51	-11.0							
A0236	2 36.4	18 9	124.25	155.78	323.2	.I....*						
	5.6	26	-36.46	-37.53	-18.4							
A0237	2 37.5	-34 44	203.10	237.31	266.0	.E...P.						
	4.1	26	-64.53	-65.72	-30.2							
A0255	2 55.1	-54 48	237.65	271.89	242.5	.SBS7*.S030			1.81	.67	1.54	I
	2.9	24	-53.84	-54.32	-30.2				2.33	2.33		
A0438	4 38.1	4 8	160.37	192.58	325.4	.S..1..W						
	5.3	12	-24.98	-26.46	-51.2							
A0509	5 9.5	-14 50	183.11	215.62	295.8							
	4.5	7	-27.18	-28.61	-65.1	N.						
A0524	5 24.0	-69 48	247.22	280.47	216.5	.SBS9......		I 9	3.7*	.07	3.65	**
	-.9	5	-32.63	-32.89	-34.1							
A0708	7 8.3	73 34	108.56	141.54	28.5	.P....*						
	12.3	-10	28.32	27.55	-.8							
A0733	7 33.0	63 4	120.69	153.60	32.0	RSBS0*.L036						
	9.1	-13	30.17	29.15	-10.9							
A0814	8 14.1	70 52	111.18	144.28	34.0	.I..9..P200		I 9	1.90	.11	1.85	XZ
	10.5	-18	33.54	32.71	-2.4			I9	6.30	6.30		
A0909	9 9.5	74 28	105.35	138.60	36.1	.SXS7..P200			1.39	.11	1.35	XZ
	10.5	-24	36.17	35.47	2.7			S6	3.45	3.45		
A0916	9 15.7	-11 53	211.12	242.93	115.8	.L.....W						
	4.8	-25	26.18	25.10	-55.1							
A0936	9 36.2	71 26	107.35	140.69	39.4							
	9.0	-27	39.41	38.66	1.4			I9				
A0937A	9 36.3	-4 37	208.29	239.94	106.5							
	5.0	-27	34.71	33.58	-48.4							
A0937B	9 36.3	-4 37	208.29	239.94	106.5							
	5.0	-27	34.71	33.58	-48.4							
A0937C	9 36.3	-4 37	208.29	239.94	106.5							
	5.0	-27	34.71	33.58	-48.4							
A0937D	9 36.3	-4 37	208.29	239.94	106.5							
	5.0	-27	34.71	33.58	-48.4							
A0944A	9 43.8	3 17	201.65	233.25	96.9							
	5.2	-27	40.94	39.70	-43.7							
A0944B	9 43.8	3 15	201.69	233.29	97.0							
	5.2	-27	40.92	39.68	-43.7							
A0947	9 47.4	28 12	168.59	200.86	71.6							
	5.8	-28	51.57	50.08	-29.1							
A0953	9 52.8	8 36	197.18	228.76	92.0	.P.....W						
	5.3	-28	45.71	44.41	-39.3							
A0955A	9 55.8	29 6	167.63	199.93	72.1	.L.....P						
	5.8	-28	53.52	52.04	-27.1							
A0955B	9 55.8	29 6	167.63	199.93	72.1	.E.....P						
	5.8	-28	53.52	52.04	-27.1							
A0956	9 56.5	30 59	164.50	196.91	70.6							
	5.8	-28	53.90	52.41	-25.8			I9				
A0957	9 57.3	5 34	201.70	233.19	96.1							
	5.2	-28	45.00	43.76	-39.6			I9				
A1006	10 5.8	12 33	194.47	225.99	89.6	.E.4.P.W						
	5.4	-29	50.45	49.11	-34.6			E P				
A1009	10 8.8	-4 28	214.86	246.23	109.8	.IB.9..P200		I 9	1.73	.09	1.70	NXZ
	5.0	-29	40.94	39.92	-40.6			I9	7.99	7.99		

NGC (IC, A)	Magnitudes				Colors				Velocities			Radio			
	m_H m_c	B(O) w	B'(O) m'_c	S(B)	(B-V)(O) w	C_o(O)	S(C)	(U-B)(O) w	V w	V_o ΔV	S(V)	ϕ_r n	ϕ(21)		Photo.
(14)	(15)	(16)	(17)	(18)	(19)	(20)	(21)	(22)	(23)	(24)	(25)	(26)	(27)	(28)	(29)
A0026									4460 4.0	4597 136	B				
A0035										−22					
A0045A									6164 1.0	6192 28	F				
A0045B									6308 1.0	6336 28	F				
A0046									6536 2.6	6595 60	D				
A0051	1.5 1.8	3.1*	14.3* 13.0	*	.35	.28	*		163 2222	−13 −177	IR				L
A0055										89					
A0058	9.0									−36					
A0103	12.8 12.30								983 1.8	1057 74	D				
A0118										141					
A0143	13.3									−104					
A0218A										164					
A0218B										164					
A0235				C*			C*		4800 .4	4939 139	B				
A0236									4037 1.5	4122 85	C				
A0237	9.5								39 11.1	−70 −110	B				
A0255	12.0 11.91		14.30							−177					F
A0438				C*			C*		4600 4.0	4528 −72	B				
A0509	13.1									−165					
A0524	0.5 0.8	1.2*	14.2* 13.8	*	.50	.40	*		264 4011	16 −247	HIR				LP
A0708									2839 1.0	2996 157	F				
A0733										107					
A0814		11.44 1.37	15.43	G	.51 2.50	.41	G		164 76.0	303 139	CR				P
A0909		13.32 1.12	14.76	G*						155					
A0916									16160 2.8	15914 −246	B				
A0936				G*	.46* 2.50		G			142					
A0937A									6577 6.3	6357 −220	F				
A0937B									6797 6.3	6577 −220	F				
A0937C									6852 11.1	6632 −220	F				
A0937D									6451 11.1	6231 −220	F				
A0944A									6110 1.5	5921 −189	E				
A0944B									6030 1.5	5841 −189	E				
A0947				D*			D*			−75					
A0953									1283 1.0	1117 −166	B				
A0955A									6409 13.7	6340 −69	K				
A0955B									6236 9.8	6167 −69	K				
A0956				G*	.44* 2.50		G			−59					
A0957				CG*	.53* 4.38		CG			−177					
A1006				G*	.97* 2.50		G			−145					
A1009				CG*	.48 4.38	.40	CG		330 171.1	118 −213	BCR				P

NGC (IC,A)	RA (1950) 100P / Dec 100P		L^I / B^I	L^{II} / B^{II}	SGL / SGB	Rev.type (S) / DDO (T,L)	Yerkes (1) / Yerkes (2)	Hu-San / Ho	log D w	log R w	log D(O)	S(D,R)
(1)	(2)	(3)	(4)	(5)	(6)	(7)	(8)	(9)	(10)	(11)	(12)	(13)
A1101	11 1.2	41 7	140.47	174.17	69.9	.P.....P			.65	.13	.60	Z
	5.6	-32	65.34	64.01	-9.3				.79	.79		
A1105A	11 4.7	18 42	196.62	227.40	90.7	.L...P.P						
	5.3	-32	65.85	64.54	-19.1							
A1105B	11 4.7	18 42	196.62	227.40	90.7	.E.....P						
	5.3	-32	65.85	64.54	-19.1							
A1107A	11 7.2	24 32	132.99	214.36	85.4							
	5.4	-32	58.41	66.98	-16.1							
A1107B	11 7.3	24 32	183.01	214.37	85.4							
	5.4	-32	58.43	67.00	-16.1							
A1108A	11 8.1	29 2	170.72	202.83	81.4	.S....*P						
	5.4	-32	69.24	67.76	-13.9							
A1108B	11 8.1	29 2	170.72	202.83	81.4	.L....*P						
	5.4	-32	69.24	67.76	-13.9							
A1108C	11 8.1	29 2	170.72	202.83	81.4							
	5.4	-32	69.24	67.76	-13.9							
A1111	11 10.8	22 26	189.15	220.14	87.8	.E.0.P.P200		E P				
	5.3	-32	68.62	67.23	-16.3			E P				
A1129	11 29.2	71 5	98.29	131.98	45.2							
	6.0	-33	45.44	44.90	8.3							
A1130A	11 29.8	53 12	112.75	147.20	61.5							
	5.5	-33	61.21	60.33	0.7							
A1130B	11 29.8	53 12	112.75	147.20	61.5							
	5.5	-33	61.21	60.33	0.7							
A1145A	11 44.5	-3 33	243.61	273.82	116.3	.SB.3..W						
	5.1	-33	55.74	55.35	-17.4							
A1145B	11 44.7	-3 33	243.69	273.89	116.3	.S..3..W						
	5.1	-33	55.76	55.37	-17.3							
A1145C	11 44.8	-3 34	243.74	273.95	116.3	.S..5..W						
	5.1	-33	55.75	55.37	-17.3							
A1157	11 57.2	37 48	130.35	166.02	77.5	.IB.9..L036						
	5.1	-33	76.17	74.96	-1.0							
A1203A	12 3.2	31 21	154.57	188.65	84.0	.E.0...P						
	5.1	-33	80.73	79.28	-2.1							
A1203B	12 3.2	31 21	154.57	188.65	84.0	.L....*P						
	5.1	-33	80.73	79.28	-2.1							
A1205	12 4.6	17 16	228.13	255.38	97.4	.S..3.*						
	5.1	-33	76.38	75.59	-6.4							
A1213	12 12.9	6 5	250.62	279.44	108.8							
	5.1	-33	67.25	67.03	-7.9							
A1214A	12 13.8	28 25	172.03	203.50	87.5	.L.....P						
	5.0	-33	83.64	82.16	-.9							
A1214B	12 13.8	28 25	172.03	203.50	87.5	.S..3..P						
	5.0	-33	83.64	82.16	-.9							
A1217	12 16.8	4 8	254.27	283.31	111.0							
	5.1	-33	65.63	65.50	-7.5							
A1230	12 30.1	9 27	260.30	288.16	106.8	.E.0...W						
	5.1	-33	71.49	71.50	-2.8							
A1232	12 32.2	6 34	262.92	291.40	109.7			I9				
	5.1	-33	68.70	68.79	-3.1							
A1244	12 44.2	26 50	293.76	240.56	91.0							
	4.9	-32	89.03	88.80	5.1							
A1245	12 45.1	27 15	321.42	222.36	90.6							
	4.9	-32	89.24	89.12	5.4							
A1246A	12 45.8	27 8	321.83	233.16	90.8							
	4.9	-32	89.05	89.24	5.6							
A1246B	12 47.2	27 10	332.47	242.92	90.8							
	4.9	-32	88.81	89.54	5.9							
A1247	12 46.8	-9 51	271.70	302.10	126.5	.SBS9..W100	S A		1.54	.10	1.50	DEW
	5.2	-32	52.41	52.75	-4.1	S 6 8*			6.32	6.32		
A1248A	12 46.7	-41 11	270.80	302.53	157.3	.L....*						
	5.5	-33	21.08	21.41	-11.3							
A1248B	12 46.8	-41 6	270.82	302.55	157.2	.L....*						
	5.5	-33	21.17	21.50	-11.3							
A1248C	12 47.4	-41 14	270.94	302.68	157.4	.L....*						
	5.5	-33	21.03	21.37	-11.2							
A1248D	12 48.9	-40 51	271.25	302.98	157.1	.L....*						
	5.5	-33	21.41	21.75	-10.9							
A1249	12 48.5	28 7	16.58	131.71	90.0	.E.0...W						
	4.9	-32	88.61	89.28	6.4							
A1253	12 52.6	0 23	275.45	304.98	117.0	.SBS7..W100			1.50	.19	1.42	EW
	5.1	-32	62.55	62.97	0.1	N *	S AF		4.33	4.33		
A1255	12 54.5	32 42	63.04	110.64	85.8	.P.....W						
	4.8	-32	84.38	84.56	8.7							
A1302	13 2.0	-3 18	279.34	309.33	121.2	.SB.7..L036			1.57	.09	1.53	N
	5.2	-32	58.62	59.14	1.3				2.36	2.36		
A1306	13 7.4	-15 29	278.67	309.49	133.3	.L...*.H030			1.36	.48	1.16	F
	5.3	-32	46.37	46.88	-.7				1.49	1.49		
A1309	13 8.8	3 40	285.74	315.13	115.0	.SB.5..P						
	5.1	-31	65.13	65.80	4.8							

NGC (IC, A) (14)	Magnitudes				Colors				Velocities			Radio			
	m_H m_c (15)	B(O) w (16)	B'(O) m'_c (17)	S(B) (18)	(B-V)(O) w (19)	C_0(O) (20)	S(C) (21)	(U-B)(O) w (22)	V w (23)	V_0 ΔV (24)	S(V) (25)	ϕ_r n (26)	ϕ(21) (27)	(28)	Photo. (29)
A1101				E*	.71* 12.50	.53	E /E	−.16	10346 2.8	10356 10	B				
A1105A									8211 1.7	8115 −96	K				
A1105B									7982 1.6	7886 −96	K				
A1107A									6314 1.1	6246 −68	E				
A1107B									5996 1.1	5928 −68	E				
A1108A									8803 100.0	8757 −46	K				
A1108B									8550 3.6	8504 −46	K				
A1108C									8839 1.0	8793 −46	K				
A1111				G*	.91* 2.50		G			−76					P
A1129									15580 1.0	15733 153	F				
A1130A									7820	7897 77	F				
A1130B									6620	6697 77	F				
A1145A									5108 4.0	4941 −167	B				
A1145B									5008 4.0	4841 −167	B				
A1145C									5396 1.8	5229 −167	B				
A1157										18					
A1203A									7010 9.2	7002 −8	K				
A1203B									6894 8.6	6886 −8	K				
A1205									6740	6670 −70	K				
A1213									2039 3.3	1927 *112	D				
A1214A									6571 8.6	6556 −15	K				
A1214B									6618 1.6	6603 −15	K				
A1217									1716 2.6	1599 −117	D				
A1230									1317 .1	1233 −86	B				
A1232				G*	.53* 2.50		G			−96					
A1244									879 2.0	876 −3	C				
A1245									7118 2.0	7118 0	C				
A1246A									6917 2.0	6917 0	C				
A1246B									7429 2.0	7430 1	C				
A1247	12.5 12.37		14.56							−147					
A1248A				M*			M* /M	*		−227					
A1248B				M*			M* /M	*		−227					
A1248C				M*			M* /M	*		−227					
A1248D				M*			M* /M	*		−225					
A1249									7700 1.0	7706 6	K				
A1253	12.9 12.65		14.49							−105					
A1255				C*			C*		13431 6.0	13460 29	BC				
A1302										−112	C*				
A1306										−150					
A1309									2990 6.3	2910 −80	K				

NGC (IC, A) (1)	RA (1950) 100 P (2)	Dec 100 P (3)	L^I B^I (4)	L^II B^II (5)	SGL SGB (6)	Rev. type (S) DDO (T, L) (7)	Yerkes (1) Yerkes (2) (8)	Hu-San Ho (9)	log D w (10)	log R w (11)	log D(O) (12)	S (D,R) (13)
A1310	13 10.2	-32 25	276.67	308.16	149.8	.S....$H030			1.86	.12	1.81	F
	5.5	-31	29.50	29.97	-4.7				2.79	2.79		
A1311	13 11.0	36 28	57.11	97.17	82.7			I9				
	4.6	-31	79.38	79.81	12.8							
A1339	13 38.8	54 35	72.89	107.90	64.4			S5				
	3.8	-30	61.25	61.34	19.3							
A1345A	13 44.9	34 6	29.35	65.69	86.2							
	4.5	-29	75.19	76.27	19.3							
A1345B	13 44.8	34 7	29.44	65.79	86.1							
	4.5	-29	75.21	76.28	19.3							
A1353	13 53.0	54 8	68.74	103.67	64.8	.IB.9..L036						
	3.7	-29	60.61	60.80	21.4			S.				
A1358	13 57.7	-45 10	283.56	315.49	164.8	.S..5*.S030			1.35	.12	1.30	I
	6.2	-29	15.12	15.76	-.1				.94	.94		
A1410	14 9.7	52 34	62.80	97.65	66.3							
	3.6	-28	60.32	60.67	24.0							
A1444	14 43.8	8 42	332.16	3.85	116.0	.P....*						
	4.9	-25	55.65	57.08	29.0							
A1447	14 46.8	-9 57	312.94	344.46	136.1	.P....*						
	5.4	-25	41.78	43.00	24.0							
A1511	15 11.0	-15 18	314.50	346.24	144.2	.SAS7..W100			1.48	.07	1.45	W
	5.6	-22	33.91	35.15	27.1	S 6 8	S A *		3.33	3.33		
A1516	15 16.3	43 3	36.58	70.56	75.0	.P....*						
	3.6	-22	55.50	56.46	36.6							
A1648A	16 48.0	45 35	37.73	70.97	62.0	.L.....P						
	3.0	-10	38.98	39.92	50.3							
A1648B	16 48.0	45 35	37.73	70.97	62.0	.S..1..P						
	3.0	-10	38.98	39.92	50.3							
A1648C	16 48.0	45 35	37.73	70.97	62.0	.L.....P						
	3.0	-10	38.98	39.92	50.3							
A1718A	17 18.1	49 8	42.47	75.61	52.3	.E.0...P						
	2.6	-6	34.07	34.92	51.4							
A1718B	17 18.1	49 8	42.47	75.61	52.3	.S..3..P						
	2.6	-6	34.07	34.92	51.4							
A1719	17 19.4	57 58	53.14	86.37	44.5							
	1.6	-5	34.12	34.72	44.2							
A1853	18 52.9	-54 36	309.15	341.85	207.4	.L....$S030			1.02	.13	.97	DEI
	8.2	8	-23.74	-22.58	19.8				2.25	2.25		
A1955A	19 55.1	40 17	43.24	75.66	1.7	.E.0...						
	3.5	16	5.19	6.03	61.9							
A1955B	19 55.1	40 17	43.24	75.66	1.7	.E.0...						
	3.5	16	5.19	6.03	61.9							
A2021	20 20.6	-44 10	323.71	356.43	224.9	.L...*.S030			1.32	.43	1.14	I
	6.9	19	-36.00	-34.64	26.9				1.26	1.26		
A2058	20 58.5	16 6	31.85	63.77	302.7	.E.1...W						
	4.7	23	-20.29	-19.22	59.8							
A2059A	20 58.8	15 55	31.74	63.67	302.3	.S..1..W						
	4.7	23	-20.46	-19.38	59.7							
A2059B	20 59.6	15 55	31.87	63.79	302.4	.L.....W						
	4.7	24	-20.61	-19.54	59.5							
A2119	21 19.5	-46 13	320.84	353.82	233.5	.S...*/S030			1.27	.85	.93	I
	6.6	25	-46.35	-45.02	19.9				.84	.84		
A2120	21 20.0	-46 0	321.14	354.12	233.7	.SA.4..S030			1.58	.57	1.35	I
	6.6	26	-46.46	-45.12	20.0				1.76	1.76		
A2144	21 44.0	-21 29	358.54	30.53	257.1	.E.0..$P200			1.68	.00	1.68	Z
	5.6	28	-49.18	-47.72	34.0				4.80	4.80		
A2208	22 7.9	-22 56	259.74	290.85	137.3	.SB.3.*						
	5.2	-33	38.66	38.70	-16.1							
A2326	23 26.1	14 29	63.87	94.79	306.5	.I..9..P200			1.57	.34	1.43	XZ
	5.0	33	-43.91	-43.54	24.3			I9	4.30	4.30		
A2339A	23 39.3	-3 54	54.85	84.64	288.4	.S..5..P						
	5.1	33	-61.82	-61.22	16.5							
A2339B	23 39.5	-3 50	55.01	84.81	288.5	.S..3..P						
	5.1	33	-61.79	-61.19	16.5							
A2340	23 40.0	-45 27	300.76	335.67	249.2	.S..7*/B060			1.45	1.05	1.03	P
	5.3	33	-68.38	-67.34	1.1				2.48	2.48		
A2359	23 59.2	-15 45	47.80	75.71	278.5	.I..9..L036						
	5.1	33	-74.39	-73.60	8.1			I9				

NGC (IC, A) (14)	Magnitudes				Colors				Velocities			Radio			
	m_H m_c (15)	B(O) w (16)	B'(O) m'_c (17)	S(B) (18)	(B-V)(O) w (19)	C_o(O) (20)	S(C) (21)	(U-B)(O) w (22)	V w (23)	V_o ΔV (24)	S(V) (25)	ϕ_r n (26)	ϕ(21) (27)	(28)	Photo. (29)
A1310										−195					
A1311				G*	.37* 2.50		G			55					
A1339				G*						137					
A1345A									4448 .9	4517 69	E				
A1345B									4912 .9	4981 69	E				
A1353				G*						143	C*				
A1358	13.0 12.87		14.11							−192					
A1410									8733 1.8	8880 147	B				
A1444									10470 1.0	10491 21	F				
A1447									1880 1.0	1833 −47	F				
A1511	12.8 12.53		14.52							−45					
A1516									12110 1.0	12271 161	F				
A1648A									9418 25.0	9641 223	K				
A1648B									9400 15.1	9623 223	KB				
A1648C									9449 2.2	9672 223	K				
A1718A									7250 17.4	7493 243	K				
A1718B									7182 2.8	7425 243	K				
A1719										248					
A1853	12.4 12.85		12.44							−75					
A1955A				C*			C*		4794 1.6	5087 292	C				
A1955B				C*			C*		4708 1.3	5000 292	C				
A2021	12.3 12.49		12.93							−5					
A2058				C*			C*		9148 .2	9407 259	B				
A2059A				C*			C*		11255 4.0	11513 258	B				
A2059B				C*			C*		11965 4.0	12223 258	B				
A2119										−15					
A2120	12.9 12.67		14.16							−14					
A2144		12.37 1.72	15.46	C	.91 1.88		C			108					
A2208										−213					
A2326		12.92 0.84	14.81	G	.59 2.50		G			214					
A2339A									6777 2.8	6919 142	B				
A2339B									7016 2.8	7158 142	B				
A2340										−45					
A2359				CG*	.41* 6.25	.36	CG		−78 25.0	2 80	B				

155

NOTES

NOTES

N 0001, 0002 Pair at 1'8 = Ho 2a, b.

0007 Edgewise S. See Helwan 22, 38.

0008, 0009 Pair at 2'7 = Ho 3a, b. N 8 looks like a dble * on Pal. Chart.

0013 Heid. 9 dim.: 0'5 x 0'5, reject. (N only).

0016 vsN. P(a) w. N 22, small SB(s) at 11'5.

0020 B * 0'3 n of N.

0021 vF no struct. B * 2' nf. Corrected coord. measured on I. Roberts 20" plate.

0023 vsBN; spir. struct. in bar; F arms, one stronger. Pseudo (R); 2'0 x 1'05. N 26 at 9'2.
      Photo. and SN 1955 P.A.S.P., 71, 162, 1959.

0024 BM, poor. res. knotty spir. arms w. dk. lane. Poss. SAB(rs).

0026 vs nct vB N; arms form series rings: 0'25 x 0'15; 0'4 x 0'35; 0'75 x 0'6. N 23 at 9'2.

0045 In Sculptor group w. N 55, 247, 253, 300, 7793 (Ap.J., 130, 718, 1959). BM, no BN, many irreg. weak, well res.
      arms; v. low surf. br. Mt. W. vel. for bright emiss. patch 0'8 nf N.

0048, 0051 In group 11 neb.; Ap.J., 51, 276, 1920 (= MWC 186).

0055 Fol. part = I 1537. In Sculptor group w. N 45, 247, 253, 300, 7793 (See Ap.J., 130, 718, 1959). Mt. W. vel.
      (+177 km/sec) for "emiss. patch 2'7 p N, p of 2". There is no emiss. there.
      Stromlo vel. for emiss. obj. 1'15 and 1'85 f N.
      Photo. P.N.A.S., 26, 33, 1940. P.A.S.P., 53, 17, 1941; 58, 232, 1946. Occ. Notes R.A.S., 3, No 18, 1956.
            Ap.J., 133, 405, 1961.
      Lum., rot., mass. Ap.J., 133, 405, 1961.
      HII reg. Zs.f.Ap., 50, 168, 1960.
      HI emiss. Epstein, Harvard Thesis, 1962.
      Radio emiss. Hdb.d.Phys., 53, 253, 1959.

0067 In N 68 group; = Ho 6g.

0068 Brightest of N 68 group. = Ho 6a. Heid. 9 and Lund 6 dim. rejected.
      Photo. A.J., 66, 568, 1961.
      Dyn. A.J., 66, 554, 566, 1961.

0069, 0070, 0071, 0072 In N 68 group; Ho 6b, c, d, f.

0072-A In N 68 group; 1'3 sf N 72.

0080, 0083 In N 83 group w. many other F gal., mostly SO and E. Dyn. A.J., 66, 554, 1961.

0095 vseBN, sev. F filam. arms form B irreg. ring struct. w knots.; asym.

0100 = Ho 9a; Ho 9b at 3'5 is probably a *.

0124 In group w. N 114, 118, 120. sBN, sev. B knotty branch. arms.

0125 In N 125-130 group. N 124 of Pettit (1954) is N 125.

0127 In N 125-130 group. P(b) w. N 128 at 0'9.

0128 Brightest of N 125-130 group. P(b) w. N 127, vB peanut-shaped N, narrow flat comp. 0'8 x 0'08 is distorted.
      Photo. Ap.J., 130, 20, 1959. N 130: U,B,V mag. by Hodge (1963).

0131 P(a) w. N 134 at 9'4.

0132 sBN, one arm more irreg. and better res. than the other; lens: 0'4 x 0'2.

0134 vsBN partly hidden by dk. lanes, many filam. knotty arms. P(a) w. N 131 at 9'4. Drawing: Helwan 9.

0145 sB bar w. no def. N, 2 strong knotty arms w. some branch., one stronger and longer forming incompl. loop.

0147 esB stel. N. e. low surf. br. dwarf. Pair w. N 185 in M 31 group.
      Monog. Ap.J., 100, 147, 1944 = MWC 697.
      Photom. Medd. Lund, II, 128, 1950.

0148 Note correc. to NGC R.A., after Helwan 22. H.A., 88,2 dim.: 1'2 x 0'5 (series a').

0150 esvBN in weak bar: 0'5 x 0'17, incompl. (r): 1'7 x 0'6, v.F. out. arms. Drawing: Helwan 9.

0151 SBN w. dk. matter, F. blobs at ends of bar, asym. arms, (r): 1'05 x 0'6. N 153 is star at end of one arm.

N 0157 vsvBN, many B knotty inner arms, v.F. out. extens. (B-V) source G discordant, rejected.
      Photo. Ap.J., 134, 874, 1961.
      Spect. Ap.J., 135, 698, 1962.
      Rot., mass, Ap.J., 134, 874, 1961.

  0160 vsN isolated in center of F. double (R). P(a) w. N 169 at 11'. MWC 626 correction N 160 = N 162, is an error. N 162 exists, mentioned in Lick 13 and Heid. 9, is 1'2 nff.

  0163, 0165 Pair at 7'3.

  0169 Close pair w. I 1559. P(a) w. N 160 at 11'.

  0175 vBN, strong narr. bar: 0'6 x 0'08. B (r): 0'8 x 0'6.

  0178 = I 39; in N 210 group. B peanut shaped bar: 0'6 x 0'2 w. F. *, asym., part. res. arms, one stronger; miniature of LMC. P. w. another asym. anon. SB(s)dm at 7'7.

  0182 In N 200 group.

  0185 Pair w. N 147 in M 31 group. Low surf. br. dwarf, dk. mark. in B M, no def. N. Additional Mt. W. vel. for glob. cluster, 1'1 sf N: -102 km/sec.
      Photo. and Monog. Ap.J., 100, 147, 1944, = MWC 697.
      Photom. Medd. Lund, II, 128, 1950. A.J., 68, 691, 1963.

  0191 = Ho 13a; pair w. I 1563 (= Ho 13b) at 0'8.

  0194 In N 200 group.

  0198 vsvBN in weak (r): 0'2 x 0'2, sev. knotty filam. arms w. branch. In N 200 group.

  0200 vsvBN in bar: 0'35 x 0'03, pseudo (r): 0'55 x 0'3, 2 main filam. arms, pseudo (R): 1'4 x 0'55. Brightest of N 200 group; many fainter gal. in field.

  0205 P(b) w. N 224 in M 31 (Local) Group. (B-V) increases w. log A/D(0); interpolated value.
      Photo. Ap.J., 76, 44, 1932 = MWC 452. Publ. Michigan X, 10, 1951.
      Monog. Ap.J., 100, 137, 1944 = MWC 696.
      Photom. M.N., 94, 519, 1934; 98, 618, 1938. Medd. Lund, II, 128, 1950. A.J. USSR, 20, 54, 1943.
      Spect. A.J., 61, 97, 1956.
      Polar. Bull. Abastumani, No 18, 15, 1955.

  0210 Brightest of N 210 group including N 178, 207, I 41. eBN in B isolated lens: 1'3 x 0'75 w. dk. lanes. 2 main detached filam., part. res. arms, pseudo (R): 4'1 x 2'2. P. w. s. anon. SBb 7' nf (= Ho 14a).

  0214 vsBN, weak bar, strong knotty (r): 0'3 x 0'2, sev. knotty filam. arms.

  0221 = M 32, P(a?) w. N 224 in M 31 (Local) Group. (B-V) constant, interp. value.
      Photo. Ap.J., 64, 325, 1926; 71, 235, 1930 (see also ref. to N 224).
      Monog. Ap.J., 82, 192, 1935; 100, 137, 1944.
      Photom. Ap.J., 50, 384, 1919; 71, 231, 1930; 83, 424, 1936; 108, 415, 1948; 120, 439, 1954. M.N., 96, 601, 1936. Medd. Lund, II, 128, 1950. A.J. USSR, 20, 54, 1943. L'Astronomie, 76, 359, 1962.
      Spect. Ap.J., 74, 36, 1931; 83, 15, 1936; 135, 732, 1962; 136, 695, 1962. A.J., 61, 97, 1956.
      Polar. Bull. Abastumani, No 18, 15, 1955.
      Rot. mass, Ap.J., 133, 393, 1092, 1961; 134, 272, 910, 1961; 136, 695, 1962. A.J., 59, 273, 1954.
      HI emiss. Ap.J., 126, 471, 1957. (not confirmed).

  0224 = M31, brightest in M31 (Local) Group.
      Photo. Ap.J., 76, 44, 1932; Ritchey, L'Evolution de l'Astrophotographie..., S.A.F., Paris, 1929.
      Monog. Ap.J., 69, 103, 1929 (= MWC 376); 76, 44, 1932 (= MWC 452); 100, 137, 1944 (= MWC 696); 101, 179, 1945; 102, 377, 1945. Stockholm Ann., 19, No 2, 1956. P.A.S.P., 50, 99, 1938.
      Photom. M.N., 74, 132, 1913; 87, 112, 1926; 94, 805, 1934; 97, 416, 1937; 110, 416, 1950. P.N.A.S., 20, 93, 1934. Publ. Michigan, VIII, No 7, 103, 1941. Stockholm Ann., 13, 10, 1941; 19, 2, 1956. Medd. Lund II, 128, 1950; II, 137, 1959. Ap.J., 50, 384, 1919; 83, 424, 1936; 108, 413, 1948; 128, 465, 1958; 133, 309, 1961. Zs.f.Ap., 34, 137, 1954; 56, 194, 1962. Izv. Pulkovo, 20, No 156, 87, 1956. A.J. USSR, 32, 16, 1955. L'Astronomie, 76, 359, 1962. Ap.J., 138, 1317, 1963.
      Orient. P.A.S.P., 54, 72, 1942. Ap.J., 104, 220, 1946.
      Spect. Ap.J., 88, 605, 1938; 108, 415, 1948; 135, 725, 1962. P.A.S.P., 48, 17, 1936; 69, 293, 1957; 72, 76, 1960. Lick Bull., 19, 498, 41, 1939. A.J., 61, 97, 1956.
      Polar. Stockholm Ann., 14, No 4, 1942. Bull. Abastumani, No 18, 15, 1955.
      Rot., mass, Ap.J., 55, 406, 1922; 95, 24, 1942; 97, 112, 1943; 136, 352, 1962. P.N.A.S., 4, 21, 1918. P.A.S.P., 50, 174, 1938; 53, 270, 1941; 72, 76, 1960. Lick Bull., 19, 498, 41, 1939. Zs.f.Ap., 35, 159, 1954. B.A.N., 14, 17, 1957. A.J., 59, 273, 1954.
      HII reg. Obs., 79, 54, 1959. Zs.f.Ap., 50, 168, 1960.
      SN 1885. Ap.J., 83, 245, 1936; 88, 289, 1938; 89, 141, 1939.
      HI emiss. B.A.N., 14, 1, 1957.
      Radio emiss. M.N., 110, 508, 1950; 111, 357, 1951; 119, 297, 1959; 121, 413, 1960; 122, 479, 1961. Nature, 174, 320, 1954; 175, 202, 1955; 180, 60, 1957; 183, 1251, 1959. Ap.J., 126, 585, 1957. A.J., 67, 580, 1962; 68, 70, 274, 1963.

  0237 vsBN, pseudo (r): 0'45 x 0'2, sev. knotty arms.

  0244 = Haro 14, Bol. Tonantzintla, 14, 11, 1956.

  0245 vsvBN, eccentric in pseudo (r): 0'7 x 0'6. 100-in. plate underexp., prob. lens only.

N 0247   In Sculptor group w. 45, 55, 253, 300, 7793 (Ap.J., 130, 718, 1959). esvBN, or *, low surf. br., well res.,
         emiss. obj., asym. Mt. W. vel. for B emiss. patch 5'0 sf N: +1 km/sec.
         Desc. and drawing, Helwan 9.
         Photom. Medd. Lund, II, 128, 1950.
         HII reg. Zs.f.Ap., 50, 168, 1960.
         HI emiss. Epstein, Harvard Thesis, 1962.

0252   = Ho 23b. Brightest of a small group.

0253   In Sculptor group w. 45, 55, 247, 300, 7793 (Ap.J., 130, 718, 1959). esBN, v. complex cent. lens: 7'0 x 2'1.
       Mt. W. vel. (-72 km/sec) for "emiss. patch 2'7 n N", not found by Evans (1956), Burbidge (1962).
       Photo. P.A.S.P., 58, 235, 1946. Ap.J., 136, 339, 1962.
       Photom. M.N., 94, 806, 1934. Ap.J., 83, 424, 1936.
       Orient. Ap.J., 127, 487, 1958.
       Spectr. Ap.J., 135, 698, 1962.
       Rot., mass, M.N., 116, 659, 1956. Ap.J., 136, 339, 1962.
       HII reg. Zs.f.Ap., 50, 168, 1960.
       SN 1940, H.A.C. 552; Hdb.d.Phys., 51, 774, 1958.
       Radio emiss. Austr.J.Phys., 8, 368, 1955; Hdb.d.Phys., 53, 253, 1959; M.N., 122, 479, 1961; P.A.S.P., 72, 368,
                   1960. Observatory, 83, 20, 1963.

0255   svB elong N, weak bar, many branch. eF outer arms, incomplete (r): 0'75 x 0'55. Photo. P.A.S.P., 43, 351, 1931.

0259   = Ho 22a. vF anon. at 3'5 (not same object as Ho 22b which is a *).

0260   = Ho 23c. In multiple system w. N 252 (N 258 = Ho 23d).

0273   vsvBN. In N 274-275 group.

0274   = Ho 26b. P(b) w. N 275 at 0'8. vseBN; proj. on one arm of N 275.

0275   = Ho 26a. P(b) w. N 274 at 0'8. B narr. bar: 0'35 x 0'05; one strong asym. arm forms loop passing near N 274,
       one shorter B arm. Drawing, Helwan 9.

0278   LBN, sev. knotty massive arms. B part has sharp edge.
       Photo. M.N., 72, 408, 1912.
       Spectr. Lick Bull., 497, 1939.

0289   sBN, bar: 0'55 x 0'08, (r); 0'7 x 0'4, 4 main knotty filam. arms w. v.F. out. extens. at large dist.
       Pseudo (R): 2'9 x 2'5.

0300   In Sculptor group w. 45, 55, 247, 253, 7793 (Ap.J., 130, 718, 1959). esBN or *, well res., dk. lanes, emiss.
       obj. Mt. W. vel. for "brighter of two emiss. patch 2'8 sp N.": +200 km/sec.
       Photo. Occ. Notes R.A.S., 3, No 18, 1956.
       Photom. Ap.J., 136, 107, 1962.
       HII reg. Obs., 79, 54, 1959. Zs.f.Ap., 50, 168, 1960.
       HI emiss. Epstein, Harvard Thesis, 1962.
       Radio emiss. Aust.J.Phys., 8, 368, 1955. Hdb.d.Phys., 53, 253, 1959.

0309   = Ho 27a. P. w. F. anon. (= Ho 27b) at 4'1. I 1602 at 13'5 sp. svBN in weak bar, sharp knotty (r): 0'4 x 0'3,
       many filam. knotty B arms, w. much branch.

0315   = Ho 28a. N 313, 316 (= Ho 28c, b) are *. N 311 at 5'5 sp., N 318 at 5'5 nf.

0327, 0329   = Ho 30a, b. Pair at 3'8. F anon. spindle at 2' np.

0337   Aysm., emiss. knots, resembles N 1313.

0337-A Anon.; LF dwarf Spiral of low surf. b. 26'6 sf N 337. See also Helwan 30.

0357   Brightest of group of 10 in 12' circle. P(a) w. N 355 (type Lp; 1' x 0'2) at 6'3. vsvBN in strong bar:
       0'6 x 0'1, weak (r): 0'85 x 0'55, traces of out. struct. Heid. dim. (0'4 x 0'4) rej., N only.

0375, 0379, 0380, 0382, 0383, 0384, 0385, 0386, 0388 Group of E, L; brightest is N 383.
       Photo. P.A.S.P., 71, 191, 1961.
       Dyn. P.A.S.P., 73, 191, 1961. A.J., 66, 545, 554, 1961.
       Spect. N 379 Ap.J., 83, 15, 1936. N 385 Ap.J., 74, 36, 1931.

0403   N 400, 401, 402 are *. N 399 at 7'8 sp. Anony. at 2'7 sf.

0404   vseBN w. dk. crescent and patches; traces of whorls or dk. lanes in lens, smooth neb. Possibly in Local Group?
       (neg. vel.). Photo. and Photom. Ap.J., 133, 314, 1961.

0406   Poor res. out. arms? Desc. M.N., 81, 601, 1921.

0407   In group of E, L, w. N 410, 414. N 408 is probably a *.

0410   In group 407-414. Photom. Ap.J., 71, 231, 1930.

0428   B. partly res. weak bar; weak, partly res. filam. arms, one stronger. Emiss. obj.; low surf. br. Lick (1956)
       vel. for 2 emiss. patches.

0434   P(b?) w. N 434-A at 3'1; P. w. N 440 at 5'1. vB cent. or bar, 2 or 3 diff. arms w. some knots form pseudo (R):
       0'9 x 0'6.

N 0434-A P(b?) w. N 434 at 3'1; prob. interacting. B spindle or lens w. 2 F anonal. arms.

0440 P. w. N 434 at 5'1. vB cent., B arms, poor. res., sharp outline.

0442 vsBN, traces of dk. lanes.

0450 vsBN, broad diff. compl. cent. w. 2 main broad knotty arms. Out. part. projects in front of s. anon. spiral (0'85 x 0'3) at 1'35.

0467 Group N 467-470-474. P(a) w. N 470 at 11'2. B diff. N w. weak narrow dk. lane; F. smooth arcs or whorls in envel. Lick 13 dim. (0'2 x 0'2) rej., N only.

0470 Group N 467-474. P(a) w. N 474 at 5'5. seBN in cent. of B lens w. many knotty B arms, pseudo (r): 0'75 x 0'5, F. out. filam. arms. Radio S. poss. identif., Aust.J.Phys., 11, 360, 1958.

0473 vsBN, v. weak bar, knotty (r): 0'35 x 0'2. P(a) w. N 463, SB: at 19'.

0474 Group N 467-474. P(a) w. N 470 at 5'5. svB diff. N in B diff. lens, vF smooth arcs or whorls in envel. Lick 13 dim. rej. N only.
      Photo. Ap.J., 135, 2, 1962.
      Radio S. poss. identif., Aust.J.Phys., 11, 360, 1958.

0488 vB diff. N in weak smooth (r): 0'9 x 0'7, many filam. knotty arms, pseudo (R): 4'5 x 3'2. N 490 at 8' nf.
      Photo. Ap.J., 92, 236, 1940.

0491 B * 0'8 sp. Revised type from Yale 26-in. pl.

0491-A vF out. arms?.

0495, 0499, 0507 In group, N 507 is the brightest.

0509 N 505 7'1 np.

0514 vsBN, weak bar w. dk. lanes, knotty, hexag. pseudo (r): 0'8 x 0'55, sev. knotty filam. arms.

0520 Nearly edgewise, P(c) of early spirals? Lick 1962 vel. of sp fainter comp. + 2857 (obs.). (B-V)(0) interpolated. B(0) from source A only.

0521 vsBN in narrow bar: 0'55 x 0'06; (r): 0'7 x 0'7, sev. filam. branch. arms. P(a) w. N 533 at 14'5.

0524 eBN in vB inner smooth part: 0'9 x 0'8, v. weak narrow rings of arcs outline lens. All dim. for B part. In group of 3 L and Sa sp. + others. Photo. and Photom. Ap.J., 133, 314, 1961.

0533 P(a) w. N 521 at 14'5. Radio S. poss. identif., Aust.J.Phys., 11, 360, 1958.

0545, 0547 = Ho 42a, b. P(a) at 0'6; N 547 is the E sf and smaller. Brightest pair in cluster. Radio emiss., Cal. Inst. Tech. Rad. Obs., 1960; Proc. 4th Berkeley Symposium, Vol. III, 245, 1960. P.A.S.P., 70, 146, 1958, w. photo.

0550 Photo. and SN 1961 P.A.S.P., 74, 215, 1962.

0560 In group, at ~ 5' from N 564.

0564 = Ho 44a. (Ho 44b at 0'8 is probably a *); I 120 at 6'8.

0578 vsBN in diff. complex bar w. dk. lanes: 0'55 x 0'1, pseudo (r): 0'6 x - , 3 main, part. res. filam. arms. 2 s. spirals seen through out. parts.

0584 = I 1712. = Ho 45b. P(a) w. N 586 at 4'3 (Ho 45c is a *). svB diff. N, smooth neb.
      Photom. Ap.J., 71, 231, 1930.
      Radio S. poss. identif., Aust.J.Phys., 11, 360, 1958.

0586 = Ho 45a. P(a) w. N 584 at 4'3. vsvBN, w. abs. lanes on one side, v. poor. res.

0598 = M 33, Local Group.
      Photo. Ap.J., 63, 236, 1926. Ritchey, L'Evolution de l'Astrophotographie ..., S.A.F., Paris, 1929.
      Photom. Ap.J., 83, 424, 1936; 91, 528, 1940; 108, 415, 1948; 130, 728, 1959. M.N., 97, 423, 1937. Medd. Lund, I, 175, 1950; II, 128, 1950. Izv. Pulkovo, 20, No 156, 87, 1956. A.J. USSR, 32, 16, 1955.
      Spect. Ap.J., 95, 52, 1942. P.A.S.P., 51, 112, 1939; 72, 283, 1960.
      Polar. Bull. Abastumani, No 18, 15, 1955.
      Dyn., rot., mass, Ap.J., 63, 67, 1926; 95, 5, 24, 1942; 97, 117, 1943; 104, 223, 1946. Zs.f.Ap., 35, 159, 1954. A.J., 59, 273, 1954; 67, 592, 1962.
      HII reg. Obs., 79, 54, 1959. Zs.f.Ap., 50, 168, 1960.
      HI emiss. P.A.S.P., 69, 356, 1957. B.A.N., 14, 19, 323, 1957. A.J., 67, 217, 1962.
      Radio emiss. M.N., 119, 297, 1959; 122, 479, 1961. P.A.S.P., 72, 368, 1960. Ap.J., 133, 322, 1961. A.J., 68, 70, 295, 1963.

0613 seBN in B bar w. dark lane, pseudo (r): 2'5 x 1'1. 4 main arms or 2 dble., one stronger, slightly asym. w. B knots, threshold of res.
      Photo. Helwan 9.
      Spect. Ap.J., 135, 697, 1962.

0615 vBN in B (r): 0'7 x 0'2; reg. knotty dble. arms.

N 0628 = M 74. vsBN in smooth cent. reg.: 0'15, as in M 33. 2 main well res. arms w. dk. matt. and m. branch. See also M.N., 85, 144, 1924. HI emiss. A.J., 66, 294, 1962; 67, 437, 1962. Harvard Rad. Ast. Rep., 101, 1962.

0643-B, C See Mem. Com. Obs., No 13, 1956. N 643 (mag. = 13.0 in H.A. 88,2) is a cluster in Small Magellanic Cloud; see P.A.S.P., 69, 252, 1957.

0660 B bar w. complex dk. lane: 2'85 x 0'7, vF smooth arms. Heid. 9 dim. (2'2 x 0'7) rej., bar only.

0672 = Ho 46a. P(b?) w. I 1727 (Ho 46b) at 9'. B E bar: 1'2 x 0'2, no N, dk. patches. Photo. and Spect. IAU Symp., 5, 1958 = Lick Cont., II, 81, 1958.

0676 vsBN w. B * almost superposed, poor. res.

0678 In group N 678-697.

0680 P. w. I 1730 at 3'7 nf.

0681 vsvBN in cent. of B extend. bulge, strong dk. lane on one side, asym. spiral patt.

0685 (r): 1'1 x 0'9.

0691 In 678-697 group.

0694 In 678-697 group. Dim. Lick 13 (0'5 x -), Heid. 9 (0'4 x 0'25) rej., N only.

0695, 0697 In 678-697 group. N 697 is the brightest.

0701 = Ho 47a. (Ho 47b at 3'3 is probably a *). P(a) w. I 1738 at 5'4. Sh. vB bar: 0'3 x 0'05. 2 main knotty arms, poor res.

0702 B complex lens w. dble. N, F out. whorls or (R): 1'75 x 1'55. Prob. interacting system.

0718 eBN in sB lens: 0'8 x 0'5. 2 main smooth arms form pseudo (R): 1'4 x 1'2.

0720 Heid. 9 dim. (0'7 x 0'5) rej., N only.

0736, 0740 In N 733-740 group.

0741 = I 1751. Brightest in group of Ellipt. N 742 at 0'8.

0750, 0751 P(c) of 2 E. w. vBN at 0'4. N of F comp. off cent., long asym. spur. m_H for 750 + 751. Pettit (1954) and Bigay et al. (1953) have mag. and colors for both comp. together. Photo. Erg. exakt. Naturwiss., XXIX, 372, 1956. Photom. Ap.J., 98, 47, 1943.

0753 vsvBN; hexag., pseudo (r): 0'33 x 0'3, many weak filam. arms w. knots. P(a) w. N 759 at 23'5.

0759 P(a) w. N 753 at 23'5.

0761 N 760 at 1'6 is a dble * (see MWC 626).

0770 P(b?) w. N 772 at 3'3.

0772 P(b?) w. N 770 at 3'3. svB diff. N, many weak tightly coiled arms, one abnormally strong.

0777 Dim. are for B part only. P(a) w. N 778 at 7'0.

0779 vBN, v. much forshort. weak bar in strong (r): 0'7 x 0'3, many weak, poor. res. arms. P. w. s. anon. SB(s)m? at 11'3.

0782 sBN, narrow bar, (r): 0'85 x 0'75, * 0'5 nf on (r).

0788 BN in diff. lens, v. weak out. whorls or (R), v. poor. res. P(a) w. I 184 at 18'5 p. Interacting chain of 3 Spirals (Ho 53a, b) at 24' sp.

0808 Dim. of B cent. part only. See Helwan 22.

0821 Chart: M.N., 74, 238, 1914.

0829 Pair w. N 830 at 4'5. N 842 at 13'2 from N 830.

0833, 0835, 0838, 0839, 0848 Group. N 833, 835 interact. pair at 1'.

0842 At 13' 2 of N 830.

0864 vsvBN in broad diff. weak bar, pseudo (r): 0'8 x 0'7. Spect. A.J., 61, 97, 1956.

0871 Strong bar: 0'2 x 0'06, asym. knotty arms. P. w. N 870 (E 0) at 1'6 and F anon. Sd at 4'4.

0876 Close p. w. N 877 at 2'1.

0877 Close p. w. N 876 at 2'1. Brightest of N 870-1-6-7 group. vsBN in B complex lens w. dk. lanes, hexag., pseudo (r): 0'7 x 0'5, 2 main knotty filam. arms w. branch.

N 0890 vsBN in vF envel. w. suggestion of dk. crescent near N. P(a) w. sF spiral at 14'5.

0891 In N 1023 group.
      Photo. Hdb.d.Ap., 5, 2, 843, 1933.
      Photom. Ap.J., 91, 539, 1940. Medd. Lund II, 114, 1945; 128, 1950. A.J., 56, 89, 1951.
      HII reg. Zs.f.Ap., 50, 168, 1960.
      Radio emiss. Hdb.d.Phys., 53, 253, 1959. P.A.S.P., 72, 368, 1960.

0895 (N 894 is part of it). vsBN, 2 main knotty arms w. m. branch. Desc. Ap.J., 46, 29, 1917, = MWC 132.

0908 vsBN, sev. knotty filam. arms. Photo. M.N., 65, 228, 1905.

0922 BN in sh. narrow bar: 0'5 x 0'08, sev. knotty filam. arms; strong, asym., hexag. outline, pseudo (R): 1'3 x 1'1.
      P(b?) w. anon. SB(s)b: at 13'.

0925 In N 1023 group. No BN(?), well res., 2 main knotty filam. arms w. branch. Dk. matt. in cent. part, sh. pseudo
      bar. Sev. dwarf Im nearby. Minor diam. in Heid. 9 rejected. (B-V) constant, interp. value.
      Photo. and Spect. IAU Symp. 5, 1958 = Lick Cont. II, 81, 1958.
      HII reg. Zs.f.Ap., 50, 168, 1960.

0936 vB diff. N or inner lens: 0'6 x 0'4, B smooth bar: 1'2 x 0'2, (r): 1'5 x 1'2, B at ends of bar, F arcs in envel.
      P(a) w. N 941 at 12'6.

0941 vsBN, pseudo (r): 0'5 x 0'25:, filam. knotty poor. res. arms. P(a) w. N 936 at 12'6 and anon. Sp at 13'6.

0942, 0943 = Ho 59a, b. Lund 6 dim.: 0'4 x 0'4, 0'8 x 0'2.

0945, 0948 = Ho 58a, b. P. at 2'7.

0949 B v. poor. res. spir. struct. in cent., vF envel.

0955 Desc. Ap.J., 46, 30, 1917 = MWC 132; Ap.J., 51, 281, 1920 = MWC 186.

0972 vB complex cent. bulge w. sN?, many dk. lanes and smooth out. arms. Pease (1917) dim. for minor axis is
      obviously an error (prob. should read 1'0 for 1'9).

0976 sBN, B inner arms, v. poor. res.; pseudo (r): 0'3 x 0'2, inner lens: 0'4 x 0'3.

0986 vBN in B bar w. dk. lanes: 1'4 x 0'45, F(r): 1'5 x 1'0, 2 main reg. arms, outer parts form vF (R): 3'4 x 2'5.

0991 In N 1052 group. vsBN in broad bar; knotty (r): 0'8 x 0'8; sev. filam. arms w. m. branch. Anon. 34'sp (Hel. 30).

1003 In N 1023 group. No BN, B bulge: 0'4 x 0'15, dk. mark., well res., many arms. Cluster of spirals in background.
      Photo. Ap.J., 88, 418, 1938.
      Spect. A.J., 61, 97, 1956.
      HII reg. Zs.f.Ap., 50, 168, 1960.
      SN 1937, Ap.J., 88, 289, 418, 1938; 89, 156, 1939; 96, 28, 1942. P.A.S.P., 50, 216, 238.
              Hdb.d.Phys., 51, 781, 1958.

1022 In N 1052 group. P(a) w. s. anon. SB(r) 0/a at 13'3. svBN, short bar: 0'5 x 0'2 w. dk. matt., smooth arms,
      pseudo (r): 0'9 x 0'8, pseudo (R): 1'85 x 1!85.

1023 Brightest of N 1023 group. eBN in cent. diff. bar: 1'3 x 1'0 near minor axis of projected lens, vF asym.
      extens. or satellite near one end of major axis. See also Ap.J., 46, 30, 1917 = MWC 132.
      Photom. Ap.J., 120, 439, 1954.
      Radio emiss. (upper limit), M.N., 123, 279, 1961.

1035 In N 1052 group.

1042 In N 1052 group. Misidentified as N 1048 in HA 88,2 and also by Morgan (1959) van den Bergh (1960). vsvBN in
      smooth lens, F(r): 0'9 x 0'5, 2 main part. res. filam. arms w. m. branch.

1047 In N 1052 group. sBN.

1048-A, B In N 1052 group. Close pair at 0'9. Poor. res. The object listed as N 1048 in HA 88,2 is actually
      N 1042. Mag. and colors by Pettit (1954) for both comp. together.

1052 Brightest in N 1052 group. Diff. vB cent., smooth. Spect. P.A.S.P., 48, 17, 1936. Ap.J., 129, 583, 1959.

1055 In N 1068 group.

1058 In N 1023 group. svBN in smooth cent. part, many part. res. arms, out. parts of low surf. br. P. w. fine anon.
      SA(r)0⁺ at 8'. New corrected Vel. by Zwicky (Ann. Rep. Mt. W.-P., 1962-63): +583 km/s.
      HII reg. Zs.f.Ap., 50, 168, 1960.
      SN 1961, Cont. Osserv. As. Asiago, No 142, 1963.

1068 = M 77. Brightest in N 1068 group. vBN, B pseudo (r): 0'5 x 0'35. Peculiar (B-V) relation for type.
      Photo. Ap.J., 97, 114, 1943; 130, 26, 1959. B.A.N., 16, 1, 1961.
      Photom. Ap.J., 50, 384, 1919; 108, 415, 1948. B.A.N., 16, 1, 1961.
      Spect. Ap.J., 97, 28, 1943; 130, 26, 1959; 135, 732, 1962. P.A.S.P., 53, 231, 1941. A.J., 61, 97, 1956.
      Orient., rot. Ap.J., 97, 117, 1943 = MWC 674; 127, 487, 1958.
      Radio emiss. Hdb.d.Phys., 53, 253, 1959. Cal. Inst. Tech. Rad. Obs., 5, 1960. P.A.S.P., 72, 368, 1960.
              Ap.J., 133, 322, 1961. Proc. 4th Berkeley Symp., Vol. III, 285, 1960.

N 1073 In N 1068 group. vsBN in narrow bar: 1'2 x 0'2, w. B knots, smooth, part. res. (r): 1'7 x 1'6, many filam.
arms. SN 1962, H.A.C. 1577, 1962. L'Astronomie, 76, 392, 1962. I.A.U. Circ. 1809, 1962; 1820, 21, 1963.

1079 svBN, weak bar: 0'9 x 0'4, pseudo (r): 1'3 x 0'65, outer arms form vF double (R): 4'3 x 2'7.

1084 vsBN, filam. knotty arms. Photo., rot., mass, Ap.J., 137, 376, 1963. SN 1963, I.A.U. Circ. 1843, 1856.

1087 In N 1068 group. P. w. N 1090 at 15' and N 1094 at 20'. Sh. B bar or double N, v. many knotty irreg. arms.
(B-V) relation constant.

1090 In N 1068 group. P. w. N 1087 at 15'. BN in narrow bar, pseudo (r): 1'0 x 0'5.
SN 1962, P.A.S.P., 75, 236, 1963.

1094 In N 1068 group. P. w. N 1087 at 20' and s. anon. S at 1'1.

1097 eBsN: 0'5 x 0'4 w. innermost N and spir. struct. form pseudo (r): 0'4 x 0'3, broad bar: 3'0 x 1'0 w. dk. lanes,
2 main filam. knotty arms form (R): 6'2 x 5'0. Small ellipt. companion N 1097-A at 3'5.
Photo. M.N., 8, 1019, 1925. P.N.A.S., 26, 33, 1940. P.A.S.P., 52, 309, 1947. Obs., 78, 125, 1958.
Ap.J., 132, 30, 1960.
Photom. Revista Ast., XXIX, No 13, 1957. Obs., 78, 123, 1958.
Spect. Ap.J., 132, 30, 1960; 135, 697, 1962.

1097-A Small E companion of N 1097 at 3'5. = No 174 in Lund 7.

1104 In N 1068 group. Heid. 9 dim. (0'2 x 0'2) rej., N only.

1136 vsvBN on F bar, (r): 0'9 x 0'8. (R)? P. w. s. anon. gal. at 3'0.

1140 vBN w. traces of spir. struct.; asym., part. res. short filam. arms. P(b) w. outlying neb. knots?

1143, 1144 P(b) at 0'7. Heid. 9 and Pal. 200-in. dim. for bright parts only.

1156 Highly res. dwarf w. traces of spir. struct., bar-like core, peanut-shaped. Heid. 9 dim. for bar only. Mt. W.
vel. refers to 2 emiss. patches p cent. neb.

1169 vsBN close to *, vF (r): 0'95 x 0'6, sev. vF filam. arms, v. low surf. br.

1175 BN in cent. of (r). Saturn-like, similar to N 7020. P. w. N 1177 (= I 281) at 2'5.

1179 vsBN, v. weak bar, knotty (r): 1'35 x 1'1, sev. F knotty filam. arms.

1186 Desc. Ap.J., 46, 31, 1917 = MWC 132.

1187 vsvBN, (r): 1'4 x 0'8, sev. filam. knotty arms. P(a) w. s. anon. SAB(r)0/a? at 21'. Error on corr. redshift in
HMS (Lick vel.). Spect. A.J., 61, 97, 1956.

1199 Brightest in N 1199 group. Heid. 9 and MW 60" dim. for bright part only.

1201 vB diff. N in B lens: 1'1 x 0'6, w. weak traces of (r) struct.: 0'9 x - .
Photo. and Photom. Ap.J., 133, 314, 1961.

1209 In N 1199 group. Heid. 9 dim. for B part only.

1232 vsB diff. N in weak broad bar, pseudo (r): 0'8 x 0'55, many knotty, part. res. filam. arms w. m. branch. P(a)
w. N 1232-A at 4'0. 1 aberrant val. of B-V (source C) rejected. Photo. P.A.S.P., 53, 269, 1941.

1232-A At 4'0 of N 1232. B bar: 0'3 x 0'08 w. asym. loop: 0'8 x 0'75. = No 212 in Lund 7 (0'7 x 0'5).
Typical dwarf SB(s)m system.

1241 = Ho 68a. P(a) w. N 1242 at 1'5. vsvBN, (r): 0'7 x 0'5, 2 main arms, weak filam. out. arms.

1242 = Ho 68c. P(a) w. N 1241 at 1'5; N 1243 (= Ho 68b) at 3'1 is a dble *. vsBN, poor. res. (r): 0'25 x 0'15, 3
main arms v. poor. res.

1248 svBN in B lens w. traces of (r) or dk. matt., pseudo (r): 0'25 x 0'19, F traces of whorls in lens and envel.
P(a) w. anon. SBp at 2'6.

1249 sh. B bar, no BN, asym.

1255 vsvBN, 2 main knotty filam. arms w. m. branch.; pseudo (r): 0'85 x 0'3. vF out. extens.

1270 In Perseus Cl. Error in HA 88,2; the obj. of mag. 12.7 is N 1275.
Photo. and Spect. Ap.J., 71, 355, 1930.
Photo. Ap.J., 119, 222, 1954.

1272, 1273, 1274 Perseus Cl. for ref. see N 1270 or N 1275. 1274: Heid. 9 dim. (0'15 x 0'15) rej.

1275 Perseus Cl. Misidentif. as N 1270 in HA 88,2. Mag. and colors reduced for type E.
Photo. Ap.J., 119, 221, 1954. Hdb.d.Phys., Vol. 53, 386, 1959.
Spect. Ap.J., 97, 28, 1943. Radio Astronomy, I.A.U. Symp. No 4, Cambridge, 1957, p. 113.
Radio emiss. Nature, 173, 164, 818, 1954. Ap.J., 119, 222, 1954; 133, 322, 1961. Proc. R.S.A., 248, 289, 1958.
P.A.S.P., 72, 368, 1960. Obs., 81, 14, 1961. Calif. Inst. Tech. Rad. Obs., 5, 1960.

N 1277, 1278, 1281, 1282 Perseus Cl.

1291 vBN, bar: 3'3 x 1'0, (R): 8'2 x 7'3. See also M.N., 82, 486, 1922.
      <u>Photo.</u> and <u>Photom.</u> Occ. Notes R.A.S., 3, No 18, 1956. M.N., 111, 526, 1951.
      <u>Spect.</u> Mem. R.A.S., 68, 69, 1961.

1292 sB cent. w. 2 main knotty arms and some branch., poor. res.

1293, 1294 Pair of Ellipt. at 2'.

1300 vseBN in narrow bar: 2'3 x 0'5, pseudo (r): 2'7 x 2'0, 2 main reg. part. res. arms form loops: 3'9 x 3'5;
      4'3 x 3'5.
      <u>Photo.</u> P.A.S.P., 59, 309, 1947. Hdb.d.Ap., 5, 2, 843, 1933.
      <u>Spect.</u> I.A.U. Symp., 5, 1958 = Lick Contr. II, 81, 1958. Ap.J., 135, 697, 1962.

1302 eBN in sh. bar: 0'6 x 0'3, smooth (r): 1'0 x 0'9, weak whorls or rings in envel., F(R): 3'3 x 2'9. P. w. anon.
      S sp. at 22'5. <u>Photo.</u> Ap.J., 92, 236, 1940.

1309 sBN, 2 main knotty arms, one stronger, poor. res.

1310 Fornax I Cl.

1313 vsBN, fairly B bar: 1'1 x 0'4, 2 main knotty, part. res. arms, one stronger, v. asym., many outlying knots and
      part. res. groups of *. Anon. small S at 16'5 sf. Mt. Stromlo vel. for emiss. neb. 1'4 ssf cent. bar.
      <u>Photo.</u> and <u>Photom.</u> Ap.J., 137, 720, 1963.
      <u>SN 1962,</u> Disc. by Sersic, unpubl.

1315 sBN, pseudo (r): 0'9 x - , poor. res. In N 1315-32 group.

1316 Fornax I Cl. vB diff. cent. w. dk. clouds, smooth neb. P(a) w. N 1317 at 6'3.
      <u>Photo.</u> Obs., 74, 248, 1954.
      <u>Photom.</u> Revista Ast., XXIX, No 13, 1957.
      <u>Spect.</u> Mem. R.A.S., 68, 69, 1961.
      <u>Radio emiss.</u> Fornax A, Obs., 73, 252, 1953; 74, 248, 1954. Ap.J., 125, 1, 1957; 133, 322, 1961. Aust.J.Phys.,
          11, 400, 517, 1958. P.A.S.P., 72, 368, 1960. Cal. Inst. Tech. Rad. Obs., 5, 1960.

1317 = 1318 Fornax I Cl. P(a) w. N 1316 at 6'3. eBN in pseudo (r): 0'45 x 0'35, weak diff. bar, vF out whorls form
      F(R): 1'9 x 1'8. HA 88,2 dim. (series a) (0'7 x 0'6) rej., N only.

1319 P(a) w. N 1325 at 6'8.

1325 P(a) w. N 1319 at 6'8, N 1332 at 28'5. sBN, F knotty filam. arms, v. poor. res.

1325-A = Ho VI (1958). P(a) w. N 1325 at 13'6, N 1332 at 20'6. sBN, weak bar, (r): 0'7 x 0'7.

1326 Fornax I Cl. vBN, smooth narrow bar: 0'85 x 0'2, smooth (r): 1'0 x 0'85, vF (R): 2'6 x 2'0.

1326-A, B Fornax I Cl. Pair in contact at 3'. Both F.

1331 = I 324?. P. w. N 1332 at 3'0. In N 1315-32 group.

1332 vB diff. N in B lens, smooth neb. P. w. N 1331 in 3'0. In N 1315-32 group. <u>Spect.</u> Sky & Tel., 8, 2, 1948.

1337 FN w. dk. lane, 2 main filam. spir. arms w. m. branch.

1341 Fornax I Cl. * 1'2 ssf.

1344 = 1340. B cent., smooth neb., no struct. <u>Photom.</u> M.N., 111, 526, 1951.

1350 Fornax I Cl.
      <u>Desc.</u> Helwan 9. Note corr. to NGC and HA 88,2 coord.
      <u>Photo.</u> and <u>SN 1960,</u> P.A.S.P., 72, 208, 1960.

1351 Fornax I Cl. vBN.

1353 vsvBN, weak bar w. dk. mark., pseudo (r): 1'05 x 0'4, sev. F filam. arms.

1355 vsvBN. Possibly edgewise S(r). P(a) w. N 1358 at 6'8.

1357 sB diff. N, 2 main arms w. a few condens., cent. smooth lens.

1358 vsvBN in sh. narrow bar: 0'55 x 0'1, weak arms form pseudo (r): 1'5 x 1'3. P(a) w. N 1355 at 6'8.

1359 Pec.; sh. knotty bar-like axis: 0'4 x 0'1 surrounded by incomp. pseudo (r): 1'4 x 0'75 w. extraneous asym. arm.
      P(a) w. anon. SAB(r)O$^+$ at 8'5. <u>Spect.</u> A.J., 61, 97, 1956.

1365 Fornax I Cl. eB complex N w. twisted dk. lane, narrow bar: 2'5 x 0'55 w. dk. lanes, 2 main, part. res. arms
      form pseudo (R): 10'05 x 5'9.
      <u>Photo.</u> Occ. Notes R.A.S., 3, No 18, 1956. Stockholm Ann., 17, No 3, 1951. Ap.J., 132, 30, 1960; 136, 118, 1962.
      <u>Spect.</u> Mem. R.A.S., 68, 69, 1961. Ap.J., 135, 697, 1962.
      <u>Rot., mass,</u> Ap.J., 132, 30, 1960; 136, 118, 1962. A.J., 67, 112, 1962.
      <u>SN 1957,</u> Carn. Inst. Yearbk., 57, 1958. Hdb.d.Phys., 51, 785, 1958.

N 1371 = 1367. svBN in sh. twisted bar, weak pseudo (r): 1'2 x 0'8, surrounded by weak out. whorls form pseudo (R): 5'2 x 3'3.

1374 Fornax I Cl. P. w. N 1375 at 2'4. BN.

1375 Fornax I Cl. P. w. N 1374 at 2'4. The negative vel. in Lick 1962 is probably spurious (night sky?).

1376 sBN, many filam. knotty arms. v. similar to M 101. P(a) w. anon. S sp at 5'3.

1379 Fornax I Cl. BN.

1380 Fornax I Cl. vBN, * 0'85 sp N. Photom. M.N., 111, 526, 1951.

1380-A Fornax I Cl. = Hel. 51 (Helwan 15). sBN.

1380-B Fornax I Cl. = Hel. 53 (Helwan 15) = N 1382? w. NGC coord. corrected. See Mem. Com. Obs., No 13, 1956.

1381 Fornax I Cl. svBN, disc 0'2 thick.

1385 B bar w. knots and dk. mark., 2 main part. res. arms, one extends in F asym. loop forming pseudo (R): 2'6 x 1'7. Spect. Ap.J., 135, 698, 1962.

1386 Fornax I Cl. sBN.

1387 Fornax I Cl. vBN, lens: 0'8 x 0'7, vF envel.

1389 Fornax I Cl. BN.

1393, 1394 In N 1383-1407 group.

1395 vB cent., smooth neb.

1398 LBN in narrow bar: 1'2 x 0'2, (r): 1'6 x 1'3, 2 main narrow, part. res. branch. arms, pseudo (R): 4'8 x 3'3. Photo. Ap.J., 92, 236, 1940. P.A.S.P., 59, 309, 1947.
Spect. Ap.J., 135, 697, 1961.

1399 Fornax I Cl. BN, * 0'3 n N. P(a) w. N 1404 at 10'2. Photom. M.N., 111, 526, 1951.

1400 sB diff. N w. weak dk. cresc. on one side. P(a) w. N 1407 at 11'8. In N 1383-1407 group.

1401 Dim. on Lick 36-in. pl.: 1'2 x 0'2:.

1404 Fornax I Cl. BN, * 0'9 sf. P(a) w. N 1399 at 10'2. Photom. M.N., 111, 526, 1951.

1407 Brightest of N 1383-1407 group. P(a) w. N 1400 at 11'8. sB diff. N.

1411 vBN. 0'3 x 0'25.

1415 vBN in B isol. lens: 1'4 x 0'55, w. spir. patt. of dk. lanes, eF (R): 3'1 x 1'7. P(a) w. N 1416 at 9'3.

1416 vsBN. P(a) w. N 1415 at 9'3. NGC coord. are correct (MWC 626), but separation from N 1415 indicates DIII corr. was justified.

1417 = Ho 70a. P(a) w. N 1418 at 5'0. svBN in bar, pseudo (r): 0'4 x - , sev. B arms w. some knots. Note error on Dec. in H.A. 88,2. Radio emiss. (possible identif.), Austral.J.Phys., 11, 360, 1958.

1418 = Ho 70b. P(a) w. N 1417 at 5'0. sBN, 2 main arms v. poor. res.

1421 vsBN in complex cent. part w. dk. lane. Classif. difficult.

1422 P(a) w. N 1426 at 31'.

1424 = 1429 vsvBN in pseudo (r): 0'3 x 0'17, 3 main arms, some knots. P(a) w. N 1417 at 19', N 1418 at 14'5.

1425 Fornax I Cl.? vsvBN in smooth cent. part w. traces of pseudo (r): 0'6 x 0'25, sev. filam. arms and lanes of dk. matter.

1426 sBN, smooth neb. P(a) w. N 1422 at 31', N 1439 at 30'.

1427 Fornax I Cl. sBN, * 1'8 p.

1427-A Fornax I Cl. F.

1428 Fornax I Cl. Noted w. sBN or * in Mt. Stromlo survey. The neg. vel. in Lick 1962 confirms that there is a * superimposed on N.

1433 seBN 0'7 x 0'35 tilted on smooth bar w. dk. lane: 2'4 x 0'8, (r): 2'8 x 2'2, w. some knots, 2 main F almost smooth arms w. sh. branch. form pseudo (R): 5'8 x 5'0. Spect. Mem. R.A.S., 68, 69, 1961.

1437 Fornax I Cl. vsBN, (r): 1'5 x 1'0.

1439 vsBN, P(a) w. N 1426 at 30'.

N 1440   = 1442. P(a) w. N 1452 at 22'.

1441   svBN, poor. res. In N 1441-1453 group. P. w. N 1449 at 4'2, N 1451 at 6'1.

1448   = 1457. sBN. See also M.N., 81, 601, 1921. HB 914, 6, 1940. Note correction to H.A. 88,2 R.A.

1449, 1451 In N 1441-1453 group.

1452   = 1455. The obj. N 1455 in Lick 13 w. NGC coord. corrected is same as N 1452 in HA 88,2; Publ. Dunlap Obs., II, No 6, 1960, and Yerkes 1958 list. P(a) w. N 1440 at 22'.

1453   Brightest in N 1441-1453 group. vBN. Photo. and Spect. IAU Symp., 5, 1958 = Lick Cont. II, 81, 1958.

1461   vsB diff. N, traces of (r): 1'4 x - .

1469   See H.A., 105, 229, 1937 (Dim: 2'0 x 0'6).

1482   P. w. N 1481 at 3'3. SN 1937, P.A.S.P., 51, 36, 1939. Rev. Mod. Phys., 12, 66, 1940. Ap.J., 96, 28, 1942.

1483   See HB 914, 6, 1940 (Dim: 1'4 x 0'9).

1485   See HA 105, 229, 1937 (Dim: 3'0 x 0'9).

1487   Pec., coll? systems. 2 BN in contact at 0'25 + E condens. at 0'35 from B (north) comp. + F knots at 0'2 s of F comp. w. out. streamers; overall extens. 6': x 2'5. Photom. Zs.f.Ap., 47, 9, 1959.

1493   vsBN, sh. bar, (r): 1'2 x 1'1, knots in (r) and arms.

1494   no BN, many ill-def. F arms.

1507   B knotty bar: 0'7 x 0'1, asym. arm or loop w. dk. matt.

1510   vBN, strongly condensed. NGC descr. (F, pL) is in error. P(a) w. N 1512 at 5'0.

1511   no BN, B bulge. Corr. to NGC dec. in M.N., 81, 601, 1921, is an error. Suspected SN = HV 11970 (HB 917, 1943) was not confirmed, see Harv. Rep. 387.

1512   vBN, strong bar and (r): 2'5 x 1'9, vF out. envel. 7': x 6': w. resid. spir. arcs 5'7 x 4'5. P(a) w. N 1510 at 5'0. Spect. Mem. R.A.S., 68, 69, 1961.

1515   vB cent., 2 main arms, dk. lanes on one side. P(a) w. N 1515-A at 2'0 and sev. s. gal. in field.

1515-A   at 2'0 of N 1515. svBN on narrow bar: 0'35 x 0'1, reg. (r): 0'45 x 0'45, brighter at ends of bar; sev. weak poor. res. arms.

1518   B bar part. res: 0'7 x 0'17, 2 main part. res. arms, one stronger. P(a) w. N 1521 at 22'. Spect. A.J., 61, 97, 1956.

1521   P(a) w. N 1518 at 22'. MWC 626 correction to NGC R.A. not verified. Correction for gal. rot. in HMS cat. is in error.

1527   vBN in s. lens: 1'2 x 0'5; N betw. 2 * at 1'2 n and s. See also M.N., 81, 601, 1921.

1530   vsvBN w. surround. spir. patt., broad bar: 1'2 x 0'5 w. dk. lanes, (r): 1'7 x 1'2; 2 main filam. arms form pseudo (R): 4'3. Mag., Ap.J., 85, 325, 1937.
         Photo. Hdb.d.Ap., 5, 2, 843, 1933.
         Spect. Ap.J., 135, 697, 1962.

1530-A See Ap.J., 82, 74, 1935; 85, 325, 1937. (= I 381? for which IC coord. are 4^h37^m8, + 75°34' (1950)).

1531, 1532 Pair at 1'8. Drawing in Helwan 9.

1533   vBN, traces of sh. bar.

1536   vsBN, bar: 0'6, asym.

1537   H.A. 88,2 dim.: 1'2 x 0'6 (series a').

1543   vBN, bar: 2'5 x 1'0, (R): 4'7 x 4'7.

1546   vsBN, asym. dk. lane. Mt. Stromlo 30-in. dim. (0'9 x 0'3, 1'6: x 0'6:) N and lens only.

1549   vBN. Photom. M.N., 111, 526, 1951.

1553   eBN, lens: 1'8 x 1'0, slight brightening at rim of lens forms F(r): 1'2 x 0'7. P(a) w. I 2058 at 21'5. Photom. M.N., 111, 526, 1951.
         Spect. Mem. R.A.S., 68, 69, 1961.

1558   See M.N., 81, 601, 1921. D x d = 3' x 1' (90°).

1559   No N, sh. B bar, B arms, knots, asym., high surf. br. Photo. P.N.A.S., 26, 34, 1940.

1560   BM, no def. N, F part. res. arms, low surf. bright. Lick 13 dim. (6' x 1') is for B parts only.

N 1566 svBN, asym., vF out. arms.
        Photo. P.N.A.S., 26, 34, 1940. Observatory, 77, 146, 1957.
        Photom. Revista Astr., XXIX, No 143, 1957. Observatory, 77, 146, 1957.
        Spect. Mem. R.A.S., 68, 69, 1961.

1569 vB core, dk. mark., well res., little trace of spir. struct. Sugg. as possible Local Group member by Hubble
      (1942) because of low velocity. Photo. and Spect. P.A.S.P., 47, 319, 1935.

1574 vBN in s. lens w. L F envel., * 0'35 sf N, B * 1'2 sf N.

1587 = Ho 76a. P. w. N 1588 (Ho 76b) at 1'2. N 1589 at 12' n.

1596 vBN, * 0'6 p N. P. w. N 1602 at 3'0.

1599 In N 1600 group. N 1579 in Helwan 38 is a misprint.

1600 Brightest in group. P(a) w. N 1601 at 1'6, N 1603 at 2'5. For other group members N 1603, 04, 06, 07, 09, 11,
      12, 13, see dim. data in Heid. 9, Lick 13, Helwan 38. Discordant val. of (B-V) (source A) rejected.
      Spect. Ap.J., 135, 733, 1962.

1601 In N 1600 group. P(a) w. N 1600 at 1'6.

1602 BM, no BN, (r): 0'95: x 0'7:, P. w. N 1596 at 3'0. See also M.N., 81, 601, 1921.

1614 eBN, 2 main mass. B arms, strong asym., F out. streamer. Radio emiss. possible identif. w. Mills source 04-012,
      Aust.J.Phys., 10, 162, 1957.

1615 Inner dim. on Lick 36-in. pl.: 1'3: x 0'3:.

1617 vBN, bar: 1'8, poor. res.

1618 (r): 1'1 x 0'55. In N 1618-1625 group. P(a) w. N 1622 at 7'8.

1622 = Ho 77a. (Ho 77b at 1'4 is probably a *); N 1618 at 7'8, N 1625 at 10'2. Heid. 9, Lund 6 dim. (0'9 x 0'2)
      are for (r) only.

1625 In N 1618-1625 group. P(a) w. N 1622 at 10'2. Pseudo (r): 0'85 x - .

1637 vsvBN in sh. bar: 0'6 x 0'2, pseudo (r): 1'0 x 0'7, strong asym. vF but res. out. arms.

1638 vBN. Heid. 9 dim., N only.

1640 sBN in strong narrow bar, (r): 1'0 x 0'75. Photo. and Spect. IAU Symp., 5, 1958 = Lick Cont. II, 81, 1958.

1642 sBN, similar to M 101.

1659 vsBN, s. B (r): 0'17 x 0'07, many knotty filam. arms, strong, asym. and sharp outline.

1666 vBN, F(r): 0'5 x 0'5. P(a) w. N 1667 at 15'.

1667 vsBN, weak bar, knotty (r): 0'33 x 0'24, sev. knotty arms w. branch. P(a) w. N 1666 at 15'.

1672 vBN, bar: 2'4, ansae.

1688 sh. B bar, asym.

1699 P. w. N 1700 at 6'6. vsBN, (r): 0'3 x 0'2. See also Ap.J., 51, 283, 1920 = MWC 186.

1700 P. w. N 1699 at 6'6. vBN, smooth. See also Ap.J., 51, 283, 1920 = MWC 186. Heid. 9 dim: 0'5 x 0'3, N only.
      Velocity by Pease (+ 800) was an error, see A.J., 61, 97, 1956. Fairly large scatter of (B-V) values.
      Spect. Ap.J., 135, 733, 1962.

1703 sBN, F bar, (r): 0'7 x - .

1705 vBN, asym. wings ? * 14.5 superposed.

1720 vsvBN in B bar w. strong dk. lane: 0'5 x 0'2, 2 main smooth arms form pseudo (R): 1'35 x 1'2. P(a) w. N 1726 at
      8'2. Heid. 9 dim. 1'1 x 0'3 for B part only.

1726 svB diff. N, smooth neb. w. weak dk. lane on one side. P(a) w. N 1720 at 8'2, and I 398 at 17'5.

1741 v Pec., P(c); P(b) w. s. B object (= IC 399) at 2'2 sf.

1744 Narrow, knotty B bar: 1'3 x 0'3; sev. part. res. filam. arms; asym.; v. low surf. bright.

1771 See M.N., 81, 601, 1921. Dim: 1' x 0'5.

1779 P. w. I 402 at 14'5.

1784 vsBN in narrow bar w. dk. mark., many knotty arms, (r): 1'3 x 0'7. Lick 13 dim. for (r) only.

1792 vsBN, B arms. Drawing in Helwan 9.

N 1796   no BN, sh. bar, asym.

1800   HA 88,2: 0'8 x 0'4 Dim. (series a').

1808   vB complex N incl. sev. B knots: 0'34 x 0'14 in B isol. lens w. many dk. lanes, eF out. whorls form
       pseudo (R): 6'5 x 3'9.

1832   svBN in strong bar: 0'4 x 0'15; (r): 0'6 x 0'4; sev. B arms part. res. w. m. branch.
       Spect. Ap.J., 135, 699, 1962.

1888, 1889   Close pair P(b) at 0'3; anon. Sc sp. at 10'8 nf. Mag. and colors for 1888+89 by Pettit (1954). Helwan 22
       has N 1888 "in E 145°"; p.a. 60° in Lick 13 is an error. Spect. A.J., 61, 197, 1956. IAU Symp., 5, 1958
       = Lick Cont., II, 81, 1958.

1947   B diff. N cut by strong dk. lane, + other dk. lane on one side. Rich LMC star field. NGC dec. is in error by
       1°. Radio emiss. (not confirmed), Observatory, 73, 252, 1953; 74, 130, 248, 1954.

1954   Pair at 5'1 w. N 1957. See Helwan 21, 30.

1961   = I 2133. vsBN, hexag. pseudo (r): 0'95 x 0'8?, 2 main branch arms w. some knots. Mag., Ap.J., 85, 325, 1937.

1964   svBN with vB * superposed in B lens: 1'2 x 0'4 w. dk. lanes, 2 main arms w. branch. form pseudo (R): 2'3 x 1'0.

2082   s elong. N, (r): 0'75 x 0'5, poor. res. Rich LMC field.

2090   sB diff. N in B lens: 1'65 x 0'6 w. sev. knotty arms and dk. lanes, poor. res., vF knotty out. arms.

2139   = I 2154. Note correction to HA 88,2 (after NGC); IC coord. are correct. sBN in narrow reg. bar: 0'35 x 0'06,
       sev. branch. knotty arms, slightly asym., sev. B emiss. knots. Spect. A.J., 61, 97, 1956.

2146   Pec., L bulge w. many irreg. abs. mark., 2 main smooth arms, one w. dk. lane, asym. P(b?) w. N 2146-A at 19'.
       Mag., Ap.J., 85, 325, 1937. Mag. source F rejected from mean B(0). Photo. and Spect. and Rot., mass,
       Ann.d'Ap., 13, 362, 1950. Ap.J., 130, 740, 1959.

2146-A P(b?) w. N 2146 at 19'. See Ap.J., 51, 276, 1920 = MWC 186; 82, 74, 1935; 85, 325, 1937. Dim. 8' x 2' in
       MWC 186 maybe misprint for 3' x 2'.

2179   B diff. N, smooth neb. w. traces of spir. arcs or whorls in out. parts.

2188   sBN in sh. bar-like struct.: 0'6 x 0'17 from which extend asym. smooth wings or arms. Poss. rear end-on view of
       edgewise SB(s)m. P. w. anon. RSB(r)O⁺ at 16'.

2196   B diff. N in smooth bulge w. F smooth arcs forming hexag. pseudo (R): 1'5 x 1'4, slightly asym.

2207   Interacting pair P(b) w. I 2163 at 1'4. vBN, pseudo (r): 0'8 x 0'5, 2 main knotty filam. arms, out. part on one
       side over I 2163.

2217   vB diff. N, smooth narrow bar: 1'4 x 0'25, (r): 1'3 x 1'2, weak spir. arcs form (R): 3'2 x 2'9. Note corr. to
       RA of HA 88,2; NGC correct.

2223   sBN w. * close, weak bar in F(r): 0'95 x 0'85, sev. filam. arms, low surf. bright.

2256, 2258 See H.A., 105, 229, 1937. N 2256, D: 1'6 x - ; N 2258, D: 1'3 x - .

2268   vsvBN, weak bar, (r): 0'5 x 0'3, many filam. arms, poor. res. Heid. 9 dim. for B only.
       Mag., Ap.J., 82, 62, 1935; 85, 325, 1937.

2273-B See Ap.J., 82, 74, 1935. N 2273 (Sa) at 40' nf 2273-B.

2276   svBN, weak bar, hexag. pseudo (r): 0'52 x 0'43, many knotty filam. arms, sharp outline. Heid. 9 dim., B part
       only. P. w. N 2300 at 6'3.
       Spect. A.J., 61, 97, 1956.
       Mag., Ap.J., 82, 62, 1935; 85, 325, 1937.

2280   sB diff. N, 2 main knotty filam. arms w. m. branch., low surf. bright.

2290, 2291, 2294 Group of S w. N 2288, 89. Photo. Ap.J., 51, 286, 1920 = MWC 186.

2300   vsBN in sB lens: 0'5 x 0'4. Possibly SAB(s)O⁻. P. w. N 2276 at 6'3, and I 1455 at 10'; other gal. in field.
       Heid. 9 dim., lens only. Mag., Ap.J., 82, 62, 1935; 85, 325, 1937.

2310   sBN. HA 88,2 dim. 2'0 x 0'5 (a') for B part only.

2314   vBN. P(a) w. I 2174 (SO) at 5'7.

2326-A See Ap.J., 82, 74, 1935. N 2326 (SB(s)) at 5' np.

2336   vsN in weak bar, (r): 1'2 x 0'7, many weak filam. arms w. knots. P(a) w. I 467 at 20'. Heid. 9 dim. for B
       part only.

2339   vsvBN in weak compl. bar: 0'55 x 0'14 w. dk. lanes, hexag. pseudo (r): 0'65 x 0'6, F knotty arms.

2344   See Ap.J., 84, 270, 1936 = MWC 549 where source of vel. (+ 520) is unknown and has not been confirmed.

N 2347 esvBN in B (r): 0'2 x 0'1, traces F (R): 1'4 x 0'75. P(a) w. I 2179 (E1) at 13'2. Yerkes type k E 2 is an error or applies to I 2179.

2366 Well res. bar: 3'5 x 0'8, weak out. arms extens., emiss. obj.; outlying res. patch 3' sp center; see also Ap.J., 46, 34, 1917. Lick 1956 vel. for emiss. patch sp. center.: + 229 km/sec.
Photo. and Spect. P.A.S.P., 47, 320, 1935.
Photom. Medd. Lund II, 128, 1950.
HII reg. Zs.f.Ap., 50, 168, 1960.

2369 sBN, B bar w. dk. lanes: 0'9 x 0'25. F arms.

2379 In N 2389 group.

2389 Brightest in group. vsvBN in pseudo (r): 0'25 x - , many knotty filam. arms, poor. res. P(a) w. N 2388, SB(s)b, at 3'4. Wrong sign of correction for gal. rot. in HMS cat. (Lick vel.).

2403 In M 81 group. N 2404 is a detail. BM no BN or esN or *, many well res., irreg. arms, broad bar.
Desc. Ap.J., 51, 287, 1920; 56, 200, 1922.
Photom. Ap.J., 91, 531, 1940. Medd. Lund II, 128, 1950.
HII reg. Observatory, 79, 54, 1959. Zs.f.Ap., 50, 168, 1960.
Radio emiss. P.A.S.P., 72, 368, 1960.
HI emiss. A.J., 66, 294, 1962; 67, 437, 1962.

2415 Haro obj. No 1; Bol. Tonantzintla, 14, 9, 1956.

2417 sN, reg., asym., * 0'8 s of N.

2424 vsBN in narrow bar: 0'95 x 0'1, dk. lane on one side.

2427 vFvsN, 2 main knotty F arms, strongly asym. Photo. Occ. Notes R.A.S., 3, No 18, 1957.

2441 vsBN in incompl. (r): 0'6 x 0'35, v. weak bar, sev. knotty arms, poor. res. See also HA 105, 229, 1937.

2442 vsBN. N 2443 is part of same. Dim. in HA 88,2 (series a') should read 6'0 x 5'0.
Photo. Occ. Notes R.A.S., 3, No 18, 1957.
Orient. Ap.J., 127, 487, 1958.

2444-45 Desc., Photo., Vel., Ap.J., 130, 12, 1959; 138, 863, 886, 1963. Heid. 9 dim.: 2444: 0'2 x 0'2 (for E compan.), 2445: 1'2 x 1'2 (probably for mass of emiss. knots). U,B,V photom. Ap.J., 138, 863, 1963.

2460 vBN, spir. struct. in lens: 0'7 x 0'5, vF smooth arms form pseudo (R): 4'3 x 3'1. P(a) w. I 2209 at 5'5 sp.

2466 sBN, * 0'65 sf N, poor. res. P. w. s. B anon. gal. 3'7 np.

2468, 2469 Mag. in Ap.J., 85, 325, 1937.

2475 Close pair w. N 2474.

2500 vsBN in sh. bar: 0'6 x 0'17, many well res. clumpy arms, pseudo (r): 0'9 x 0'9. In group w. N 2541, 2552.

2507 = Ho 92a. (Ho 92b is a *). F out. whorls.

2521 Mag. in Ap.J., 85, 325, 1937. Heid. 9 dim.: 0'3 x 0'3 (N?).

2523 sB diff. N on narrow B bar: 0'6 x 0'1, (r): 0'9 x 0'75, sev. filam. arms w. knots. P(a) w. 2523-B at 8'8, and anon. SB(s)b at 7'2.

2523-A See Ap.J., 82, 74, 1935. HA 105, 229, 1937.

2523-B P(a) w. N 2523 at 8'8. See Ap.J., 82, 74, 1935. HA 105, 229, 1937. Exact minor replica of N 5746.

2523-C See Ap.J., 82, 74, 1935. HA 105, 229, 1937.

2525 esBN or * in sh. bar: 0'55 x 0'15, pseudo (r): 0'8 x - , B mass., part. res. arms form pseudo (R): 2'1 x 1'4.

2532 vsvBN, sev. B knotty arms, high surf. bright., pseudo (r); 0'4 x 0'3.

2534 Mag. in Ap.J., 85, 325, 1937. Heid. 9 dim.: 0'3 x 0'3 (N?).

2535 = Ho 94a. P(b) w. N 2536 at 1'8. sBN, (r): 0'6 x 0'6, arm extends to 2'8. SN 1901, A.N., 221, 47, 1924.
Ap.J., 88, 289, 1938.

2536 = Ho 94b. P(b) w. N 2535 at 1'8.

2537 B partly res. bar: 0'5 x 0'17 w. strong asym. arm, part. res. v. weak out. loop. P(a) w. I 2233 at 19' and 2537-A at 4'5. See also Ap.J., 51, 287, 1920. Mt. W. and Lick 1956, 1962 vel. for emiss. NW of center. Lick 1962 vel. for cent. bar: +421 km/sec. Mag. of source F rejected (error of identif?).
Photo. Observatory, 74, 130, 1954.

2537-A P(a) w. N 2537 at 4'5.

2541 vsFN in smooth cent. as in M 33, many well res. arms. In group w. N 2500, 2552. Heid. 9 dim. (4'0: x 1'8:) for B part only.

N 2543   = I 2232, vsvBN, broad bar w. dk. matt.; 0'5 x 0'25, pseudo (r): 1'0 x 0'6, F reg. arms.

2544   See also HA, 105, 229, 1937.

2545   vsvBN, F smooth bar: 0'4 x 0'08, B(r); 0'55 x 0'3, smooth F out. arms form pseudo (R): 1'0 x 0'8.

2549   eB elong. N in elong. lens: 1'5 x 0'4 w. traces of brightening at tips, F out. envel. Mag. 85, 325, 1937.

2550   See HA, 105, 229, 1937.

2550-A See Ap.J., 82, 74, 1935. HA 105, 229, 1937.

2551   B diff. N in smooth lens: 1'0 x 0'8 w. traces F whorls or dk. lanes. Sev. other F S in field.

2552   vsFN, highly res., irreg. spir. struct., v. low surf. bright. In group w. N 2500, 2541.

2562, 2563 In a group.

2565   SN 1960, P.A.S.P., 73, 175, 1961.

2573   vsvBN. Close to South Celestial Pole, note RA and Precession.

2578   sBN in B bar: 0'55 x 0'02, incompl. (r): 0'8 x - . P. w. anon. SB(s) at 3'0.

2591   Mag.: Ap.J., 85, 325, 1937.

2601   vsBN, 2 * involv.

2608   2 * superp. on bar, pseudo (r): 1'0 x 0'35. SN 1920, A.N., 210, 373, 1920. Ap.J., 88, 290, 1938.
       P.A.S.P., 35, 116, 1923.

2613   svBN in B bulge, many reg. filam. arms w. absorpt. on one side, similar to M 31. Helvan 15 dim. (5' x 1') is
       for B part only. Rot. Ap.J., 97, 117, 1943 = MWC 674.

2614   See also H. A., 105, 229, 1937; D: 2'5 x - .

2623   Poss. radio source (unconfirmed); see Humason et. al. (1956).

2629   See H.A., 105, 229, 1937; D: 1'2 x - . P. w. N 2641 at 6'5 ssf.

2633   vsvBN, B bar w. dk. lanes: 0'7 x 0'25 in lens 0'8 x 0'4, 2 main reg. arms form pseudo (R): 1'9 x 0'95. P(a) w.
       N 2634 at 8'2. Brightest in a group. See HA, 105, 229, 1937.

2634   P(a) w. N 2633 at 8'3 and anon. 2634-A at 2'. See H.A. 105, 229, 1937; D: 1'2 x - .

2634-A P(a) w. N 2634 at 2'. Poor. res., dim. for B part only.

2636   vBN, compact; dim. for B part only; see H.A., 105, 229, 1937; D: 0'5 x - .

2639   vsvBN, B(r): 0'45 x 0'2 in lens 0'9 x 0'45; part. obsc. on one side; rev. type doubtful, possibly SA(r)0$^+$.

2642   svBN in weak bar: 0'55 x 0'14, (r): 0'65 x 0'55, 4 or 5 knotty, filam. arms. P(a) w. anon. Sm? at 3'2.
       B(0) = 13.59 (Source C, w = 0.45).

2646   sBN on F bar, traces of (r): 0'43 x 0'38:. Dim. for B part only. The object identif. as N 2646 in HA, 88, 2 is
       I 520. See HA 105, 229, 1937; D: 0'7 x - .

2650   See H.A., 105, 229, 1937; D x d : 1'1 x 0'9. (r) = 0'55. Heid. 9 dim. for N only.

2654   Mag.: Ap.J., 85, 325, 1937.

2655   vB vL N w. asym. dk. matt. in lens (?): 1'9 x 1'4, vF smooth out. whorls, center similar to N 1316. Whole
       object similar to I 5267. See also M.N., 74, 239, 1914. Yerkes type E4p (Morgan, 1958) is an error, probably
       refers to N only. Heid. 9 dim. for B part only. Mag., Ap.J., 82, 62, 1935; 85, 325, 1937.

2672   = Ho 99a. Close P(a) w. N 2673 at 0'6. Brightest in a group, incl. N 2667, -73, -77 and sev. IC obj.
       Photom. M.N., 96, 602, 1936.
       SN 1938 ? C.P. Gaposchkin, "Galactic Novae", 1957.

2673   = Ho 99b. P(a) w. N 2672 at 0'6. Rev. type doubtful, poss. SOp.

2681   eBN in smooth (r): 0'6 x 0'6, F whorls in lens, pseudo (R): 2'1 x 2'0.
       Photo. Ap.J., 104, 219, 1946. Stockholm Ann., 14, 1942; 15, 1948.
       Orient. Stockholm Ann., 15, No 4, 1948. (Note: 200-in. photog. show outer whorls to be of same sense as inner
              spiral pattern).

2683   svBN in peanut-shaped bulge, many filam. arms w. dk. lanes on one side, pseudo (R): 7'3 x 0'85.
       Spect. Ap.J., 135, 733, 1962.
       Rot. Ap.J., 97, 117, 1943 = MWC 674.

2685   vB much elong. bar-like core w. asym. dk. lanes on one side, assoc. w. anomalous whorls, whose axis of rot. is
       apparently in the main equat. plane marked by outer F(R): 4'1 x 1'8; a very strange object. H.A., 88,2 dim.
       (m_c series: 2'0 x 0'5) is for core only.
       Photo. Ap.J., 130, 20, 1959. Mag. Ap.J., 85, 325, 1937.

N 2693   P(a) w. N 2694 at 1'. BN. Heid. 9 dim. for B part only. Photom. M.N., 98, 618, 1938. Mag. and colors for
         N 2693 + 94 sources B, F, H.

  2694   Compact EO at 1' of N 2693.

  2698   In a group w. N 2690, 95, 97, 99, 2702, 06.

  2701   vsBN, v. weak bar w. dk. lanes, pseudo (r): 0'95 x 0'5, knotty spir. arms. Yerkes type I (Morgan 1958) is an
         error. Object is similar to N 2712.

  2708   Pair w. N 2709 at 8'.

  2712   vsBN, smooth narrow bar: 0'55 x 0'03, (r): 1'0 x 0'55, sev. knotty branch. arms.

  2713   svBN in strong bar w. dk. lanes, pseudo (r): 1'1 x 0'55, 2 main filam. arms w. some knots form pseudo (R):
         2'95 x 0'85. P(a) w. N 2716 at 11'.

  2715   vsBN, pseudo (r): 0'75 x 0'33, sev. filam. knotty arms, sharp outline.
         Photom. Medd. Lund II, 128, 1950.
         Mag. Ap.J., 85, 325, 1937.

  2716   = Ho 104a. P(a) w. N 2713 at 11' (Ho 104b at 1'8 is a dble *). Close to cl. of F gal. vsvBN, B(r):
         0'2 x 0'17, v. poor. res., traces of (R): 0'8 x - .

  2719, 2719-A = Ho 105a, b. Pair at 0'4. Anon. F SB at 9'5 nff.

  2722   Note corr. to NGC coord. (see Helwan 21). Heid. 9 dim: 0'3 x 0'3 (N?).

  2723   Heid. 9 dim.: 0'2 x 0'2 (N?).

  2726   Mag.: Ap.J., 85, 325, 1937.

  2732   vsvBN. P(a) w. anon. SO sp. w. eBN at 4' f. Heid. 9 dim. (0'4 x 0'3) rej., N only? Mag. Ap.J., 85, 325, 1937.

  2742   sBN, sev. filam. knotty arms. Mag. Ap.J., 85, 325, 1937.

  2742-A See Ap.J., 82, 74, 1935; Mag.: 85, 325, 1937.

  2744   B complex center, 2 main smooth arms, poss. long extens. Interacting system? In N 2749 group.

  2748   vB center w. sN, sev. knotty arms w. dk. lanes, poor. res.
         Mag. 82, 62, 1935; 85, 325, 1937.
         Spect. IAU Symp., 5, 1958 = Lick Cont. II, No. 81, 1958.

  2749   Brightest in group incl. N 2744, -45, -47, -51, -52.

  2763   vB sh. bar: 0'17 x 0'06 w. sN, pseudo (r): 0'45 x 0'3, 2 main filam. knotty arms w. branch.

  2768   vsvB center, smooth neb. in lens 1'4 x 0'5 and ext. env. Abs. patch noted by Hubble on a 60-in. plate of 1923
         is a defect. Lick 13 dim. are for lens only. Mag., 85, 325, 1937. 1 aberrant value of (B-V) (source C)
         rejected. Photom. M.N., 96, 602, 1946. Ap.J., 120, 439, 1954.

  2770   = Ho 111a. P. w. F anon. w. 2 nuclei (Ho 111c) at 3'0 (Ho 111b at 3'3 np is a *). vsBN, pseudo (r),
         poss. SAB(rs).

  2775   sB diff. N in B smooth lens: 0'8 x 0'6, many knotty branch. arms form (r): 1'4 x 1'1, strong narrow out. dk.
         lane. P. w. N 2777 at 11'. Orient. Ap.J., 127, 487, 1958.

  2776   svBN, pseudo (r): 0'3 x - , 2 main knotty arms w. m. branch; similar to M 101.

  2777   P. w. N 2775 at 11'.

  2781   vsBN, weak bar, (r): 1'0 x 0'35. Dim. for B part only. Palomar Sky Survey chart shows F(R): 3'3 x 1'2.

  2782   eBN, smooth broad bar w. strong dk. lane, hexag. pseudo (r): 1'0 x 1'0, asym. smooth arms w. dk. lanes, asym.
         extens. ext. to 2'5. See also M.N., 74, 239, 1914. P(b?) w. anon. SB(s) sp at 11'8.
         Rot. C.R. Acad. Sc., Paris, 250, 2516, 1960.

  2784   vsvB diff. N, traces of (R).

  2787   svBN in B inner lens: 0'5 x 0'3, strong narrow bar w. blobs. F(r): 1'4 x 0'75. See also M.N., 74, 242, 1914.
         Heid. 9 dim. (0'7? x 0'5?) rej., N only.

  2788   no BN, BM, * 0'4 s. Coord. meas. on Rey. 30-in. plate.

  2793   B knotty bar: 0'3 x 0'14, strong asym. knotty arm poss. due to interact. w. small anon. SB(rs)? at 1'7.
         Similar to N 2537.

  2798   = Ho 117a. P(b) w. N 2799 at 1'5. eBsN, forsh. B bar: 0'34 x 0'14 (w. ansae) in lens 0'6 x 0'4, 2 smooth F
         out. arms. Heid. 9, Lund 6 dim. for lens only.

  2799   = Ho 117b. P(b) w. N 2798 at 1'5. B cent. and bar, 2 main smooth arms nearly edgewise. Lund 6 minor dim.
         (0'5) is an error.

N 2805 = Ho 124b. In multiple interacting syst. w. N 2814, 2820 at 13'. vsBN in cent. pseudo (r): 1'5 x 1'0, many irreg. res. vF knotty arms. Similar to M 101.

2811 vBN in weak forsh. bar, smooth (r): 1'0 x 0'25, in lens 1'7 x 0'4, weak out. whorls w. some dk. lanes. Heid. 9, Helwan 22 and HA 88,2 dim. for lens only.

2814 = Ho 124c. P. w. N 2820 at 3'7. B, poss. SB(s): sp?

2815 B cent. in bulge, 2 main filam. arms, poor. res., pseudo (r): 1'9 x 0'6.

2820 = Ho 124a. P. w. N 2814 at 3'7 and 2820-A at 2'1. In group w. N 2805. v flat cent. bulge w. dk. lanes, knotty out. arms probably interacting with N 2820-A. Mag., Ap.J., 85, 325, 1937.

2820-A = Ho 124d (dim.: 0'4 x 0'4). = I 2458? P(b) w. N 2820 at 2'1.

2822 Inner dim. only; lost in glare of β Eri. Coord. meas. on Rey. 30-in. plate.

2825, 2826 In N 2832 group.

2830, 2831, 2832 In group. = Ho 123b, c, a. N 2832 brightest. Desc.: M.N., 74, 240, 1914. Ap.J., 46, 36, 1917.

2835 vsFN in weak bar, sev. res. F arms, pseudo (r): 1'15 x 0'85. See also HB, 914, 6, 1940.
Spect. IAU Symp., 5, 1958 = Lick Cont. II, No 81, 1958. A.J., 61, 97, 1956.

2836 F, amorphous, sev. * involv.

2841 LBN, many knotty arms, pseudo (r): 3'2 x 1'2, not well def.
Photom. Ap.J., 50, 384, 1919; 120, 439, 1954.
Spect. IAU Symp., 5, 1958 = Lick Cont. II, No 81, 1958. Ap.J., 135, 733, 1962.
Orient., rot. Ap.J., 97, 117, 1943; 127, 487, 1958.
Radio emiss. Hdb.d.Phys., vol. 53, 253, 1959.
SN 1912 P.A.S.P., 29, 213, 1917. Ap.J., 88, 290, 1938.
SN 1957 Sky & Tel., 16, 374, 1957.

2844 Brightest in a group w. N 2852 at 17'5, N 2853 at 16'5. vsBN, B(r): 0'3 x 0'1, in lens: 0'4 x 0'2 poor. res.

2848 = Ho 128a. N 2847 (= Ho 128c?) is a * inv. in neb. of N 2848 (see Helwan 30). Ho 128b at 1'1 is probably a *. P(a) w. N 2851 at 5'2. B cent. w. * close, 2 main knotty arms w. m. branch.

2852 P(a) w. N 2844 at 17'5. (r): 0'3 x 0'15 in lens 0'35 x 0'2. Heid 9 dim. rej., N only.

2853 P. w. N 2844 at 16'5.

2855 vB diff. N, traces innermost (r): 0'35 x 0'31, smooth (r): 0'75 x 0'6 in lens: 1'3 x 1'0 w. dk. lanes, v. weak out. whorls or incompl. (R): 3'2 x 2'2. Similar to I 5267. P(a?) w. small anon. SB(s)b at 7'0. Heid 9, HA 88,2 dim. for lens only.

2859 vBN in diff. bar: 1'0 x 0'2 w. diff. blobs, smooth F (r): 1'3 x 1'2, in lens 1'4 x 1'3, weak diff. (R): 3'4 x 2'6. Heid 9 dim. for lens only. Photo. Ap.J., 64, 326, 1926. See also M.N., 74, 242, 1914.

2865 sB diff. N w. * at 7" on minor axis.

2872 = Ho 130a. P(b?) w. N 2874 at 1'3.

2874 = Ho 130b. P. w. N 2872 at 1'3. N 2874 is largest of triplet w. N 2872 and 2873 (= Ho 130d). Identification as N 2875 in Lund 6 is an error; 2875 is * inv. 0'7 nf center of 2874 (see Heid 9). N 2871 (= Ho 130c) is also a *.

2880 svBN in sh. bar near minor axis. See also M.N., 74, 238, 1914. Mag., Ap.J., 85, 325, 1937.

2884 sBN, vF (r?): 0'75 x 0'33. P(a) w. N 2889 at 12'8.

2888 sBN, poor. res., * at 15" s.

2889 vsBN, pseudo (r): 0'5 x 0'45, 2 main filam. arms w. m. branch. P(a) w. N 2884 at 12'8.

2892 See H.A. 105, 229, 1937, D: 0'6 x - .

2902 vB diff. N in B lens 0'6 x 0'45; similar to N 1553.

2903 vBN in sh. B bar, complex patt. of B, part. res. arms, pseudo (r): 2'5 x 1'4, weak, part res. out. arms. N 2905 is a detail. Unusual (B-V) relation in nucleus (emiss.?).
Photo. Ap.J., 132, 640, 1960. P.A.S.P., 75, 222, 1963.
Photom. Ap.J., 50, 384, 1919.
Spect. IAU Symp. 5, 1958 = Lick Cont., II, No 81, 1958. Ap.J., 135, 698, 1962.
Rot., mass, Ap.J., 132, 640, 1960.
HI emiss. A.J., 66, 294, 1961; 67, 437, 1962.

2907 vsBN, B bulge, dk. lane; a miniature of N 4594. P(a) w. anon. S sp. at 5'4. Other F gal. in field.

2911 svBN, diff. neb. w. dk. lane on one side. P(a) w. N 2912 at 1'3, 2914 at 4'8. In N 2911-2919 group. Perhaps similar to N 1316.

2914 svBN, 2 main reg. arms, poor. res. Dim. for B part only. Heid 9 dim. rej., N only. P(a) w. N 2911 at 4'8. In N 2911-19 group.

N 2915 BN, poor. res.

2919 sBN in weak bar, (r): 0'7 x 0'3:; in N 2911-19 group.

2935 eBN in B lens 0'85 x 0'6 w. dk. lanes, 2 main, narrow filam. part. res., arms, form pseudo (R): 2'8 x 2'5.

2942 sBN, 2 main branch. arms, F, poor. res.

2950 eBN, strong short bar w. blob: 0'7, traces of (r) 1'0 x 0'65 at edge of lens: 1'2 x 0'7. v. weak (R):
      1'9 x 1'4. Heid 9 dim., lens only. Mag. Ap.J., 85, 325, 1937.

2955 svBN in s. B(r): 0'25 x 0'1, many filam. knotty arms in B part 1'4 x 0'6, pseudo (r): 1'35 x 0'55, vF pseudo
      (R): 2'4 x 1'3:. Lund 9 maj. dim. (0'7) is an error.

2957 P. w. N 2963 at 2'8 sf.

2959 See HA 105, 229, 1937.

2961 Same obj. as N 2959-A in Ap.J., 82, 74, 1935. See also H.A., 105, 229, 1937.

2962 svB diff. N in B lens 1'0 x 0'5 slightly brighter at rim, (r): 0'85 x 0'3:, 2 smooth arcs form F(R): 2'2 x 1'3.

2964 sBN, vF bar, 2 main knotty arms, pseudo (r): 0'6 x 0'3. See also Ap.J., 51, 288, 1920. P(a) w. N 2968 at 5'8.
      Lund 9 dim. for B part only.

2967 vsBN in B cent. part: 0'53 x 0'47, 2 main part. res., mass. arms w. some branch. Heid 9 dim. for B part only.

2968 sBN w. narrow dk. lane, poorly res. Poss. Sp sp. See also Ap.J., 51, 288, 1920. P(a) w. N 2964 at 5'8.
      Brightest of group.

2970 In N 2968 group. See Ap.J., 51, 289, 1920. Lund 9 dim. (1'0 x 1'0) rej., is an error.

2974 vBN, * at 0'7.

2976 M 81 group. Chaotic inner struct. w. many dk. lanes, vsB stellar N, many stellar condens., B inner part has
      sharp edge. See HA 105, 229, 1937.
      Photom. M.N., 94, 806, 1934. Medd. Lund II, 128, 1950. Dennison, Univ. of Michigan Thesis, 1954.
      Polar. Bull. Abastumani, No 18, 15, 1955.
      HII reg. Zs.f.Ap., 50, 168, 1960.

2977 Low surf. bright. Note corr. to NGC coord.; see Heid. 9. Mag.: Holmberg (1958). No color, no type.

2978, 2980 Pair at 10'; note corr. to NGC coord. of 2980; see Helwan 38.

2983 vsvBN in B inner lens: 0'33 x 0'22 on B narrow bar: 0'6 x 0'1, pseudo (r): 1'5 x 0'55.

2985 s. diff. vBN, many poor. res. knotty arms, weak out. whorls form pseudo (R): 2'6 x 1'9. P(a) w. N 3027 at 25'.
      Heid 9 dim. (1'6 x 1'4) for B part only.

2986 vB cent., smooth neb. P. w. anon. SA sp, at 2'4.

2990 vsBN, 2 main arms. Poor. res. Yerkes class I? not confirmed.

2992 P(b) w. N 2993 at 2'9. sBN, asym. arms w. dk. lane, vF out. extens.

2993 P(b) w. N 2992 at 2'9. vB dble N w. asym. arm or loop. F out. extens.

2997 vsvB complex N, smooth inner part. w. complex spir. patt. of dk. lanes, pseudo (r): 2'1 x 1'5, 2 main, part. res.
      filam. arms. Similar to M 101.

2998 = Ho 144a. P(a) w. anon. SB(s)mp at 4'5 sf. Brightest in N 2998-3010 group; N 3000 (= Ho 144e) is a dble * .
      vsBN, pseudo (r): 0'35 x 0'17, many filam. knotty arms.

3003 No def. N, BM, dk. mark. and knots, filam. arms; class. doubtful, poss. SB(s)d.
      SN 1961, A.J., USSR, 220, 1961. IAU Circ. 1753.

3020, 3024 = Ho 147a, b. In multiple system w. N 3016, 3019 (Ho 147c, d).

3021 vsvBN, many filam. B knotty arms, poor. res., high surf. bright. Heid 9 dim. for B part only.

3027 Possible member of M 81 group? (See Lund, II, 136, 1958) sh. bar, 2 main knotty arms, one longer.
      P(a) w. N 2985 at 25'.

3031 = M 81. Slow decrease of (B-V) w. log A/D(0), interp. value.
      Photo. Ap.J., 32, 34, 1910; 92, 22, 1940. Ritchey, l'Evolution de l'Astrophotographie ..., Soc. Ast. de France,
        Paris, 1929. P.A.S.P., 71, 102, 534, 1959. Hdb.d.Ap., 5, 2, 843, 1933.
      Photom. Ap.J., 46, 206, 1917; 50, 384, 1919; 83, 434, 1936; 91, 528, 1940. M.N., 94, 806, 1934. Medd. Lund II,
        128, 1950. Dennison, Univ. of Michigan Thesis, 1954. A.J., USSR, 32, 16, 1955. Izv. Pulkovo, 20,
        No 156, 87, 1956.
      Spect. P.A.S.P., 71, 102, 1959. Lick Obs. Bull. 497, 1939. Ap.J., 135, 733, 1962.
      Struct. Ap.J., 104, 221, 1946. P.A.S.P., 71, 534, 1959.
      Rot. Ap.J., 97, 117, 1943. A.J., 62, 28, 1957. P.A.S.P., 71, 102, 1959.
      Polar. Bull. Abastumani. No 18, 15, 1955.   (Continued).

N 3031   (Continued).
      <u>HII reg.</u> Observatory, 79, 54, 1959. Zs.f.Ap., 50, 168, 1960.
      <u>Radio emiss.</u> Nature, 172, 853, 1953. M.N., 122, 479, 1961. Ap.J., 134, 659, 1961. Hdb.d.Phys., 53, 253, 1959.
      <u>HI emiss.</u> Ap.J., 126, 471, 1957. P.A.S.P., 72, 368, 1960. B.A.N., 15, 307, 1961.
      <u>Nova 1950,</u> P.A.S.P., 62, 116, 1950.

3032   svBN in sh. stubby bar: 0'27 x 0'18, smooth (r): 0'5 x 0'4 in lens 0'7 x 0'6, vF envel. Lund 9 dim. rej., N
      only. Heid 9 and HA 88,2 dim. rej., bar only.

3034   = M 82. In M 81 group.
      <u>Photo.</u> Ap.J., 64, 325, 1926; Ap.J., 137, 1005, 1963. B.A.N., 15, 309, 1961.
      <u>Photom.</u> Ap.J., 46, 206, 1917; 50, 384, 1919; 83, 424, 1936. M.N., 94, 806, 1934. Medd. Lund II, 128, 1950.
            Dennison, Univ. of Michigan Thesis, 1954.
      <u>Spect.</u> Sky & Tel., 8, 2, 1948. A.J., 61, 97, 1956. Ap.J., 135, 696, 1962; 137, 1005, 1963.
      <u>Polar.</u> Bull. Abastunmani, No 18, 15, 1955. A.J., 67, 271, 1962. Sky & Tel., XXIII, 254, 1962.
      <u>Radio emiss.</u> Ap.J., 134, 659, 1961; 137, 1005, 1963.
      <u>HI emiss.</u> B.A.N., 15, 307, 1961.

3041   sBN, sev. F knotty arms, poor. res.

3044   No def. N, B knotty cent., poor. res.

3052   sBN, (r): 0'5 x 0'3, 3 main filam. knotty arms. P(a) w. N 3045 at 16'5.

3054   sBN, weak bar, (r): 0'75 x 0'45, sev. smooth filam. arms.

3055   vsvBN in sh. narrow bar, 2 main knotty arms. w. m. branch., one stronger and longer. Heid 9 dim. (1'2 x 0'6)
      for B part only. <u>Spect.</u> Lick Obs. Bull. 497, 1939.

3056   B diff. N 0'3 x 0'2, vF (r or R?): 1'0 x 0'55 w. * on it. Poss. SA(r)0$^+$. HA 88,2 dim. (ser. a') for N only.

3059   vB narrow bar: 0'35 x 0'08, pseudo (r): 1'2 x 1'1. Similar to N 2082.

3065   svBN w. inner B cent., weak (r): 1'0 x 0'8 at edge of lens, vF envel. P(b) w. N 3066 at 3'0. Heid 9 and HA
      88,2 dim. for N only. B(0): source F rejected. <u>Spect.</u> IAU Symp., 5, 1958 = Lick Cont., II, No 81, 1958.

3066   BN in sh. bar, one B v. sh. arm, other forms complete loop, pseudo (R): 0'9 x 0'8, some distortion. P(b) w.
      N 3065 at 3'0. <u>Spect.</u> IAU Symp., 5, 1958 = Lick Cont., II, No 81, 1958.

3067   B complex bar or lens w. B knots and dk. lanes. Similar to N 972.

3073   = Ho 156b. P. w. N 3079 (Ho 156a) at 10'.

3077   In M 81 group. B cent. reg. w. irreg., roughly radial dk. filam., smooth unres. neb.
      <u>Photom.</u> Ap.J., 46, 206, 1917; 50, 384, 1919. M.N., 94, 806, 1934. Medd. Lund II, 128, 1950. Dennison, Univ.
            of Michigan Thesis, 1954.
      <u>Spect.</u> Lick Obs. Bull., 497, 1939.
      <u>Polar.</u> Bull. Abastumani, No 18, 15, 1955.
      <u>Radio emiss.</u> Ap.J., 134, 659, 1961.

3078   vBN, HA 88,2 dim. (ser. a': 0'5 x 0'4) for B part only.

3079   = Ho 156a. P. w. N 3073 at 10' p and anon. at 6'5 np. B peanut-shaped bar: 1'4 x 0'3 w. dk. lanes on one side,
      2 main part. res. arms, one longer forms out. loop or (R): 6'2 x 0'5. Almost edgewise and probably similar to
      N 4631. Lick (1956) vel. for condens. 60" SE cent.: +1593 km/sec. Lick (1962) 2 vel. at 99" n of N, 30" s of
      N: +1008, +1237 km/sec.

3081   vBN w. innermost SB(r) struct., v. weak bar, strong reg. (r): 1'1 x 0'7, eF (R): 2'0 x 1'8: HA 88,2 dim. (ser.
      a': 1'5 x 1'2) for B part only. <u>Photo.</u> Ap.J., 92, 236, 1940.

3089   svBN, pseudo (r): 0'5 x 0'4, 2 main knotty arms w. branch., poor. res.

3091   BN. P(a) w. N 3096 at 4'8, and anon. EO at 1'3.

3095   vsvBN, pseudo (r): 0'95 x 0'5, dk. lanes in bar. P(a) w. N 3100 at 10'0.

3098   sBN, B lens, flat compon. 0'06 thick.

3100   vBN, F bar w. narrow dk. lane on one side near N. P(a) w. N 3095 at 10'0.

3109   Part. res. elong. star cloud of low surf. bright.
      <u>Photo.</u> A.J., 61, 97, 1956.
      <u>HI emiss.</u> Epstein, Harvard Thesis, 1962.

3115   vBN in flat disc: 2'7 x 0'1 w. some weak knots near tips, extens. envel. Poss. E$^+$7. P. w. vF dwarf E w.
      stellar N at 5'5.
      <u>Photo.</u> Ap.J., 64, 325, 1926; 71, 235, 1930; 98, 47, 1943. Hdb.d.Ap., 5, 2, 843, 1933.
      <u>Photom.</u> Ap.J., 71, 231, 1930; 91, 289, 1940; 120, 439, 1954. Ann. d'Ap., 11, 247, 1948. B.A.N., 16, 1, 1961.
      <u>Spect.</u> Ap.J., 135, 734, 1962.
      <u>Dyn., rot., mass,</u> Ap.J., 91, 296, 1940. A.J., 59, 273, 1954. P.A.S.P., 71, 104, 1959.
      <u>SN 1935?,</u> suspected, Lund Ann. 7, 161, 1938.

3124   vsBN, F bar: 0'55 x 0'06, (r): 0'65 x 0'55, 2 main knotty arms w. branch.

N 3136 BN, possibly S0⁻. HA 88,2 and HA 88,4 dim. (1'2 x 0'7) for B part only.

3143 Dim. for B part only; P(a) w. N 3145 at 9'.

3145 svBN in F bar, pseudo (r): 0'7 x 0'4, 2 main knotty, filam. arms w. branch. P(a) w. N 3143 at 9'.

3147 vBN, many filam. narrow arms in lens, no def. (r) struct. Heid 9 dim. (2'0 x 1'7) for B part only.

3151, 3152 In N 3158 group. 3152: Heid. 9 dim. (0'3? x 0'3?) rej.

3156 In N 3166 group.

3158 Brightest in a group. P(a) w. N 3160 (S sp.) at 4'8.

3159, 3161 = Ho 172c, a. Pair of E at 1'3. In N 3158 group.

3162 svBN, pseudo (r): 0'5 x 0'3, 2 main knotty arms w. m. branch., asym. out. part. Upsala 21, Heid 9, and Lund 9 dim. for B part only.

3163 = Ho 172b. In N 3158 group.

3166 = Ho 173a. Brightest of group. P(b) w. N 3169 at 7'7, P. w. N 3165 at 4'8. vsvBN in sh. smooth bar: 0'5 x 0'14, spir. patt. in lens, pseudo (r): 0'52 x 0'48, v. weak extens. envel. Lund 6 dim. for B part only.

3169 = Ho 173b. In N 3166 group. P(b) w. N 3166 at 7'7. svBN in B bulge, w. dk. lane on one side, some distortion in out. part. caused by 3166. Lund 6 dim. for B part only.
      Spect. IAU Symp., 5, 1958 = Lick Cont. II, No 81, 1958.
      Rot. Ap.J., 97, 117, 1943.

3175 vsBN in cent. of bar or complex lens w. dk. lanes, v. weak out. parts. P(a) w. anon. S sp. at 5'0. HA 88,2 dim. (from Helwan 15: 2'0 x 0'5) for B part only.

3177 vsvBN in B pseudo (r): 0'14 x 0'08:, 2 main knotty B arms, F out. whorls. Lund 9, Heid 9, and HA 88,4 dim. for B part only. SN 1947 at 40" from N on outer arm. P.A.S.P., 60, 15, 1948. Ann.Rep. Mt. W., 46, 20, 1946-47.

3182 (r): 0'17 x 0'12.

3183 = Ho 177a. Ho 177b at 3' is a *, but vF small comp. at 2'2 nf. Lund 6 dim. for B part only.

3184 svBN, smooth lens w. spir. patt. of dk. mark., hexag. pseudo (r): 0'85 x 0'85, 2 main part. res. knotty arms w. m. branch.
      SN 1921, P.N.A.S., 25, 569, 1939.
      SN 1937, H.A.C., 494, 1939. B.S.A.F., 55, 159, 1941. Ap.J., 96, 28, 1942.

3185 In N 3190 group. svBN, knotty (r): 1'3 x 0'75 in lens: 1'6 x 1'0, weak out. arms form (R): 2'5 x 1'8. Heid 9, Lund 9, and HA 88,4 dim. for lens only. Photo. P.A.S.P., 59, 161, 1947.

3187 In N 3190 group. P(b) w. N 3190 at 4'8. Knotty cent. lens 1'5 x 0'4 w. no def. N, 2 anomal. arms. distorted by 3190. Heid 9, Lund 9 dim. for lens only. Photo. P.A.S.P., 59, 161, 1947.

3190 = Ho 175a. Brightest of group. P(b) w. N 3187 at 4'8. N 3189 is part of same system; L, B cent. bulge: 1'3 x 0'5, strong dk. lane w. out. arms tilted to principal plane.
      Photo. Ap.J., 97, 114, 1943; 104, 219, 1946. P.A.S.P., 59, 161, 1947.
      Orient., rot. Ap.J., 97, 117, 1943; 127, 487, 1958.

3193 = Ho 175b. In N 3190 group. vB cent. in smooth neb. Lund 9 dim. for B part only.
      Photo. P.A.S.P., 59, 161, 1947.

3198 svBN in bar part. obscured on one side, pseudo (r): 1'75 x 0'5, sev. knotty, part. res. branch. arms. Lund 9, Heid 9 dim. for B part only. Spect. IAU Symp., 5, 1958 = Lick Cont. II, No 81, 1958. Ap.J., 135, 698, 1962.

3200 vsBN in weak (r): 1'2 x 0'4, 2 main v. weak filam. arms. Class. doubtful.

3203 vBsN. (r): 0'7 x - . Good example of edgewise SA(r)0⁺. Sev. small gal. nearby.

3206 sh. B bar: 0'3 x 0'05, one main knotty arm forms loop or pseudo (R): 2'1 x 1'9:, a few * and emiss. obj. are part. resolved.

3214, 3200 = Ho 182a, b. Pair at 5'1.

3221 SN 1961, Disc. by P. Wild, unpubl.

3223 = I 2571. B diff. nuclear reg., traces of (r) struct.; sev. F filam. arms. See HB 914, 7, 1940.

3226 = Ho 187b. P(b) w. N 3227 at 2'2. B diff. N, poss. some dk. lanes and spots as in N 3077. Lund 6 dim. for B part only.

3227 = Ho 187a. P(b) w. N 3226 at 2'2. vseBN, B complex lens: 2'25 x 1'25 w. dk. mark., 2 main smooth arms, one touching N 3226; slight distortion? Lund 6 dim. for lens only.

3238 Heid. 9 dim. (0'3 x 0'3) rej., N only.

3239 Highly res., B * superp., rich field. Somewhat like N 4027. Heid 9, Lund 9 dim. for bar only.

N 3241 sBN, (r): 0'75 x 0'45. Dim. for B part only.

3244 Not res., * 0'5 s att.

3245 eBN in vB smooth lens: 0'6 x 0'3, diff. envel. P(a) w. N 3245-A at 8'8.

3245-A P(a) w. N 3245 at 8'8. B bulge, knotty equat. plane, fairly B smooth arms, almost exactly edgewise.

3250 BN, 2 * 0'5 f.

3250-A F spindle, B * 0'7 f.

3250-C sBN, * 0'15 n.

3250-E BN, class. doubtful.

3252 Mag.: Ap.J., 85, 325, 1937. Note corr. to NGC coord.; see Heid. 9.

3254 svBN w. dk. lanes, spir. patt. of nearly uniform surf. bright. SN 1941 H.A.C., 578, 1941.
P.A.S.P., 53, 192, 1941.

3256 Coll. system includes 2 or 3 N in contact forming a vB mass: 0'6 x 0'3 w. fragment: 0'5 x 0'15 at 0'3 sp. vF
streamers up to 4' from N, overall extens.: 7'5: x 2'5:.
Photo., photom. Zs.f.Ap., 47, 9, 1959. Mag.: 11.85 (pg).
Spect. Mem. R.A.S., 68, 69, 1961.

3256-C No BN, ill-defined arms eB * 4'2p. Sersic (1959) suggests P(b) w. N 3256 at 14'.
Photo., Photom. Zs.f.Ap., 47, 9, 1959. Mag.: 11.6 (pg).

3257 vBN, v. weak bar? P. w. N 3258 at 4'5.

3258 sBN, * 0'8 np. P. w. N 3257 at 4'5, N 3260 at 2'6.

3258-B At 3'0 nnp N 3273. Class. diff.

3259 vsBN, pseudo (r): 0'4 x 0'2, many knotty arms, poor. res. P(a) w. N 3266 at 18'. HA 88,2 dim. (m$_c$ series:
1'1 x 0'6) for B part only.

3260 * 0'4 s. P. w. N 3258 at 2'6.

3261 vBN, F(r): 0'9 x 0'7, strong narrow bar, 2 main reg. filam. arms w. branch. P(a) w. anon.
SA (1'5 x 0'45) at 8'0.

3262, 3263 Pair at 2'6.

3266 vsBN; dim. for B part only. P. w. N 3259 at 18'.

3267 In N 3267-3281 group. P. w. N 3268 at 2'5. vsBN, vF bar? (r): 1'15 x 0'6.

3268 In N 3267-3281 group. P. w. N 3267 at 2'5. sBN. Note Corr. to NGC coord.; see Mem. Commonw. Obs. No 13, 1956.

3269 In N 3267-3281 group. vBN, (r): 1'6 x 0'6.

3271 = I 2585. In N 3267-3281 group. vBN, F bar w. blobs. HA 88,2 dim. (a': 1'0: x 0'6:) for B part only. Note
corr. to NGC coord.; see Mem. Commonw. Obs. No 13, 1956.

3273 In N 3267-3281 group. P. w. N 3258-B at 3'0. Many others gal. in field. vBN, F(r): 0'95 x 0'35.

3275 sBN, weak bar, (r): 0'95 x 0'75 w. F * on it; other F * 0'2 sf N. P. w. N 3275-A S sp (0'85 x 0'2) at 9'8.

3277 vsvBN, vB (r): 0'3 x 0'2:, poor. res. inner arms. Similar to N 6753, but no (R) visible. Lund 6, Heid 9, and
Lick dim. for B part only.

3281 In N 3267-3281 group. Poor. res. See also Helwan 22. HA 88,2 dim. (after Helwan 9, 15) for B part only.

3281-C, D In N 3281 group. Class. doubtful.

3285 P(a) w. 3285-A at 12', 3285-B at 18'. seBN, dk. lane on bar, vF arms.

3285-A, B P(a) w. N 3285 at 12' and 18'.

3287 B bar: 0'34 x 0'06 w. vsFN, 2 main knotty branch. arms, strong asym.

3288 = 3284? P. w. N 3286 at 4'0. See also H.A. 105, 229, 1937.

3289 Note Corr. to NGC coord.; see Mem. Commonw. Obs. No 13. Class. doubtful.

3294 = Ho 202a. N 3291 (Ho 202b) at 4'8 is a *; N 3304 at 18'. vs diff. BN, pseudo (r): 0'4 x 0'2, sev. knotty B
branch. arms. SN 1955 A.J., 61, 338, 1956.

3299 BM no BN or eFN, 2 main knotty arms, v. low surf. bright. P(a) w. N 3306 at 11'8.

3300 vBN w. sh. bar, traces of (r); poor image. Dim. for B part only.

N 3301 eBN, B pseudo (r): 1'0 x 0'25, 2 F smooth arms form pseudo (R): 2'1 x 0'55.
HA 88,2 maj. dim. (1'4) for lens only.

3304 svBN, 2 main arms, pseudo (R): 1'0 x 0'3. Poor image; dim. for B part only. P(a) w. N 3294 at 18'.

3306 Poor. res. P(a) w. N 3299 at 11'8. Lund 9 dim. (0'7 x 0'4) for B part only.

3307 Hydra I Cl. Note correction to NGC coord. (see MWC 626).

3308 Hydra I Cl., eBN, B lens: 0'55 x 0'45, vF diff. bar in envel.

3309 Brightest in Hydra I Cl. P(a) w. N 3311 at 1'7. More condensed and brighter than N 3311.

3310 vBvsN, weak bar in vB (r): 0'35 x 0'25, sev. filam. knotty arms, asym. out. arm and filam. extens., max. ext.
6'9 x 3'6 (no obvious interacting comp. nearby). See also Ap.J., 51, 289, 1920. Heid 9, Lund 9 dim. for lens
only. Spect. Lick Obs. Bull., 497, 1939.

3311 Hydra I Cl. P(a) w. N 3309 at 1'7. B part: 0'45 x 0'3, more diff. and fainter than N 3309.

3312 = I 629. Hydra I Cl. eBN, asym. dk. lane; perhaps distorted by N 3309-3311. Coll. pair? at 22'5. Pec.
pair at 7'5.

3314 Hydra I Cl.; esvBN, bar: 1'2 x 0'25, w. dk. lanes, F out. asym. arm, perhaps P(c)?

3316 Hydra I Cl.; eBN, bar: 0'5 x 0'3, pseudo (r): 0'45.

3318 vBN, vF bar, pseudo (r): 0'9 x 0'4. P. w. N 3318-B at 10'5. See also H.B., 914, 7, 1940.

3318-A F, poor. image., class. diff., B * 0'4 nf.

3318-B F. P. w. N 3318 at 10'5.

3319 vB narrow bar: 0'85 x 0'08, 3 main branch., part. res., filam. arms.

3320 sBN, filam. knotty arms; poor. res., dim. for B part only.

3329 vBN or (r): 0'14 x 0'08, poor. res. B lens 0'9 x 0'45, traces F(R). Poss. SA(rs). P(a) w. anon. SBc at 7'2.
Brightest of a group of about 12 gal. Heid 9 dim. (0'65 x 0'5) for lens only.

3338 Leo Group. svBN in smooth inner lens: 0'33 x 0'17, pseudo (r): 0'55 x 0'35, 2 main knotty arms w. some branch.
vB * at 2'7.
HII reg. Zs.f.Ap., 50, 168, 1960.
Photo., SN 1915? Lundmark, Vistas in Astronomy, Vol. 2, 1614, 1956.

3344 vsBN in weak bar, knotty (r): 0'9 x 0'85, 3 main part. res. branch. arms, outer parts form weak (R): 6'0 x 6'0.
Lick 13, Upsala 21, Heid 9, and Lund 9 dim. for B part only.

3346 vB sh. central segment in bar: 0'14 x 0'03, part. res. pseudo (r): 0'5 x 0'4, many part. res. filam. branch.
arms. HII reg. Zs.f.Ap., 50, 168, 1960.

3347 svBN, 2 * or emiss. patch in northern arm. P(a) w. N 3354 SB: at 3'5 (inner dim: 0'45 x 0'35) and N 3358 at 8'5.

3347-A, B, C 3 F anon.; poor. images. Class. diff.

3348 B and compact, * 0'18 from N. Heid 9 dim. (0'3 x 0'3) for B part only. Mag., Ap.J., 85, 325, 1937.

3351 = M 95. Leo Group. eBN in strong smooth bar: 1'4 x 0'3 w. dk. lanes, (r): 2'1 x 1'9 in lens: 2'5 x 2'3.
Branch. knotty out. arms. Lick 13 dim. (3'0 x 3'0) for B part only. (B-V) constant, interp. value.
Photo. Hdb.d.Ap., 5, 2, 845, 1933.
HII reg. Zs.f.Ap., 50, 168, 1960.

3353 = Haro 3 (Bol. Tonantzintla, 14, 8, 1956). Color suggests type Imp? See also HA 105, 230, 1937.
Photom. Ap.J., 128, 443, 1958.

3358 vBN, outer arms form pseudo (R): 2'6 x 1'3. P. w. N 3347 at 8'5.

3359 sB complex bar w. vsN, highly res., F branch. out. arms, one stronger, (r): 1'8 x 1'1, in lens 2'2 x 1'9:.
Photo. P.A.S.P., 61, 124, 1949.
Spect. I.A.U. Symp., 5, 1958 = Lick Cont., II, No 81, 1958.

3364 Mag.: Ap.J., 85, 325, 1937.

3367 vseBN, narrow bar: 0'5 x 0'05, (r): 0'55 x 0'45, 3 main knotty filam. arms, strong asym., sharp semi-circular
outline on side opposite to N 3377 at 22'. See also M.N., 76, 647, 1916. Projects in Leo group, but redshift
is more than 3 times mean redshift of group (see Humason et al., 1956).

3368 = M 96. Leo group. sBN in broad diff. bar w. many dk. lanes, (r): 2'4 x 1'5, F out. arms form F (R):
6'2 x 3'9. Lund 9, Upsala 21 dim. for B part only.
Photo. Ap.J., 92, 236, 1940.
Spect. Ap.J., 135, 734, 1962.
Orient. Ap.J., 127, 487, 1958.
HII reg. Zs.f.Ap., 50, 168, 1960.

N 3370 sBN, sev. knotty, filam. branch arms; poss. SAB(rs). Lund 9 dim. for B part only.

3377 Leo Group. vB cent. smooth neb., some glob. clust.? See also Ap.J., 51, 291, 1920. P. w. N 3377-A at 7'0.
Lund 9, 10, Lick 13, Upsala 21, Heid 9, and HA 88,2 dim. for B part only.
Photom. M.N., 98, 618, 1938. Ap.J., 50, 384, 1919.

3377-A P. w. N 3377 at 7'0. vF bar-like core, 2 main arms one larger and stronger, part. res.

3379 = M 105. = Ho 212a. Leo Group. P. w. N 3384 at 7'2, N 3389 at 10'3. vBN, in lens 1'5 x 1'5, some glob.
clust.? Lund 10 dim. for lens only. One discordant val. of B-V (source C) rejected.
Photo. Ap.J., 64, 325, 1926; 71, 235, 1930.
Photom. Ap.J., 50, 384, 1919; 71, 231, 1930; 136, 713, 1962; 137, 733, 1963. M.N., 98, 619, 1938. Ann.d'Ap.,
       11, 247, 1948. P.A.S.P., 74, 146, 1962. A.J., 67, 120, 1962. Dennison, Univ. of Michigan Thesis, 1954.
Spect. Ap.J., 135, 734, 1962.
Mass, mass/lum. Ap.J., 134, 251, 1961; 134, 910, 1961. Ap.J., 138, 849, 1963.

3384 = Ho 212b. Leo Group. P. w. N 3379 at 7'2. eBN in sh. weak bar: 0'7 x 0'2, smooth struct. Lund 9 dim. for B
part only. Photo., photom. Dennison, Univ. of Michigan Thesis, 1954. Ap.J., 50, 384, 1919.

3389 = Ho 212c. Leo Group. vsBN, w. main knotty arms w. branch. Lund 9 and HA 88,2 dim. for B part only. HII reg.
Zs.f.Ap., 50, 168, 1960.

3395 = Ho 215a. I 2605 is one arm. P(b) w. N 3396 at 2'. vsvBN in pseudo B(r): 0'3 x 0'14, 2 main B knotty arms,
part. res., distorted out. part. Lund 6, Heid 9, and HA 88,2 dim. for B part only.
Photo. Ap.J., 116, 64, 1952.
Spect. Ap.J., 116, 64, 1952. A.J., 61, 97, 1956. P.A.S.P., 69, 386, 1957. I.A.U. Symp., 5, 1958 =
       Lick Cont. II, No 81, 1958.

3396 = Ho 215b. P(b) w. N 3395 at 2'. vB bar: 0'7 x 0'2, part. res. distorted arm. Lund 6, Lund 9 dim. for B part
only; HA 88,2 maj. dim. (0'8, after Pease) for bar only. Spect. see refer. for N 3395.

3398 = I 644? See H.A. 105, 230, 1937.

3400 In N 3414-18 group.

3403 v. poor. res., vF out. arms. Mag.: Ap.J., 85, 325, 1937. Heid 9 dim. for B part only.

3404 = I 2609 (see Helwan 15). vsBN.

3408 See H.A., 105, 230, 1937.

3412 Leo Group. vBN in sh. B diff. bar or lens: 0'55 x 0'3, vF envel. Photom. Ap.J., 50, 384, 1919.

3413 = Ho 218c. P. w. N3424 at 9'9, N 3430 at 15'.

3414 Class. doubtful. P. w. N 3418 at 8'2.

3418 Class. doubtful. P. w. N 3414 at 8'2.

3419 eBN in weak bar, F(r): 0'45 x 0'35 in lens: 0'6 x 0'45, vF(R): 1'1 x 0'85. * on lens. P(a) w. N 3419-A at 4'5.
Lund 9 dim. rej., N only; Heid 9 dim. rej., N or lens only.

3419-A P(a) w. N 3419 at 4'5.

3423 vsBN, sev. part. res., filam. branch. arms. HII reg. Zs.f.Ap., 50, 168, 1960.

3424 = Ho 218a. P. w. N 3413 at 9'9, N 3430 at 6'2. Lund 6, Lund 9 dim. for B part only.

3430 = Ho 218b. P. w. N 3424 at 6'2, N 3413 at 15'. sBN, vF bar, pseudo (r): 0'5 x 0'3, sev. filam. knotty
branch. arms.

3432 B narrow knotty bar: 1'4 x 0'3, F knotty out, arms. Neb patch 4' sp.
Spect. A.J., 61, 97, 1956.
Rot. Ap.J., 97, 117, 1943.

3433 sBN in smooth cent. part, 2 main knotty, filam. arms w. m. branch.; small anon. S sp. at 3'0 of N, and a dozen
others in field. Lund 9 dim. (2'0 x 1'8) omitted by mistake. Lund 9, Heid 9 dim. for B part only.

3437 sBN, hexag. cent. part., knotty filam. arms, poor. res.

3440 See H.A., 105, 230, 1937. In N 3440-3445-3458 group. Dim. for B part only.

3445 sBN in complex bar-like core, one knotty mass. arm ending in elong. patch: 0'4 x 0'1. In N 3440-3445-3458 group.
See HA, 105, 230, 1937.

3447 Low surf. bright. In contact w. N 3447-A. Heid 9 dim. (1'8 x 0'75) for B part only.

3447-A Im in contact w. N 3447; dim: 1'3 x 0'5 (Lick 36-in.).

3448 B complex bar or lens: 1'9 x 0'5, F out. extens. Class. doubtful, poss. SB(s)O/a p. P(b) w. vF anon.
SB(s)d p at 3'8.

3450 Note corr. to NGC coord. (see Helwan 21).

N 3454 = Ho 221b. P(a) w. N 3455 at 3'8. B bar w. knots and dk. mark., F smooth out. arms, edgewise.
       Heid 9, Lund 9 dim. for B part only.

   3455 = Ho 221a. P(a) w. N 3453 at 3'8. B complex cent., sBN in sh. bar, Hexag. pseudo (r): 0'3 x 0'2, outer arms
       form pseudo (R): 2'1 x 1'0. Heid 9, Lund 9 dim. for B part only.

   3456 Heid. 9 dim. rej., N only.

   3458 svBN, Lund 9 dim. rej. N only. Heid 9 dim. B part only. In N 3440-3445-3458 group. See HA 105, 230, 1937.

   3470 See H.A., 105, 230, 1937.

   3485 svBN, narrow smooth bar, (r): 0'7 x 0'6, sev. knotty filam. arms. Heid 9, Lund 9 dim. for B part only.

   3486 B diff. N in weak bar: 0'55 x 0'1, part. res. knotty (r): 0'7 x 0'5, many part. res. filam. branch. arms.
       Similar to N 6744. HA 88,2 dim. for B part only.

   3488 See H.A., 105, 230, 1937.

   3489 Leo Group. vsvBN in B inner lens: 0'37 x 0'17, pseudo (r) w. dk. lane: 0'6 x 0'3, pseudo (R): 1'4 x 0'45.
       Lund 9, Heid 9 dim. for B part only. Photo. Stockholm Ann., 14, No 3, 1942.

   3495 vs not vBN, many knotty arms and dk. lanes, low surf. bright. HA 88,2 minor dim. (1'8 mc series) is an error or
       misprint for 0'8.

   3504 eBN in B lens: 1'4 x 0'8 w. dk. lanes, F smooth out. whorls form (R): 2'05 x 1'9. P(a) w. N 3512 at 12'.
       Photo., rot., mass, Ap.J., 132, 661, 1960.
       Spect. Ap.J., 135, 697, 1962.

   3506 sBN, 2 main B arms, suggestion of bar, poor. res. Lund 9 dim. for B part only.

   3509 = VV 75. Heid. 9 maj. diam.: 2'. Note corr. to NGC coord. Photo., spect., vel. Ap.J., 138, 873, 1963.

   3510 = Haro 26 (Bol. Tonantzintla, 14, 11, 1956). B knotty bar: 0'85 x 0'08, F out. extens.
       Photom. Ap.J., 128, 443, 1958.
       Spect. I.A.U. Symp., 5, 1958 = Lick Cont. II, No 81, 1958.

   3511 esN or *, sugg. of SAB struct. in cent., complex knotty, mass. arms w. dk. lanes. P(a) w. N 3513 at 10'8.

   3512 vBsN, pseudo (r): 0'25 x 0'2, 2 main knotty filam. arms w. m. branch. P(a) w. N 3504 at 12', N 3515 at 13'5.
       Spect. A.J., 61, 97, 1956.

   3513 eBsN, strong bar: 0'5 x 0'06, pseudo (r): 0'85 x - , 2 main mass., knotty arms, vF extens. form pseudo (R):
       2'4 x 1'5. P(a) w. N 3511 at 10'8. Helwan 21, 22 and Lund 7 dim. for B part only.

   3515 P(a) w. N 3512 at 13'5.

   3516 eBN on sh. B bar: 0'4 x 0'1, vF (R): 0'95 x 0'95. Heid 9 dim. for N or lens only.
       Spect. P.A.S.P., 53, 231, 1941. Ap.J., 97, 28, 1943.

   3517 See H.A., 105, 230, 1937.

   3521 vsvBN in complex hexag. lens: 4'2 x 1'4, many filam. knotty arms and dk. lanes, F filam. out. arms.
       HA 88,2 major dim. for B part only.

   3547 s elong N or bar, pseudo (r?): 0'3 x - , v. poor. res.; poss. SB(rs). P(a) w. anon. SB(rs)0+ at 10'4.

   3549 vsBN, 2 main knotty arms w. branch., poor. res. Lund 9 dim. (4'0 x 1'2) appear excessive and may be an error.

   3556 Broad not vB bar seen end-on, sev. complex part. res. arms w. many dk. lanes on one side. Class. diff.
       See H.A. 105, 230, 1937.
       Orient. Ap.J., 127, 487, 1958.
       Photo., rot., mass, Ap.J., 131, 549, 1960.
       Spect., Ap.J., 135, 697, 1962.

   3557 BN, perhaps S0? P(a) w. N 3564 at 7'5, N 3568 at 11'5.

   3557-A, B 2 F anon., class. doubtful.

   3564 svBN. P(a) w. N 3557 at 7'5.

   3568 No BN, B knot off cent. P(a) w. N 3557 at 11'5.

   3571 = N 3544 (See Helwan 15).

   3577 vsvBN in strong narrow bar: 0'5 x 0'05, F reg. (r): 0'57 x 0'52, 2 main narrow, smooth F arms.
       P(a) w. N 3583 at 5'0 and sF anon. SB(s)m at 2'7.

   3583 vBvsN in B complex lens: 0'8 x 0'5 w. dk. lanes, 3 main arms w. knots, vF (R): 3'3 x 1'9? suspected. P(a) w. N
       3577 at 5'0. Small EO satellite at 0'9. Lund 9 dim. for B part only.

   3585 Poss. S0⁻p. HA 88,2 dim. (after Helwan) for B part only.

N 3593　In N 3607 group. BN w. L bulge and dk. lane.

3596　svBN, 2 main mass. knotty reg. arms. Dim. for B part only; HA 88,2 gives 4'0 x 4'0 (ser. a').

3599　In N 3607 group. Heid 9 dim. (0'5 x 0'5) rej., N only.

3605　In N 3607 group. = Ho 240c. P(a) w. N 3607 at 2'7. Photom. M.N., 96, 602, 1936.

3607　Brightest of a group. = Ho 240a. P(a) w. N 3605 at 2'7, N 3608 at 5'8. svBN in B lens: 0'8 x 0'7 w. strong dk. crescent on one side, pseudo (r): 0'5 x - . Photom. M.N., 96, 602, 1936.

3608　In N 3607 group. = Ho 240b. sB diff. N. P(a) w. N 3607 at 5'8. Lick 13 and MWC 324 dim. for B part only. Photom. M.N., 96, 602, 1936.

3610　vsvBN, trace of flat compon., poss. SO sp. See HA 105, 230, 1937. Photom. M.N., 98, 619, 1938. Mag. Ap.J., 85, 325, 1937.

3611　svBN w. B inner whorls, F smooth out. whorls, traces of incompl. (R). 2 F anon. SB(s)m at 3'0 and 10'0.

3613　sB diff. N. P(a) w. N 3619 at 16'. See HA 105, 230, 1937. Photom. Ap.J., 50, 384, 1919. Mag. Ap.J., 85, 325, 1937.

3614　sBN, trace of F bar, narrow F (r): 0'43 x 0'2, 2 main knotty, filam. branch. arms, beginning of res., P. w. N 3614-A at 2'5. Lund 9 dim. for B part only.

3614-A P. w. N 3614 at 2'5. F narrow bar: 0'25 x 0'1, weak asym. arm; poss. dwarf physical companion of N 3614. The pair is similar to N 1232 and SBm companion.

3619　vsvBN v. weak spir. patt., pseudo (r): 0'7 x - . F incomplete (R) suspected. P(a) w. N 3625 at 9'5. Lund 9 dim. rej., N only. See HA 105, 230, 1937. Photom. Ap.J., 50, 384, 1919. Mag. Ap.J., 85, 325, 1937.

3621　vsBN in complex patt. of part. res. irreg. arms and dk. lanes. See also H.B., 914, 7, 1940. HA 88,2 dim. (after Helwan 9) for B part only. Photo. H.A., 105, 242, 1937.

3623　= M 65. = Ho 246b. P(a) w. N 3627 at 20' (Leo group). s diff. vBN in smooth broad diff. bar w. dk. lanes, 2 main smooth arms w. strong dk. lane in front of lens; arms form pseudo (R): 5'9 x 1'4. Lund 9, Lund 10 dim. for B part only. (B-V) source C, rejected. Photo. Ap.J., 97, 114, 1943; 120, 444, 1954; 134, 233, 1961. Photom. Ap.J., 50, 384, 1919; 120, 439, 1954. Medd. Lund II, 114, 1945; 128, 1950. Izv. Pulkovo, 20, No 156, 　　　　87, 1956. A.J. USSR, 32, 16, 1955. Spectr. Ap.J., 135, 699, 734, 1962. Orient., rot., mass, Ap.J., 127, 487, 1958; 134, 232, 1961. HII reg. Zs.f.Ap., 50, 168, 1960.

3625　P(a) w. N 3619 at 9'5. sBN in complex bar, 2 main arms, poor. res. Mag.: Ap.J., 85, 325, 1937. See also HA 105, 230, 1937.

3626　= 3632. seBN, B(r): 0'65 x 0'3 w. dk. matt., vF (R): 1'4 x 1'1.

3627　= M 66. = Ho 246a. P(a) w. N 3623 at 20' (Leo group). svBN in complex bar and lens w. many dk. lanes, 2 main part. res. arms. Photom. Ap.J., 50, 384, 1919. Izv. Pulkovo, 20, No 156, 87, 1956. A.J. USSR, 32, 16, 1955. Spectr. Ap.J., 135, 734, 1962. Rot., Ap.J., 97, 117, 1943. HII reg. Zs.f.Ap., 50, 168, 1960.

3628　Ho 246c. In M 65-66 group. Edgewise, has two equat. planes marked by dk. matter tilted a few degrees to each other. Heid 9 maj. dim. (17'0) is excessive. Drawing, Erg.d. Exakt. Naturwiss., XXIX, 376, 1956. Photom. Izv. Pulkovo, 20, No 156, 87, 1956. A.J. USSR, 32, 16, 1955.

3629　= Ho 247a. (Ho 247b at 3'5 is a *). vsBN, many knotty filam. arms.

3630　vBN. Cluster of vs gal. at 22'. In N 3630-3645 group.

3631　sBN in B core: 0'3 x 0'3, 2 main mass., part. res. reg. arms w. some branch.

3633　In N 3630-3645 group.

3636　sBN, vB * at 1'7. P(a) w. N 3637 at 3'8. Heid 9 dim. for B part only.

3637　vBN in B bar: 0'5 x 0'08 w. blobs on F(r): 0'5 x 0'5 in lens 0'6 x 0'7, vF (R): 1'35 x 1'05. P(a) w. N 3636 at 3'8. Heid 9 dim. for N only; HA 88,4 dim. for lens only.

3640　In N 3630-3645 group. P(a) w. N 3641 at 2'5. sB diff. N. Lund 9 and HA 88,2 dim. for B part only.

3641　In N 3630-3645 group. P(a) w. N 3640 at 2'5. vsB and compact.

3642　vsvBN, F(r): 0'43 x 0'38, many narrow arms w. some knots, outer arms form traces of pseudo (R). Lund 9, Heid 9 dim. for inner B part only. Mag. Ap.J., 85, 325, 1937.

N 3643 = 3645. In N 3630-3645 group. Classif. doubtful. Inner dim. on Lick 36-in. pl.: 0'6: x 0'2:.
Heid 9, Lund 9 dim. rej., N only.

3646 sBN, (r): 0'7 x 0'3, v. strong knotty (R): 2'1 x 1'0, knotty branch. arms outside (R); (r) and N not in center
of (R). P(a) w. N 3649 at 7'8. Lick (1956) and Burbidge (1961) vel. in agreement for emiss. patch 70" SW:
+4080 km/sec.
Photo., rot., mass, Ap.J., 134, 236, 1961; 138, 887, 1963.
Spectr. Ap.J., 135, 699, 1962.

3649 svBN, B inner lens: 0'45 x 0'3, smooth reg. arms. P(a) w. N 3646 at 7'8. Lund 9, Heid 9 dim. for bar
and lens only.

3650 Absorpt. lane, similar to N 4565.

3655 sBN, * at 7", sev. B irreg. knotty arms; perhaps SAB(rs). Poor. res.

3656 SN 1963, I.A.U. Circ., 1834, 1963. HAC 1605, June 1963. Photo. L'Astronomie, 77, 9, 1963.

3657 Looks stellar on small-scale plates.

3658 Poss. SO. P(a) w. N 3665 at 15'.

3659 V poor. res. Lund 9 and Mt. W. 60-in. dim. for B part only.

3664 B knotty narrow bar: 0'85 x 0'08, w. gap in cent.; reg. out. loop w. some knots: 1'5 x 1'4. P(b) w. N 3664-A at
6'2 and anon. SAB(r)O$^+$ at 12'.

3664-A P(b) w. N 3664 at 6'2. Coord. from Zwicky's catal. (1961).

3665 vB diff. N in B lens: 0'7 x 0'5 w. strong dk. crescent. P(a) w. N 3658 at 15'. Lund 9 dim. for lens only.

3666 sB cent., many knotty arms, poor. res. See also Ap.J., 46, 38, 1917. Lund 9 dim. for B part only.

3669 Mag.: Ap.J., 85, 325, 1937.

3672 sBN, pseudo (r): 0'7 x 0'3, many filam. knotty arms. Lund 9 dim. for B part only. P(a) w. anon. SAO$^+$ at 13'5
nnf; and I 688 at 20' p.

3673 sBN in weak bar w. dk. mark., (r): 1'5 x 0'7, in lens 2'0 x 1'0; F filam. arms. HA 88,2 dim. (after Helwan) is
for lens only.

3674 svBN. Mag.: Ap.J., 85, 325, 1937. Dim. for B part only. P(a) w. N 3683 at 13'5 and F anon. SB(r)O$^-$ at 7'9.

3675 sB diff. N, 2 main knotty, reg. arms, strong absorpt. lane on one side. HA 88,2 dim. (after Lick 13) for
B part only.

3681 B diff. N in smooth B inner lens or bar: 0'35 x 0'25, (r): 0'6 x 0'55, many filam. knotty branch. arms. P(a) w.
N 3684 at 14'. Lund 9 dim. for B part only.

3682 Classif. doubtful. Dim. for B part only.

3683 Mag.: Ap.J., 82, 73, 1935; 85, 325, 1937. P(a) w. N 3674 at 13'5.

3683-A See Ap.J., 82, 74, 1935. P(a) w. N 3683 at 20'. sBN in sh. bar, pseudo (r): 0'5 x - , sev. knotty filam.
arms, poor. res.; poss. SAB.

3684 sBN, 2 main branch. knotty arms. P(a) w. N 3681 at 14' sp, N 3686 at 14' nf. Lund 9, HA 88,2 dim. for
B part only.

3686 vseBN, bar: 0'4 x 0'13, 2 main knotty arms, F smooth out. whorls. P. w. N 3684 at 14'.

3689 sBN, pseudo (r): 0'2 x 0'1, 3 main knotty hexag. arms, poor. res.

3690 Coll. pair P(c) w. I 694, 2 v. complex N: 0'3 separ., irreg. spiral-like arms. Yerkes 2 (Morgan, 1959) classif.:
a? Ip + a? Ip. Mag. Ap.J., 85, 325, 1937.

3705 = Ho 259a. P. w. 2 anon. (Ho 259b, c) at 8'6 and 7'5. sBN w. B * nearby in broad diff. bar, (r): 1'2 x 0'5,
sev. F knotty arms w. F out. extens. Lund 9 dim. for B part only.

3717 sBN in broad bulge, absorpt. lane on one side, weak out. parts. P. w. I 2913 at 7'5. HA 88,2 dim. for
B part only.

3718 vsvBN, partly hidden by strong dk. lane in smooth lens: 3'8 x 2'4, weak pseudo (r): 3'3 x 1'9, vF smooth arms.
P(b) w. N 3729 at 11'5. See also HA 105, 230, 1937. Photo. Stockholm Ann., 15, No 4, 1948.

3719, 3720 = Ho 260b, a. Pair at 2'3.

3726 svBN, (r): 1'4 x 0'75, sev. part. res. B mass. arms. B(0) source B rejected (wrong identif.?).

3729 sBN in bar: 0'5 x 0'1, knotty (r): 1'15 x 0'6 in lens: 1'4 x 0'7, F out. neb. w. asym. condens., no def. arms.
P(b) w. N 3718 at 11'5. Heid 9 and Lick 13 dim. for lens only. See also HA 105, 230, 1937.
Photo. Stockholm Ann., 15, No 4, 1948.

N 3732   = 3730. vBvsN in vB lens: 0'3 x 0'17 w. some spir. struct., smooth loop forms incompl. pseudo (r): 0'5 x - , vF out. whorls or R suggested. Brightest of rich group. Heid 9, Lund 9 dim. for B part only.

3733   Mag.: Ap.J., 85, 325, 1937; see also H.A. 105, 230, 1937. P. w. N 3737 at 8'3., classif. uncertain.

3735   sBN, sev. knotty arms, poor. res., poss. SB(rs)c?

3737   = Ho 266a. P. w. anon. (Ho 266b) at 1'2 and several others F gal. nearby, N 3733 at 8'3. See also HA 105, 230, 1937. All dim. for inner part.

3738   B in cent., no N, peanut-shaped bar or core: 0'6 x 0'35. Similar to N 5253? P(a) w. N 3756 at 16'. Lund 9 dim. for B part only. See also HA 105, 230, 1937. Mag. Ap.J., 85, 325, 1937. 2 val. source F rej. from B(0).

3755   sBN, sh. bar: 0'3 x 0'06, pseudo (r): 0'55 x 0'22, sev. knotty filam. B arms, sharp outline. Interacting system?

3756   sBN, pseudo (r?): 0'55 x 0'25, 2 main knotty filam. arms w. m. branch. P(a) w. N 3738 at 16'. See also HA 105, 230, 1937. Mag.: Ap.J., 85, 325, 1937.

3759   See H.A. 105, 230, 1937. P. w. I 2943 np 2'2. Heid 9 dim., N only?

3759-A   See Ap.J., 82, 74, 1935; H.A., 105, 230, 1937.

3769   = Ho 270a. P(b) w. N 3769-A at 1'2. sh. B bar w. off cent. N and dk. mark., (r): 0'95 x 0'3. Yerkes 2 (Morgan, 1959) classif: or gD.

3769-A   = Ho 270b. P(b) w. N 3769 at 1'2.

3773   vBN w. * att.; dim. for B part only.

3780   sBN, many filam. knotty arms. P(a) w. N 3804 at 13'5. Mag. Ap.J., 85, 325, 1937.

3782   B cent. part w. B narrow bar: 0'3 x 0'05, many knotty filam. arms w. F out. extens., poor. res. Similar to N 3504. Yerkes class. "aI? Like M 82?" not confirmed. Heid 9, Lund 9 dim. for B part only.

3783   vsvBN, (r): 0'6 x 0'5, F out. arms, B * 1'2 sf. HA 88,2 class. E: is an error.

3786   = Ho 272b. P. w. N 3788 at 1'5. vB diff. N, v. weak bar, B lens: 1'0 x 0'55 w. dk. lane, pseudo (r): 0'75 x 0'35, F smooth out. whorls and (R): 1'8 x 0'85:, + vF extens. Heid 9, Lund 9 dim. for lens only. Photo., spectr. Ap.J., 116, 64, 1952.

3788   = Ho 272a. P. w. N 3786 at 1'5; N 3793 at 4'7 is probably a *. eBN and inner lens, vB lens: 0'9 x 0'2 w. dk. mark. and B v. m. forsh. narrow bar, 2 main arms form (r?): 1'4 x 0'25, F out. extens. Photo., spectr. Ap.J., 116, 64, 1952.

3799, 3800   V. close pair. Photo., spectr. Ap.J., 116, 65, 1952.

3804   = N 3794. P(a) w. N 3780 at 13'5. Lund 9, Heid 9 dim. for B part only.

3810   vsBN in B cent. part: 0'85 x 0'7, pseudo (r): 0'55 x 0'4, many part. res. filam. arms. Rather similar to N 1068. Heid 9 dim. for B part only. HII reg. Zs.f.Ap., 50, 168, 1960.

3813   vsvBN, sev. knotty vB arms, poor. res.

3818   sBN, poss. SO⁻? P(a) w. anon. Pec. at 21'. Yerkes 2 class.: "red plate: kE6".

3824   See HA, 105, 230, 1937.

3829   See H.A. 105, 230, 1937.

3846   In N 3846-3898 group. See H.A. 105, 230, 1937.

3846-A   In N 3846-3898 group. See Ap.J., 82, 74, 1935; H.A. 105, 230, 1937.

3850   In N 3846-3898 group. Mag.: Ap.J., 85, 325, 1937.

3865   = Helwan 260? (Helwan 22); many s. gal. in field.

3872   sBN. Lund 9, Heid 9 dim. for B part only.

3877   BM no BN but * superp. v. near, 2 main knotty arms, some branch. poor. res.

3885   vBN, B lens: 0'85 x 0'4 w. dk. lane on one side, weak envel.

3887   sBN in smooth bar w. dk. lane, (r): 1'05 x 0'08, sev. knotty branch. arms.

3888   In N 3846-3898 group. P(a) w. N 3898 at 16'. svBN, pseudo (r): 0'5 x 0'3, 2 main filam. knotty arms, poor. res. Heid 9, Lund 9 dim. for B part only. Mag. Ap.J., 85, 325, 1937.

3892   vsvBN, B bar, (r): 1'15 x - ; Lund 9 dim. rej., N only.

3893   = Ho 293a. P. w. N 3896 at 3'9. vsBN in sh. bar: 0'27 x - , pseudo (r): 0'53 x 0'27, 2 main knotty filam. arms w. some branch., one stronger. Lund 9 dim. for B part only.

N 3894 = Ho 294a. P(a) w. N 3895 at 2'0. All dim. for B part only.

3895 = Ho 294b. P(a) w. N 3894 at 2'0. svBN, sh. B bar: 0'4 x 0'1, (r): 0'5 x 0'3, poor. res. All dim. for B part only.

3896 = Ho 293b. P(b) w. N 3893 at 3'9. Type IOp? from Pal. Survey chart.

3898 Brightest of N 3846-3898 group. P(a) w. N 3888 at 16'. vBLN: 0'6 x 0'35, B inner spir. struct., pseudo (r): 2'3 x 0'9 in lens: 2'55 x 1'05, vF part. res. out. arms. Lund 9, Heid 9 and HA 88,2 dim. for B part (lens) only. Mag. Ap.J., 85, 325, 1937.

3900 BN, (r): 1'2 x 0'5, dk. lane on one side; poss. SAB(r)0⁺.

3904 BN. P(a) w. N 3923 at 37'.

3912 = 3899.

3913 = Ho 296a. (Ho 296b at 1'7 not found in given position); P(b?) w. 3921 at 17'. Heid 9 and Lund 6 dim. rej., N only. See H.A., 105, 230, 1937. Mag.: Ap.J., 85, 325, 1937. Type SA(s)d w. F outer arms on Pal. Sky Survey chart. SN 1963, I.A.U. Circ. 1831, 1837, 1963.

3916 P. w. N 3921 at 4'5. See H.A. 105, 230, 1937. Lund 9 dim. for B part only.

3917 sB cent. part, many knotty branch. arms, poor. res. P(a) w. N 3931 at 11', and anon. S sp (1'9 x 0'15) at 6' np. N 3917-A in Ap.J., 82, 74, 1935, is an E 9' n and 4'5 f N 3917.

3921 P. w. N 3916 at 4'5; P(b?) w. N 3913 at 17'. Heid. 9 dim. rej., N only. See H.A. 105, 230, 1937. Photo. Ap.J., 138, 883, 1963.

3923 sBN. P(a) w. N 3904 at 37'. Helwan 22 major dim. (3') is excessive. Spectr. P.A.S.P., 52, 140, 1940.

3928 N 3932 sf 5'5 is a star. See also Heid 9.

3930 = Ho 300a. P. w. anon. (Ho 300b) at 3'3.

3931 Note corr. to NGC coord. after Lund 9. P(a) w. N 3917 at 11'. vsBN in Lens: 0'5 x 0'3. Heid 9 dim. rej., N only. Mag. Ap.J., 85, 325, 1937. See also HA, 105, 230, 1937.

3938 sB diff. N in B inner lens: 0'34 x 0'28, sev. B filam. knotty, part. res. arms. Transition type between M 74 and M 101. See HA, 105, 230, 1937. Spectr. A.J., 61, 97, 1956. SN 1961, Sp. and photo.: Mem. Soc. Ast. Italiana, XXXIV, 1, 1963.

3941 svBN in vB bar: 0'8 x 0'3, weak whorls in lens. Poss. 0⁺.

3945 vsBN in inner lens: 0'43 x 0'15 on F bar: 0'95 x 0'25 w. small blobs. All dim. for B part only. F(R): 4'5 x 2'0 on Palomar Survey Chart.

3949 = Ho 301a. B cent., sev. knotty B arms, poor. res. N 3950 (Ho 301b) at 1'6 noted as a * in Ap.J., 91, 350, 1940 = MWC 626; however it appears nebulous on Pal. chart. Lund 9 dim. for B part only.

3953 svBN in B inner lens: 0'5 x 0'3, (r): 1'2 x 0'55, many knotty filam. arms, beginning of res. Similar to N 6744. See also HA 105, 230, 1937.

3955 B complex bar w. knots and dk. lanes. Possibly similar to M 82 or Pec. HA 88,2 class. E: is an error.

3956 svB bar or N: 0'25 x 0'08, sev. knotty filam. arms. Classif. uncertain. Heid 9 dim. for B part only.

3957 sBN in rectang. bulge: 0'55 x 0'2, w. dk. lane.

3958 P(a) w. N 3963 at 8'2. Lens: 0'7 x 0'3.

3963 svBN in B bar: 0'5 x 0'3, pseudo (r): 0'5 x - , 2 main mass., knotty B arms. Heid 9 dim. for B part only. P(a) w. N 3958 at 8'2. Mag.: Ap.J., 85, 325, 1937.

3972 = Ho 304a. P(a) w. N 3977 (Ho 304b) at 5'2. sBN, 2 main knotty arms. See also HA 105, 230, 1937. Mag.: Ap.J., 85, 325, 1937.

3975 = Ho 306b. P. w. N 3978 at 2'0.

3976 = Ho 305a. P. w. Fanon (Ho 305b) at 4'8. sB diff. N, 2 main knotty arms, poor. res.

3977 = 3980? = Ho 304b. P(a) w. N 3972 at 5'2. svBN in B cent. part or lens: 0'7 x 0'6, poor. res., F(R): 1'5 x 1'5 w. vF out. arms. Similar to N 1068. Heid. 9 and Lund 6 dim. rej., lens only. See also HA, 105, 230, 1937. SN 1946, Ann. Rep. Mt. Wilson Obs., 45, 19, 1945-46.

3978 = Ho 306a. P. w. N 3975 at 2'0.

3982 svBN, (r): 0'33 x 0'29, sev. knotty arms w. F out. extens. Lund 9, Heid 9 dim. for B part only. See also HA, 105, 230, 1937. Mag.: Ap.J., 85, 325, 1937.

3985 sB bar: 0'2 x 0'1, no def. N, 2 main strong arms, poor. res. All dim. for B part only. Yerkes Class.: or pf?

3986 sBN. P. w. I 2978 at 4'8. Other gal. nearby.

N 3990   = Ho 310b. P(a) w. N 3998 (Ho 310a) at 3'2. svBN or lens: 0'25 x 0'15. See also HA 105, 230, 1937.
         Spectr. I.A.U. Symp., 5, 1958 = Lick Cont. II, No 82, 1958.

3991   = Ho 309c. Multiple interacting system w. N 3994-3995. Knotty bar-like core w. 2 asym. B knots at one end.
       Pec. Heid 9 major dim. (0'3) is an error and was rej.
       Photo. Sky & Tel., 17, 231, 1958.
       Spectr. P.A.S.P., 69, 564, 1957. Haro obj. 5 (Bol. Tonantzintla, 14, 8, 1956).
           Lick 1962 vel. for fainter comp.: + 3040.

3992   vB diff. N, B smooth bar w. dk. lane: 1'7 x 0'5, (r): 2'5 x 1'7, 3 main part res. filam. arms w. some branch.
       See also HA, 105, 230, 1937.
       Photo. Stockholm Ann., 17, No 3, 1951.
       SN 1956, Hdb.d.Phys., Vol. 51, 774, 1958; Spectr.: A.J., 65, 54, 1960.

3993   = Ho 308a. In multiple system w. N 3987, 89, 97.

3994   = Ho 309b. In multiple system w. N 3991, 3995. P. w. N 3995 at 1'8. sBN, pseudo (r): 0'25 x 0'1, poor. res.,
       F out. streamer toward N 3995.
       Photo. Sky & Tel., 17, 231, 1958.
       Spectr. P.A.S.P., 69, 386, 1957.

3995   = Ho 309a. Multiple interacting system w. N 3991, 3994. P. w. N 3994 at 1'8, N 3991 at 3'7. sBN off center in
       cardioid-shaped lens or (r), 3 knotty irreg., asym. arms.
       Photo. Sky & Tel., 17, 231, 1958.
       Spectr. P.A.S.P., 69, 386, 1957. I.A.U. Symp., 5, 1958 = Lick Cont. II, No 82, 1958.

3997   = Ho 308b. In multiple system w. N 3987, 89, 93.

3998   = Ho 310a. P(a) w. N 3990 at 3'2. vBN: 0'5 x 0'4, B uniform lens: 1'4 x 1'2. See also HA, 105, 230, 1937.
       Mag.: Ap.J., 85, 325, 1937. Spectr. I.A.U. Symp., 5, 1958 = Lick Cont. II, No 81, 1958.

4008   sBN. Lund 9 dim. for B part only.

4010   = Ho 314a. P. w. N 4001 (Ho 314b) at 7'.

4013   B diff. peanut-shaped bulge w. B * superp., no BN, strong equat. dk. lane; exactly edgewise. V. similar to N
       891. See also HA 105, 230, 1937. Photo. Hdb.d.Ap., 5, 2, 843, 1933.

4024   sBN in weak diff. bar, F envel. Heid 9 minor dim. (0'25) is for bar only.

4025   Asym. Similar to N 1313.

4026   vsvBN, B lens: 0'75 x 0'35, v. thin flat compon. Similar to N 4111. See also HA 105, 230, 1937. The object
       4085-A found by Keenan (Ap.J., 82, 74, 1935) of mag. 11.6 is most likely N 4026.

4027   sB elong. core in B bar, one main asym. arm w. addit. branch. Similar to LMC. P(a?) N 4038-39 at 41'.
       See also M.N., 82, 487, 1922.
       Photom. H.B., 913, 13, 1940.
       Spectr. P.A.S.P., 52, 140, 1940. A.J., 68, 278, 1963 (Abst.).

4030   sBN, many knotty filam. arms; poss. (rs) type. F anon. Im at 16'5 sf. Lick 13 major dim. (2') for B part only.

4032   = N 4042?

4033   svBN in B diff. lens: 0'34 x 0'17. HA 88,2 dim. (0'7 x 0'4, ser. a') for B part only.

4035   Heid. 9 R.A. is 0^{m}6 less.

4036   vBN w. few patches of dk. matt. in B diff. lens: 0'95 x 0'3. P(a) w. N 4041 at 15'. Lund 9, Heid 9 dim. for B
       part only. Yerkes 1 class.: or D K.

4037   vsBN in weak bar: 0'7 x 0'25, vF pseudo (r), traces of out. struct., v. low surf. bright. Lund 9 dim.
       for B part only.

4038, 4039 Coll. system. B complex cent. w. dk. mark. and vB knots, long smooth out. streamers. N 4038 is north
       comp. See also M.N., 82, 487, 1922. All dim. are for both comp. P(a?) w. N 4027 at 41'.
       Photo. Ap.J., 57, 140, 1923. P.A.S.P., 53, 16, 1941. P.N.A.S., 26, 35, 1940. Proc. 3rd
           Berkeley Symp., Vol. III, 1955.
       Photom. HB, 913, 13, 1940.
       Spectr. P.A.S.P., 52, 139, 1940. Ap.J., 116, 66, 1952.
       Radio source, Aust.J.Phys., 11, 360, 1958.
       SN 1921, Medd. Lund, I, No 155, 1939.

4041   vB cent. w. complex struct.: 0'52 x 0'48, sev. knotty filam. arms. P(a) w. N 4036 at 15'; 2 F anon. SB(s)m at
       12' and 17'. Heid 9, Lund 9 dim. for B part only.

4045   = Ho 320a. P. w. anon. (Ho 320b) at 1'6. vsvBN, weak bar, incompl. (r): 0'57 x 0'53, F out. arms form pseudo
       (R): 1'7 x - . Heid 9, HA 88,4 dim. for B part only; Lund 6 minor dim. (2'5) is an error.

4047   vsvBN surrounded by many knotty, poor. res. arms in B lens: 1'05 x 0'85, eF (R): 2'4 x 2'4. Similar to N 1068.
       Heid 9, Lund 9 dim. for lens only.

4050   vsvBN in broad bar: 1'4 x 0'5, w. dk. mark., (r): 1'7 x 1'3, in lens: 2'2 x 1'4. F smooth out. arms. Heid 9
       and HA 88,2 (after Helwan) dim. for B part only.

N 4051 vseBN or *, pseudo (r): 1'8 x 0'8:, 2 main part. res. branch. arms. See also HA 105, 230, 1937.
        Photo. Ap.J., 130, 26, 1959.
        Spectr. Ap.J., 97, 28, 1943. Broad em. lines.
        HII reg. Zs.f.Ap., 50, 168, 1960.

4062   vsBN, many knotty arms, traces of pseudo (r): 0'7 x - ; transition type between SA(rs) and SA(s).
       Upsala 21, Lick 13 and Lund 9 dim. for B part only.

4064   B complex bar w. dk. lanes and innermost vB segment: 0'3 x 0'06, vF out. part. Lund 9 dim. rej., bar only.
       Yerkes 1 class.: or I ? F.

4068   See H.A., 105, 230, 1937.

4073   In a group w. N 4077 and other F gal.

4081   = N 4125-A in Ap.J., 82, 74, 1935 (mag. = 13.8, dim.: 1'2 x 0'3).

4085   = Ho 326b. P(a) w. N 4088 at 11'. No def. BN, complex knotty arms, poor. res. Mag. Ap.J., 85, 325, 1937.
       B(0) source F rejected. For N 4085-A (Ap.J., 82, 74, 1935) see N 4026.

4088   = Ho 326a. P(a) w. N 4085 at 11'. vsBN complex broad lens, w. many dk. lanes, pseudo (r?): 1'3 x - . Lick
       (1962) vel. for 2 emiss. 52" SW and 105" NE of nucl.: +996, +616 km/sec.
       Photo. Ap.J., 104, 218, 1946.
       Rot. Ap.J., 97, 117, 1943.

4096   sBN or bar, perhaps F * superp., sev. B knotty filam. arms w. branch. Lund 9, Lund 10 dim. for B part only.
       SN 1960, P.A.S.P., 73, 175, 1961. I.A.U. Circ. 1731. HAC 1489.

4100   vsBN, 2 main knotty reg. arms, weak (R): 4'5 x 1'3. Lund 9, Heid 9, Lick 13 dim. for B part only.

4102   sBN in vB isol. lens: 0'5 x 0'25, 2 main detached B knotty arms form pseudo (r) or (R): 1'2 x 0'6. Heid 9, Lund
       9 dim. for B part only. See also HA, 105, 231, 1937.

4105   P(b?) w. N 4106 at 1'15.

4106   P(b?) w. N 4105 at 1'15. vBN, F smooth bar: 0'8 x 0'35 vF out. extens. Probably interacting w. N 4105.

4108   Mag.: Ap.J., 85, 325, 1937.

4108-A, B See Ap.J., 82, 74, 1935. N 4108-A at 8' np (dim.: 1'2 x 0'4), N 4108-B at 5' nf (dim.: 0'9 x 0'6).

4109   = Ho 333b. P. w. N 4111 at 4'8. See H.A. 105, 231, 1937.

4111   = Ho 333a. P. w. N 4109 at 4'8. vsvBN cut by dk. lane, e thin, smooth equat. compon., traces of ansae or (r?):
       0'7 x - in lens: 1'0 x 0'2.
       Photo. B.A.N., 16, 1, 1961.
       Photom. M.N., 98, 619, 1938. B.A.N., 16, 1, 1961.
       Spectr. I.A.U. Symp., 5, 1958 = Lick Cont. II, No 81, 1958. Ap.J., 135, 734, 1962.

4114   Heid. 9 dim. rej.

4116   B narrow bar w. vsBN, pseudo (r): 0'7 x - , sev. part. res. filam. arms, slightly asym. P(a) w. N 4123 at 14'.
       Lund 9 dim. for B part only.
       Spectr., I.A.U. Symp., 5, 1958 = Lick Cont. II, No 81, 1958.

4117, 4118 = Ho 334 a, b. Pair at 1'6. 4118: 0'4 x 0'4 in Lund 6, B part only. See also HA, 105, 231, 1937.

4120   Mag.: Ap.J., 85, 325, 1937.

4121   = Ho 335b. P. w. N 4125 at 3'6.

4123   vsvBN on F bar w. dk. lanes, (r): 1'4 x 1'2, sev. filam. part. res. arms. P(a) w. N 4116 at 14'.
       Lund 9 minor dim. (1'5) is too small.

4124   vsvBN in B (r): 0'25 x 0'1 w. inner dk. matter, lens 0'4 x 0'2, B out. envel.

4125   = Ho 335a. P(a) w. N 4121 at 3'6. Spectr., Ap.J., 132, 325, 1960. Mag.: Ap.J., 85, 325, 1937.
       For N 4125-A see N 4081.

4128   = Ho 337a. P. w. anon. (Ho 337b) at 2'. svBN. Mag.: Ap.J., 85, 325, 1937.

4129   B complex bar and lens w. dk. mark., vF arms. Heid 9, Lund 9 dim. for B part only. Yerkes 2 class.: or I?

4136   svBN, fairly B bar: 0'4 x 0'1, (r): 0'75 x 0'45, sev. part. res. arms w. branch. Similar to N 6744.
       SN 1941, HAC 581. May, 1941.

4137   See also H.A., 105, 231, 1937.

4138   sBN w. * att., (r): 0'65 x 0'4 w. strong inner dk. lane. See also HA, 105, 231, 1937.

4143   sB diff. N, v. weak bar and traces of spir. struct. See also HA, 105, 231, 1937.

4144   BM no BN, poor. res. Lund 9 dim. for B part only.

N 4145 = Ho 342a. P. w. anon. (Ho 342b) at 13', Sp. w. small satel. attached.

4146 <u>SN 1963,</u> HAC 1584, Jan. 28, 1963.

4150 vsvBN w. F dk. crescent on one side.

4151 = Ho 345a. P(a) w. N 4156 at 5'2 and Ho 345c at 8'8. seBN, vB inner lens: 0'4 x 0'3, broad bar or lens w. spir. patt. of dk. matt., pseudo (r): 2'1 x - . vF outer arms form pseudo (R): 6'5 x 6'0.
<u>Photo.</u> P.A.S.P., 46, 134, 1934.
<u>Spectr.</u> P.A.S.P., 46, 134, 1934; 48, 107, 1936; 53, 231, 1941; 61, 132, 1949. Ap.J., 97, 28, 1943; 135, 734, 1962. Strong nuclear emission; (B-V) increases w. log A/D(0).

4152 sBN or bar, pseudo (r): 0'3 x 0'2, sev. knotty filam. arms. Heid 9, Lund 9 dim. for B part only.

4156 = Ho 345b. P(a) w. N 4151 at 5'2. and anon. (Ho 345c) at 7'. sBN, narrow bar, pseudo (r): 0'34 x - . Lund 9 minor dim. (0'3) is an error.

4157 B cent. part obsc. by dk. lane on one side, sev. knotty filam. arms, v. poor. res.
<u>SN 1937,</u> P.A.S.P., 49, 205, 1937. Ap.J., 88, 291, 1938; 96, 28, 1942.

4158 vBN, (r): 0'22 x 0'17, many filam. arms, v. poor. res. Heid 9, Lund 9 dim. for B part only.

4162 vBN w. * att. at 0'2, pseudo (r): 0'45 x 0'3, eF (R): 3'65 x 2'25 suspected (?).

4165 sBN, (r): 0'67 x 0'43, bar v. weak or absent, classif. doubtful. P(a) w. N 4168 at 2'7.

4168 P(a) w. N 4165 at 2'7. Brightest in a group.

4178 = I 3042. sB narrow bar: 0'7 x 0'1, sev. F part. res. branch. arms.
<u>Spectr.</u> I.A.U. Symp., 5, 1958 = Lick Cont. II, No 81, 1958.
<u>SN 1963,</u> I.A.U. Circ., 1830, 31, 32, 1963.

4179 Classif. uncertain; poss. E$^+$ 7.

4183 B in cent., no def. N, knotty filam. arms and dk. lane, v. poor. res. Heid 9 dim. for B part only. Seyfert's comment in HA 105, p. 232; "In HA 88,2, N 4160 should read N 4183. N 4160 is probably a star" is correct. Note also wrong coord.

4186 Note corr. to NGC coord. (see MWC 626). = Ho 348b. P. w. N 4192 at 11'5.

4189 = I 3050. sBN, sev. knotty branch. filam. arms, poor. res. In group w. N 4164, 93.

4192 = M 98. = Ho 348a. P. w. N 4186 at 11'5 sf (= Ho 348b) and Ho 348c at 9'5 sp. vseBN part. hidden by dk. lane, smooth bar or lens 5'0 x 0'85 w. many dk. lanes, part. res. spir. arcs near edge; smooth out. arms form pseudo (R): 7'9 x 1'7. <u>Photom.</u> Izv. Pulkovo, 20, No 156, 87, 1956. A.J. USSR, 32, 16, 1955.

4193 sBN, poor. res. In N 4189 group. Lund 10 major dim. (0'6) is an error.

4194 eBN, asym., F out. struct. Heid 9, Lund 9 dim. for B part only. <u>Spectr.</u> IAU Symp., 5, 1958 = Lick Cont. II, No 81, 1958.

4203 vB diff. N in B lens: 0'7 x 0'6 w. traces of bar fairly B envel. w. weak traces of arcs or ring.
<u>Polar.</u> Bull. Abastumani, No 18, 15, 1955.

4206 = Ho 353b. In multiple system w. N 4216 (at 10'7), 4222 and I 771 (Ho 353d). vsBN, many knotty arms, dk. lane in front, poor. res.

4210 sBN in narrow B bar, (r): 0'6 x 0'4, 2 main B arms, poor. res. Lund 9 dim. for B part only.
<u>Mag.</u> Ap.J., 85, 325, 1937.

4212 = 4208. BN, sev. knotty arms w. some branch., poor. res.

4214 = 4228. Sh. B, part. res. bar-like core w. dk. mark.: 1'6 x 1'0, traces of spir. struct., highly res. whorls. Lund 9 minor dim. (0'4) is an error. (B-V) val. interpolated.
<u>Photo.</u> Ap.J., 64, 328, 1926.
<u>Spectr.</u> A.J., 61, 97, 1956.
<u>HII reg.</u> Zs.f.Ap., 50, 168, 1960.
<u>Radio emiss.</u> (unobserved) M.N., 123, 279, 1961.
<u>HI emiss.</u> Epstein, Harvard Thesis, 1962.
<u>SN 1954,</u> Publ. Bologna, VI 12, 1955. L'Astronomie, 69, 393, 1955. Zs.f.Ap., 35, 205, 1955. HAC, 1250.
        P.A.S.P., 72, 100, 1960; 75, 133, 1963.

4215 esvBN, e thin disk, lens: 1'1 x 0'1 w. ansae or (r:): 0'95 x - .

4216 = Ho 353a. In multiple system w. N 4206, 4222 and I 771 (Ho 353d). seBN, part. hidden by dk. lanes, knotty reg. whorls w. v. strong dk. lanes, pseudo (R): 5'6 x 0'7. Lund 9, MWC 132, 186 dim. for B part only. (B-V) value interpolated.
<u>Photo.</u> Ap.J., 97, 114, 1943; 104, 218, 1946. Mem. Soc.R.Sc. Liege, 4, XV, 1, 1956.
<u>Photom.</u> Stockholm Ann., 18, No 9, 1956. Mem. Soc.R.Sc. Liege, 4, XV, 1, 1956.
<u>Orient., rot.</u> Ap.J., 97, 117, 1943; 127, 487, 1958. Nature, 169, 1042, 1952.

4217 = Ho 354a. P. w. N 4226 at 7'4. <u>Photom.</u> Izv. Pulkovo, 20, No 156, 87, 1956. A.J. USSR, 32, 16, 1955.

N 4218   P(a) w. N 4220 at 15'.

4220   sBN, (r): 0'95 x 0'25, poor. res. P(a) w. N 4218 at 15'. Lund 9 dim. for B part only. Yerkes 2 class.: or D G.

4221   vsvBN on B bar, (r): 1'05 x 0'85, in lens: 1'3 x 1'1, eF (R): 2'4 x 2'4. Lund 9 dim. rej., N only; Heid 9 dim. (r) only? Mag. Ap.J., 85, 325, 1937.

4222   = Ho 353c. In multiple system w. N 4206, 4216 and I 771 (Ho 353d). Exactly edgewise, knots and dk. lanes, poor. res.

4231, 4232   = Ho 356a, b. Pair at 1'1.

4234   = 358a. (Ho 358b at 1'9 is a *).
       Spectr. Haro obj. 7 (Bol. Tonantzintla, 14, 8, 1956).
       Radio emiss.? Aust.J.Phys., 11, 360, 1958. Proc. 4th Berkeley Symp., vol. III, 245, 1960.

4235   = I 3098. = Ho 359a. P(a) w. N 4246 at 12', N 4247 at 13'. svB diff. N in B bulge, smooth spir. arms w. dk. lane on one side. Lund 9 dim. for B part only. Yerkes 1 class.: or D G.

4236   = Ho 357 a. P. w. anon. (Ho 357b) at 9'. v. long F bar: 3'9 x 0'4, highly res. weak out. arms. See also Ap.J., 46, 39, 1917 = MWC 132. Lick 1956 vel. for brightest emiss. patches in SE end, 5'5 from center: + 186 km/sec (may be affected by rotation). HII reg. Zs.f.Ap., 50, 168, 1960.

4237   sBN, pseudo (r): 0'75 x 0'3, many knotty arms, poor. res.

4242   Low surf. bright., weak diff. bar, sev. filam. vF arms, part. res. See HA, 105, 231, 1937.

4244   vsBN or * ? dk. lane. Lick 13, Lund 9, 10 dim. for B part only. (B-V) interp.
       Photo., orient. P.A.S.P., 53, 269, 1941. Ap.J., 127, 487, 1958.
       Radio emiss. M.N., 122, 479, 1961.
       HI emiss. A.J., 66, 294, 1962; 67, 437, 1962.

4245   vsvBN in inner lens: 0'17 x 0'14 w. spir. struct., strong bar and (r): 1'2 x 0'9, in lens: 1'5 x 1'3.
       P. w. N 4253 at 16'5. Heid 9 dim. for lens only.

4246   = I 3113. = Ho 359b, in multiple system w. N 4235 at 12', 4247 at 5'3. sBN, 2 main reg. knotty arms w. some branch. Lund 6, 9 dim. for B part only.

4247   = Ho 359c in multiple system w. N 4235, 4246. vB elong. N w. dk. lane, weak bar, pseudo (r) or (R): 1'0 x 0'85, poor. res. Lund 9 dim. for B part only.

4248   = Ho 363b. P. w. N 4258 at 13'3. Lick 13 minor dim. (0'1) is an error or misprint.

4250   vsvBN in innermost lens: 0'3 x 0'3 w. some (r) or spir. struct., F bar, (r): 1'4 x 0'85. Mag. for N 4250-A in Ap.J., 82, 74, 1935 refers probably to N 4250.

4251   svB diff. N, strong narrow bar or lens: 0'1 thick, B part: 0'95 x 0'35, weak envel. Photom. Ap.J., 50, 384, 1919.

4253   Poss. SB(s)a:. P. w. N 4245 at 16'5.

4254   = M 99. svBN in complex cent. lens w. many dk. lanes, pseudo (r): 0'8 x 0'8, 2 part. res., mass. arms w. m. branch. Similar to M 33.
       Photo. Ap.J., 135, 7, 1962.
       Photom. Izv. Pulkovo, 20, No 156, 87, 1956. A.J., USSR, 32, 16, 1955.
       HII reg. Zs.f.Ap., 50, 168, 1960.

4256   sBN in B bulge, strong dk. lane on one side. v. similar to N 5746. Error on δ in H.A., 88.2.

4258   = Ho 363a. P. w. N 4248 at 13'3.
       Photo. Ap.J., 97, 114, 1943; 104, 218, 1946; 138, 375, 1963.
       Photom. Izv. Pulkovo, 20, No 156, 87, 1955. A.J. USSR, 32, 16, 1955.
       Orient., rot., mass. Ap.J., 97, 117, 1943; 127, 487, 1958; 138, 375, 1963.
       Spectr. Ap.J., 135, 698, 1962.
       HII reg. Zs.f.Ap., 50, 168, 1960.
       Radio emiss. Phil. Mag., 43, 137, 1952. Hdb.d.Phys., vol. 53, 253, 1959. M.N., 122, 479, 1961.
                    P.A.S.P., 72, 368, 1960.

4259   = Ho 368e. In group w. N 4273. Lund 6 dim. for N only.

4260   svBN in B broad bar w. blobs, pseudo (r): 1'1 x - , 2 reg. smooth arms.

4261   P. w. N 4264 at 3'5. Radio emiss. Aust.J.Phys., 11, 360, 1958. Cal.Inst.Techn.Rad.Obs., 5, 1960. Proc. 4th Berkeley Symp., Vol. III, 245, 1960.

4262   eBN in sh. B bar: 0'45 x 0'1, smooth B lens: 0'9 x 0'8, vF envel. Lund 7 dim. rej., N only; Heid 9, Lund 9, HA 88,4 dim. for lens only.

4264   BN in strong bar, (r): 0'35 x 0'35. P(a) w. N 4261 at 3'5. All dim. for B part only.

4266   In group w. N 4273.

4267   vB diff. N in sh. diff. B bar: 0'55 x 0'15:. P. w. I 775 at 14'5. Lund 9 dim. rej., bar only.
       Photom. Ap.J., 132, 306, 1960.

N 4268 = Ho 368d. In group w. N 4273.

4269 = Ho 365a. Close pair w. I 3155 (Ho 365b) at 1'. vB * 2' n. Lund 6 dim. rej., N only.

4270 = Ho 368c. In group w. N 4273.

4273 = Ho 368a. Brightest of group. Interp. value of (B-V)(0).
Photo. P.A.S.P., 48, 111, 1936.
SN 1936, Ap.J., 88, 291, 1938; 89, 192, 1939. P.A.S.P., 48, 108, 226, 1936.

4274 vBN in s. bar seen almost end-on, w. dk. lanes, B (r): 2'7 x 1'0 in lens: 3'2 x 1'2, F out. arms form pseudo
(R): 5'8 x 1'55. Lick 13, Upsala 21 dim. for B part (lens) only.

4277 = Ho 368f. In group w. N 4273. Mag. 13.9 in Lund 6, 15.9 in Lund 9 (?). Lick 13, Lund 9 dim. for B part only.

4278 = Ho 369a. P. w. N 4283 at 3'5. vB center, smooth struct., many glob. cl.
Photom. Ap.J., 50, 384, 1919; 71, 231, 1930.
Spectr. Ap.J., 116, 66, 1952; 132, 325, 1960.
Rot., mass, mass/lum. Ap.J., 132, 325, 1960; 134, 910, 1961.

4281 = Ho 368b. In group w. N 4273.

4283 = Ho 369b. P. w. N 4278 at 3'5, N 4286 at 5'2. svB cent., steep luminos. gradient. Lick 13, Upsala 21 dim.
for B part only.
Photom. Ap.J., 71, 231, 1930.
Spectr. Ap.J., 116, 66, 1952.

4286 P. w. N 4283 at 5'2. Poss. SA(r)a.

4288 = Ho 371a. P. w. anon. (Ho 371b) at 2'2.

4290 = Ho 373a. P. w. N 4284, Sc? (Ho 373b) at 4'5 (w. small corr. to NGC Dec. of N 4284). vsvBN, B bar, pseudo
(r): 0'9 x 0'65.

4291 P(a) w. N 4319 at 7'4.

4292 = Ho 375a. P. w. anon. (Ho 375b) at 2'2.

4293 vsBN, partly hidden by strong dk. lane in bar, lens: 2'6 x 0'7, vF (R): 4'2 x 2'0. Lund 9 dim. for lens only.

4294 = Ho 376a. P. w. N 4299 at 5'5. Long narrow bar, no N, asym., highly res. Lund 6 minor dim. (2'8) is an error
or misprint for 0'8.

4298 = Ho 377a. P(a) w. N 4302 at 2'4. vsBN, many knotty filam. arms w. dk. lanes.

4299 = Ho 376b. P. w. N 4294 at 5'5. No def. N or bar, one out. arm, irreg.

4301 Probably = Ho 379b (1'1 x 1'1) w. NGC coord. correct. according to Heid 9 and MWC 626. P. w. N 4303 at 10'.

4302 = Ho 377b. P. w. N 4298 at 2'4. BM, N hidden by strong dk. lane.

4303 = M 61. = Ho 379a. P. w. N 4301 at 10'. eBN in broad diff. bar w. many dk. lanes, hexag. pseudo (r):
1'6 x 1'6, part. res. filam. out. arms form pseudo (R): 5'4 x 5'2.
HII reg. Zs.f.Ap., 50, 168, 1960.
SN 1926, P.A.S.P., 38, 182, 1926; 48, 111, 1936; 52, 306, 1940. H.B., 836, 1926. Ap.J., 88, 291, 1938;
89, 193, 1939.
SN 1961, P.A.S.P., 74, 215, 1962.

4305, 4306 = Ho 381 a, b. Pair at 3'.

4307 = Ho 380a. P. w. anon. (Ho 380b) at 3'2.

4309 = Ho 382a. P. w. anon. (Ho 382b) at 1'6. (r): 1'0 x 0'55.

4312 = Ho 387b. P. w. N 4321 at 18', and group of F anon. gal.

4313 = Ho 385a. (Ho 385b at 4'3 is a *). sBN.

4314 eBN w. spir. struct.: 0'5 x 0'35, vB bar: 2'1 x 0'3, weak smooth (r): 2'2 x 1'7, in lens: 3'0 x 2'1, smooth out.
arms form pseudo (R): 3'6 x 3'0. Heid 9 and HA 88,4 minor dim. rej., bar or lens only?
Spectr. Ap.J., 135, 697, 1962.

4319 vsvBN in B bar: 0'4 x 0'13, pseudo (r): 1'1 x 0'6, 2 main F arms, poor. res. P. w. N 4291 at 7'4.
Heid 9 dim. for (r) only.

4321 = M 100. = M 387a. P. w. N 4312 at 18'. vBN w. inner spir. struct: 0'4 x 0'3, broad weak diff. bar: 1'9 x 1'2,
spir. patt. of dk. lanes in lens, pseudo (r): 1'9 x 1'7, part. res. reg. arms, pseudo (R): 5'0 x 3'9. Lick 13,
Heid 9, Lund dim. for B part only. (B-V) const. w. log A/D(0).
Photo. A.J., 61, 160, 1956. Ap.J., 127, 522, 1958; 135, 7, 1962. Hdb.d.Ap., 5, 2, 803, 1933.
Photom. Izv. Pulkovo, 20, No 156, 87, 1956. A.J., USSR, 32, 16, 1955.
HII reg. Zs.f.Ap., 50, 168, 1960. Observatory, 79, 54, 1959.
SN 1901, P.A.S.P., 29, 180, 1917. Lick Obs. Bull., 300, 1917. Ap.J., 88, 292, 1938.
SN 1960, P.A.S.P., 73, 175, 1961.

N 4322   = 4323. 4' n of 4321 (= Ho 387 f? 0'5 x 0'5).

4324   = Ho 388a. (Ho 388b at 1'1 is a *). svBN, (r): 0'7 x 0'3, w. dk. lane, knots on (r). poss. SAB? Lund 6 dim.
       for lens only. Photo. Ap.J., 92, 236, 1940.

4326   Lund 9 dim. rej., N only.

4329   sBN, smooth neb. Heid. 9 dim. rej., N only? P(a) w. anon. S sp (1'3 x 0'3) w. dk. lane at 3'0.
       Many others in field.

4332   B bar: 0'95 x 0'35, 2 F smooth arms. Lund 9 dim. for bar only.

4333   vsBN, B narrow bar: 0'3 x 0'06.

4334   vBsN on fairly B thin bar. Lund 9 dim. for bar only?

4340   = Ho 391b. P(a) w. N 4350 at 5'6. svBN, broad bar w. blobs, (r): 1'9 x 1'2, lens: 2'5 x 1'4. Heid 9, Lund 6,
       9 dim. for lens only.

4341, -42, -43 The identifications of N 4341 -2 -3 are uncertain; the identifications shown in Fig. 8 which differ
       from the Heidelberg and Mt. Wilson identifications have been adopted in consultation with Dr. Mayall.

4341   = I 3260. Identified as N 4343 in Heid. 9, Holmberg (1958). In Morgan (1958) Dec of 4341,43 must be exchanged.

4342   = I 3256. Identif. as N 4343 in Humason et al. (1956). vseBN in B lens: 0'45 x 0'15. vs E2 comp. at 0'5. N
       4342 in Yerkes 2 list (Morgan 1959) is said to be southern most of group of 5; class. therefore applies to N
       4343 (new identif.). In Morgan (1958) the class. kE1 may apply to I 3267?

4343   Identified as N 4341 in Heid. 9, Holmberg (1958) and Morgan (1958) and as N 4342 (Morgan 1959). vBN in B bulge,
       many knotty filam. arms w. dk. lane on one side, poor. res.

4344   = Ho 390a. (Ho 390b at 1'7 is a *).

4350   = Ho 391a. P(a) w. N 4340 at 5'6. vsvBN; B lens: 1'0 x 0'25. Photom. Ap.J., 132, 306, 1960.

4351   = N 4354. Asym.

4359   See HA 105, 231, 1937.

4363   Mag.: Ap.J., 85, 325, 1937.

4365   vB cent., smooth neb., many glob. clusters. P(a) w. N 4370 at 10'.
       Photom. Ap.J., 132, 306, 1960.
       Spectr. A.J., 61, 97, 1956. Zwicky, Morph. Astr., p. 154, 1957.

4369   vB complex. cent. 0'45 x 0'4 w. spir. arms and dk. lane, F out. arms and F(R): 1'4 x 1'4.

4370   Rev. class. S0+. P(a) w. N 4365 at 10'.

4371   vBN: 0'6 x 0'3 on smooth bar: 1'1 x 0'4, weak (r): 1'9 x 1'1, stronger near extremities of bar.

4373   BN, * 0'6 n. P. w. I 3290 at 2'0.

4374   = Ho 403b. P(a) w. N 4387 at 10'5. vB cent., smooth neb., some glob. clusters?
       Photo. Ap.J., 135, 6, 1962.
       Photom. Ap.J., 71, 231, 1930; 132, 306, 1960.
       Spectr. Ap.J., 135, 734, 1962.
       Radio emiss. Observatory, 80, 325, 1960; 81, 202, 1961.
       SN 1957, A.N., 284, 141, 1958. A.J., 63, 146, 1958; 65, 54, 1960.

4375   SN 1960, P.A.S.P., 73, 175, 1961.

4377   svBN, smooth lens, one vs gal. vis. through lens, other through envel.

4378   svB diff. N, F whorls form pseudo (R): 2'8 x 2'0.

4380   vsBN, v. weak filam. arms and dk. lanes, v. poor. res., classif. doubtful.

4382   = M85. = Ho 397a. P. w. N 4394 at 7'8. eB diff. N, weak smooth whorls in lens, vF diam. distorsion toward s.
       anon. comp. at 3'0.
       Photo. B.A.N., 16, 1, 1961. Ap.J., 135, 6, 1962.
       Photom. Ap.J., 71, 231, 1930. B.A.N., 16, 1, 1961.
       HII reg. Zs.f.Ap., 50, 168, 1960.
       SN 1960, H.A.C., 1521, 1960. Mem. Soc. Ast. Ital., III, 74, 1962. Photo: Ann. Guebhard, 39, 263, 1963.

4385   vsvBN in strong bar w. dk. lane, pseudo (r): 1'05 x 0'7:.

4387   P. w. N 4374 at 10'5. Poss. SAO⁻.

4388   = Ho 403c. Irreg. dk. lane, perhaps bar seen end-on. Minor diam. (3'2) in Lund 10 is an error, or misprint
       and was rejected.

4389   sB narrow bar: 0'5 x 0'1, crossed by dk. lane; pseudo (r): 1'5 x 0'65.

N 4391　Heid. 9 and Lund 9 dim. rejected (0'25 x 0'25 and 0'3 x 0'3).

4394　= Ho 397b.　P. w. N 4382 at 7'8.　eBN in B bar: 1'3 x 0'2 w. dk. lanes, (r): 1'6 x 1'3, (R): 2'8 x 2'6.
Spectr. Ap.J., 135, 734, 1962.

4395　Details = N 4399, 4400, 4401.　Lick 1956 vel. for 2 emiss. patch in 4401; +312 km/sec.　v. low surf. bright, irreg. arms, partly res.　See also HA, 105, 231, 1937.
HII reg. Zs.f.Ap., 50, 168, 1960.

4396　= Ho 400a.　(Ho 400b at 6'2 is a dble　*).

4402　= Ho 403d.　P(a) w. N 4406 at 10'.　Strong, complex curved dk. lanes.　Classif. diff.; Poss. IO?

4406　= M 86.　= Ho 403a.　P(a) w. N 4402 at 10'.　vB cent., smooth neb., traces of zonal struct., some glob. cl.?　F
envel. in out. parts.　Desc. Ap.J., 46, 231, 1917 = MWC 132.
Photo. Ap.J., 135, 6, 1962.
Photom. Ap.J., 71, 231, 1930; 132, 306, 1960.
Spectr. Ap.J., 135, 734, 1962.

4410-A, B　Close pair at 0'3.　Heid. 9 and Lund 9 dim. for both components.　See Holmberg (1958), mag. and cal.
for 4410 A + B.

4411-A, B　Pair at 4'4.　See Holmberg (1958).

4412　sBN in B bar, B knotty incompl. (r): 0'65 x 0'6, vF out. arms.

4413　= Ho 403f.　Dim. in Lund 9 are for B part only.

4414　B diff. N in B bulge, many filam. part. res. arms w. dk. lanes and m. branch.　See also HA, 105, 231, 1937.

4417　= 4437.　elong. N.　Photom., Ap.J., 132, 306, 1960.

4419　B bar in bulge, smooth arms w. strong dk. lane on one side.

4420　= 4409.　No def. N, B knotty bar: 0'75 x 0'3, sev. knotty arms w. absorp., poor. res.

4424　Lund 9 minor diam. (0'3) rej., bar only?　SN 1895, A.N., 226, 76, 1925.　Ap.J., 88, 292, 1938.

4425　= Ho 403e.　Photom. Ap.J., 132, 306, 1960.

4428　= Ho 407b.　P(a) w. N 4433 at 7'0.　B knotty arms, pseudo (r): 0'35 x 0'2, branch. arms.　Dim. in Heid 9, Lund
6, Lund 9 for B part only.

4429　vBN: 0'6 x 0'4 w. strong dk. crescent, smooth (r) or (R): 2'7 x 0'8, vF envel.　See also M.N., 94, 806, 1934.

4431　= Ho 408c.　P(a) w. N 4436 at 3'5, N 4440 at 6'8.

4433　= Ho 407a.　P(a) w. N 4428 at 7'0.　B complex lens: 1'2 x 0'4 seen end-on, vF detach. out. arms.　Dim. in Heid
9, Lund 6, and Lund 9 for lens only.

4435　= Ho 409b.　P(b) w. N 4438 at 4'3.　vBN in B bar w. spherical envel.　Photo. Ap.J., 138, 876, 1963.

4436　= Ho 408a.　P(a) w. N 4431 at 3'5, N 4440 at 3'3.

4438　= Ho 409a.　P(b) w. N 4435 at 4'3.　vsvBN in B bulge part. hidden by strong complex dk. lane, F irreg. out. part
and dk. mark., strongly distorted by 4435.　Photo. Ap.J., 138, 876, 1963.

4440　= Ho 408b.　P(a) w. N 4436 at 3'3, N 4431 at 6'8.　vB diff. N in narrow B bar: 0'6 x 0'1 w. blobs, pseudo (r):
1'05 x 0'6, smooth reg. out. arms.　Photo. P.A.S.P., 59, 309, 1947.

4441　Heid 9 and Lund 9 dim.: 0'4 x 0'4.　Mag. Ap.J., 85, 325, 1937.

4442　vB diff. N in B lens and diff. bar.　Photom. M.N., 94, 806, 1934.　Ap.J., 132, 306, 1960.

4448　B diff. N in B forshort bar w. dk. lanes, (r): 1'0 x 0'5, 2 main reg. arms w. dk. lane on one side.

4449　B cent. core or bar w. N or *, part. res., irreg. dk. lanes, sev. v. irreg., well-res. branches.
Photo. Ap.J., 64, 325, 1926; 135, 697, 1962.　Hdb.d.Phys., 5, 2, 843, 1933.
Spectr. P.A.S.P., 69, 297, 1957.　Ap.J., 135, 696, 1962.
Polar. Bull. Abastumani, No 18, 15, 1955.
HII reg. Zs.f.Ap., 50, 168, 1960.
Radio emiss. M.N., 123, 279, 1961.
HI emiss. Epstein, Harvard Thesis, 1962.

4450　svB diff. N in smooth bulge w. strong reg. dk. lane, smooth arms w. few condens., pseudo (R): 3'4 x 2'1.

4454　vsBN, broad weak bar, (r): 0'9 x 0'75, traces of out. (R): 2'1 x 1'7?.

4457　vBN in isolated B lens: 1'4 x 1'0 w. spir. arms and dk. lanes, smooth (R): 2'0 x 2'0.　Heid 9, Lund 9 dim. are
for lens only.

4458　= Ho 411b.　P(a) w. N 4461 at 3'7.　(B-V) source H rejected.

N 4459 svBN in smooth (r): 0'3 x 0'25, strong dk. crescent. N 4468 at 8'5, N 4474 at 13'5.
        Photom. Ap.J., 132, 306, 1960.
        Misprint in, Zs.f.Ap., 50, 168, 1960, for N 4559.

   4460 B elong. cent.: 0'5 x 0'15, no def. N, F * superp.

   4461 = Ho 411a. P(a) w. N 4458 at 3'7. vsvB diff. N, slight bright. at edge of lens. Lund 9 dim. for B part only.

   4462 vBN in B bar, (r): 1'1 x 0'4, F out. arms.

   4466 = Ho 412a. (Ho 412b at 2'1 is a *).

   4467 = Ho 413c. P. w. N 4472 at 4'2.

   4469 vBN, part. obsc., 2 smooth loops or arms w. dk. matter.

   4472 = M 49. = Ho 413a. P. w. N 4467 at 4'2, F anon. dIm at 5'5, and N 4470 (Pec) at 10'5. vB cent., smooth neb.,
         many glob. cl.
         Photo. B.A.N., 16, 1, 1961. Ap.J., 135, 6, 1962.
         Photom. Ap.J., 71, 231, 1930; 132, 306, 1960. B.A.N., 61, 1, 1961. M.N., 94, 806, 1934.
         Spectr. Ap.J., 135, 734, 1962.
         Radio emiss. M.N., 123, 279, 1961.

   4473 Lund 9 dim. for B part only.
         Photom. Ap.J., 132, 306, 1960.
         Spectr. Ap.J., 83, 15, 1936.

   4476 vBN w. narrow dk. crescent? P(a) w. N 4478 at 4'5. Upsala 21, Heid 9 dim. for B part only.

   4478 eB cent., smooth neb. w. steep gradient. P(a) w. N 4476 at 4'5. Lick 13, Heid 9 dim. for B part only.

   4485 = Ho 414b. P(b) w. N 4490 at 3'5. Smooth part. res. core w. dk. mark., asym., part. res. arm or branch toward
         N 4490. Lund 9 dim. B part only.
         Spectr. Ap.J., 116, 66, 1952.

   4486 = M 87 = eB cent. w. blue jet, smooth neb. many glob. cl. 3 other E or S0 in field.
         Photo. Ap.J., 56, 166, 1922; 114, 222, 1954; 130, 342, 1959. M.N., 85, 888, 1925. P.A.S.P., 61, 123, 1949.
              B.A.N., 16, 1, 1961.
         Photom. Ap.J., 71, 231, 1930; 132, 306, 1960; 135, 187, 1962. M.N., 94, 806, 1934. B.A.N., 16, 1, 1961.
         Spectr. I.A.U. Symp., 5, 1958 = Lick Cont. II, No 81, 1958. Ap.J., 132, 325, 1960; 135, 734, 1962.
         Polar. Ap.J., 123, 550, 1956; 130, 340, 1959.
         Mass, Ap.J., 134, 910, 1961.
         SN 1919, A.N., 215, 215, 1922. P.A.S.P., 35, 261, 1923. Ap.J., 88, 292, 1938.
         Radio emiss. (Virgo A) Nature, 164, 101, 1949. Aust.J.Phys., 6, 4, 452, 1953. Ap.J., 119, 221, 1954; 133, 322,
              1961. P.A.S.P., 72, 368, 1960. Observatory, 76, 141, 1956; 81, 202, 1961. Cal. Inst. Techn. Rad.
              Obs., 5, 1960.

   4486-A At 7'5 ssf N 4486 noted by E. Herzog. See Lowell Obs. B., No 97, 1959.

   4486-B svB, sharp outline; P(a) w. N 4486 at 7'3. The U-B, B-V relation may be peculiar,
           see Ap.J., Suppl. No 48, 1961.

   4487 vsvBN or *, part. res. branch. arms.

   4490 = Ho 414a. P(b) w. N 4485 at 3'5. B core, part. res. w. irreg. dk. mark., distorted by N 4485, with connecting
         streamer. Lick (1962) vel. for 2 emiss. 25" and 60" NW of center: +633 km/sec. (B-V) source A rejected.
         Spectr. Ap.J., 116, 66, 1952.
         HII reg. Zs.f.Ap., 50, 168, 1960.
         Radio emiss. M.N., 122, 479, 1961.

   4492 = I 3438.

   4494 vB cent., smooth neb. Lund 9 dim. for B part only. Photom. Ap.J., 50, 384, 1919; 91, 286, 1940.

   4496-A, B = 4505. = Ho 415a, b. Two overlap. systems. P(c?) at 0'9. sh. narrow bar, sev. filam. branch. arms in
         comp. A. Mag. and colors for both components together. SN 1960, I.A.U. Circ. 1721, 1723, 1725, 1734, 1736.
         H.A.C. 1480. C.R. Acad. Sc., Paris, 250, 3952, 1960. P.A.S.P., 73, 175, 1961.

   4500 eBN, B lens: 0'8 x 0'3 w. ansae, 2 smooth reg. arms. Lund 9, Heid 9 dim. for lens only.

   4501 = M 88. vsBN, pseudo (r): 1'1 x 0'55, many knotty filam. arms w. dk. lanes. (B-V) source A rej. Unusual rela-
         tion, (B-V) interpolated.
         Photo. Hubble, Obs. App. to Cosmo., plate II, 1936. Ap.J., 135, 7, 1962.
         HII reg. Zs.f.Ap., 50, 168, 1960.

   4503 svBN, B lens. Photom. Ap.J., 132, 306, 1960.

   4504 vsBN in B cent. part, 2 main mass. reg. arms w. beginning of resol., v. similar to N 300.

   4507 = HA 88,2 "New 2". Note corr. to NGC R.A. and H.A. 88,2 Dec. See also Mem. Com. Obs., 13, 1956. vsvBN, (r):
         0'8 x 0'6. Lund 9 dim. for B part only.

   4509 See H.A., 105, 231, 1937.

N 4517 B in cent., no N visible, complex struct. w. many dk. lanes. P(a) w. N 4517-A at 17'. Note error in HA 88,2 coord., NGC correct.

4517-A P(a) w. N 4517 at 17'. = Reinmuth 80 in HA 88,2. vF narrow bar, 2 main knotty vF arms, some branch. asym.

4519 = Ho 418a. P. w. anon. (Ho 418b) at 3'. B diff. bar w. elong. inner core, 3 main knotty filam. arms w. m. branch., asym.

4520 Heid. 9 dim. (0'2 x 0'2) and Lund 9 (0'4 x 0'3) rej., N only? P(a) w. I 799 at 4'5.

4523 F asym. arm, low surf. bright., <u>Desc.</u>, A.J., 61, 71, 1956.

4526 sB diff. N in B diff. inner lens: 0'55 x 0'4 w. dk. crescent simulating (r), B forsh. bar, in lens 2'9 x 0'7, F envel.
      <u>Photo.</u> Ap.J., 120, 444, 1954. B.A.N., 16, 1, 1961.
      <u>Photom.</u> M.N., 94, 806, 1934. Ap.J., 120, 439, 1954; 132, 305, 1960. B.A.N., 16, 1, 1961.
      <u>Radio emiss.</u> Observatory, 80, 216, 1960. M.N., 123, 279, 1961.

4527 vseBN or *, B bulge or bar: 1'5 x 0'4, 2 main knotty part. res. arms w. complex dk. lanes on near side.
      <u>Photo., and rot.</u> Ap.J., 97, 114, 1943.
      <u>SN 1915,</u> Lick Bull., 300, 1917. P.A.S.P., 29, 180, 1919. Ap.J., 88, 293, 1938.

4532 B bar: 0'85 x 0'3 w. dk. patches and B knots, F out. streamer or extens.

4533 P(a) w. N 4536 at 8'2.

4534 = Ho 419a. (Ho 419b at 0'7 is a condens. in the gal. or a *). See H.A., 105, 231, 1937.

4535 = Ho 420a. P. w. anon. (Ho 420b) at 5'. v. sharp, vseBN or *. Smooth bar or lens w. dk. lane, 2 main part. res. arms w. m. branch.
      <u>Photo.</u> Ap.J., 135, 7, 1962.
      <u>HII reg.</u> Zs.f.Ap., 50, 168, 1960.

4536 vseBN, forsh. bar w. strong dk. lane, pseudo (r): 2'9 x 1'0, 2 main filam. reg. arms w. knots. P(a) w. N 4533 at 8'2. Unusual increase of (B-V) w. log A/D(0), interp. value. <u>Photom.</u> M.N., 94, 806, 1934.

4540 = Ho 421a. P(a) w. I 3519 (Ho 421b?) at 1'5 nf (and not np as in IC). I 3528 at 1's is a *. BM no def. N, v. many B knotty arms w. dk. lanes, poor. res. Heid 9, Lund 6 and 9 dim. for B part only.

4545 <u>SN 1940,</u> H.A.C. 530. P.A.S.P., 52, 331, 1940.

4546 sB diff. N in B diff. lens. Lund 9 dim. B part only.

4548 B diff. N in strong bar: 1'7 x 0'3 w. dk. lane, (r): 2'0 x 1'4, B part. res. filam. arms, pseudo (R): 4'2 x 3'1. P(a) w. N 4571 at 27'. Heid 9, Lund 9 dim. B part only.

4550 = Ho 422a. P(a) w. N 4551 at 3'. Lund 9 dim. (0'9 x 0'3) rej., lens only.

4551 = Ho 422b. P(a) w. N 4550 at 3'.

4552 = M 89. <u>Photom.</u> Ap.J., 71, 231, 1930; 132, 306, 1960.

4553 svBN, (r): 0'9 x 0'3.

4559 = Ho 423a. 3 s anon. nearby (Ho 423b, c, d) vs not vB N in sh. bar, pseudo (r): 1'1 x 0'55:, sev. part. res. filam. branch. arms.
      <u>SN 1941,</u> H.A.C. 576. P.A.S.P., 53, 130, 194, 1941. Observatory 68, 121, 1948.
      <u>HII reg.</u> Zs.f.Ap., 50, 168, 1960 (4459 is a misprint).

4561 = I 3569. sh. B bar: 0'3 x 0'08, no BN, sev. knotty branch. asym. arms.

4564 <u>Photom.</u> Ap.J., 132, 306, 1960.
      <u>SN 1961,</u> H.A.C., 1528, 1961. J.R.A.S. Canada, 55, 173, 1962. Mem. Soc. Ast. Ital., XXXIII, 77, 1962.

4565 = Ho 426a. 3 s anon. nearby (Ho 426b, c, d).
      <u>Photo.</u> B.A.N., 16, 1, 1961. Hdb.d.Ap., 5, 2, 843, 1933.
      <u>Photom.</u> Ap.J., 104, 214, 1946. Izv. Pulkovo, 20, Nr 156, 87, 1956. A.J. USSR, 32, 16, 1955.
              B.A.N., 16, 1, 1961.
      <u>Spectr.</u> P.A.S.P., 69, 302, 1957.
      <u>Orient.</u> Ap.J., 127, 487, 1958. Stockholm Ann., 15, No 4, 1948.
      <u>Radio emiss.</u> M.N., 122, 479, 1961.

4567 = Ho 427b. P(b?) w. N 4568 at 1'2. vB diff. N ?, pseudo (r): 0'55 x 0'4, many B knotty, branch. arms in lens, smooth F (R). Misidentified as N 4568 in Upsala 21. Lund 9, Upsala 21 dim. for B part only.
      <u>Photo.</u> Hdb.d.Ap., 5, 2, 843, 1933.
      <u>Spectr.</u> Ap.J., 116, 66, 1952. I.A.U. Symp., 5, 1958 = Lick Cont. II, 81, 1958.
      <u>Photom.</u> Medd. Lund II, 128, 1950.

4568 = Ho 427a. P(b) w. N 4567 at 1'2. vsBN, v. many B knotty arms w. dk. lanes, pseudo (r): 0'8 x 0'3. Overlaps N 4567. Misidentified as N 4567 in Upsala 21. Heid 9, Lund 6, Lund 10, Upsala 21 dim. for B part only. For refer. see N 4567.

N 4569 = M 90. P(a) w. I 3583 at 6'0. Poss. interacting. vseBN in B diff. bar w. m. dk. matt., smooth reg. arms or whorls. Early Mt. Wilson velocity (MWC 531) was for * superposed near N; see A.J., 61, 110, 1956. Yerkes 1 color class.: or g.
Photo. Ap.J., 135, 7, 1962.

4570 svBN, B diamond-shaped lens. Photom. M.N., 94, 806, 1934. Ap.J., 132, 306, 1960.

4571 = I 3588. P(a) w. N 4548 at 27'. vs not vBN, pseudo (r): 0'47 x 0'4, many weak part. res. filam. arms. Heid 9 dim. for B part only.

4578 = Ho 429a. P. w. anon. (Ho 429b) at 3'5. Photom. Ap.J., 132, 306, 1960.

4579 = M 58. sB diff. N in smooth lens w. dk. lanes, pseudo (r): 2'2 x 1'5, smooth out. whorls form pseudo (R): 4'1 x 3'0.
Photo. Ap.J., 135, 7, 1962.
Photom. M.N., 94, 806, 1934.
HII reg. Zs.f.Ap., 50, 168, 1960.

4580 vsBN, traces of bar in B lens, strong knotty hexag. (r): 0'55 x 0'4, smooth out. arms. Lund 9 dim. for B part only.

4586 sBN in B bulge, dk. lane on one side.

4589 B diff. N, smooth neb. P(a) w. N 4572 at 7'5, N 4648 at 22'. Heid 9 dim. for B part only.
Mag. Ap.J., 85, 325, 1937.

4592 BM no BN, part. res. eF filam. extens., slightly asym. Lund 9, Heid 9 dim. for B part only.

4593 vBN in smooth bar: 1'5 x 0'25, weak (r): 1'8 x 1'3 in lens: 2'1 x 1'6, 2 main asym. arms form pseudo (R): 3'4 x 2'4. Lund 9, HA 88,4 minor diam. (0'7, 0'8) rej., bar only.

4594 = M 104. vB cent. bulge, narrow patchy arms in lens, strong dk. lane in front, many glob. cl. Lund 7 dim. for B part only.
Photo. Ap.J., 97, 114, 1943; 98, 47, 1943; 120, 444, 1954. B.A.N., 16, 1, 1961. Hdb.d.Ap., 5, 2, 843, 1933.
Photom. M.N., 106, 171, 1946. Ann.d'Ap., 11, 247, 1948. Ap.J., 83, 424, 1936; 98, 47, 1943; 120, 439, 1954.
      B.A.N., 16, 1, 1961.
Spectr. Ap.J., 135, 716, 1962.
Orient., Rot. Ap.J., 127, 487, 1958. P.A.S.P., 63, 133, 1951. P.N.A.S., 2, 517, 1916. Ap.J., 97, 117, 1943.
HII reg. Observatory, 79, 54, 1959. Zs.f.Ap., 50, 168, 1960.
Radio emiss. (unobserv.), M.N., 123, 279, 1961.

4596 vB diff. N in strong bar w. blobs, F (r): 1'8 x 1'3. P(a) w. almost identical twins w. N 4608 at 19', Lund 9 dim. for B part only.

4597 sh. F bar, part. res. asym. filam. arms. vs comp. or knot near weaker arm.

4601 vsBN. P. w. N 4603 at 3'3.

4602 sBN, pseudo (r): 0'6 x 0'25?. sev. knotty branch. arms w. dk. lanes. Dim. in HA 88,2 from Helwan should read: 3'0 x 0'5. Lund 10, Lund 9, Heid 9 dim. for B part only. P. w. I 804 at ~ 10'.

4603 F, sBN, poor. res., 2 B * involv. P. w. N 4601 at 3'3. HA 88,2 dim. (2'5 x 1'2, mf series) for B part only.

4605 B complex bar and lens: 3'2 x 0'85 w. dk. matt., F envel. Lick 13, Heid 9 and Lund 9 dim. for lens only.
Spectr. Lick Obs. Bull., 497, 1939.

4606 = Ho 436a. P. w. N 4607 at 4'0. BN, dk. patch. Lund 9 dim. (0'8 x 0'3) rej., N only? Lund 6, Heid 9 dim. for B part only.

4607 = Ho 436b. P. w. N 4606 at 4'0. Sev. knots, classif. doubtful.

4608 vB diff. N, strong narrow B bar: 1'3 x 0'15, F(R): 1'4 x 1'4. Heid 9 dim. for B part only. P(a) w. N 4596 at 19', almost identical.

4612 svB diff. N in diff. bar: 0'6 x 0'2, in lens: 1'4 x 0'9, weak smooth (R): 2'2 x 1'5. Heid 9 dim. for lens only.

4616 * 0'7 f. classif. doubtful.

4618 = Ho 438a. P(b?) w. N 4625 at 8'3, possibly interacting? Similar to LMC-SMC pair. B bar w. inner B axis: 0'4 x 0'08 and dk. lane, one main mass., part. res. arm or loop, other F, pseudo (R): 2'7 x 2'5.
HII reg. Zs.f.Ap., 50, 168, 1960.

4619 See HA, 105, 231, 1937.

4621 = M 59. B diff. N, smooth neb. Lund 9 dim. for B part only.
Photo. Ap.J., 64, 325, 1926; 71, 235, 1930. B.A.N., 16, 1, 1961.
Photom. Ap.J., 71, 231, 1930; 132, 306, 1960. B.A.N., 16, 1, 1961.
Spectr. Ap.J., 135, 734, 1962.
SN 1939, Ap.J., 96, 28, 1942.

4622 sBN, (r): 1'05 x 1'0.

4625 = I 3675. = Ho 438b. P(b?) w. N 4618 at 8'3, interacting? Similar to LMC-SMC pair. sBN or sh. bar; one main part. res. arm, one fainter; strong asym., Lund 9 dim. for B part only.

N 4627   = Ho 442b. P(b) w. N 4631 at 2'5. BM no BN, smooth neb. w. weak abs. mark., some glob. cl.; out. parts distorted by N 4631. Similar to N 205. See also HA, 105, 231, 1937.

   4631   = Ho 442a. P(b) w. N 4627 at 2'5. Prob. end-on front view of late SB(s), complex dk. mark., part. res. asym. out. arms. See also HA, 105, 231, 1937. Mean vel. of brightest emiss. patch, 1'3 f center: +662 km/sec (sources B, D, G, J).
          Photo. M.N., 85, 1019, 1925.
          Photom. Ap.J., 91, 528, 1940. Izv. Pulkovo, 20, Nr 156, 87, 1956. A.J. USSR, 32, 16, 1955.
          Spectr. P.A.S.P., 69, 302, 1957.
          Rot., mass, A.J., 67, 113, 1962. Ap.J., 137, 363, 1963.
          HII reg. Zs.f.Ap., 50, 168, 1960.
          Radio emiss. M.N., 122, 479, 1961.
          HI emiss., Epstein, Harvard Thesis, 1962.

   4632   BM no def. BN, sev. B knotty branch. arms w. dk. lane on one side, poor. res. Lund 9 dim. for B part only.
          Photom. M.N., 94, 806, 1934.
          SN 1946, Ann. Rep. Mt. Wilson Obs., 45, 19, 1946.

   4633   = I 3688. = Ho 445b. P. w. N 4634 at 3'5. B bar: 1'6 x 0'2. Recorded as N 4634b in Lund 6.

   4634   = Ho 445a. P. w. N 4633 at 3'5.

   4636   = N 4624? vBN in smooth neb., many glob. cl. Beginning of differentiation of lens: 1'2 x 1'1. HA 88,2 dim. from Helwan (1'2 x 1'1) are lens only.
          Photom. M.N., 94, 806, 1934.
          Spectr. P.A.S.P., 51, 121, 1939.
          SN 1939, Bull. S.A.F., 53, 44, 1939. P.A.S.P., 51, 166, 1939. Ap.J., 96, 28, 1942.

   4637   P. w. N 4638 at 1'5. Heid. 9 remark "not found = N 4647?" is an error; it is the eeF neb vs E 90°, 1'5 sf N 4638. Dim.: 0'8 x 0'3, Lick 36-in.

   4638   vB cent. P. w. N 4637 at 1'5. Lick 13 and Upsala 21 dim. for B part only.

   4639   Lick 13 and Upsala 21 dim. for B part only.

   4643   vB diff. N in strong narrow bar: 1'65 x 0'25, weak (r): 1'65 x 1'55, lens: 1'8 x 1'7, surrounded by cont. dk. rings and traces of filam. arms. Lund 9, Heid 9 and HA 88,2 (after Helwan) dim. for B part only.
          Photom. M.N., 94, 806, 1934.
          Spectr. I.A.U. Symp., 5, 1958 = Lick Cont. II, 81, 1958.

   4645   sBN.

   4645-A, B Pair at 5'. 4645-A: B * 0'8 ssf; 4645-B: B * 0'25 sp.

   4647   = Ho 448b. P(a) w. N 4649 at 2'5. vsBN in sh. bar-like struct., pseudo (r): 0'5 x 0'3, v. many knotty arms, out. dk. lane on one side. Upsala 21 dim. (0'7 x 0'2) are an error or misprint. (rej.).
          Photo. Ap.J., 56, 166, 1922; 116, 64, 1952. M.N., 98, 613, 1938.
          Spectr. Ap.J., 116, 66, 1952. A.J., 61, 97, 1956. IAU Symp., 5, 1958 = Lick Cont. II, 81, 1958.

   4648   vBN. P. w. N 4589 at 22'. Lens: 0'95 x 0'7. Mag. Ap.J., 85, 325, 1937. Heid 9 dim. (0'6 x 0'6) for lens only.

   4649   = M 60. = Ho 448a. P(a) w. N 4647 at 2'5. Upsala 21, Lick 13, and Heid 9 dim. for B part only. vB cent. smooth neb., many glob. cl. B mag. (source F) for 4647 + 4649.
          Photo. Ap.J., 56, 166, 1922; 116, 64, 1952; 135, 6, 1962. M.N., 98, 613, 318. B.A.N., 16, 1, 1961.
          Photom. Ap.J., 71, 231, 1930; 132, 306, 1960. M.N., 94, 807, 1934; 98, 619, 1938. Ann. d'Ap., 11, 247, 1948; 14, 347, 1951. B.A.N., 16, 1, 1961.
          Spectr. Ap.J., 112, 66, 1952; 135, 734, 1962. A.J., 61, 97, 1956.

   4651   vB diff. N in B lens: 1'0 x 0'6, pseudo (r): 0'75 x 0'4:, sev. filam. knotty branch arms. F spur and blob attached. Drawing, Erg. d. Exakt. Naturwiss., XXIX, 376, 1956.

   4653   In Group w. N 4666, 4668. Pseudo (r): 0'4 x 0'4, 2 main knotty filam. arms w. m. branch. Lund 9, Heid 9 dim. for B part only.

   4654   = I 3708. Sh. knotty bar: 0'35 x 0'08, pseudo (r?): 1'1 x 0'5, sev. part. res. filam., branch. arms w. many dk. lanes, slightly asym. Lick 13, Upsala 21 dim. for B part only.

   4656, 4657 Prob. interact. pair of Magell. systems; perhaps like N 4038-4039. Lick 13, Lund 9 dim. for B part only. See also HA, 105, 231, 1937.
          Photom. Error on V mag. in Ap.J. Suppl. 48, 1961, V = 11.81.
          Spectr. P.A.S.P., 69, 386, 1957.
          HII reg. Zs.f.Ap., 50, 168, 1960.
          HI emiss. Epstein, Harvard Thesis, 1962.

   4658   B bar: 0'5 x 0'1, w. complex dk. lanes, 2 main reg. arms + third weaker arm. P(a) w. N 4663 at 7'2.

   4663   = I 811. P. w. N 4658 at 7'2. vBN, narrow B bar: 0'35 x 0'05, smooth lens: 0'6 x 0'5.

   4665   = N 4664. B diff. N, fairly B diff. bar: 1'5 x 0'2, traces of smooth arms form pseudo (R): 2'4 x 1'5. See also M.N., 94, 806, 1934.

   4666   = Ho 453a. P(a) w. N 4668 at 7'3. B nucl. reg., many knotty branch. arms w. dk. lanes. Lund 9 dim. for B part only. Photom. M.N., 94, 806, 1934.

N 4668   = Ho 453b. P(a) w. N 4666 at 7'3. Poor res. Lick 13, Lund 9 dim. for B part only.

4670   seBN, strong bar: 0'55 x 0'08 w. some struct., 2 F smooth arcs, F out. whorls, strongly asym. Haro No 9 (Bol. Tonantzintla, 14, 8, 1958). P(a) w. N 4673 at 5'6. Heid 9 dim. for B part only.

4672   3 * superp.

4673   P(a) w. N 4670 at 5'6. Heid 9 dim. for B part only.

4674   SN 1907, H.A.C. 399, 1936. Hdb.d.Phys., 51, 774, 1958 (where coord. are in error).

4676-A, B = I 819, 820. = Ho 459a, b. P(b) at 0'6. See HA, 105, 231, 1937.
       Photo. Ap.J., 130, 23, 1959; 138, 878, 1963.
       Desc. Astr. Zirk. USSR, No 178, 19, 1957.
       Masses, Ap.J., 135, 726, 1961.

4677   sBN.

4679   Note corr. to HA 88,2 coord., see Mem. Com. Obs. No 13, 1956. * involv. 0'25 s N.

4683   BN, * 0'7 sf.

4684   vB e. forsh. N and bar on minor axis, (r): 0'25 x 0'06:, lens: 0'4 x 0'1, almost edgewise. Lund 9 dim. for B part only.

4688   = Ho 461a. P. w. anon. small Im (Ho 462a) at 6'8.

4689   vsBN in B compl. cent. reg., w. many filam. part. res. arms w. dk. lanes, B hexag. outline forms pseudo (r): 1'4 x 1'4. Upsala 21 dim. for B part only.

4691   vB compl. bar: 1'2 x 0'4, w. dk. mark., asym. loop or (r): 1'55 x 1'3, vF asym. (R): 2'7 x 2'3. Lund 9 dim. rej., bar only.

4692   Color P-V = 0.90 (Proc. 4th Berkeley Symp. III, 209, 1960).

4694   vBN in 3 lens or bar w. irreg. dk. lanes; similar to N 1316? Lund 9 dim. for B part only.
       Photom. Ap.J., 132, 306, 1960.

4696   svBN, * 0'75 np. Brightest in cluster, see Mem. Commonwealth Obs., II, No 13, 1956. Possible radio source? (Austral.J.Phys., 13, 694, 1960).

4696-A, B, C, D, E See Mem. Commwealth obs., III, No 13, 1956.

4697   vB cent. smooth neb., sev. glob. Cl. P(b) w. anon. SAB(s)cp at 5'9. Lick 13 minor dim. is in error, Heid 9 dim. for B part only.

4698   vB diff. N in B bulge, smooth inner reg., 2 main smooth arms w. strong dk. lane on one side. Similar to N 4594. One aberrant val. B-V (source C) rejected.

4699   vsvBN in weak bar: 0'4 x 0'06, pseudo (r): 0'4 x - , many arms w. dk. lane in lens, many filam. arms form pseudo (R): 2'7 x 1'7. Similar to N 2775 and N 2841. SN 1948, Ann. Rep. Mt. W. Obs., 47, 20, 1948.

4700   BN in B bar w. dk. mark., spir. struct. not res. because of tilt. P(a) w. anon. Sp ? at 10'. Heid 9 dim. for B part only. Yerkes 2 class.: or I A.

4701   vsBN, complex B cent. part w. many knotty branch. arms, F filam. out. arms. Heid 9 for B part only. HA 88,2 class. (E:) is an error.

4703   Similar to N 4565.

4706   vBN. Helwan neb. 276 (Helwan Bull. 22) is not N 4706. See Mem. Commonwealth Obs., III, No 13, 74, 1956.

4708   = Ho 463a. (Ho 463b at 0'4 is a condens. in the gal.).

4709   vBN; sB neb. 1'2 sf.

4710   sBN, part. hidden by strong dk. lane, ansae; (r): 1'6 x - , strong flat compon. 0'09 thick.
       Photo. and Photom. B.A.N., 16, 1, 1961.

4712   = Ho 468b. P(a) w. N 4725 at 12'. Lund 9 minor dim. is in error (rej.). sBN, 2 main reg. knotty arms, poor. res. Yerkes 1 class.: or A F.

4713   sBN in sh., B bar: 0'35 x 0'06, pseudo (r): 0'4 x - , 2 main knotty filam. arms w. m. branch. Lund 9 dim. for B part only.

4724   = Ho 470b. P. w. N 4727 at 1'. See also HB 914, 6, 1940. Heid 9 dim. for B part only.

4725   = Ho 468a. P. w. N 4712 at 12'. vseBN in F smooth broad bar w. dk. lanes, strong part. res. (r): 4'3 x 2'5, one main arm forms incomplete pseudo (R): 10'0 x - . Lick 13 dim. for B part only.
       Photom. Ap.J., 46, 206, 1917; 50, 384, 1919.
       SN 1940, H.A.C. 522, 1940. P.A.S.P., 52, 206, 1940.

4727   = Ho 470a. P. w. N 4724 at 1' and N 4726 = N 4740 at 11'. In group w. I 3799, 3819, 3822, 3824, 3825, 3827, 3831, 3838. See HB 914, 6, 1940.

N 4728 = Ho 469a. P. w. anon. (Ho 469b, c) at 2'2 and 3'6. Color, P-V = 0.78 (Proc. 4th Berkeley Symp.III, 201, 1960).

4731 = Ho 472a. P(a) w. anon. dIBm (Ho 472b): 0'9 x 0'45 at 10'5. Narrow B bar: 1'1 x 0'2, w. B cent. part.: 0'5 x 0'1, 2 main knotty filam. arms. Heid 9 minor dim. (0'3) rej., bar only; Helwan 30, 38 dim. for B part only.

4733 = Ho 473a. (Ho 473b at 0'9 is a *).

4736 = M 94. eBN in B(r): 1'6 x 1'2, v. many smooth arms in lens: 6'0 x 4'7, F(R): 11'2 x 8'5.
Photo. Ap.J., 135, 366, 1962. Hdb.d.Ap., 5, 2, 843, 1933.
Photom. Ap.J., 46, 206, 1917; 50, 384, 1919; 83, 424, 1936; 108, 415, 1948.
Spectr. Lick Obs. Bull., 497, 1939. IAU Symp., 5, 1958 = Lick Cont. II, No 81, 1958. Ap.J., 135, 698, 734, 1962.
Orient., rot., mass, Ap.J., 127, 487, 1958; 97, 117, 1943; 135, 366, 1962.
HII reg. Zs.f.Ap., 50, 168, 1960.
Radio emiss. M.N., 122, 479, 1961.

4747 = Ho 468c. P. w. N 4725 at 24'. Lund 9 minor dim. for bar only?

4749 Mag. Ap.J., 85, 325, 1937.

4750 vsvBN, strong (r) of spir. arcs: 0'5 x 0'4, B part or lens: 0'85 x 0'55, F(R): 1'4 x 1'3.
Mag. Ap.J., 85, 325, 1937.
Spectr. IAU Symp., 5, 1948 = Lick Cont. II, No 81, 1958.

4753 esBN part. hidden by filam. dk. lanes in smooth neb. Pec. Perhaps similar to N 3077 or N 5195.

4754 = Ho 478b. P(a) w. N 4762 at 10'5. vB diff. N on F bar: 0'7 x 0'3 w. traces of blobs, B part or lens: 0'85 x 0'7. Lund 6 second set of dim. (0'7 x 0'7) for lens only. Photom. Ap.J., 132, 306, 1960.

4757 P(a) w. N 4760 at 12'. Addit. dim. in Lund 7.

4760 P(a) w. N 4757 at 12'. Classif.EO from weak plate is doubtful, probab. N of SO (confirmed by Yerkes class. kD2). All dim. except HA 88,4 are for B inner part or N.

4762 = Ho 478a. P(a) w. N 4754 at 10'5. vsvBN in narrow B flat compon.: 1'7 x 0'1, exactly edgewise w. F twisted brushes. Lund 6, Lund 9, and HA 88,2 dim. for B part only. Photo. and Photom. B.A.N., 16, 1, 1961.

4765 eB, not res., classif. doubtful, perhaps IO (supported by Yerkes class. E?4 or Ip).

4766 Identif. doubtful. "Not found" in Lick 13, but found in Lund 7 and Helwan 15, 21, 38.

4767-A Betw., 2 *, * 0'6 n.

4767-B Poor. res., classif. doubtful. * 0'6 n, * 0'7 s.

4771 BM no def. N, many filam. arms w. dk. lanes, v. poor. res., class. uncertain from weak plate.

4772 B diff. N in B bulge, smooth arcs or arms w. strong dk. lane on one side. Probably similar to N 4594, classif. from weak plate.

4775 vsBN, sev. part. res. filam. branch. arms, asym.

4777 Lund 9 dim. (0'3 x 0'3) rej., N only?

4780 = Ho 482a. P. w. anon. (Ho 482b) at 2'.

4781 = Ho 483a. P(a) w. N 4784 at 5'7, N 4790 at 18'5. sh. B narrow bar: 0'5 x 0'1, sev. knotty filam. arms, asym. Helwan and Lund 9 dim. are for B part only.

4782, 4783 = Ho 485a, b. P(b) at 0'7, connected. N 4782 at sp.; ident. by Page, 1952 are in error (interchange NGC numbers) - HA 88,4 dim. are for both gal. together. Note also corr. to HA 88,2 Dec.
Photo. P.N.A.S., 26, 35, 1940. Ap.J., 116, 64, 1952.
Spectr. Ap.J., 116, 64, 1952; 133, 335, 1961; 135, 681, 1962.
Radio emiss. (Source 3C278) Aust.J.Phys., 11, 360, 1958. Cal. Inst. Tech. Rad. Obs., 5, 1960. Proc. 4th Berkeley Symp., vol. III, 245, 1960. Ap.J., 133, 335, 1961; 135, 681, 1962.

4784 = Ho 483b. P. w. N 4781 at 5'7. Maj. diam. in Heid. 9 and Lund 9 rej., N only?

4789 B * 0'6 n. Gal. long. in Humason et. al., (1956) is in error. P. w. N 4789-A at 5'. N 4787 at 3' p.

4789-A P. w. N 4789 at 5'. Dim.: 2'5 x 1'5 on weak Lick 36-in. plate.

4790 BN, struct. v. poor. res. P(a) w. N 4781 at 18'5.

4792 sBN, 7' n of N 4794.

4793 vsvBN in cent. of B complex lens w. many knots and dk. lanes, pseudo (r): 0'6 x 0'3, 3 weak out. arms, one possibly extending toward dwarf satellite. Lund 9 dim. for B part only. Lick 1956 vel. for emiss in arm 30" NE of center: + 2544 km/sec.

4794 svBN, B forsh. bar: 0'4 x 0'08, 2 main smooth arms. P(a) w. N 4782-4783 at 9', N 4792 at 7' n. Heid. 9 and Lund 9 dim. rej., lens only. Small Ssp or IO? at 11'5 nf.

N 4800   vBN, B(r): 0'5 x 0'25, many filam. arms form pseudo (R'): 1'05 x 0'95.   poor. res. Lund 9 dim. for B part only.

4802   = 4804, see Helwan 15. Lund 9 dim.: 0'5 x 0'3. Ellipt. w. B * inv.

4808   vsBN, many B filam. part. res. arms, F out. extens. or loop suspected. Similar to N 7793. P(a) w. anon.
       SAB(s)d: at 17'5.

4809   = Ho 486a. North compon. of P(b) w. N 4810 at 0'7. Note corr. to NGC coord. according to Lund 6; confirmed in
       Zwicky's cat. (1961). Knotty core, partly res. on one side, F extens., distorted.
       Photo. and Spectr. Ap.J., 116, 66, 1952.

4810   = Ho 486b. South compon. of P(b) w. N 4809 at 0'7. Note corr. to NGC coord. according to Lund 6; confirmed in
       Zwicky's cat. (1961). B knotty core, out. part distorted. Photo. and Spectr. Ap.J., 116, 66, 1952.

4814   svBN in B lens w. filam. arms and dk. lanes, 2 main fairly smooth filam. arms and dk. lanes. Lund 9, Heid 9
       dim. for B part only.

4819   = Ho 490a. P. w. N 4821 at 1'8. Color P-V: 0.86 (Proc. 4th Berkeley Symp., vol. III, 1960).

4821   = Ho 490b. P. w. N 4819 at 1'8. Color P-V: 0.78 (Proc. 4th Berkeley Symp., vol. III, 1960). Heid. 9 and Lund
       6 dim. (0'2 x 0'2) rej.

4825   B diff. N w. trace of dk. lane. In group w. N 4820, 4823, 4829 and others SO sp. Heid 9 dim. for B part only.

4826   = M 64. eBN part. hidden by vs dk. lane, pseudo (r): 1'5 x 0'7 in B part 3'9 x 2'0, 2 main smooth out. arms
       form pseudo (R): 6'0 x 2'6. Note + 10' correction to HA 88,2 declination.
       Photom. Ap.J., 46, 206, 1917; 50, 385, 1919; 83, 424, 1936; 108, 415, 1948.
       Spectr. Ap.J., 135, 699, 734, 1962.
       Rot. Ap.J., 97, 117, 1943.
       Radio emiss. M.N., 122, 479, 1961.

4835   vBN, 2 or 3 main knotty arms w. dk. lanes. P(a) w. vs anon. dIBm: at 1'7.

4839, 4842   P-V = 0.92, 0.87 (Proc. 4th Berkeley Symp. vol. III, 1960). 4842: Heid 9 dim. (0'25 x 0'25) rej.

4841-A, B = Ho 492a, b. Pair at 0'7. Mag. and col. for 4841 A + B.

4845   sB diff. N in B bulge, part. hidden by dk. lane on one side, smooth spir. struct. and dk. lanes. Lund 9 dim.
       2'9 x 0'6 for B part only.

4849   = Ho 495a. P. w. I 838 (= Ho 495b) at 1'9. P-V = 0.93 (Proc. 4th Berkeley Symp. vol. III, 1960).

4856   sB diff. N in B inner lens: 0'5 x 0'25, diff. bar, traces of smooth arms.

4861   B core, 2 main filam. knotty arms, one longer, asym., poor. res. weak 60 in pl. Lick 1956 vel. for emiss. in SW
       end of system V_O = + 829 km/sec (may be affected by rotation). Photo. Ap.J., 138, 885, 1963.

4864   Heid 9 dim. (0'2 x 0'2) rej.

4866   vseBN part. hidden by dk. lanes in lens, (r): 2'4 x 0'3. Yerkes 2 class.: or D GK.

4869   Heid 9 dim. (0'25 x 0'25) rej.

4872   Error in HA 88,2. Dim. and mag. fit N 4889 = 4884. N 4872 is 0'8 sp. See Ap.J., 115, 288, 1952.

4874   Photo. Hubble, Obs. Appr. to Cosmo., plate III, 1936.
       Spectr. Ap.J., 135, 734, 1962.

4877   B diff. N or lens, F spir. arms and dk. lane, poor. res.

4880   = Ho 497a. (Ho 497b at 1'7 is a *). Lund 6 dim. for B part only.

4881   (B-V)(0) interpolated.

4889   = N 4884. Misidentif. as N 4872 in HA 88,2. N 4872 is 0'8 sp., N 4886 is 1'1 np.
       Photo. Hubble, Obs. App. to Cosmo., plate III, 1936.
       Spectr. Ap.J., 74, 36, 1931; Ap.J., 135, 734, 1962.

4895-A 2'7 sp N 4895. Color P-V = 0.58:. See Proc. 4th Berkeley Symp. Vol. III, 1960.

4898   Noted double by Pettit (1954).

4899   sBN, pseudo (r): 0'45 x 0'1, sev. knotty filam. branch arms. Heid 9 dim. for B part only.

4900   Sh. B narrow inner bar: 0'3 x 0'06 w. svBN, complex knotty filam. pseudo (r): 1'1 x 1'0.
       Desc. Ap.J., 46, 42, 1917 = MWC 132.

4902   vsBN in narrow B bar: 0'65 x 0'1, strong narrow (r): 0'9 x 0'8, sev. branch. filam. arms. Helwan 9, 15 and
       Heid 9 dim. for B part only.

4904   B narrow bar: 0'4 x 0'06, sev. knotty arms w. some branch.

4911   = Ho 499a. P. w. s. anon. (Ho 499b) at 0'6.

N 4915 P(a) w. N 4918 at 6'3, and anon. Pec. at 12'6. Lund 9, Heid 9 dim. for B part only. HA 88,4 dim. (0'7 x 0'4) are inconsistent.

4921 SN 1959, P.A.S.P., 72, 208, 1960. A.J. USSR, 216, 1, 1960.

4922 Desc. as double in Heid. 9 w. overall dim.: 0'9 x 0'4;v. pec.

4926, 4926-A A is 3'4 nf 4926; color P-V = + 0.55 (see Proc. 4th Berkeley Symp. vol. III, 1960).

4928 svBN, 2 main B knotty arms, v. compact and B. Anon. Sbc sp. (2'8 x 0'4) at 23'5 sp. Heid 9 dim. for B part only.

4933-A, B = Ho 502a, b. Interacting close pair at 0'8. (A): B glob. N w. strong dk. lane, smooth neb. (B): vBN, B asym. extens. HA 88,2 and 88,4 dim. for both compon. together. m_H probably for both comp. P(a) w. anon. SB(r)0/a at 4'3.

4936 B diff. N, * at 0'2. P(a) w. I 844 at 12'7.

4939 vsvBN, B cent. lens w. pseudo (r): 1'3 x 0'7, 2 main knotty filam. arms w. some branch. Lund 9 dim. for B part (lens) only.

4941 svBN in weak diff. bar, knotty (r): 1'7 x 0'8 in lens: 2'4 x 1'05, eF (R) (or out. whorls): 3'1 x 2'4. Heid 9, Lund 9 and all Helwan dim. for B part only.

4945 Note corr. of -12' to NGC declination (R. Shobbrook, Mt. Stromlo, unpublish.) A large late-type spiral partly obscured at a low galac. lat. See also M.N., 81, 601, 1921. HA 88,2 dim. (11'5 x 2'0, ser. a') for B part only.
Photo. Occ. Notes R.A.S., 3, No 18, 1956.
Orient. Ap.J., 127, 487, 1958.
Radio emiss. Hdb.d.Phys., 53, 253, 1959. Observatory, 83, 20, 1963.

4947 sBN, (r): 0'85 x 0'5.

4947-A F, BM, no BN, vF * attach. at n tip.

4948 = Ho 505a. (Ho 505b at 1' sf is a dble *, but v. F comp. at 1'1 np). N 4948-A at 12'5 sf, another vF anon. SB(s)dm at 5'5 nf asym.

4948-A = Ho 506a. (Ho 506b at 3'3 sf not found). N 4948 at 12'5. Also noted in Lund 9 (0'6 x 0'6) where major dim. is too small.

4951 sBN, pseudo (r): 0'6 x 0'25, w. dk. lanes; s * on (r) at 8" from N, sev. filam. branch. arms, poor. res. Lick 13 major dim. (1'2) for B part only.

4952 Color P-V = 0.92 (see Proc. 4th Berkeley Symp. vol. III, 1960.)

4957 P. w. N 4961 at 12'5. B diff. N. Heid. 9 dim.: 0'5 x 0'4.

4958 P. w. N 4948-A at 13'5 and N 4948 at 14'. vBN in B lens: 1'8 x 0'45 w. F ansae, (r?): 1'2 x - . Helwan 21, 22 dim. for B part only.

4961 P(a) w. N 4957 at 12'5. sBN in B lens or bar: 0'4 x 0'25, sev. filam. knotty branch. arms, F asym. extens. Heid 9, Lund 9 dim. for B part only.

4976 BN. HA 88,2 dim. (2'0 x 1'5: ser. a) for B part only. Photom. M.N., 112, 606, 1952.

4981 svBN, F narrow bar: 0'6 x 0'05, (r): 0'7 x 0'5, sev. filam. knotty branch. arms, B * at 1' from N. Lund 9, Heid 9, Lick 13 and Helwan 21, 22 dim. for B part only.

4984 eBN, B smooth lens: 1'3 x 1'1 w. spir. patt. of dk. lanes, F(R): 2'8 x 1'8. Lund 7, Helwan 30 dim. (4' x 0'5) rej., wrong identif.?

4995 vBN, hexag pseudo (r): 0'6 x 0'55, sev. B knotty arms. Helwan 21 dim. rej.

4999 svBN, B narrow bar: 0'5 x 0'05, (r): 0'95 x 0'6, 2 main reg. arms, perhaps each dble.

5003 Note corr. to NGC coord. (Lick 13).

5005 eBN in B inner lens: 0'8 x 0'3, sev. knotty arms w. strong dk. lanes. Lund 9 dim. (5'0 x 0'9) are inconsistent; Lund 10 and MWC 132 dim. for B part only.
Photo. Ap.J., 133, 815, 1961.
Desc. Ap.J., 46, 43, 1917 = MWC 132.
Spectr. Ap.J., 135, 698, 1962.
Orient., rot., mass, Ap.J., 97, 117, 1943; 127, 487, 1958; 133, 814, 1961.

5011 vBN, vF out. envel. ?

5012 svBN, hexag. (r): 0'6 x 0'3, sev. knotty filam. branch. arms. P(a) w. anon. Pec or Sm at 15'5.

5016 sBN, weak bar, (r): 0'2 x 0'15, sev. knotty filam. arms w. m. branch.

5018 vBN, dk. patches or defect in lens. P(a) w. N 5022 at 7'2.

5022 No BN, B narrow bar? : 0'5 x 0'05, * superp. P(a) w. N 5018 at 7'2.

N 5026   sBN betw. 2 *, vF arms.

5028   * at 0'45.

5030   In N 5049 group.

5033   svB diff. N in B bulge w. spir. patt. of dk. lanes, sev. part. res. filam. arms w. branch. HA 88,2 dim.
       (6' x 3', after Lick 13) for B part only. Unusual dec. of B-V w. log A/D(0), interp. value.

5035   In N 5049 group. vBN, weak bar, (r): 0'75 x 0'5.

5037   In N 5049 group. BN in bulge, pseudo (r): 1'3 x 0'35.

5044, 5046   In N 5049 group.

5047   In N 5049 group. sBN, v. thin flat compon.

5049   Only one in group w. rad. vel., but N 5044 the brightest.

5054   Near N 5049 group. svB complex N, pseudo (r?): 0'85 x 0'5, 3 main B part. res. arms. P. w. s. anon. SBm?
       sp at 2'7 n.

5055   = M 63. vsvB stell. N in B inner lens: 1'7 x 0'95, many filam. part. res. arms, (r): 1'35 x 0'6. Lund 9 dim.
       much too small (rej.). B-V const. w. log A/D(0), interp. value.
       Photo. Ap.J., 131, 282, 1960; 134, 883, 1961.
       Photom. Stockholm Ann., 15, No 9, 1949. A.J., 66, 283, 1961; Ap.J., 134, 880, 1961.
       Spectr. Lick Obs. Bull. 497, 1939. Ap.J., 135, 698, 735, 1962.
       Polar. Stockholm Ann., 17, No 4, 1951.
       Orient., rot., mass, Ap.J., 127, 487, 1958; 131, 282, 1960; 136, 352, 1962.
       HII reg. Zs.f.Ap., 50, 168, 1960.

5061   vB diff. N.

5064   BN, not res. Classif. uncertain.

5068   sh. B bar: 0'8 x 0'1 w. vs N, pseudo (r): 1'6 x 1'9:, 2 main knotty part. res. arms w. m. branch. Helwan 30, 38
       min. dim. much too small. Spectr. A.J., 61, 97, 1956.

5077   = Ho 514b. P(a) w. N 5079 at 3'0. Brightest of a group. vB diff. N, * at 16".

5078   vB diff. N in B bulge w. v. strong dk. lane, edgewise; similar to N 4594 or N 5746. P(a) w. I 879 at 2'3.

5079   = Ho 514a. P(a) w. N 5077 at 3'0, N 5076 at 3'2. Not vBN not in center, sev. knotty arms form pseudo (r):
       0'6 x 0'4, vF extens.

5082   sBN, s * 0'6 f, detail or defect near N. SN 1958 and Photo. P.A.S.P., 72, 208, 1960.

5084   svBN, v. thin flat compon.: 0'3 w. some struct. near N.

5085   vsBN in B inner lens: 0'35 x 0'3, 2 main knotty arms w. dk. lane, some branch.; similar to M 51.
       Helwan 30, 38 dim. for B part only.

5087   vsvBN, B lens: 0'4 x 0'25 w. poor. res. dk. crescent. Heid 9 and HA 88,2 dim. for B part only.

5088   = Ho 515a. (Ho 515b at 3'7 is a *). In N 5077 group. vBN, poor. res. arms, dk. lane on one side. Lund 6,
       Lund 9 dim. for B part only.

5090   s * 0'5 f, vB * 5' n. P. w. N 5091 at 1'3.

5090-A sBN, sev. * nearby.

5090-B sBN, probably late SA type.

5091   Asym. N, vB * 5'n. P. w. N 5090 at 1'3.

5101   vB diff. N, narrow B smooth bar: 1'75 x 0'2 w. s. blobs, weak (r): 1'6 x 1'4, vF smooth out. whorls form pseudo
       (R): 5'0 x 4'3. HA 88,2 minor dim. (0'6: ser. a) rej., error or bar only?

5102   vBN in B lens: 1'2 x 0'7. Iota Cen is 17' sp. HA 88,2 dim. for lens only. Photom. M.N., 112, 606, 1952.

5107   P. w. N 5112 at 13'5.

5112   Sh. B inner bar: 0'5 x 0'1, sev. filam. knotty branch. arms. P. w. N 5107 at 13'5.

5116   vsBN, v. narrow bar, 2 main filam. branch. arms, v. poor. res. Lund 9 dim. for B part only.

5121   BN, B envel., dk. crescent? HA 88,2 dim. (0'6: x 0'6:; ser. a') for N only.

5121-A vF, s * near center.

N 5128   One of the most peculiar bright galaxies = radio source Centaurus A.
      Descr. see Helwan 21; HB 898, 1935; and photo. ref. Struct. A.J., 68, 76, 1963.
      Photo. H.B. 898, 1935. M.N., 109, 98, 1949. Ap.J., 119, 223, 1954; 129, 272, 1959. Zs.f.Ap., 51, 64, 1960.
         Hdb.d.Phys., vol. 53, 267, 1959.
      Photom. M.N., 109, 94, 1949. Observatory, 78, 24, 1958. IAU Symp., 4, 1955 (Cambridge U.P., p. 169, 1957).
      Spectr. Zs.f.Ap., 51, 64, 1960.
      Polar. A.J., 67, 271, 1962.
      Rot., mass, Ap.J., 129, 271, 1959.
      Radio emiss. Nature 164, 101, 1949. Ap.J., 119, 123, 1954; 125, 1, 1957; 133, 322, 1961. Aust.J.Phys, 6, 452,
         1953; 11, 517, 1958. P.A.S.P., 72, 368, 1960. Cal. Inst. Tech. Rad. Obs., 4, 1959; 2, 1961.
         IAU Symp., 4, 1955.

5134   vsvBN in B bulge, smooth lens w. dk. lane, 2 F main arms w. some knots, Classif. uncertain.
      P(a) w. I 4237 at 10'7.

5135   vBN in B bar: 1'3 x 0'3. P(a) w. I 4248 at 13'5.

5147   Diff. bar, no N, 2 main mass. part. res. branch. arms, B * superp., strongly asym. Heid 9, Lund 9 dim.
      for B part only.

5156   sBN, s * 0'4 f, s neb. knot 1'2 np.

5169   P(a) w. N 5173 at 5'5. Lund 9 dim. for B part only.

5170   vsvBN in sB bulge part. obsc. by dk. lane. Similar to N 4565.

5172   sBN, pseudo (r): 1'35 x 0'6, 3 main knotty arms, poor. res. Heid 9, Lund 9 dim. for (r) only.

5173   P(a) w. N 5169 at 5'5. All dim. for B part only.

5194, 5195 = M 51. = Ho 526a, b. Well-known interacting pair P(b) at 4'8. In M 101 group. B mag.
(source F) 5194 + 95.
      Photo. Ap.J., 32, 34, 1910, Ritchey, L'Evolution de Astrophographie..., S.A.F., Paris 1929. Hdb.d.Ap., 5, 2,
         843, 1933. Medd. Lund I, 170, 1950. P.A.S.P., 67, 232, 1955; 75, 222, 1963.
      Photom. Ap.J., 46, 206, 1917; 50, 385, 1919; 83, 424, 1936; 91, 528, 1940; 108, 415, 1948. A.J. USSR, 32, 16,
         1955. Izv. Pulkovo, 20, No 156, 87, 1956. Publ. Burakan, XXV, 15, 1958. Medd. Lund, I, 170, 1950;
         II, 128, 1950.
      Spectr. Ap.J., 116, 66, 1952; 135, 734, 1962.
      HII reg. Observatory, 79, 54, 1959. Zs.f.Ap., 50, 168, 1960.
      Radio emiss. M.N., 122, 479, 1961. Ap.J., 133, 322, 1961. Hdb.d.Phys., 53, 253, 1959.
      HI emiss. Ap.J., 126, 471, 1957. P.A.S.P., 72, 368, 1960. B.A.N., 15, 506, 314, 1961.
      SN 1945, (in N 5195) P.A.S.P., 57, 174, 1945.

5198   vBvs diff. N, in lens: 0'5 x 0'4 smooth neb. Yerkes 2 class. "S" (1959) is an error or misprint. Heid 9, Lund
      9 dim. for lens only.

5204   In M 101 group. no def. N, BM, highly res. irreg. arms. Heid 9, Lund 9 dim. for B part only. Lick 1956 vel.
      for 2 emiss patches 30" SW of center: +416 km/sec.
      Photo. P.A.S.P., 61, 123, 1949. Mag.: Ap.J., 85, 325, 1937.
      HII reg. Zs.f.Ap., 50, 168, 1960.

5216   P(b) w. N 5218. vB cent. smooth struct., long streamer connects direct w. 5218: 3'3 x 0'l, opposite streamer:
      1'1 x 0'14.
      Photo. Ap.J., 81, 355, 1935. Erg.d.Exakt.Naturwiss., XXIX, 344, 1956.
      Spectr. I.A.U. Symp., 5, 1958 = Lick Cont. II, 81, 1958.

5218   P(b) w. N 5216. B complex bar and lens w. dk. lanes, smooth distorted arm, + F extens. opposite to 5216.
      For ref. see N 5216.

5230   vsBN, sev. knotty filam. arms w. m. branch., asym. v. similar to M 101.

5236   = M 83. eBN in B complex bar w. dk. lanes, 2 main part. res. arms. w. m. branch. (B-V)(0) interpolated.
      Photo. M.N., 85, 1019, 1925. P.N.A.S., 26, 33, 1940.
      Radio emiss. Hdb.d.Phys., 53, 253, 1959. M.N., 122, 479, 1961. P.A.S.P., 72, 368, 1960.
         Observatory, 83, 20, 1963.
      HI emiss. Epstein, Harvard Thesis, 1962.
      SN 1923, P.A.S.P., 35, 166, 1923; 48, 320, 1936. H.B. 786, 787, 1923. Ap.J., 88, 293, 1938.
      SN 1950, H.A.C. 1074, 1950.
      SN 1958, (or Nova?) H.A.C. 1394, 1958. Sky & Tel., 17, 287, 1958.

5247   B complex N, 2 main part. res. reg. arms, 1 or 2 addit. F arms. Similar to M 74 or M 99. Photo. Helwan 9, 1912.

5248   eBN'in vB lens w. many dk. lanes, pseudo (r): 2'4 x 1'1, B part or lens: 3'6 x 2'1, F part. res. out. arms form
      pseudo (R): 6'6 x 4'5.
      Photo., rot., mass, Ap.J., 136, 128, 1962.
      HII reg. Zs.f.Ap., 50, 168, 1960.

5253   vB core: 0'55 x 0'3 w. traces of res. and complex dk. lanes in B part: 1'55 x 0'55, smooth out. neb. Pec., class.
      difficult, poss. IO or Im?
      Photo. Observatory, 72, 133, 1952.
      Spectr. Observatory, 72, 133, 1952. Bol. Tonantzintla, 14, 8, 1956. P.A.S.P., 69, 564, 1957.
         Ap.J., 135, 696, 1962.
      SN 1895, (Z cen), H.A., 84, 7, 1923. Ap.J., 83, 173, 1936; 88, 293, 1938; 89, 193, 1938.

N 5257 = Ho 532a. P(b) w. N 5258 at 1'3. NW comp; vsBN, narrow spiral in B lens: 0'5 x 0'4, one arm linking w. N 5258.
Lund 6 dim. for lens only. Lund 9, Heid 9 dim. for B part only. Photo., Spectr. Ap.J., 116, 64, 1952.
Hdb.d.Phys., vol. 53, 381, 1959.

5258 = Ho 532b. P(b) w. N 5257 at 1'3. Lund 6, 9 and Heid 9 dim. for B part only. B complex lens: 0'3 x 0'2, 2
main B smooth arms, a third linking w. N 5257. Photo., Spectr. Ap.J., 116, 66, 1952.
Hdb.d.Phys., vol. 53, 381, 1959.

5266 sBN or lens: 0'7 x 0'35. HA 88,2 dim. for B part only.

5266-A F anon., poorly res.

5273 = Ho 535a. P(a) w. N 5276 at 3'3. sB diff. N w. 2 weak dk. patches, vF spir. whorls in lens: 1'4 x 1'2, smooth
neb. HA 88,2 dim. (1'0 x 1'0: ser. mc) is for N or lens only. Lund 9 dim. for lens only.

5276 = Ho 535b. P(a) w. N 5273 at 3'3. vB bar or lens, 2 filam. arms, one forms out. loop: 0'9 x 0'55.

5278, 5279 Pair (b) at 0'6. 5278: vsvBN, pseudo (r): 0'4 x 0'25, strongly asym.; 5279: vsvBN, sh. bar, 2 main smooth
arms, distorted: at end of arm of 5278.

5290 B bulge part. hidden by dk. lane and asym. abs. Poss. edgewise SBb?

5291 P(b) w. anon. at 0'6.

5293 vsBN, smooth (r): 0'22 x 0'2, 2 main filam. arms w. some knots and branch., 2 F addit. arms.

5296 P(b?) w. N 5297 at 1'6. sBN. Heid. 9 dim. (0'25 x 0'25) rej. N only.

5297 P(b?) w. N 5296 at 1'6. vsBN, B lens w. sev. narrow knotty arms and dk. lane, 2 F out. smooth arms.
Lund 9 dim. for B part only.

5298 vBN, F bar, pseudo (r): 0'45 x 0'4, poor. res. P(a) at 5'6: w. anon. SB(r)b: (1'3 x 0'65), (r): 0'45 x 0'2.

5301 B bulge part. obs. by dk. lane, vSN or no def. N, 2 main arms w. strong dk. lane.

5302 vBN, F bar, poor. res.

5304 BN, 2 * involv. classif. uncertain. Dim.: 0'8 x 0'45 on Boyden 60-in. pl.

5308 vBN, diamond-shaped. See also Ap.J., 46, 43, 1917.

5322 B diff. N, smooth neb. Possibly SO⁻ ? Heid 9, Lund 9 and HA 88,2 dim. for B part only. Mag. Ap.J., 85, 325, 1937.

5324 B diff. N, many knotty filam. arms w. m. branch. Poss. SA(r?). Lund 9, Heid 9 and HA 88,2 (after Helwan) dim.
for B part only.

5328 Poss. SO?. P. w. N 5330 (EO?) at 1'7.

5334 = I 4338. Low surf. bright.

5350 = Ho 555c. In small group w. N 5353, -54, -55, vsvBN in B bar, (r): 0'7 x 0'5, 2 main filam. knotty arms w.
some branch.

5351 = Ho 554a. P. w. N 5341 at 12'5. N 5349 at 3'4. sBN, (r): 0'43 x 0'25, knotty arms form pseudo (R):
1'2 x 0'5, poor. res. Lund 9 dim. for B part only.

5353 = Ho 555b. In small group w. N 5350, -54, -55, N 5354 at 1'2. vsBN, lens: 0'6 x 0'15, diamond-shaped.

5354 = Ho 555a. In small group w. N 5350, -53, -55, N 5353 at 1'2. Similar to N 1316.

5360 = Ho 557b. P(a) w. N 5364 at 8'7. Pec.

5363 2 B diff. N in contact or one BN w. narrow dk. lane and * superp., F out. extens. w. dk. lane. Pec. P(a) w.
N 5364 at 14'5.

5364 = Ho 557a. P(a) w. N 5360 at 8'7. sBN in smooth cent. w. dk. matter, narrow (r): 1'2 x 0'65, in lens:
1'8 x 1'1, 2 main part. res. filam. arms form pseudo (R): 6'0 x 4'3. HII reg. Zs.f.Ap., 50, 168, 1960.

5365 svBN, vF envel. Note corr. to Mt. Stromlo (1956) class.

5365-A B * attach. 0'7 f N at one end.

5365-B At 9' f N 5365. Asym.

5368 Dim.: Heid. 9 (0'5 x 0'5) and Lund 9 (0'6 x 0'3). Mag. Ap.J., 85, 325, 1937.

5371 = 5390. vsB diff. N, weak bar, pseudo (r): 1'0 x 0'7, sev. knotty filam. reg. arms w. some branch.

5376 In group w. N 5379, -89. sBN, weak bar, (r): 0'5 x 0'4. All dim. for B part only.

5377 seBN w. dk. lane, B bar in lens 2'2 x 0'7, vF out. whorls or (R): 3'65 x 2'0.

5378 Heid. 9 dim. (0'7? x 0'7?) rej., N only. P. w. N 5380 at 11'.

N 5379   = Ho 561b. P. w. N 5389 at 4'2. vsBN, (r): 0'5 x 0'35.

5380   P. w. N 5378 at 11'.

5383   eBN w. complex struct., weak bar and lens w. dk. lanes, 2 main sh. arms. P(a) w. F anon. SB(s)c at 3'1.
       (See M.W.C. 132).
       <u>Photo., rot., mass,</u> Ap.J., 136, 704, 1962.
       <u>Spectr.</u> Ap.J., 135, 696, 1962.

5389   = Ho 561a. P. w. N 5379 at 4'2. vBN, (r): 1'4 x 0'3, w. strong dk. lane on one side. Poss. SAB?

5394   = Ho 563b. P(b) w. N 5395 at 1'9. eBN or *, complex abnormal lens: 0'7 x 0'3 w. dk. lanes, 2 main reg. arms,
       one connecting w. N 5395. Heid 9, Lund 6, 9 dim. for lens only.

5395   = Ho 563a. P(b) w. N 5394 at 1'9. sBN in B bulge, one main arm w. some knots, strong dk. lanes on one side,
       signs of distorsion by 5394. Lick 13 dim. for B part only.

5398   H.A. 88,2 dim.: 1'5: x 1'5: (ser. a').

5403   = Ho 564a. P. w. anon. (Ho 564b) at 1'8.

5419   H.A. 88,2 dim.: 1'0: x 0'7: (ser. a').

5422   = Ho 567a. (Ho 567b at 2'2 is a *). svBN, B lens: 0'85 x 0'3 w. traces of dk. lane.
       <u>Photom.</u> Ap.J., 50, 385, 1919 (listed as N 5423, prob. misprint).

5426   = Ho 573b. P(b) w. N 5427 **at** 2'3. South comp., B diff. N, B cent., sev. filam. knotty arms, 2 extending to N
       5427. Heid 9 minor dim. (0'7) is much too small; HA 88,2 dim. (after Helwan) for B part cnly. (B-V) source E
       rejected. <u>Photo., Spectr.</u> Ap.J., 116, 64, 1952.

5427   = Ho 573a. P(b) w. N 5426 at 2'3. vBN in B lens: 0'23 x 0'17, 2 main B spir. arms, knots and branch.
       <u>Photo., Spectr.</u> Ap.J., 116, 64, 1952.

5430   = Ho 569a. (Ho 569b at 0'4 may be * ?) svBN in B lens w. B rim: 0'5 x 0'3, 2 main reg. arms, * superp. 22"
       from N.

5443   = Ho 578a. (Ho 578b at 1'8 is a *). <u>Mag.</u> Ap.J., 85, 325, 1937.

5444   P. w. N 5445 at 7'.

5448   svBN w. dk. matt. on one side, F bar, F(r): 1'6 x 0'5, 2 F arms form pseudo (R): 3'3 x 1'4.

5457   = M 101. Details (HII reg.) = N 5447, 53, 55, 58, 61, 62, 71. Lick 13 dim. for B part only.
       <u>Photo.</u> Ritchey, L'Evolution de l'Astrophotographie..., S.A.F., Paris, 1929.
       <u>Photom.</u> Ap.J., 50, 385, 1919; 83, 424, 1936; 91, 528, 1940; 108, 415, 1948. Medd. Lund II, 128, 1950. A.J.USSR
              82, 16, 1955. Izv. Pulkovo, 20, No 156, 87, 1956. Publ. Burakan, XXIV, 2, 1958. Error on V mag. in
              Ap.J. Suppl. No 48, 1961, V = 12.36 for A/D(0) = 0.025.
       <u>HII reg.</u> Ap.J., 91, 261, 1940. Observatory, 79, 54, 1959. Zs.f.Ap., 50, 168, 1960.
       <u>Radio emiss.</u> Hdb.d.Phys., 53, 253, 1959. P.A.S.P., 72, 368, 1960. M.N., 122, 479, 1961.
       <u>HI emiss.</u> B.A.N., 14, 323, 1959. A.J., 67, 317, 1962.
       <u>SN 1908/9,</u> A.N., 180, 375, 1909. Ap.J., 69, 103, 1929; 88, 293, 1938.

5468   = Ho 585a. Detail or * = N 5467 (see Helwan 38, MWC 626). P(a) w. N 5472 at 5'1. svB elong. N or bar, 2 main
       part. res. filam. arms w. m. branch., pseudo (r): 0'3 x - . Poss. SA(s)cd w. pec. N.

5472   = Ho 585b. P(a) w. N 5468 at 5'1. sB elong. N not in cent. of B lens: 0'25 x 0'1, pseudo (r): 0'22 x 0'08?
       v. poor. res.

5473   svBN, sh. bar, F lens. <u>Mag.</u> Ap.J., 85, 325, 1937.
       <u>Photom.</u> Ap.J., 50, 384, 1919.
       <u>Spectr.</u> IAU Symp., 5, 1958 = Lick Cont. II, 81, 1958.

5474   Low surf. bright., smooth part. res. cent. w. vsFN, sev. part. res. arms, strongly asym. In M 101 group.
       <u>Photom.</u> Medd. Lund II, 128, 1950.
       <u>HII reg.</u> Zs.f.Ap., 50, 168, 1960.

5475, 5477 <u>Mag.</u> Ap.J., 85, 325, 1937.

5480   = Ho 588a. P(a) w. N 5481 at 3'1. Note corr. to HA 88,2 and NGC RA (see MWC 626). svBN, sev. filam. branch.
       arms poor. res.

5481   = Ho 588b. P(a) w. N 5480 at 3'1. Note corr. to NGC RA (see MWC 626).

5483   No N, BM.

5484   P(a) w. N 5485 at 3'9. Dim.: 0'3 x 0'3 (Heid. 9, Lund 9, Crossley 36-in.).

5485   P(a) w. N 5484 at 3'9, N 5486 at 6'5. sBN in B diff. lens w. curved dk. lane. Similar to N 1947 and possibly
       N 5128. <u>Photom.</u> Ap.J., 50, 385, 1919. <u>Mag.</u> Ap.J., 85, 325, 1937.

5486   P(a) w. N 5485 at 6'5. <u>Mag.</u> Ap.J., 85, 325, 1937.

5490   = Ho 595a. P. w. anon. (Ho 595b) at 1'8 nf. In group w. I 982, 983 and others.

N 5490-C At 4'7 nf N 5490, 7' s of I 983. In group w. I 982, 983 and anon.

5493 vB diff. N in B diamond-shaped lens: 0'6 x 0'15, F nearly circular envel.

5494 BM, 3 main knotty filam. branch. arms, 2 B * superp.

5496 v. poor. res.

5506 = Ho 604a. P(a) w. N 5507 at 4'. I 985 at 25'.

5507 = Ho 604b. P(a) w. N 5506 at 4'. Lick 13 dim. (0'3 x 0'3) rej., N?

5523 BM, no def. N, many filam. knotty arms w. m. branch. and dk. lanes v. poor. res. Lund 9 dim. for B part only.

5529 v. poor. res., almost exactly edgewise.

5530 B * superp. on N. Helwan 30, 38 dim. for B part only.

5533 vBN in pseudo (r): 0'7 x 0'3, weak irreg. out. arms. Lund 9 dim. (0'9 x 0'9) is an error or N only.

5534 = Ho 623a. Anon. (Ho 623b) at 0'5 may be a *.

5544 SW compon. of P. w. N 5545 at 0'6. eBN, (r): 0'37 x 0'35, F out. whorls, pseudo (R): 0'75 x 0'7. Lick 13, Lund 9 dim. for lens only.
Photo. Hdb.d.Phys., 53, 377, 1959.
Desc. Ap.J., 46, 44, 1917; 51, 298, 1920.
Spectr. Ap.J., 116, 66, 1952.

5545 NE compon. of P. w. N 5544 at 0'6. svBN, B cent lens (or bar): 0'2 x 0'08, 2 main B arms, a few knots, in front of N 5544. For ref. see N 5544.

5548 eBN, F spir. patt. in lens: 0'5 x 0'5, outer whorls form pseudo (R): 1'0 x 0'85. Heid 9, Lund 9 dim. for lens only. Broad em. lines in N. Spectr. L'Astronomie, 73, 3, 1959.

5556 Sh. B bar: 0'4 x 0'06, no def. N, sev. F part. res. filam. branch. arms, pseudo (r): 0'55 x - , asym. Similar to M 101. P(a) w. anon. Sm at 9'6. HA 88,2 dim. for B part only.

5557 BN, no struct. Lick 13, Heid 9 dim. for B part only. Photom. M.N., 98, 620, 1938.

5560 = Ho 630b. P(b) w. N 5566 at 5'0, N 5569 at 7'. vBN in strong forsh. bar: 0'8, weak extens. of arms, distorted by 5566. Desc.: Ap.J., 46, 44, 1917. Lick 13, Lund 6 dim. for lens only.

5566 = Ho 630a. P(b) w. N 5560 at 5'0, N 5569 at 4'2. eBN, smooth bar w. (r): 1'4 x 0'75, F smooth out. arms w. strong dk. lane, one vF extens. towards 5560. Desc.: Ap.J., 46, 44, 1917. Lund 6 dim. rej., (r) only. Lund 9, 10 dim. for B part only.
Photo., photom. B.A.N., 16, 1, 1961.
Orient. Ap.J., 127, 487, 1958.

5569 = Ho 630c. P(a) w. N 5566 at 4'2, N 5560 at 7'. vsN in B sh. bar, F poor. res. arms. Lund 6 dim. much too small (rej.); Lund 9, Heid 9 for B part only.

5574 = Ho 632b. P. w. N 5576 at 2'7. svBN, diff. lens w. less flattened envel.

5576 = Ho 632a. P. w. N 5574 at 2'7. B diff. N. Lund 6 dim. (0'6 x 0'6) rej., N only?

5577 sBN, v. fine arms.

5584 sh. B bar in lens, pseudo (r): - x 0'3, sev. part. res. branch. filam. arms, v. similar to M 101.

5585 In M 101 group. BM, no def. N, weak irreg. arms well res. up to cent. reg., low surf. bright. Lund 6, Heid 9 dim. for B part only.
Mag. Ap.J., 85, 325, 1937.
Photom. Medd. Lund II, 128, 1950.
HII reg. Zs.f.Ap., 50, 168, 1960.

5595 = Ho 638a. P. w. N 5597 at 4'2. sBN, F bar, 2 main knotty arms w. some branch.

5597 = Ho 638b. P. w. N 5595 at 4'2. vseBN, F bar, sev. filam. arms form pseudo (R): 1'4 x 1'1. Lund 6 minor dim. rej., much too small.

5600 vB core or N, pseudo (r?): 0'4 x 0'2, asym. out. arms.

5612 vF envel? * involv., classif. uncertain.

5613 svBN, broad eF bar, smooth (r): 0'3 x 0'25, in lens 0'35 x 0'3, F(R): 1'0 x 0'65. P(b) w. N 5614 at 2'0. Heid 9 dim. for (r) only.

5614 svBN, B smooth pseudo (r): 0'33 x 0'3, smooth strongly asym. spir. struct., poor. res., strong dk. lanes. P(b) w. N 5615 which is B knot on pseudo (R), w. smooth irreg. tail. Heid 9 dim. for lens only. HA 88,2 class. (E:) is erroneous.

5631 vB diff. N w. F dk. crescent on one side, in lens 0'5 x 0'5, F envel. Heid 9, Lund 9 dim. for lens only.
Mag. Ap.J., 85, 325, 1937.

N 5633 sBN in complex lens w. B knots, pseudo (r): 0'4 x 0'3, B part: 0'9 x 0'55, F(R): 1'9 x 1'0. Heid 9, Lund 9 and
HA 88,2 dim. for B part only.

5636 = Ho 653b. P(a) w. N 5638 at 2'0. vsBN, F bar, (r): 0'8 x 0'5.

5638 = Ho 653a. P(a) w. N 5636 at 2'0.

5643 vsvBN, vF bar, hexag. pseudo (r): 1'1 x 1'0. 2 main part. res. arms w. branch. HA 88,2 dim. (2'5 x 2'3: ser.
a) for B part only; see HB 914, 7, 1940. Photo. Occ. Notes R.A.S., 3, No 18, 1956.

5645 B bar: 0'25 x 0'05, sev. knotty arms w. some branch., asym. Heid 9 dim. for B part only.

5653 vBN, B pseudo (r): 0'17 x 0'1, in B part: 0'5 x 0'4, sev. B knotty arms, F smooth pseudo (R): 1'05 x 0'85.
Heid 9, Lund 9 dim. for B part only. HA 88,2 class. (E:) is an error.

5660 svBN, pseudo (r): 0'2 x - , sev. knotty branch. arms. P. w. F anon. IBm at 2'5. N 5676 at 30'5.
Mag. Ap.J., 85, 325, 1937.

5665 sBN or condens., F bar: 0'4 x 0'05, one asym. arm forms out. loop: 1'3 x 0'75. Lund 9, Heid 9, HA 88,2 dim.
for B part only.

5668 vs not vB N, BM, many part. res. irreg. branch. arms. Similar to N 300. Lund 9, Heid 9 dim. for B part only.
SN 1954, H.A.C. 1425. P.A.S.P., 72, 97, 1960. L'Astronomie, 68, 210, 1954. A.J., 65, 54, 1960. Pub. Bologna,
VI, 12, 1955. Hdb.d.Phys., 51, 782, 1958.

5669 sh. B bar: 0'2 x 0'05 in pseudo (r): 0'4 x 0'3, 2 main part. res. filam. arms w. some branch. Lund 9, Heid 9
dim. for B part only.

5672 Proj. on Bootes Cl. Photo. Hubble, Obs. Approach to Cosmol., Plate VI.

5673 Mag. Ap.J., 85, 325, 1937.

5676 sBN in B cent., pseudo (r): 0'6 x 0'35, many B knotty filam. arms w. branch., asym. out. part. P(a) N 5660 at
30'5. I 1029 at 26'5. One aberrant val. B-V (source C) rejected. Lund 9 dim. for B part only.
Mag. Ap.J., 85, 325, 1937.

5678 vsBN in B bar w. complex patt. of dk. lanes, pseudo (r): 1'3 x 0'5, smooth out. arms, slightly asym. P. w.
anon. s. E3 at 1'8.

5682 = Ho 663a. P. w. N 5683 at 1'4, N 5689 at 8'3. sh. B bar: 0'2 x 0'1, 2 main reg. arms.

5683 = Ho 663b. P. w. N 5682 at 1'4. eBN or *.

5687 B diff. N, eF envel. Heid. 9 and Lund 9 dim. rej., N only. B(0) = 13.18 (Source C, w = 0.45).

5689 vB diff. N in B bulge w. strong dk. lane on one side, lens: 1'2 x 0'5, F smooth out. whorls. P(a) w. 5682-83 at
8'3, 5693 at 11'8, and others. Brightest of a group. Lund 9 dim. for lens only.

5690 BM no def. N, sev. arms w. dk. lanes, class. diff., poss. SB?, vB * at 3'1. Lund 9 dim. are in error or for
core only. (rej.).

5691 vB bar or core: 0'25 x 0'06 in B complex core or lens: 0'6 x 0'45 w. dk. lane, one smooth, mass. out. whorl,
strong asym. Lund 9 dim. for core only.

5693 sh. B bar, one main knotty arm, strong asym. P. w. N 5689 at 11'8.

5701 svB diff. N, B inner lens: 0'55 x 0'55, B bar w. blobs: 1'3 x 0'3, F(r): 1'3 x 1'3, narrow filam., part. res.
spir. arcs form F(R): 3'4 x 3'4, small anon. S visible betw. lens and (R). Lund 9 dim. for B part only.

5705 vF, bar: 0'6 x 0'1.

5707 Mag.: Ap.J., 85, 325, 1937.

5713 sh. vB bar w. eBN, B clumpy inner arms, strongly asym. incompl. F(R): 1'75 x 1'65. P(b) w. N 5719 at 12'.
Spectr. A.J., 61, 97, 1956.

5716 v. poor. res., class. uncertain. P(a) w. N 5728 at 23'. All dim. for B part only.

5719 P(b) w. N 5713 at 12'. vBN in sh. bar, strong dk. lanes on lens and on near side, out. part. distorted by interact. w. N 5713. Similar to N 3190. Lund 9 dim. for B part only.

5728 vBN w. spir. patt. of dk. lanes, broad F bar w. dk. lane, narrow (r): 1'8 x 0'9. P(a) w. N 5716 at 23', small
anon. SB(s)m at 3'2.

5739 Heid 9 dim. rej., N only.

5740 vBN, weak bar, pseudo (r): 0'7 x 0.'4, sev. branch. arms, poor. res. Lund 9 dim. for B part only. P(a) w. N
5746 at 18'. One aberrant val. B-V (source C) rejected. Desc. Ap.J., 46, 45, 1917.

5746 vsBN in B cent. bulge, strong dk. lane in front. P(a) w. N 5740 at 18'.
Photo., photom. B.A.N., 16, 1, 1961.
Orient., rot., Ap.J., 97, 117, 1943; 127, 487, 1958.

N 5750   seBN in diff. inner lens: 0'35 x 0'17, broad diff. bar w. dk. lane, strong (r): 1'1 x 0'55, F smooth out. arms or arcs. Similar to N 5566. Heid 9, Lund 9, HA 88,2 dim. for B part only. Yerkes 2 (1959) class.: or F.

5756   = Ho 676a. (Ho 676b at 2' is probably a *).

5757   eBN, strong bar: 0'5 x 0'05, F(r): 0'5 x 0'5, out. arms form pseudo (R): 1'2 x 1'2. P. w. anon. S sp. at 3'6.

5768   sBN, pseudo (r): 0'5 x 0'3?, sev. knotty branch. arms, poor. res. Heid 9, HA 88,2 (m$_c$) dim. for B part only.

5772   vBN, (r): 0'5 x 0'35, poor. res. All dim. for B part only.

5774   = Ho 685b. P(a) w. N 5775 at 4'5. sh. B bar: 0'3 x 0'05, no N, 2 main part. res. filam. F branch. arms. Lund 6, 9 dim. are much too small.

5775   = Ho 685a. P(a) w. N 5774 at 4'5. B bulge: 0'5 x 0'25, sev. knotty arms w. strong dk. lane, seen edgewise.

5783   <u>Mag.</u> Ap.J., 85, 325, 1937.

5791   B diff. N. Class. uncertain, poss. S0⁻. P(a) w. I 1077 at 20'.

5792   vsBN in broad diff. bar w. strong dk. lane, (r): 2'2 x 0'75 in lens: 3'5 x 1'1, 2 main filam. arms w. some knots form pseudo (R): 6'7 x 1'3. Similar to N 5566. <u>Radio S.,</u> poss. ident., Aust.J.Phys., 11, 360, 1958.

5793   B bulge, strong dk. lane. P. w. N 5796 at 4'3.

5796   B diff. N, small * at 10". P. w. N 5793 at 4'3.

5806   In N 5846 group. P(a) w. N 5813 at 21'. eBN in B lens w. spir. patt. of dk. lanes, pseudo (r): 0'9 x 0'55. F smooth out. arms. Lick 13, Heid 9 dim. for B part only.

5811   In N 5846 group. B bar: 0'3 x 0'08. F. asym. loop, poor. res. All dim. for B part only.

5812   P. w. I 1084 sf 5'0.

5813   In N 5846 group. = Ho 688a. P. w. N 5814 at 4'8, N 5806 at 21'. Lick 13 dim. for B part only.

5820   vsBN in B lens: 0'6 x 0'2.   P. w. N 5821 at 3'6 nf and anon. S at 9'6 sp. N 5821 = Ho 687a. in Lund 6 and has another vF companion at 1'3.

5831   In N 5846 group.

5832   No BN, F bar, F asym. spir. struct. Class. uncertain, poss. SB(s)m?

5838   In N 5846 group. P(a) w. N 5848 (S0 sp.?) at 17'5. B diff. N, fairly B lens. Lick 13 dim. much too small. <u>Photo., photom.</u> B.A.N., 16, 1, 1961.

5839, 5845   In N 5846 group.

5846   = Ho 694a. Brightest in group (see Ap.J., 131, 595, 1960). P(a) w. 5846-A at 0'7. B diff. N, smooth neb. Mag., colors for N 5846 + 46-A (Sources A, B, C, E, F). <u>Spectr.</u> I.A.U. Symp., 5, 1958 = Lick Cont. II, 81, 1958.

5846-A = Ho 694b. P(a) w. N 5846 at 0'7.

5850   In N 5846 group. P(a) w. N 5846 at 10'. vBN w. innermost bar-struct. and N, narrow smooth bar: 1'75, part. res. (r): 2'0 x 1'75, F part. res. out. arms form pseudo (R): 4'2 x 3'8. Similar to N 1433. Lick 13, Heid 9 dim. for B part only. <u>Photo.</u> M.N., 85, 1019, 1925. Ap.J., 64, 326, 1926.

5854   In N 5846 group. vs diff. N in B smooth lens: 0'85 x 0'25 w. sugges. of bar and spir. pattern, F smooth whorls in B envel.

5857   P(b?) w. N 5859 at 2'0. vsvBN in B lens: 0'3 x 0'25, pseudo (r): 0'3 x 0'2, 2 main reg. arms. Heid 9 dim. for lens only. B mag. (Source C) for 5857 + 59.

5858   Class. uncertain, poss. S0⁻ sp. P(a) w. N 5861 at 9'6.

5859   P(b?) w. N 5857 at 2'0. vBvsN in B lens: 0'7 x 0'25 w. dk. lanes, 2 main reg. knotty arms; little or no distorsion.

5861   F bar w. vF or no N, pseudo (r): 0'35 x 0'25, 2 main filam. arms w. some branch. P(a) w. N 5858 at 9'6 np. I 1091 at 9'6 nnp.

5864   In N 5846 group. sB diff. N in B lens: 1'0 x 0'25 w. blobs. Poss. SB(r)? Similar to N 5854.

5866   = M 102. vBN w. narrow sharp dk. lane and ansae. B flat compon.: 1'6 x 0'1, in B lens: 2'2 x 0'9. Wide pair w. N 5907. Lund 9 dim. for lens only. N 5867 is a small E neb. at 1'5 sp.
       <u>Mag.</u> Ap.J., 85, 325, 1937.
       <u>Photo.</u> Ap.J., 131, 224, 1960. B.A.N., 16, 1, 1961. Hdb.d.Ap., 5, 2, 843, 1933.
       <u>Photom.</u> B.A.N., 16, 1, 1961.
       <u>Spectr.</u> Sky & Tel., 8, 2, 1948. Ap.J., 135, 735, 1962.

5866-B See Ap.J., 82, 74, 1935 (dim.: 2'2 x 1'7).

5874, 5875, 5876 <u>Mag.</u> Ap.J., 85, 325, 1937.

N 5878 B diff. N, 2 main arms w. little branch., poor. res. HA 88,2 dim. for B part only.

5879 vsBN, many filam. knotty arms, poor. res. Mag.: Ap.J., 85, 325, 1937. SN 1954, H.A.C. 1275, 1954.
P.A.S.P., 72, 104, 1960.

5885 sBN, vF bar, (r): 0'55 x 0'1, sev. filam. branch. arms. HA 88,2 dim. (2'0 x 2'0, after Helwan 30) for B part
only. Lund 10 dim. (3'7 x 4'0) may be misprint for 3'7 x 3'0.

5893 = Ho 701b. P. w. N 5895-6 at 4'3. N 5896 is a F neb. 1' n of 5895 which is elong. 25°. N 5895 in Heid 9 and
Lund 6 must be a defect.

5898 P(a) w. N 5903 at 5'6.

5899 P(a) w. N 5900 at 9'5. svBN, sh. bar: 0'3 x 0'1, hexag. pseudo (r): 0'5 x 0'35, sev. knotty branch. arms,
strong asym.

5900 = Ho 702a. P(a) w. N 5899 at 9'5. N 5901 (= Ho 702b) at 1'3 may be a *.

5903 P(a) w. N 5898 at 5'6.

5905 sBN on bar: 0'7 x 0'15, strong (r): 0'9 x 0'8, 2 main filam. arms w. some knots and branch. P(a) w. N 5908 at
13'. Lund 9, Heid 9 dim. for B part only. Mag. Ap.J., 85, 325, 1937. SN 1963, I.A.U. Circ. 1842.

5907 = Ho 704a. P. w. anon. (Ho 704b) at 12'. vs bulge nearly hidden by strong dk. lane. N 5906 is part of it.
Desc.: Ap.J., 46, 46, 1917.
Photo. P.A.S.P., 52, 146, 1940.
Photo., Orient. Ap.J., 127, 487, 1958.
SN 1940, H.A.C., 519. P.A.S.P., 52, 146, 1940. Spectr. Hdb.d.Phys., vol. 51, 781, 1958.

5908 vsBN in B bulge, strong dk. lane; similar to N 4594. P(a) w. N 5905 at 13'.
Mag. Ap.J., 82, 62, 1935; 85, 325, 1937.

5915 P(b) w. N 5916 at 4'8, N 5916-A at 4'6. vB bar, 2 main B arms, F asym. loop or (R): 1'1 x 0'8, eF out. extens.
Heid 9 dim. (0'7 x 0'3) rej., bar only.

5916 P(b) w. N 5915 at 4'8. vsvBN, weak bar obscured by dk. lane, pseudo (r): 0'55 x 0'2:, 2 main smooth arms, F
out. whorls, distorted by interaction w. N 5915. Heid 9, Helwan 38 dim. for B part only.

5916-A P(b) w. 5915 at 4'6. = Hel 479 (Helwan 38). B bar, 2 main arms one sh. and B, other forms asym. loop.

5921 eBN in B bar: 0'85 x 0'3 w. dk. lanes, strong (r): 1'1 x 0'85, sev. part. res. filam. arms.
Spectr. Ap.J., 135, 697, 1962.
Photo. Hdb.d.Ap., 5, 2, 843, 1933.

5929, 5930 = Ho 710b, a. Conn. pair at 0'5. Faint I syst. at 5'5 nf. Spectr. Ap.J., 116, 65, 1952.

5936 B bar w. * superp., pseudo (r): 0'5 x 0'35, 2 main B reg. knotty arms.

5949 vsBN, many B knotty arms, (r) struct. doubtful. Similar to N 2841?

5951 = Ho 713a. (Ho 713b at 1'9 is a *).

5953, 5954 = Ho 714b, a. Pair at 0'8. Spectr. Ap.J., 116, 66, 1952. P.A.S.P., 168, 386, 1957.

5957 Weak, (r): 0'9 x 0'8.

5962 = Ho 716a. (Ho 716b at 1'5 is a *). svBN w. B arcs, knotty B (r): 0'4 x 0'3, v. many filam. knotty arms,
pseudo (R): 2'5 x 1'9. Heid 9, Lund 6, 9 dim. for B part or lens only.

5964 = I 4551? Narrow B bar: 1'2 x 0'1, vsFN, sev. part. res. branch. F arms, low surf. bright. Heid 9 dim. for
B part only.

5967 F, vsBN, (r): 0'8 x 0'8. P. w. N 5967-A at 9'.

5967-A P. w. N 5967 at 9'. vF, sev. F * involv. Poss. SBc?

5968 sBN, sh. bar, (r): 0'65 x 0'55, 2 or 3 reg., smooth filam. arms, low surf. bright.

5970 vsBN in vB bar: 0'5 x 0'1, narrow (r): 0'6 x 0'4, sev. knotty branch. filam. arms, high surf. bright. Heid 9
dim.: 3'0 x 1'0. P. w. I 1131 at ~ 8'.

5976 In group w. N 5981, 82, 85.

5981 = Ho 719c. P(a) w. N 5982 at 6'3. Heid 9, Lund 6 dim. for B part only. sBN, strong narrow dk. lane.
Similar to N 4565.

5982 = Ho 719a. P(a) w. N 5981 at 6'3, N 5985 at 7'7. vBN. Lund 6 dim. for B part only.

5984 B v. narrow bar; 0'5 x 0'05 w. brighter segment; v. poor. res.

5985 = Ho 719b. P(a) w. N 5982 at 7'7. sBN, sh. B bar: 0'3 x 0'1, narrow (r): 0'95 x 0'5, 3 main narrow filam. arms.

6015 vsBN in complex cent. w. many dk. lanes, many knotty arms in B lens, pseudo (R): 5'2 x 1'8. Heid 9 dim. for
B part only.

N 6027-A, D In small, dense Seyfert's group. Note that the designation in HMS (1956) is different from Seyfert's. 6027-A = Seyfert's 6027b; 6027-D = Seyfert's 6027. <u>Dyn.</u> A.J., 66, 544, 1961. <u>Photo. and Desc.</u> P.A.S.P., 63, 72, 1951.

6041, 6044, 6045, 6047 In Hercules Cl. Anon. 6050-A, V = 11173 (Ap.J., 130, 629, 1959). <u>Photo.</u> Erg. Exakt. Naturwiss., 29, 369, 1956. <u>Photo., dyn.</u> Ap.J., 130, 629, 1959.

6052 = 6064. vBN in B bar or core: 0'25 x 0'06, sev. B, irreg. knotty sh. arms, v. high surf. bright, pec.

6055 or 6053? Hercules Cl. <u>Spectr.</u> Ap.J., 130, 629, 1028, 1959.

6056, 6061 Hercules Cl.

6068, 6068-A = Ho 727a, b. Pair at 2'0.

6070 = Ho 729a. P. w. 2 anon. (Ho 729b, c) at 4'3 and 5'5.

6106 vs B diff. N w. * at 5", sev. knotty branch. arms. Similar to M 33. P(a) w. s. anon. S at 12'. Heid 9 dim. for B part only.

6118 s not vBN, 3 main reg. knotty filam. arms w. some branch., low surf. bright.

6140 <u>Mag.</u>: Ap.J., 85, 325, 1937. Rev. class. SA(s)c, pec. N, B part: 2'5 x 1'5, dim. 6'5 x 4'5, on Palomar 48-in. chart.

6143 vsBN in sh. bar or core, pseudo (r): 0'15 x - , 2 main knotty branch. arms, poor. res. <u>Mag.</u>: Ap.J., 85, 325, 1937, where class. (E1) is an error.

6166, 6166-A, B, C, D = Ho 751a, b, c, d, e. <u>Desc. and Photo.</u> P.A.S.P., 70, 143, 1958. A.J., 66, 558, 1961. Ap.J., 136, 1134, 1962. <u>Color, mag., vel.</u> A.J., 66, 558, 1961. <u>Radio emiss.</u> P.A.S.P., 70, 143, 1958. Cal. Inst. Tech. Radio Obs., 5, 1960.

6181 vsBN in vB lens: 0'7 x 0'35 w. spir. struct. and dk. lanes, 3 main part. res. B arms, F out. whorls form pseudo (R): 2'1 x 0'85. Heid 9 dim. much too small, lens only? <u>SN 1926,</u> P.A.S.P., 53, 125, 1941.

6196 = I 4613. In a group. Dim. on a Lick 36-in. pl.: 0'6: x 0'3:. Heid 9 dim. (0'2 x 0'2), N only, rej.

6207 No def. N, BM, B * near cent. (early Mt. Wil. vel. -250: was for *), complex knotty arms in lens, F out. arms, pseudo (R): 2'9 x 1'2.

6211 <u>Mag.</u>: Ap.J., 85, 325, 1927.

6215 B, vsBN. P. w. N 6221 at 18'.

6215-A F, B * 1'3 sf.

6217 svBN, broad diff. weak bar, pseudo (r): 1'2 x 1'0 formed by bright knotty arms in lens: 1'6 x 1'3, F pseudo (R): 2'5 x 2'4. Desc.: Ap.J., 46, 47, 1917. Lick 13, Heid 9, Lund 10 dim. for lens only. <u>Spectr.</u> Lick Bull., 497, 1939. A.J., 61, 97, 1956. <u>Mag.</u>: Ap.J., 85, 325, 1937.

6221 svBN in complex bar: 0'65 x 0'4 w. dk. lanes, 2 main arms one stronger and longer. P. w. N 6215 at 18'.

6239 B complex bar, one sh. B arm, double out. loop (helix?), vF asym. extens., a most peculiar system! Small coll. pair at 7'5. Heid 9 dim. for B part only. One aberr. value B-V (Source C) rej., interp. value.

6240 Complex core w. strong dk. lane, distorted, F out. filam. No nearby obj. of similar size. Another v. pec. object.

6246, 6246-A Pair at 10'. <u>Mag.</u> Ap.J., 82, 62, 1935; 85, 325, 1937.

6300 FN, sev. * superp., dk. lane on bar, (r): 2'0 x 1'1. See also HB, 914, 8, 1940. <u>Photo.</u> Occ. Notes R.A.S., 3, No 18, 1956.

6306, 6307 = Ho 769b, a. Pair at 1'4. Lund 6 dim. for 6306: 0'3 x 0'3. <u>Mag.</u>: Ap.J., 85, 325, 1937.

6308 sBN, (r): 0'4 x 0'3.

6310 <u>Mag.</u>: Ap.J., 85, 325, 1937.

6314, 6315 Pair at 3'2. Dk. lane in N 6314. Heid 9 dim. rej., N only?

6340 sBN in B bulge: 0'6 x 0'6 w. dk. lanes; lens: 1'0 x 1'0, F out. whorls form pseudo (R): 1'9 x 1'6. HA 88,2 dim. for lens only; class. (E) is erroneous. I 1251, 1254 at 6' n and 8' nf.

6359 sBN. P. w. small SB(s)b at 11' np. Heid 9 dim. rej., N only. <u>Mag.</u>: Ap.J., 85, 325, 1937.

6381 <u>Mag.</u>: Ap.J., 85, 325, 1937.

6384 sBN in F bar, (r): 1'0 x 0'7, 4 filam. arms, part. res. w. branch. Similar to N 6744. Heid 9 dim. for B part only.

N 6412   sBN, 2 main knotty arms w. m. branch. Similar to M 33.

6438, 6438-A Close pair. See P.N.A.S., 26, 35, 1940.

6478 = 6466. <u>Desc.</u>: Ap.J., 46, 47, 1917.

6482 B * att. Heid 9, Lick 13 dim. N only? Mean B(0) = 12.87. Source A, C discordant (resid.: -0.33 (A), +0.45 (C)).

6493-A See Ap.J., 82, 74, 1935 (dim.: 1'6 x 0'7). = N 6491 ? w. NGC coord. corrected. It is 3'1 nf N 6493 (SA(r)0⁺)
        and not np. Anony. faint SB(s)d at 4'5 np N 6493.

6500, 6501 Pair at 2'3 in a small group. Heid 9 dim. rejected.

6503 vsvBN, v. many knotty B arms in lens, vF out. extens. Heid 9, Lick 13 dim. for B part only.
      <u>Spectr.</u> Lick Bull., 497, 1939. Ap.J., 135, 698, 1962.
      <u>Rot.</u> Ap.J., 97, 117, 1943 = MWC 674.

6555 = Ho 774a. (Ho 774b at 1'8 is a dble *). sBN or bar: 0'15 x 0'05, pseudo (r): 0'4 x 0'25, sev. B knotty
      branch. arms, poor. res. Lund 6 dim. for B part only.

6570 B bar: 0'3 x 0'1, sev. knotty arms, strong asym., a miniature of LMC. Heid 9 dim. for B part only.

6574 sB diff. N or bulge, sev. mass. knotty arms w. some branch., poor. res. Heid 9 dim. for B part only.

6587 Class. uncertain, poss. E 5?

6621-2 = VV 247. <u>Photo., spectr. vel.</u> Ap. J., 138, 873, 1963.

6627 Weak. sBN, bar: 0'5. Heid 9 dim., N only.

6643 vsBN, v. many knotty arms, pseudo (r): 0'9 x 0'5. <u>Mag.</u>: Ap.J., 85, 325, 1937. <u>Spectr.</u> Ap.J., 135, 698, 1962.

6651 <u>Mag.</u>: Ap.J., 85, 325, 1937.

6654 svB diff. N in B bar, 2 main vF spir. arms form pseudo (R): 1'85 x 1'3. <u>Mag.</u>: Ap.J., 85, 325, 1937.

6654-A See Ap.J., 82, 74, 1935; 85, 325, 1937. Anon. Sm of v. low surf. br. at 2'5 np.

6658 vBN, smooth diamond-shaped lens. P(a) w. N 6661 at 9'6. Misidentif. as N 6661 by Bigay (1951). Heid 9 dim.
      for lens only.

6661 = 6660. B diff. N or bulge in lens: 0'65 x 0'4, traces of whorls and dk. lanes in envel. P(a) w. N 6658 at
      9'6. Misident. as N 6658 by Bigay (1951). Heid 9 dim. for lens only.

6667 <u>Mag.</u>: Ap.J., 85, 325, 1937.

6674 vBN in B bar: 0'5 x 0'17, (r): 0'9 x 0'6, sev. filam., F branch. arms w. some knots, low surf. bright. Heid. 9
      dim. (0'2? x 0'2?) rej., N only.

6684 BN, (r): 1'2 x 0'8. Note revis. of Mt. Stromlo (1956) class.

6684-A vF, no BN. Dim. for B part only.

6690 BM no def. N, F, v. poor. res. <u>Mag.</u>: Ap.J., 85, 325, 1937.

6699 sBN. See also HB 914, 7, 1940.

6702 Heid. 9 dim. (0'2 x 0'2) rej., N only. Mt. W. early vel. +2250 (1931) refers to N 6703 (see A.J., 61, 97, 1956).

6703 BN, nearly uniform disk. <u>Desc.</u>: Ap.J., 46, 49, 1917; 51, 30, 1920. Heid. 9 dim. (0'3 x 0'3) rej., N only?
      Class. uncertain, poss. SA(r)0⁺?

6707 P. w. N 7608 at 6'. <u>Desc.</u>: M.N., 81, 601, 1921 (dim.: 3' x 1'); 110, 436, 1950.

6721 sBN, vs * att. 0'2 sf.

6744 B diff. N in weak bar: 2'0 x 0'4, F broken (r): 3'2 x 1'9, sev. filam., part. res. arms. F outlying irreg.
      cloud: 1'6 x 0'4 np 10'5 at end of vF anomal. arm. See also M.N., 81, 601, 1921; HB 914, 7, 1940. HA 88,2 dim.
      (9'0 x 9'0: ser. a) much too small rej. Upsala 21 dim. (10' x 6') for B part only.
      <u>Photom.</u> M.N., 112, 606, 1952. Ap.J., 138, 934, 1963.
      <u>Radio emiss.</u> Hdb.d.Phys., vol. 53, 253, 1959.

6753 vBvsN in vB smooth (r): 0'32 x 0'24, B inner part. w. sev. knotty poor. res. arms, B knotty (R): 2'0 x 1'6. S.
      anon. Sp 5'9 sf and 12' sf. Similar to M 94. Note corr. to (r) dim. of Mt. Stromlo (1956) survey.
      <u>Photo.</u> P.N.A.S., 26, 34, 1940.

6754 s not BN, pseudo (r): 1'1 x 0'35; P(a) w. SAB0⁻ (0'2 x 0'15) at 1'2.

6761 sBN, (r): 0'85 x 0'95. Poor. res.

6769 P(b) w. N 6770 at 1'9, P(a) w. N 6771 at 3'5. vB diff. N in narrow incompl. (r): 0'6 x 0'45 in lens 0'7 x 0'5,
      sev. filam. arms w. knots. Linked to N 6770. HA 88,2 class. (E:) is erroneous.
      <u>Mass of group,</u> A.J., 66, 544, 1961.

N 6770 P(b) w. 6769 at 1'9, P(a) w. N 6771 at 3'2. vBN on weak smooth bar w. F inner blobs, pseudo incompl. (r): 0'9: x 0'85, 2 main arms, one forms straight link to N 6769, vF out. whorls. For ref. see N 6769.

6771 P(a) w. N 6769 at 3'5, N 6770 at 3'2. vBN, (r): 0'9 x 0'2, w. inner dk. matt. on one side, vF rings. For ref. see N 6769.

6776 vBN, * 0'4 np. Note corr. to HA 88,2 and NGC RA (see Mem. Commonw. Obs. No 13, 1956).

6776-A Elong. knot 0'4 p N; poss. SBm on edge ? * 0'3 n N.

6780 sBN, pseudo (r): 0'65 x 0'4. Similar to M 101 but more reg.

6782 vBN, vF (R): 1'8 x 1'3.

6796 Mag.: Ap.J., 82, 325, 1937.

6808 sBN, B(r): 0'6 x 0'25, asym. arm. Note rev. of Mt. Stromlo (1956) class.

6810 vBN, dk. lane? P. w. large vF, anon. gal. 12' sp.

6814 vsvBN in weak diff. bar, sev. knotty arms form pseudo (r): 0'75 x 0'75, weak out parts. Heid 9 dim. for B part only.

6821 B bar: 0'2 x 0'06, no def. N, F asym. spir. struct., poor. res. Heid 9 dim. for B part only.

6822 In local group. Mt. W. vel. for I 1308 (emiss. neb. in object): + 102 km/sec. Lick (1962) vel. for 2 objects without emiss., probably glob. clusters.
Monog., photo. M.N., 82, 489, 1922. Ap.J., 62, 409, 1925 = MWC 304. B.A.N., 15, 308, 1961.
Photom. Medd. Lund, I, 175, 1950: II, 128, 1950.
HII reg. Observatory, 79, 54, 1959. Zs.f.Ap., 50, 168, 1960.
Radio emiss. M.N., 123, 279, 1961.
HI emiss. B.A.N., 15, 307, 1961. A.J., 68, 274, 1963.

6824 vBN or bulge, 2 main B arms, v. poor. res. Heid 9 dim. for B part only.

6835 BN, 2 main B inner arms seen almost edgewise; v. poor. res. P(a) w. N 6836 at 7'5. SN 1962, IAU Circ. 1806, 1962. L'Astronomie, 76, 392, 1962.

6836 BM no BN, vF spir. arms or arcs, v. poor. res., low surf. bright. P(a) w. N 6835 at 7'5.

6850 sBN; v. poor. res.

6851 vBN, class. uncertain, poss. SAO⁻?

6851-A, B Pair of F anon. at 1'5.

6854 vsBN, s * 0'15 np N; vs B anon. gal. (1'4 x 0'9) at 1'9 nf.

6861 = I 4949. vBN or lens 1'1 x 0'45, * 0'7 np. In group w. N 6868, 6870 and others. Class. uncertain, poss. SAO⁻?

6861-D, E, F In group w. N 6861, 68, 70 etc., see Mem. Com. Obs. No 13, 1956.

6868 In Group. P(a) w. N 6870 at 6'3. BN.

6870 In group. P(a) w. N 6868 at 6'3. sBN, v. poor. res.

6872 P(b) w. I 4970 at 1'1 n. vBN, weak narrow bar: 0'6 x 0'5, pseudo (r): 0'8 x 0'65, 2 main reg. narrow arms w. vF distorted extens., one diverging away from I 4970. See also M.N., 81, 601, 1921.

6875 vBN, * 3' sf.

6875-A No BN. Spindle, diff. to class. At ~ 19' of N 6875.

6876 vB cent., smooth neb., * 0'5 s. P(a) w. N 6877 at 1'45, I 4971 at 4'5, N 6872 at 9'.

6877 vB cent., no struct. Poss. SO? P(a) w. N 6876 at 1'45.

6878 B diff. N, 2 reg. arms; similar to M 81. Sev. other gal. in field. P(a) w. anon. SAO⁻ (0'6 x 0'2) at 6'8.

6878-A F, poor. res., (r): 0'6 x 0'4. At 18' of N 6878.

6880 svBN, vF bar? traces of (s) struct., * 0'35 np. P. w. I 4981 at 1'1.

6887 F, BM no BN, poor. res. See also M.N., 81, 602, 1921.

6890 vsBN in B inner lens w. 2 main poor. res. arms, pseudo (r): 0'5 x 0'3, out. part has fairly sharp edge w. traces of spir. struct. forming pseudo (R): 0'95 x 0'65. HA 88,2 class. (E:) is erroneous.

6893 eBN in B lens: 0'85 x 0'5 w. dk. crescent, fairly B envel. Close pair of anon. S, SO at 19' sf. HA 88,2 dim. for B part only.

6902 vBN, F bar, (r): 0'7 x 0'6, F out. arms. Helwan 38 dim. for B part only. See also M.N., 81, 601, 1921; 110, 436, 1950.

N 6906 BN, (r): 0'8: x 0'3:, 2 main arms, v. poor. res., class. uncertain. P(a) w. I 5000 at 18'. Desc.: Ap.J., 51, 301, 1920.

6907 = 6908. vsBN in B inner lens, strong bar or lens: 0'85 x 0'4, w. dk. lanes, 2 main knotty arms, slightly asym. Similar to N 1097. Drawing: Helwan 9.

6909 BN, 3 * 0'6 p N. See also M.N., 81, 601, 1921. HA 88,2 dim. for B part only.

6915 BN, vF bar, (r): 0'3: x 0'2:; dim. of B part on Crossley 36-in. pl.: 0'4 x 0'3.

6921 P. w. vF anon. S at 1'5. Heid. 9 dim. (0'3? x 0'3?) rej.

6923 H.A. 88,2 dim.: 2'0: x 1'0: (ser. a').

6925 B diff. N in B bulge, sev. filam. knotty arms w. some branch. Drawing: Helwan 9.

6927-A Anon. at 2'0 sp N 6927 (See Humason et. al., 1956). In N 6928 group.

6928 Brightest in group. P(a) w. N 6930 at 3'7. B bar w. dk. lanes, 2 main arms, some knots, pseudo (R): 1'5 x 0'35. Desc. Ap.J., 51, 301, 1920.

6930 In N 6928 group. P(a) w. N 6928 at 3'7. sBN in B lens or bar. F arms, poor. res. Desc.: Ap.J., 51, 302, 1920. Mag. and colors reduced as Sb.

6935 sBN, vF bar, (r): 0'7 x 0'65, vF out. arms. P(a) w. N 6937 at 4'5. HA 88,2 dim. for B part (r) only. Desc., Photo. M.N., 82, 490, 1922. P.N.A.S., 26, 34, 1940.

6937 sBN, F bar, (r): 0'7 x 0'6. 3 main F knotty arms. P(a) w. N 6935 at 4'5. HA 88,2 dim. for B part (r) only. For ref. see 6935.

6943 sBN, poor. res. See also M.N., 81, 601, 1921.

6944 sBN. Heid. 9 dim. (0'3? x 0'3?) rej., N only? P. w. 6944-A at 6'5.

6944-A P. w. 6944 at 6'5. vsBN.

6946 esBN, hexag. pseudo (r): 2'4 x 2'2, 3 or 4 main mass. part. res. arms w. m. branch., low surf. bright. Poss. membership in Local Group not confirmed. Mt. W. vel. for emiss. patch 4'1 nf N: + 222 km/sec; Lick 1956 vel. for 2 emiss. patches: + 221 km/sec.
Photo. P.A.S.P., 60, 266, 1948; 61, 98, 1949.
Dist. P.A.S.P., 50, 238, 1938.
Radio emiss. M.N., 122, 479, 1961.
HI emiss. Epstein, Harvard Thesis, 1962.
SN 1917, P.A.S.P., 29, 211, 1917. Ap.J., 88, 294, 1938; 89, 195, 1938.
SN 1939, Ap.J., 96, 28, 1942. L'Astronomie, 55, 159, 1941.
SN 1948, P.A.S.P., 60, 266, 1948; 61, 97, 1949. H.B. 919, 26, 1949.

6951 = 6952. eBN w. innermost (r) and esN, broad bar: 1'2 x 0'3 in lens 2'3 x 1'4, 3 main part. res. arms w. some branch. Mag. Ap.J., 85, 325, 1937.

6958 vBN, * 0'7 n. HA 88,2 dim. for B part only.

6962 Brightest and largest of a dense group. B diff. N in sh. diff. B bar 0'4 x 0'2, vF (r): 0'7 x 0'5, 2 main F. out. arms w. some knots form pseudo (R): 2'4 x 1'7. P(a) w. N 6964 at 1'9. Heid 9 dim. for N or bar only.

6963, 6964 In N 6962 group.

6970 B, sBN, (r): 0'4 x 0'3.

6982 vs * 0'1 n, * 1'1 n. P. w. N 6984 at 6'.

6984 (r): 0'35 x 0'25, Asym.; B * 1'3 f. P. w. N 6982 at 6'. Note revis. of Mt. Stromlo (1956) class.

7013 B diff. N w. dk. lane, (r): 0'8 x 0'2, poor. res. Poss. SAB?

7020 vBN, (r): 1'1 x 0'4, (R): 2'65 x 1'25.

7029 eBN, vB diff. cent., smooth neb., F anon. Spir. at 6'5 ssf.

7038 F, vsBN, poor. res. See also M.N., 81, 601, 1921.

7041 Poor. resolv., classif. uncertain; poss. SAab not res.? HA 88,2 dim. (0'8 x 0'4: ser. a') for B part only.

7049 vBN, * att. 0'3 np. Dk. crescent in B lens: 0'8 x 0'5. HA 88,2 dim. for lens only.
Photo. M.N., 112, 606, 1952.

7059 B diff. N w. dk. lanes, weak pseudo (r): 1'4 x 0'6:, 2 main knotty F arms. See also M.N., 81, 601, 1921.

7064 B cent. part (bar?): 2'0 x 0'2 w. some knots, 2 main arms.

7065 (r): 0'4 x 0'4, * on bar near N. P. w. N 7065-A at 4'1 sf. Heid 9 dim. rej., N only.

7065-A P. w. N 7065 at 4'1. vsBN isolated in incompl. (r): 0'5: x 0'4.

N 7070   P(a) w. N 7070-A at 21' nf, N 7072 at 4'5 ssf.   sBN 2 main knotty arms w. m. branch.   Similar to M 33.

7070-A   P(a) w. N 7070 at 21'.   Poss. S0p.   Dk. lanes.

7072   P(a) w. N 7070 at 4'5, N 7072-A at 3'6 ssp.   sB cent., sev. B knotty arms.   Poss. SBm.

7072-A   P(a) w. N 7072 at 3'6.   Poor. res.

7079   vB elong. N tilted on B cigar-shaped bar: 0'55 x 0'25, traces of struct. in B lens: 1'4 x 0'8, vF envel.   HA 88,2 dim. (0'5: 0'5: ser. a') for N only.

7083   sB diff. N, sev. knotty filam. arms w. dk. lanes.   See also M.N., 81, 601, 1921.

7090   B complex cent. part. w. dk. lane on one side, smooth out. parts, slightly asym.; diff. to classif. poss. SB(s)m, after Sersic (Rev. Ast. 1957).   Photom. Revista Ast., XXIX, II, 1957.

7096   Dk. crescent?   Poor. res. Dble * 1'4 nf; F anon. 1'2 n.

7097, 7097-A   Pair at 5'9.

7098   vBN, F broad diff. bar: 1'4 x 0'8 w. blobs, F(r): 2'05 x 1'1 in lens: 2'4 x 1'2, vF out. whorls or (R): 3'8 x 1'9.   See also M.N., 81, 601, 1921.

7102   sBN, broad bar, pseudo (r): 0'7 x 0'55, F, poor. res.

7107   Poor. res.   See M.N., 81, 601, 1921.

7119-A, B   Pair in contact, cent. of B at 0'25 sp of A.   Perhaps optical?   Other small gal. in field.   A: vsBN, pseudo (r): 0'2 x 0'12, sev. B knotty arms, poor. res.; B: B part structureless. m_H for both components.

7124   sBN in smooth bar: 0'5 x 0'08, (r): 0'7 x 0'3.   2 main filam. arms w. some knots, slightly asym.   See also M.N., 81, 601, 1921.

7125   sh. vB bar: 0'24 x 0'08 in pseudo (r): 0'6 x 0'4, 2 main filam. knotty arms w. m. branch.   See also M.N., 81, 601, 1921.   P(a) w. N 7126 at 6'3, and anon. SB(rs) at 6'5 s.

7126   vsBN in B cent. part: 0'65 x 0'35 w. spir. struct., 2 main F reg. knotty arms.   Note corr. to erroneous class. in Mt. Stromlo (1956) survey.   P(a) w. N 7125 at 6'3.

7135   B diff. N in fairly B asym. coma extend. 0'8 in sp dir. w. s. condens.; long thin comet-tail extens.   2'6 in nf dir.   Sev. s. gal. in field but no interact. compan.   Distant P. w. I 5135 at 18'.   A very strange object.

7137   svBN, 3 main knotty B arms w. branch., pseudo (r): 0'25.   Heid 9 dim. for B part only.

7141   See M.N., 81, 601, 1921.

7144   vB diff. cent., smooth struct. * 1'7 np, * 1'7 sp.   P(a) w. N 7145 at 23'5.   HA 88,2 dim. (0'5: x 0'5:, ser. a') much too small, N only?

7145   vB cent., * 0'9 sf.   P(a) w. N 7144 at 23'5.   HA 88,2 dim. (0'5: x 0'5:, ser. a') much too small, N only?

7155   Bar: 0'9, w. s *, vF (r): 1'1 x 1'1.   HA 88,4 dim. inconsistent, minor dim. (0'7) too small.

7156   sBN, pseudo (r): 0'3 x 0'25, sev. F filam. branch. arms.   Similar to M 101.   All dim. for B part only.

7162   BM, no BN, sev. filam. knotty arms.   P(a) w. N 7162-A at 14'5 nf, N 7166 at 11'0.   See also M.N., 81, 601, 1921.

7162-A   Sh. not vB bar: 0'5 x 0'12, sev. filam. knotty arms.   P(a) w. N 7162 at 14'5.   Mt. Stromlo (1956) dim. for B part only.

7163   In N 7163-7176 group.

7166   eBN: 0'35 x 0'24 in B diff. lens: 1'2 x 0'4, F envel.   P(a) w. N 7162 at 11'0.   HA 88,2 dim. for lens only.

7168   B diff. N, smooth struct.   P(a) w. anon EO? (0'4 x 0'4) at 3'0 sf.   Listed by error as I 5152-A in Mem. Commonwealth Obs., III, 13, 1956, Table III.

7171   sBN in weak diff. bar, pseudo (r): 0'65 x ?, 2 main knotty arms w. m. branch.   P(a) w. I 1417 at 12'3.   Radio S. (?), Poss. ident. (unconfirmed); Aust.J.Phys., 11, 360, 1958.

7172, 7174   In N 7163-7176 group.

7177   eBN, smooth (r): 0'5 x 0'3 in lens: 1'3 x 0'8, many filam. knotty arms.   Heid 9 dim. for B part only.   Desc. Ap.J., 46, 54, 1917.   SN 1960, P.A.S.P., 73, 175, 1961.

7179   sBN, weak ansae. class. uncertain.   See also M.N., 81, 602, 1921.

7180   Spindle, classif. doubtful.

7184   vBsN in B broad diff. bar w. dk. lane, (r): 1'65 x 0'4, many knotty filam. arms w. branch.

7191   Stromlo dim. for B part only.   Class. uncertain. s * att.

N 7196 vBN, vF out. envel.?, * 0'6 f. P. w. vs B gal. 1'2 nf.

7205 sB diff. N, 2 main mass. B knotty arms w. dk. lanes and emiss. obj. P(a) w. N 7205-A at 8'5 p.

7205-A B cent., sev. knotty arms, asym., poor. res. P(a) w. N 7205 at 8'5.

7213 eBN, smooth tightly coiled arms. vF envel.: 1'9 x 1'7? Photo. M.N., 112, 606, 1952.

7214 P. w. I 5168 at 5'2.

7217 vB diff. N, B(r): 0'35 x 0'27, v. many knotty, tightly coiled arms in lens: 1'3 x 1'1, part. res. out. arms form
      (R): 2'5 x 2'1.
      Photo., photom. Hdb.d.Ap., 5, 2, 843, 1933. B.A.N., 16, 1, 1961.
      HII reg. Zs.f.Ap., 50, 168, 1960.

7218 B sh. bar: 0'3 x 0'1 w. FN, broad knotty (r): 0'8 x 0'4, sev. knotty arms, slightly asym.

7219 eBN, B(r): 0'3 x 0'2, (R): 1'25 x 0'85.

7232 (r): 0'55 x 0'1:. P(a) w. N 7233 at 2'. Note rev. of Mt. Stromlo (1956) class. and dim.

7232-A FN or no N in forsh. bar, pseudo (r): 0'7 x 0'1. Poor. res. 8'1 nnf I 5181.

7232-B vF, narrow bar, vF filam. arms. 5' nf N 7232.

7233 svBN, sh. B bar, F smooth arms. P(a) w. N 7232 at 2'. Note revis. of Mt. Stromlo (1956) class.

7236, 7237 Pair of distorted E or S0, at 30". Greenstein (1962) from 200 −in. photog. has dim. of 7236: 10", of
      7237: 60". Heid. 9 dim. rejected. F anon. gal. 0'7 sf. Radio Source 3C442.
      For mag., vel., spectr., radio emiss. see Ap.J., 135, 679, 1962.

7240 In N 7242 group; uncertain identif. in Humason et. al. (1956); desc. in Heid. 9 confirms N 7242 is 3'8 nf.

7242 Brightest in group. = Ho 789a. Ho 789b at 0'5 may be a *. I 5195 3'5 ssf, N 7240 3'8 sp.

7248 Dim. B part on Lick 36-in. pl.: 0'5 x 0'2. N 7250 at 17'5.

7252 eBN in B lens: 0'5 x 0'4 w. traces of (r): 0'3 x 0'3, traces of F(R): 2'0 x 1'4.

7290 sBN, B knotty (r): 0'35 x 0'22, many filam. knotty arms w. m. branch. Similar to M 63. Heid 9 dim. for
      B part only.

7298 sBN, pseudo (r?): 0'2 x 0'2, 2 main knotty filam. arms w. branch. P(a) w. N 7300 at 11'3. Perhaps similar to
      M 101. Heid 9 dim. for B part only.

7300 sBN, pseudo (r): 0'55 x 0'2, 3 main smooth arms, poor. res. P(a) w. N 7298 at 11'3, N 7302 at 21'5.

7302 = I 5228. vsvBN, B inner lens: 0'3 x 0'2. P(a) w. N 7300 at 21'5. Heid 9 dim. for lens only.

7307 F, FN, poor. res. See M.N., 81, 601, 1921.

7309 vBN in smooth lens, pseudo (r): 0'35 x - , 3 main knotty arms w. F out. extens. and some branch.

7313 P. w. N 7314 at 4'3.

7314 esBN in forsh. bar, pseudo (r): 3'5 x 1'5, many knotty arms. P. w. N 7313 at 4'3. Helwan 9, HA 88,2 dim. for
      B part only.

7317 = Ho 792d. Stephan's Quintet.
      Photo. Hdb.d.Phys., vol. 53, 381, 1959. Ap.J., 130, 15, 1959; 134, 244, 1961.
      Dyn., mass, Ap.J., 130, 15, 1959; 134, 244, 1961. A.J., 66, 542, 1962.

7318-A, B = Ho 792c. Col. pair. In Stephan's Quintet. A projects on arm of B; B is distorted. For ref. see N
      7317. B mag. (source C) for both comp.

7319 = Ho 792b. In Stephan's Quintet. Asym. out. filam. reaching out to 2'2 from N. For ref. see N 7317. Lick 13,
      Heid 9, Lund 6 dim. for B part only.

7320 = Ho 792a. In Stephan's Quintet, but low rad. vel. makes phys. membership doubtful (See Ap.J., 134, 244, 1961),
      for ref. see N 7317.

7320-C At 4'1 nf N 7320. Outlying member of Stephan's group? (r): 0'4 x - .

7329 vBN, (r): 1'2 x 0'85, sev. filam. knotty arms. See also H.B., 914, 7, 1940.

7331 = Ho 795a. Brightest in a group of F objects. See Note to N 7333. Lund 6 dim. for B part only.
      Photo. Ap.J., 97, 114, 1943; 133, 892, 1961.
      Photom. Stockholm Ann., 13, No 8, 1941; 14, No 3, 1942. Ap.J., 104, 212, 1946.
      Spectr. Ap.J., 135, 699, 1962.
      Orient., Rot. Ap.J., 97, 117, 1943; 127, 487, 1958.
      Polar. Stockholm Ann., 19, No 1, 1956.
      HII reg. Zs.f.Ap., 50, 168, 1960.
      SN 1959, HAC, 1438, 1959. P.A.S.P., 72, 127, 208, 1960. Ap.J., 133, 869, 1961.

N 7332 = Ho 796a. P(a) w. N 7339 at 5'0. vB peanut-shaped cent. bulge: 0'7 x 0'4, strong flat comp.: 1'2 x 0'14, smooth neb.
Desc., photo. Ap.J., 130, 20, 1959. B.A.N., 16, 1, 1961.
Photom. B.A.N., 16, 1, 1961.

7333 = Ho 795i is a *. Misidentif. in Lick 13. N 7338, 25, 27, 26 (= Ho d, f, g, h) are also *.

7335 = Ho 795c. Redshift suggests poss. outlying member of Stephan's group?

7339 = Ho 796b. P(a) w. N 7332 at 5'0. B cent. bulge or lens w. knots and dk. mark.: 0'7 x 0'25, w. strong forsh. knotty spir. arms, nearly spindle. Lick 13, Lund 6 dim. for B part only.

7343 Uncertain redshift (Humason et. al., 1956). Identification is also uncertain, N 7343 is an SB(s)b with a bright, stellar nucleus, 22's, 20'f N 7331, the object observed at Mt. W. is listed as E3 and is either the nucleus or possibly a small anon. E3 gal. 10'n, 2'p N 7343.

7361 Note corr. to HA 88,2 and NGC RA (MWC 626) v. poor. res. asym.

7368 See M.N., 81, 602, 1921.

7371 = Ho 797a. (Ho 797b at 1'0 is a *). sBN in sh. lens or bar: 0'3 x 0'1, F(r): 0'75 x 0'75, eF (R): 2'9: x 2'9:. Lick 13, Lund 6, Heid 9 dim. for B part only.

7377 B diff. N in diff. bulge w. sev. spir. dk. lanes; somewhat similar to N 1316. HA 88,2 and 88,4 dim. for B part only.

7385, 7386 Pair at 6'. Dyn., mass, A.J., 66, 554, 1961.

7392 vsvBN, 2 main knotty arms w. dk. lanes; transition toward SAB.

7393 sBN in B bar: 0'22 x 0'06, pseudo (r): 0'4 x 0'35, F out. arms. Lick 13, Heid 9 dim. for B part only.

7408 Desc.: HB 777, 1922. M.N., 110, 437, 1950.

7410 B diff. N, B lens w. bar and some spir. struct., v. poor. res.

7412 sBN, bar: 0'85, pseudo (r): 1'3 x 1'2, vB * 6' nnf.

7412-A F, asym.; poss. SBm on edge?

7416 vsBN, B bar w. dk. lane, (r): 1'2 x 0'35, 2 F reg. arms w. dk. lanes.

7418 svBN, vF bar, pseudo (r): 0'85 x 0'7, 2 main knotty filam. branch. arms. See also H.B., 914, 7, 1940. Drawing: Helwan 9. P(a) w. N 7421 at 19'5.

7418-A vsBN, vF arms, classif. doubtful. at 16' nf N 7418. Stromlo dim. for B part only.

7421 sB diff. N, narrow B bar, (r): 0'8 x 0'55, 3 main smooth arms. P(a) w. N 7418 at 19'5. See also H.B., 914, 7, 1940. Drawing: Helwan 9. Photom. Revista Ast., XXIX, 1957.

7424 sB elong. diff. N: 0'2 x 0'12 in sh. diff. bar: 0'6 x 0'3, pseudo (r): 1'2 x - , 2 main part. res. filam. arms w. m. branch. Similar to M 101. Low surf. bright.; Lund 7, 10 dim. for B part only.

7448 svBN in B knotty pseudo (r): 0'35 x 0'2, sev. B knotty spir. arms, high surf. bright., sharp outline.

7454 svB diff. N. P. w. anon. SB(s)c at 1'7. Heid 9 dim. for B part only. Photom. M.N., 98, 620, 1938.

7456 F, not well res., * 1'3 ssp. N.

7457 vsBN, smooth neb. w. v. weak traces of zones or arcs. P. w. small anon. spindle at 8'. Heid 9, Lick 13 dim. for lens only.

7462 Almost spindle, bar: 1'1 x - , B * 1'2 p N. See also M.N., 81, 602, 1921. HA 88,2 minor dim. (after Helwan) is excessive.

7463, 7464, 7465 = Ho 802a, c, b. 7465: SN 1950, IAU Circ. 1348.

7469 = Ho 803a. P(a) w. I 5283 at 1'3 nf (= Ho 803b? with $\Delta \alpha$, $\Delta \delta$ of opposite sign). eBN, pseudo (r): 0'35 x 0'22, F out. whorls form pseudo (R): 1'2 x 0'85. Isol., detached arms. Heid 9, Lund 6 dim. for B part only.
Photo. Ap.J., 137, 1023, 1963.
Spectr. Ap.J., 97, 28, 1943. Broad em. lines in N.
Rot., mass, Ap.J., 137, 1023, 1963.

7479 vsBN in bar: 1'6 x 0'3 w. strong dk. lanes, 2 main arms, part. res., one stronger, pseudo (r?): 2'5 x 2'1. Heid 9 minor dim. (0'3) rej., bar only.
Photo. Ap.J., 64, 326, 1926; 132, 654, 1960.
Spectr. IAU Symp., 5, 1958 = Lick Cont. II, 81, 1958. Ap.J., 132, 654, 1960; 135, 698, 1962.
Rot., mass, Ap.J., 132, 654, 1960. A.J., 65, 342, 1960.

7496 svBN, bar: 1'2 x - , elong. B patch in one arm, * 1'8 n N. See also M.N., 81, 602, 1921. HA 88,2 dim. for B part only.

7496-A Poor. res., classif. doubtful, Mt. Stromlo dim. for B part only.

N 7499, 7501, 7503 Triple system w. many F gal. in field. (Pegasus II cl.).

7507 P(a) w. N 7513 at 18'.

7513 P(a) w. N 7507 at 18'.

7531 B diff. N in vB (r): 0'95 x 0'4, w. dk. lanes, sev. F filam., part. res. arms. HA 88,2 dim. (1'5: x 0'5:, ser. a') for B part only.

7537 = Ho 805b. P(a) w. N 7541 at 2'7. v. poor. res. Lund 6 dim. for B part only.

7541 = N 7581, = Ho 805a. P(a) w. N 7537 at 2'7. B narrow bar: 0'55 x 0'5, many knotty filam. arms w. dk. lanes, poor. res.

7552 = I 5294. eBN in B complex bar and lens: 1'8 x 0'35, w. dk. lane, 2 smooth reg. arms w. few B knots form pseudo (R): 3'0 x 2'4.

7562 P(a) w. N 7557, E ? at 4'5 np. Heid 9 dim. (0'45 x 0'3) rej., N only.

7562-A Spindle at 2'3 sf N 7562.

7576 eBN in B lens: 0'35 x 0'3, F(r): 0'7 x 0'55. P. w. N 7585 at 10'7. Heid 9 dim. for lens only.

7582 In group w. N 7590, 7599. P(a) w. N 7590 at 9'5, N 7599 at 13'. vsBN in B complex lens and bar: 2'7 x 0'7, w. dk. lanes, 2 F smooth reg. arms form pseudo (R): 4'4 x 1'75. See also M.N., 81, 602, 1921. Photo. P.N.A.S., 26, 33, 1940.

7585 B diff. N in B bulge or lens: 0'8 x 0'55, w. traces of dk. lane, single smooth arm or loop forms pseudo (R): 1'95 x 1'7: in F envel. P(a) w. N 7576 at 10'7.

7590 In group w. N 7582, 7599. P(a) w. N 7599 at 4'9. vB inner part: 1'0 x 0'4, sev. B knotty arms. B * 1'1 nf. Photo. P.N.A.S., 26, 33, 1940.

7592 Colliding pair, 2 N 0'25 apart.

7599 In group w. N 7582, 7590. P(a) w. N 7590 at 4'9. vs not vB N, many reg. knotty arms w. some branch., dk. lane on one side. See also M.N., 81, 601, 1921. Photo. P.N.A.S., 26, 33, 1940.

7600 svBN in B diff. lens: 0'6 x 0'2. Poss. E$^+$ 6. Heid. 9 dim.: 1'6 x 0'3.

7606 B diff. N in smooth cent. part. w. dk. lane, 2 main filam. arms, w. some knots and branch.

7611, 7615, 7617, 7619, 7623, 7626, 7631 N 7619 brightest of group (Pegasus I cl.).
Desc. Ap.J., 51, 304, 1920.
Dyn., mass, Ap.J., 134, 262, 1961. A.J., 66, 545, 1961.

7625 sB complex N in B(r): 0'22 x 0'17, complex lens w. strong asym. dk. lane; v. pec. object. Heid 9 dim. for B part only. Yerkes 1 class. (1958).: or F ? "turbulent E w. dust".

7640 No def. N, BM, forsh. bar: 1'7 x 0'3 w. dk. lanes, well res. arms w. F out. extens., slightly asym. Heid 9 dim. for B part only. Spectr. IAU Symp., 5, 1958 = Lick Cont., II, 81, 1958. Ap.J., 135, 696, 1962.

7671, 7672 P(a) at 6'.

7678 svBN, pseudo (r): 0'4 x - , 2 main filam. knotty arms w. some branch., poor. res.

7679 eBN in F lens: 0'5 x 0'5 w. dk. matt. or F(r), F bar or tidal extens. P(a)? w. N 7682 at 4'5. Heid 9 dim. for lens only.

7682 Bar: 0'6, sBN, (r): 0'8. P(b)? w. N 7679 at 4'5. Not found in Heid 9 is an error; see Ap.J., 91, 350, 1940 = MWC 626.

7685 Identif. doubtful. vF.

7689 vsBN in weak pseudo (r): 0'25 x 0'2, sev. B knotty arms, v. sharp outline. Similar to M 101.

7690 vsvBN in (r): 0'24 x 0'12, surrounding spir. struct. v. poor. res., class uncertain. Mt. Stromlo 74-in. dim. for B part only.

7702 eBN in B (r): 1'0 x 0'45, brighter near ansae in lens: 1'2 x 0'55, eF out. (R): 2'2 x 1'4:.

7713 BM, no BN, knots in arms. P. w. N 7713-A at 19'. Class. uncertain, poss. SA?

7713-A P. w. N 7713 at 19'. poor. res., class. uncertain.

7714 = Ho 810a. P(b) w. N 7715 at 1'9. eBN, B distorted knotty lens 0'8 x 0'8, one main smooth arm or loop; outer extens., one link w. N 7715. Lund 6, Heid 9 dim. for lens only. Spectr. IAU Symp., 5, 1958 = Lick Cont. II, 82, 1958.

7715 = Ho 810b. P(b) w. N 7714 at 1'9. F cent. part: 0'3 x 0'1, narrow knotty extens., knotty link w. 7714. Lund 6, Heid 9 dim. for B part only. Spectr. IAU Symp., 5, 1958 = Lick Cont. II, 81, 1958.

7716 vBN, vF bar, B(r): 0'45 x 0'3, sev. F narrow filam. arms w. some branch. One aberr. val. B-V (source C) rej.

N 7721 = Ho 812a. (Ho 812b at 2' is a *). vsBN, sev. filam. knotty branch. arms, poor. res. Lick 13, Helwan 9, 15 dim. for B part only.

7723 svBN in B bar: 0'6 x 0'03, (r): 0'75 x 0'5, many knotty arms, pseudo (R): 2'4 x 1'6. Lick 13, Heid 9 dim. for B part only. Similar to N 6300. Desc. and Struct. Stockholm Ann., 19, No 2, 1956.

7727 vsB diff. N in smooth inner lens: 0'3 x 0'1, * or B knot superp.; vF smooth whcrls or arms. P(a) w. N 7724 SB(s)ab at 12'. Heid 9 dim. for B part only.

7741 B narrow bar: 0'8 x 0'2, w. dk. lanes, no BN, 2 mass., part. res. arms, one stronger. Heid 9 dim. for B part only. Interp. val. of B-V(0). Spectr. A.J., 68, 278, 1963 (Abst.).

7742 eBsN in B(r): 0'3 x 0'3, many poor. res. knotty arms, doubtful (R). Similar to N 6753. HA 88,2 classif. (E:) is erroneous. Spectr. Lick Obs. Bull., 497, 1939.

7743 vBN in sh. bar: 1'0 x 0'16, smooth arms at edge of lens: 1'9 x 1'65 form pseudo (r): 1'5 x 1'3, vF traces of (R): 3'9 x 2'7. Heid 9 dim. for lens only.

7744 = I 5348 ? sBN, B part or lens: 0'5 x 0'4. HA 88,4 dim. (0'7 x 0'4) for B part only.

7752 P(b) w. N 7753 at 2'0 (= Ho 816b?). vs and B, pec.; Lick 36-in. pl. dim.: 0'5 x 0'2. Note corr. to NGC Decl., 7752 is sp of 7753.

7753 = Ho 816a. P(b) w. N 7752 at 2'0. sBN, weak bar, (r): 0'6 x 0'4, asym. out. whorls.

7757 = Ho 817a. N 7756 at 4'5 (= Ho 817b) is a *. Similar to M 101.

7764 B complex bar: 0'5 x - , partly res. High surf. bright.

7764-A Interacting pair of Sp. and Irr. sp? + small EO comp. at 0'75 of Sp. (See Mem. R.A.S., 68, 72, 1961).

7769 = Ho 820c. P(a) w. N 7770 at 5', N 7771 at 5'4. eBN, pseudo (r): 0'75 x 0'55, F out. extens., eF(R) suspected. Heid 9, Lund 6 dim. for B part only. Mean B(0) = 13.12. Two discordant val., source C (resid.: +1.15, -0.33). Spectr. Lick Bull., 497, 1939.

7770 = Ho 820b. P. w. N 7769 at 5', N 7771 at 1'1.

7771 = Ho 820a. P. w. N 7769 at 5'4, N 7770 at 1'1. eB elong. core or N in B bar: 0'9 x - w. dk. lanes 2 smooth spir. arms. Lund 6, Heid 9 dim. for B part only.

7779 In N 7782 group.

7782 Brightest in group. sB diff. N, 2 main filam. knotty arms. Heid 9, Lick 13 dim. for B part only.

7785 Smooth N, no struct.

7793 vsvBN (or * ?) many irreg., part. res. arms w. branch. Helwan 9, 15 and Lund 7 dim. for B part only. Sd class. originally introduced by H. Shapley for this galaxy.
Photo. P.A.S.P., 53, 16, 1941. P.N.A.S., 26, 31, 1940.
Photom. H.B., 907, 1938.
HII reg. Zs.f.Ap., 50, 168, 1960.

7796 svBN.

7814 vB cent. bulge: 0'5 x 0'4, out. bulge: 2'0 x 1'2, strong thin (0'1) dk. lane seen edgewise w. secondary layer of dk. matt. Lick 13, Heid 9 dim. for B part only. Interp. val. of B-V(0).
Photo. Ritchey, L'Evolution de l'Astrophotographie ..., S.A.F., Paris, 1929. Pl. 22. Hdb.d.Ap. 5, 2, 843, 1933.
Photo., photom. Ap.J., 120, 444, 1954. B.A.N., 16, 1, 1961.

7817 Spindle, classif. uncertain.

I 10 Local Group? Mt. W. vel. for bright emiss. patch in sf part: -88 km/sec.
       Photo. P.A.S.P., 47, 317, 1935. A.J., 67, 432, 1962.
       Spectr. P.A.S.P., 53, 123, 1941.
       HI emiss. A.J., 66, 294, 1962; 67, 431, 1962. Harvard Radio Ast. Rep., 102, 1962. Epstein, Harvard Thesis 1962.

   79 Brightest in a group; see P.N.A.S., 26, 41, 1940.

  127 In group w. N 584, 586.

  167 In N 678-697 group.

  239 In N 1023 group. vsBN in smooth pseudo bar: 0'21 x 0'18, pseudo (r): 0'27 x - , 2 part. res. main arms w.
       branch., low surf. bright. Similar to M 101.

  342 vBN, weak pseudo (r): 4'1 x 3'7, extens. well res. arms; v. similar to M 101. See also HA 105, 229, 1937.
       Monog. H.B. 899, 16, 1935.
       Photo. Hubble, Realm of Neb., pl. 12, 1936. L'Astronomie, 50, 26, 1936.
       Spectr. A.J., 61, 97, 1956. Zwicky, Morph. Astro., 153, 1957.
       Radio emiss. P.A.S.P., 72, 368, 1960. M.N., 122, 479, 1961.
       HI emiss. A.J., 67, 313, 1962.

343, 346 In N 1371-1407 group.

  356 See HA, 105, 229, 1937.

  391 B, v. reg. arms.

  398 P(a) w. N 1726 at 17'5. B bar: 0'3 x 0'08, poor. res. Dim. for B part only.

  449 See HA, 105, 229, 1937.

  451 Note corr. to IC coord. (HA 105, 229, 1937) I 450 at 6'5 sp. Mag.: Ap.J., 85, 325, 1937.

  467 P(a) w. N 2336 at 20'. Poor. res., low surf. bright.

  469 Mag.: Ap.J., 85, 325, 1937.

  492 Weak, (r): 0'4 x - .

  511 vBN, poor. def.; dim. for B part only. See also HA 105, 229, 1937.

  520 Misidentified as N 2646 in HA 88,2. sB diff. N, F whorls in lens. F smooth arms form pseudo (r): 0'7 x 0'6.
       See also HA 105, 229, 1937.

  529 See HA, 105, 229, 1937.

  694 Coll. pair P(c) w. N 3690.

749, 750 = Ho 313a, b. Pair at 3'3. See also HA, 105, 230, 1937.

  751 Pair w. I 752 at 4'2. See also HA, 105, 230, 1937.

  757 Mag.: Ap.J., 85, 325, 1937.

  764 FN, sev. F filam. arms w. some branch. Poss. SAB(rs).

  775 P. w. N 4267 at 14'5.

783, 783-A See Ap.J., 115, 284, 1952.

  794 mpg = 14.5 (1'44), 14.9 (1'), Bigay et. al., 1954.

  844 P(a) w. N 4936 at 12'7.

  982 vsBN. P. w. I 983 at 2'7, N 5490 at 10'5. Lund 9 dim. (0'3 x 0'2) rej., N only.

  983 sBN, bar: 0'5, (r): 0'9 x 0'6, weak arms. B * 1'5 sf. P. w. I 982 at 2'7. Lund 9 dim. (0'3 x 0'2) rej. N only.

 1029 Mag.: Ap.J., 85, 325, 1937. P(a) w. N 5676 at 26'5.

 1067 sBN, F(r): 0'6 x 0'5, sev. filam. arms, poor. res. P. w. I 1066 (S:) at 2'2. Dim. for B part only.

 1091 sBN, poor. res. P(a) w. N 5858 at 9'6. Dim. for B part only.

 1099 SN 1940, HAC 524, 1940. L'Astronomie, 55, 159, 1941.

 1131 P. w. N 5970 at 8'. sBN.

 1173, 1181-A, B, 1183, 1185, 1186, 1194 In Hercules Cluster.

 1182-4 In Hercules Cluster. Photo., spectr., vel. Ap.J., 138, 887, 1963.

 1237, 1248 Mag.: Ap.J., 85, 325, 1937.

I 1302 In a group. P. w. I 1303 at 9'5.

1303 P. w. I 1302 at 9'5. sBN, knotty branch. arms, poor. res.

1308 Emiss. neb. in N 6822.

1417 P(a) w. N 7171 at 12'3. Dim. for B part only.

1459 = I 5265. Photo., photom. M.N., 112, 606, 1952.

1554 Note corr. to IC coord. (Helwan 22, 38; dim.: 0'5 x 0'3).

1559 Close pair w. N 169. Lick 13 dim.: 0'3; Heid. 9: 0'3 x 0'2.

1563 = Ho 13b. P. w. N 191 at 0'8. Lund 6 dim.: 0'6 x 0'6.

1613 Local Group. Note corr. to IC coord. Asym., highly res., v. low surf. bright. HII rings and glob. clusters.
      Photo. Hubble, Realm of neb., pl. II, 1936. B.A.N., 15, 308, 1961.
      Photom. Medd. Lund, II, 128, 1950; I, 175, 1950.
      HII reg. Zs.f.Ap., 50, 168, 1960.
      Radio emiss. P.A.S.P., 72, 368, 1960. M.N., 123, 279, 1961.
      HI emiss. B.A.N., 15, 307, 1961.

1727 = Ho 46b (dim.: 3'5 x 1'5). P(b?) w. N 672 at 9'. No N, F knotty bar, magellanic type, well res., low surf.
      bright.; poss. distorted by N 672. Mt. W. vel. for emiss. patch in sf end.

1731 At ～ 30' of N 672, and 36' of I 1727.

1738 P(a) w. N 701 at 5'4. (r): 0'21 x 0'17; B part: 1'2 x 1'2.

1830 = Haro 18 (Boll. Tonantzintla, No 14, 1956).

1856 Lund 7 dim.: 0'9 x 0'3.

1913 F spindle: 1'5 long (Helwan 30).

1933 BM, poor. res., B * 0'6 s. In a group incl. I 1920, -28, -42, -46.

1953 No N, sh. bar, pseudo (r): 0'52 x 0'47, 3 main knotty arms form pseudo (R) or loop. low surf. bright.

1954 sBN or *, 2 main B mass. arms w. fainter clumpy out. parts. See also M.N., 81, 602, 1921.

1970 Class. uncertain, poor. res.; see also M.N., 81, 602, 1921.

2033 Class. uncertain; Stromlo 30-in., dim.: 0'7: x 0'25.

2035 H.A. 88,2 dim.: 0'6 x 0'6 (ser. a').

2038, 2039 Pair at 1'5. 2039: 0'45 x 0'35: w. neb. patch 0'4 p.

2056 B complex N, vF (R): 1'4 x 1'3; remark in HA 88,2 "poss. planetary" suggested by (R). It is definitely not a
      planetary. HA 88,2 dim. (0'6 x 0'6, ser. a') for N only.

2058 F spindle, class. uncertain.

2082 Pec. w. small comp. (coll. ?). In center of a cluster in Doradus.
      Photo., photom. Zs.f.Ap., 53, 256, 1961.
      Radio emiss. Hdb.d.Phys., vol. 53, 261, 1958. Aust.J.Phys., 14, 497, 1961.

2163 P(b) w. N 2207. For ref. see N 2207.

2174 vsBN, vF (R). P(a) w. N 2314 at 5'7.

2179 P. w. N 2347 at 13'2.

2200, 2200-A Pair at 1'4. I 2200: asym., * 0'6 nf. class. uncertain.

2209 P(a) w. N 2460 at 5'5. vsBN, (r): 0'33 x - . Others F gal. in field. Dim. for B part only.

2233 P(a) w. N 2537 at 19'. Desc.: Ap.J., 51, 308, 1920.

2363 Photo., SN 1961, P.A.S.P., 74, 215, 1962.

2389 In a group. P(a) w. N 2636 at 8'. 2 B mass. arms. See also H.A., 105, 229, 1937.

2522, 2523 Pair at 5'.

2537 sBN, pseudo (r): 0'5 x 0'5, sev. filam. arms w. knots and branch. Similar to N 300. Anon. gal. of v. low surf.
      bright at 16'.

I 2574 In M 81 group. v. low surf. bright., v. weak bar-like core: 4'5 x 1'0, 2 main well-res. arms. See also HA, 105,
229, 1937.
Photom. Medd. Lund II, 128, 1950.
HII reg. Zs.f.Ap., 50, 168, 1960.
HI emiss. Epstein, Harvard Thesis, 1962.

2584 Helwan 22 dim. (0'8 x -) rej., N only.

2587 sBN. Stromlo 13 dim. for B part only.

2604 At 13' of close pair N 3395-3396.

2627 sBN, 2 main B arms w. F out. extens. HA 88,2 dim. (2'0 x 2'0, after Helwan) for B part only.

2943 Lund 9 dim.: 0'3 x 0'3. See HA, 105, 230, 1937. P. w. N 3759 at 2'2.

2995 Forsh. bar, no def. N, 2 main branch. arms poor. res.

3155 = Ho 365b. Close pair w. N 4269 at 1'.

3258 Asym., highly res. arm, magellanic type? m_{pg} = 15.0 (1'44), 15.5 (1'), Bigay et. al., 1954.

3290 BN. Pair w. N 4373 at 2'0. Classif. uncertain.

3303 m_{pg} = 15.0 (1'44), 15.1 (1'), Bigay et. al., 1954.

3322-A At 19' sf N 4365.

3330 See HA, 105, 231, 1937.

3370 B N: 0'5 x 0'4.

3381 m_{pg} = 14.8 (1'44, 1'), Bigay et. al., 1954.

3393 m_{pg} = 15.1 (1'44), 15.4 (1'), Bigay et. al., 1954.

3457 m_{pg} = 15.8 (1'44), 16.5 (1'), Bigay et. al., 1954.

3475 B(0), B-V(0) for D(0) = 1'. Photo., dim.: A.J., 61, 72, 1956.

3476 Poss. Sm or Im.

3481, 3481-A Connected systems; see Erg.d.Exakten Naturwiss., 29, 356, 1956.

3483 Connected to I 3481, 3481-A, according to F. Zwicky, Erg., d.Exakten Naturwiss., 29, 356, 1956. Note large
differential rad. vel.

3522 Desc.: A.J., 61, 71, 1956.

3528 = Ho 421b? P(a) w. N 4540 at 1'5.

3583 No N. Part. res. core or bar: 1'4 x 0'4. F asym. out. extens. P. w. N 4569 at 6'0, poss. interacting.

3804 = N 4711 (Heid. 9). See also HA, 105, 231, 1937.

3896-A vF out. arms ? B * 0'6 s.

3900, 3946, 3949, 3960-A (0'5 nf I 3960), 4011, 4012, 4021, 4040, 4045. In Coma Cluster.

4051 In Coma Cl. SN 1950, P.A.S.P., 62, 117, 1950.

4182 Photo. Ap.J., 88, 285, 1938.
SN 1937, P.A.S.P., 49, 283, 1937; 50, 216, 1938. Ap.J., 88, 291, 412, 1938; 89, 156, 1939; 96, 28, 1942.
Zs.f.Ap., 14, 227, 1937. L'Astronomie, 55, 25, 1941. Hdb.d.Phys., vol. 51, 777, 780, 1958.

4237 sBN, (r): 0'5 x 0'45, F, poor. res. P(a) w. N 5314 at 10'7.
SN 1962, HAC 1574, July 1962. Announced by Haro in anonymous object.

4296 H.A. 88,2 dim.: 0'6 x 0'6 (ser. a'). Photom. M.N., 112, 606, 1952.

4327 P(a) w. I 4329 at 6'7. In I 4329 group. Poor. res., class. uncertain.

4329 P(a) w. I 4327 at 6'7; brightest in a group. Anon. Sa sp. at 3'1. BN: 0'7 x 0'6.

4351 BN in B bulge part. hidden by strong dk. lane on one side, poor. res.

4448 No BN, poor. res.

4653 See H.B. 914, 8, 1940.

4662 No N, B core part. res., sev. emiss. neb.; outlying neb. patch 1'4 sf. HA 88,2 dim. (1'3 x 0'9, a) for B part
only. Photo. P.N.A.S., 26, 35, 1940.

I 4662-A B * att. nf. classif. uncertain.

4710 Low surf. bright.

4717 BN, classif. uncertain; dim. for B part only.

4719 SN 1934, H.B., 907, 1938.

4720 No BN, BM, F out. parts. See also M.N., 81, 602, 1921. Classif. uncertain. P. w. I 4721 at 9'.

4721 vsBN, * or neb. knots in F arms. See also M.N., 81, 602, 1921. P. w. I 4720 at 9'.

4796 BN. P. w. I 4797 at 5'7.

4797 BN. P. w. I 4796 at 5'7.

4806 BN or * ? B * att. 0'2 sp. N.

4810 See M.N., 81, 602, 1921.

4820 F, classif. uncertain, dim. for B part only.

4829 B * 0'4 np.

4832 sBN, * 0'8 n.

4836 Bar: 0'8. Similar to N 4027.

4837 Not vEN, B sh. bar, poor. res. P. w. I 4839 at 3'6. HA 88,2 dim. (1'4 x 1'0 ser. a) for B part only.

4837-A BN, B * superp. Spindle.

4839 sBN, diff. bar, 2 main diff. arms. P. w. I 4837 at 3'6.

4840 Asym., dble?

4845 B * 0'3 sp N. Classif. uncertain.

4889 F * 0'1 from N.

4892 S * att. at s tip. Classif. doubtful.

4943 sBN, B * 1'0 n.

4960 2 * at n tip. Stromlo 13 dim. for B part only.

4970 vsB cent. * att. 0'1 f. P(b) w. N 6872 at 1'1.

4972 vsBN, v. poor. res., narrow dk. lane. P(a) w. N 6876 at 4'5.

4981 Asym., v. poor. res. appears connected to tip of N 6880, P(b) at 1'1.

5000 = I 1316 ? BN, B bar, (r): 0'6 x 0'35, sev. F filam. arms. P(a) w. N 6906 at 18'.

5052 No N, B, asym., extremely thin. See also M.N., 81, 602, 1921.

5063 sBN. Radio Source (?), poss. ident., Aust.J.Phys., 14, 497, 1961.

5105-A No BN, BM, 2 * superp. 0'6 np, 0'5 sf.

5105-B B, * 0'9 np.

5131 eBN in v. sh. B bar: 0'3 x - . P(a) w. I 5135 at 12'.

5135 Coll.? eB cent., incompl. pseudo (r): 0'4 x 0'3, 2 main curved streamers form pseudo (R): 1'0 x 1'0. P(a) w. I 5131 at 12' and F anon. spindle, poss. SBm, at 6'5 f. Distant P. w. N 7135 at 18'.

5152 Fairly B cent., well res., traces of resid. SA struct. HD 209142 (m_{pg} = 7.8) is 1'2 nf on edge of system. See also M.N., 81, 602, 1921.

5168 P. w. N 7214 at 5'2.

5179 Note corr. to IC RA (Helwan 38).

5181 Note corr. to HA 88,2 coord. (Mt. Stromlo Mem. 13), eBN, B smooth edge-on lens: 1'6 x 0'4. P(a) w. N 7232-A at 8'1.

5186 vsBN in B incompl. (r): 0'35 x 0'2, sev. B, poor. res. knotty arms. Interacting pair of small S at 11'8 np.

5201 sh. B knotty bar: 0'6 x 0'16, traces of pseudo (r): 1'6 x 1'2:, sev. filam. knotty arms, part. res. See also H.B., 914, 7, 1940. Rich cluster of F gal. at 12' np.

5240 sBN, bar: 1'2, (r): 1'2 x 0'8 w. 2 * on it.

I 5264 = Helwan 47. Note corr. to IC coord. (Helwan 9). P. w. I 1459 = I 5265 = Helwan 48.

5267 BN in B part: 1'6 x 1'35, vF out. whorls or (R).

5267-A Poor. res.

5267-B Spindle, * att.

5269 Note corr. to HA 88,2 coord. (Mt. Stromlo Mem. 13). It is sp of 2, not np as in IC. P. w. I 5270 at 11'.

5269-A, B, C Class. uncertain, poorly res. Dim. of 5269-C for B part only. (Mt. Stromlo Mem. 13).

5270 Note corr. to IC coord. (Mt. Stromlo Mem. 13). P. w. I 5269 at 11'.

5271 H.A. 88,2 dim.: 2'0: x 0'8: (ser. a').

5273 Note corr. to HA 88,2 and IC coord. (Mt. Stromlo Mem. 13). sBN, knotty pseudo (r): 0'85 x 0'55, sev. knotty branch. arms. Poor. res., class. uncertain.

5283 = Ho 803b with $\Delta\alpha$, $\Delta\delta$ of opposite sign. P. w. N 7469 at 1'3. Pec., vF out. arms? Lund 6 major dim. (0'3) was rejected. Photo., rad., vel., Ap.J., 137, 1023, 1963.

5325 sBN, B * 1'2 sp, * 1'3 f.

5328 B diff. N, smooth struct. Close pair w. I 5328-A at 0'75 sp. Classif. uncertain, poss. SO⁻? HA 88,4 dim. for B part only.

5328-A Close pair w. I 5328 at 0'75.

5328-B At 14' ssf I 5328.

5332 vsBN, many filam. knotty arms, low surf. bright. HA 88,2 dim. (4'0: x 4'0:) for B part only.

5342 Photo., SN 1961, P.A.S.P., 74, 215, 1962.

5381 At ~ 11' of N 7814.

A 0026   At 5'6 n, 9'5 p N 128; in a group.

0035   Zwicky Obj. in Sculptor. <u>Photo.</u> Applied Mech., Th. von Karman Anniv. vol., p. 137, Pl. II, 1941.

0045-A, B Two brightest members of a "chain" of galaxies near N 247. <u>Photo., spectr., vel.</u> Ap.J., 138, 884, 1963.

0046   = Haro 15, 23' nnp N 263. See Bol. Tonantzintla, No 14, 8, 1956.

0051   Small Magellanic Cloud. Local group. P(b) w. Large Mag. Cloud at 21°. Note corr. to HA 88,2 coord.
       <u>Monog.</u> and references to 1954: Suppl. Aust.J.Sci., 17, No 3, 1954.   B(∞) = 2.79 (Ap.J., 131, 574, 1960).
       <u>Reviews</u> and additional references to 1960: Trans. I.A.U., XI A, 292, 1961.
                                        to 1962: "Advances in Astron. and Astroph.", 1,   , 1963.
                                        to 1963: I.A.U. Symposium No 20 (Canberra).

0055   <u>SN 1939,</u> H.A.C., 518. Ap.J., 96, 28, 1942.

0058   Sculptor system; E dwarf in Local Group.
       <u>Photo., monog.</u> H.B., 908, 1, 1938. Nature, 142, 715, 1938. P.A.S.P., 51, 40, 1939. P.N.A.S., 25, 565, 1939.
       <u>Star counts,</u> A.J., 66, 384, 1962.

0103   = H.A. 88,2, New 1. F diff. bar: 0'55 x 0'14; hexag. pseudo (r): 1'05 x 0'9, sev. vF part. res. branch. arms,
       v. low surf. bright. H.A. 88,4 dim. (2'7 x 2'1) for B part only. P(a) w. anon. SB sp. at 4'0.

0118   <u>SN 1936,</u> P.A.S.P., 51, 36, 1939.

0143   Dwarf Magellanic. At 3'5 nf HD 10818; see H.B., 919, 41, 1941. Dim.: 5' x 3'; mag.: 13.3.

0218-A, B Zwicky obj. in And. P(b) at 1'4. <u>Photo.</u> Applied Mech., Th. von Karman Anniv. vol., p. 137, Pl. II, 1941.

0235   <u>SN 1938,</u> P.A.S.P., 51, 36, 1939. Ap.J., 96, 28, 1942. Hdb.d.Phys., vol. 51, 774, 1958. B.S.A.F., 55, 149, 1942.
       <u>Mag., color,</u> Pettit (1954).

0236   Brightest (np) of close pair of "disrupted galaxies" described by Zwicky (see Humason et.al., 1956).

0237   Fornax system. E dwarf in Local Group. N 1049 is a glob. cl. in it (Mt. W. vel.: - 71 km/sec; mag. and color:
       Pettit 1954).
       <u>Photo., monog.</u> Nature, 142, 715, 1938. P.A.S.P., 51, 42, 1939. P.N.A.S., 25, 565, 1939. A.J., 66, 250, 1961.
       <u>Star counts,</u> A.J., 66, 250, 1961.
       <u>Glob. Cl.</u> Ap.J., 120, 422, 1954. A.J., 66, 83, 1961.

0255   F, no BN, asym. See H.B., 914, 6, 1940; dim.: 6'0 x 0'8, mag.: 12.0:.

0438   See Humason et. al., 1956. <u>Mag., color,</u> Pettit 1954.

0509   From H.A., 85, No 6; mag.: 13.1.

0524   Large Magellanic Cloud. Local Group. P(b) w. Small Mag. cloud at 21°. Note corr. to HA 88,2 coord.
       <u>Monog.</u> and references to 1954: Suppl. Aust.J.Sci., 17, No 3, 1954.   B(∞) = 0.63 (Ap.J., 131, 574, 1960).
       <u>Reviews</u> and additional references to 1960: Trans. I.A.U., XI A, 292, 1961.
                                        to 1962: "Advances in Astron. and Astroph.", 1,   , 1963.
                                        to 1963: I.A.U. Symposium No 20 (Canberra).

0708   = VV 123. (Vorontsov-Velyaminov Catal., 1959).
       <u>Photo.</u> Ap.J., 130, 23, 1959; 138, 863, 1963.
       <u>U,B,V photom.</u> Ap.J., 138, 863, 1963.

0733   Zwicky obj. No 3. Bar: 0'5, (R): 1'2 x 1'1, overall dim.: 1'7 x 1'5 (Lick 36-in. pl.); similar to N 1291.

0814   = Holmberg II (1958). In M 81 Group. BM, v. irreg., well res., low surf. bright.
       <u>Photom.</u> Medd. Lund II, 128, 1950.
       <u>Spectr.</u> A.J., 61, 97, 1956.
       <u>HII reg.</u> Zs.f.Ap., 50, 168, 1960.
       <u>HI emiss.</u> Epstein, Harvard Thesis, 1962.

0909   = Holmberg III (1958). vsN ? in weak bar, 2 F well res. arms w. branch., v. low surf. bright. B mag. reduced
       w. mean Holmberg's color for type.

0916   See Humason et. al., 1956. Radio source Hydra A. <u>Radio emiss.</u> Cal. Inst. Tech. Radio Obs., No 5, 1960.

0936   = Holmberg I (1958). In M 81 Group ? Zwicky obj., see Phys. Review, 61, 499, 1942.
       <u>Photom.</u> Medd. Lund II, 128, 1950.

0937-A, B, C, D = VV 116. (Vorontsov-Velyaminov Catal., 1959).
       <u>Desc., photo.</u> Ap.J., 130, 23, 1959; 134, 249, 1961.
       <u>Dyn., vel., mass,</u> Ap.J., 134, 248, 1961. A.J., 66, 543, 1961.

0944-A, B = I 564, 563 ? in Zwicky's catalogue (1960). = Ho 143a, b. pair at 1'7.
       Dim.: 2'0 x 0'5, 1'0 x 0'4 (Lund 6).

0947   = Haro 22 (Bol. Tonantzintla, No 14, 7, 1956).

0953   See Humason et. al., 1956. Poss. radio source ?

A 0955-A, B Zwicky's connected gal. at 35"7.
    Photo. Hdb.d.Phys., vol. 53, 383, 1959.
    Mag., vel., mass, Ap.J., 132, 627, 1960.

0956 Zwicky Obj. Leo A.
    Photo. Sci. Monthly, 51, 400, 1940. Applied Mech., Th. von Karman Anniv. vol., p. 137, Pl. I, 1941.
    Mag., dist. Mt. Wilson Rep., 20, 1939-1940.

0957 Sextans B system. See F. Zwicky, Morph. Astr., p. 225, 1957.

1006 Harrington and Wilson No 1 (Leo I = Regulus system); E dwarf in Local Group. See P.A.S.P., 62, 118, 1950.
    Photo., photom., star counts, A.J., 68, 470, 1963.

1009 Sextans A system. Zwicky obj. Square center w. only traces of bar, well res. Mt. Wil. and Lick vel. (1956) for
    emiss. patch on SE edge of system. Mean B(0): 12.84; sources C and G discordant (resid.: + 0.63 (C), - 0.89 (G)).
    Photo. Sci. Monthly, 51, 398, 1940. Applied Mech., Th. von Karman Anniv. vol., p. 137, Pl. I, 1941.
        Phys. Review, 61, 499, 1942. Morph. Astr., p. 223, 1957.
    Mag., dist. Mt. Wilson Ann. Rep., 20, 1939-1940.
    HI emiss. Epstein, Harvard Thesis, 1962.

1101 Mayall's nebula.
    Photo. P.A.S.P., 53, 188, 1941. Ap.J., 119, 225, 1954.
    Spectr. P.A.S.P., 53, 188, 1941. A 4 type, no 3727 emiss.

1105-A, B Zwicky connected gal. at 22"2. Photo., mag., vel., mass, Ap.J., 132, 627, 1960.

1107-A, B = Ho 231 a, b. Pair at 0'8. Dim.: 0'6 x 0'06, 1'2 x 0'4 (Lund 6).

1108-A, B, C Zwicky connected multiple system. Separation A-B: 55"6, B-C: 30"5.
    Photo. Erg.d.Exakt. Naturwiss., XXIX, 344, 1956.
    Mag., vel., mass, Ap.J., 133, 794, 1961.

1111 Harrington and Wilson No 2 (Leo II system); E dwarf in Local Group. See P.A.S.P., 62, 118, 1950. Sculptor
    type, well res., B foreground * in center.
    Star counts, A.J., 66, 125, 1962.

1129 = VV 172 (Vorontsov-Velyaminov Catal. 1959).
    Photo. Ap.J., 131, 742, 1960; 138, 884, 1963.
    Spectr., vel., Ap.J., 138, 884, 1963.

1130-A, B = VV 150 (Vorontsov-Velyaminov Catal., 1959).
    Spectr., vel. A.J., 66, 544, 1961.

1145-A, B, C Wild's connected triple system; see P.A.S.P., 65, 202, 1953. For precise coord. see Ap.J., 133, 794, 1961.
    Photo. Erg.d.Exakt. Naturwiss., XXIX, 365, 1956.
    Mag., vel., mass, Ap.J., 133, 794, 1961. A.J., 66, 543, 1961.

1157 Zwicky obj. No 2. v. low surf. bright., well res., asym.; forsh. cent. part, smooth bar.
    Dim.: 5' x 1'5 (Lick 36-in. pl.).

1203-A, B Zwicky's connected gal. at 73". Photo., mag., vel., mass, Ap.J., 132, 627, 1960.

1205 SN 1960, P.A.S.P., 73, 175, 1961.

1213 = Haro 6 (Bol. Tonantzintla, No 14, 7, 1956). N 4197 at 10' p.

1214-A, B Zwicky's connected gal. at 35"9. Photo., mag., vel., mass, Ap.J., 132, 627, 1960.

1217 = Haro 8 (Bol. Tonantzintla, No 14, 7, 1956).

1230 In Virgo Cl., 4'8 n, 3'0 p BD+9°2637. See Humason et. al., 1956.

1232 = Holmberg VII (1958). F companion of N 4532.

1244, 1245, 1246-A, B In Coma Cl. list; see Proc. 4th Berkeley Symp., vol. III, 1960. Note low vel. of A 1244,
    prob. foreground object.

1247 = HA 88,2 New 3. F sh. bar: 0'4 x 0'08, sev. knotty, part. res. branch. arms, one forms asym.
    outer whorls: 3'9 x 2'5.

1248-A, B, C, D = Helwan 274, 276, 280, 288; see Helwan Bull. No 22, 1921.
    U,B,V photom. R. R. Shobbrook, Mt. Stromlo Obs. Thesis, 1964.

1249 Coma Cl; SN 1961, P.A.S.P., 73, 185, 1961.

1253 = HA 88,2 New 4. vsBN in F bar, sev. part. res. F filam. arms.

1255 Zwicky obj.; see Humason et. al., 1956. Mag., color, Pettit 1954.

1302 Anon. dwarf No 447 noted by C. D. Shane on 20-in. pl.; see Humason et. al., 1956. Lick (1956) vel. for emiss.
    60" s of center: + 1239 km/sec.

1306 See Helwan 30; 16' f, 14' s of N 4984.

A 1309 Photo., vel., mag. P.A.S.P., 74, 35, 1962.
        SN 1959, P.A.S.P., 72, 208, 1960; 74, 35, 117, 1962.

1310 See Helwan 21, p. 210.

1311 = Holmberg VIII (1958). Companion of N 5033.

1339 = Holmberg V (1958). Photom. Medd. Lund II, 128, 1950.

1345-A, B = Ho 541 a, b. Pair at 1'5. Dim.: 1'0 x 1'0, 1'3 x 1'2 (Lund 6).

1353 = Holmberg IV (1958). In M 101 Group. Lick (1956) vel. for emiss. 50" nf of center: + 290 km/sec.
      Photom. Medd. Lund II, 128, 1950.

1358 = HA 72 No 2 = HN 1734.

1410 See Humason et. al. 1956; poss. radio source ?

1444 = VV 109 (Vorontsov-Velyaminov Catal., 1959). Photo., spectr., vel., Ap.J., 138, 883, 1963.

1447 = VV 140 (Vorontsov-Velyaminov Catal., 1959). Photo., spectr., vel., Ap.J., 138, 883, 1963.

1511 = Fath 703 (A.J., 28, 75, 1914). Note corr. to HA 88,2 coord. sB core, 2 main knotty filam. branch. arms, low
      surf. bright. HA 88,2 dim. (2'0 x 2'0, ser. a') for B part only.

1516 Photo., spectr., vel. Ap.J., 138, 883, 1963.

1648-A, B, C Zwicky's connected multiple system. A, B at 26",B,C at 151". Vel. of component B also in
      Humason et. al. (1956).
      Photo. Hdb.d.Phys., vol. 53, 382, 1959.
      Spectr., vel., mag., mass, Ap.J., 133, 804, 1961.
      Dyn., mass, A.J., 66, 544, 1961.

1718-A, B Zwicky's connected gal. at 3'8.
      Photo. Hdb.d.Phys., vol. 53, 382, 1959.
      Mag., vel., mass, Ap.J., 133, 794, 1961.

1719 Draco dwarf E system, in Local Group; see P.A.S.P., 67, 27, 1955. Fully res., no neb. background.
      Photo., Var. stars, A.J., 66, 300, 1961.

1853 From H.A. 85, No 6. HA 88,2 dim. (0'7 x 0'5, ser. a) for B part only.

1955-A, B In a low lat. group noted by C. D. Shane on 20-in. pl.; coord. approx. for identif.;
      see Humason et. al., 1956.

2021 = HA 88,2, New 5. sBN.

2058 At 11'6 np N 7006; see Humason et. al., 1956. Mag., color, Pettit 1954.

2059-A, B At 6'8 sp and 7'9 sf N 7006; see Humason et. al., 1956. Mag., color, Pettit 1954.

2119 Near HA 88,2 New 6 (= A 2120). Noted New 6-A in Mem. Comm. Obs., III, No 13, 1956.

2120 = HA 88,2, New 6, dim.: 4'0 x 1'0 (ser. a'). No BN, BM.

2144 Capricorn E dwarf system in Local Group. Fully res., no perceptible neb. background.
      Photo. Zwicky's Morph. Astr., 1957, Fig. 42, p. 205.

2208 Photo. P.A.S.P., 51, 136, 1939.
      SN 1960, P.A.S.P., 51, 136, 1939. Ap.J., 96, 28, 1942.

2326 Pegasus dwarf Im system. Coord. from Holmberg (1958). F, part. res., fairly smooth struct.

2339-A, B Zwicky's connected gal., 5'8 and 6'8 sf I 1505; see Humason et. al., 1956.
      Photo. Erg.d.Exakt. Naturwiss., XXIX, 363, 1956. Zwicky's Morph. Astr., 1957, p. 230. Ap.J., 136, 1148, 1962.
      Polar. Ap.J., 136, 1148, 1962.
      Spectr. I.A.U. Symp., 5, 1958 = Lick Cont. II, No 81, 1958.

2340 = HN 2871.

2359 = Wolf-Lundmark-Melotte system. Dwarf Im in Local Group. See M.N., 86, 636, 1926. Mt. Wil. vel. for 2 emiss.
      patches N of center and cluster p center.
      Photom. Medd. Lund II, 128, 1950.
      Star counts, V.J.S., 68, Heft 4, 1933 = Lund Medd. I, No 135, 1933.

APPENDIX I

Integrated Magnitudes in B System

$$X = \log A/D(0), \text{ Source, } B(X)$$

```
N0016    +008C1320 +038C1315
N0023    -046C1371 +028C1290 +030C1284
N0068    -037C1464
N0069    -004C1582
N0071    -028C1487 -007C1484
N0080    -015C1397
N0072    -010C1509 +020C1467
N0072A   0.61C1580
N0083    -011C1438
N0095    +019A1334
N0105    2.27C1392
N0125    +023C1358 +048C1329 -003L1387 -030L1415
N0127    -001L1551 -025L1548
N0128    +025A1274 +017C1276 +020C1269 -034L1315 -058L1342
N0147    +024B1127 -032B1277*-034C1264 -009C1161 +049G1065
N0130    0.68L1482 0.40L1564
N0151    -076C1422 +015C1238
N0157    -097C1440 -012C1127 +014C1108 +028C1105 +017G1127
N0160    -065C1466 +010C1367
N0178    +020C1310
N0182    +003C1349
N0185    -009B1147 -032B1167*-009C1092 +042G1037 -012H1107 -002H1099 +002H1088 -086L1278
N0194    +017C1349 +047C1316
N0205    -027B1017*-050B1067*-053C1075 -028C1006 -013C0984 -088D1189 -133D1360 -027E1011 +032F0889 +024F0899 +013F0975
N0205    +045G0899 -104L1170
N0210    -110C1369 -025C1245 +015C1178
N0214    -064C1461 +021C1298
N0221    -067A1011 -048A0979 -018A0944 -008A0941 +010B0947 -067B1027*-066C1031 +010C0942 -050D1000 -095D1083 -026E0971
N0221    +050G0913 +036K0941 -067L0995
N0224    -216A0941 -216B0957*-171B0807*-140B0727*-245D1071 -223D0987 -200D0897 -175D0809 -151D0735 -165E0782 -139E0711
N0224    -139E0711 +038E0439*   *E0436 +015G0441 -063K0562 -053K0552 +010K0448
N0227    +003C1349
N0237    +025A1376
N0247    -019C1041 +013G0962*
N0253    -007K0831 +038K0807
N0255    -076C1459 +033C1238
N0278    -068C1321 +017C1158 +020H1166 +035H1152
N0357    -017C1336 -010C1338*
N0375    -002C1577
N0379    -000C1413 +020C1407 +027C1397 -002L1413 -026L1427
N0380    -005C1416 +016C1401 +022C1384 -006L1401 -030L1424
N0382    +003L1468 -021L1472
N0383    +016C1353 -030L1480
N0384    +019C1443 -004L1437 -028L1463
N0385    +019C1439 +025C1416 -004L1424 -028L1458


N0386    +001C1556 -001L1531 -025L1562
N0388    +001C1574 +022C1575 +028C1546 -001L1591 -025L1584
N0404    +008C1152 +046G1123 -012H1158 +010H1124
N0428    -017A1241 +010C1207 +015C1195 +007G1189
N0470    +003A1272 -046L1318 -070L1390 -085L1469
N0474    -042A1314 -060C1363 -039C1326 -061L1315
N0488    -013A1171 -106C1378 -094C1350 -021C1166 +027G1118 -003H1143 +016H1108
N0499    -028L1387
N0507    -032L1373
N0514    +034C1229
N0520    -001A1271 -084C1475 +027C1216 +041C1216 +034G1243 -050L1317
N0521    -005A1277
N0524    -035A1268 -016A1227 +014A1145 +024A1131 -057C1311 -013C1238 +016C1180 -035L1247 -043L1287 -059L1280 -093L1402
N0533    +036A1301
N0560    +046C1394 +048C1395 -014L1454
N0564    -009C1416
N0578    -074C1363 +002C1175 +016C1176*+019G1151
N0584    -039A1216 -020A1188 +010A1159 +020A1147 -017C1197
N0596    -012C1249
N0598    -167A1147 -134E1028 +018E0629   *E0627 +013G0633 -032K0708 -022K0689 +003K0704
N0613    +028C1078
N0628    -054A1183 -147C1431 -026C1047 -022C1049 -004C1016 +010F0948 +004F0951 -002F1013 +011G0988
N0636    +026C1239
N0660    -002G1194
N0672    +014C1168 +026G1144
N0681    -068C1484 +017C1285
N0718    +031A1263 +018A1260 -075C1394 +010C1252
N0720    -026A1168 +006C1151
N0721    -009C1426
N0736    -004C1402 +017C1358
N0741    +012A1290 -008C1332 -001C1310
N0750    -006C1382 -031L1382 -039L1438
N0751    -002C1416 -028L1413 -036L1441
N0750.   1.15C1325 2.27C1307 0.96H1335 1.43H1310
N0753    +009C1295 +029G1303 -013H1347 +009H1324
N0770    -014C1463
N0772    -003C1143 +043F1013 +030G1120
N0779    -045C1288 +031C1188 +040C1187
N0784    +021G1227
N0788    +000C1322
N0803    +034G1302
N0821    +016A1243 -047C1355 -004C1274 +026C1206 +028C1230*+051C1186
N0864    -106C1495 -050C1346 +005C1169
N0871    +024C1408
N0877    +029A1253 +008C1263
```

```
N0890    +000C1289 -009H1336 +021H1320 -031L1334
N0891    +016C1118 +016G1093
N0908    -072C1330 +019C1099 +025G1086
N0922    +010C1243
N0925    -098C1382 -022C1158 -012C1160 +011C1070 +024G1067
N0936    -072A1232 -054A1200 -024A1147 -014A1139 +004C1128 +021G1128
N0941    +023G1298
N0949    +008H1296 +031H1293
N0972    +003C1231
N1003    +013C1242 +027G1205
N1023    -071A1168 -052A1130 -022A1086 -012A1076 +006C1054 +065F0929 +057F0926 +040F1032 +034G1054
N1042    -105C1569 +026G1157
N1048.   0.43C1555 4.07C1548
N1052    +021C1186 +043G1178
N1055    +028G1147
N1058    -002C1229 +040G1186 +000H1223 +014H1217
N1068    -085A1077 -066A1047 -036A1003 -026A0999 -107C1133 -034C1019 -008C1004 +038F0933 +026F1002 +018F1061 +027G0973
N1073    -011C1204 +014G1157
N1079    +031C1245
N1084    -045A1235 -026A1171 +004A1126 +014A1122 -067C1357 +007C1122*+032C1122
N1087    -078C1434 +012C1160 +021C1151 +030G1159
N1090    +031G1263
N1097    -031C1091 -013C1055
N1097A   0.68C1415
N1140    +042C1284 -034L1321
N1156    +001C1281 +027C1229 +043G1199 -058L1392
N1169    -044H1346 -014H1299
N1175    +001H1435 +031H1388
N1199    -030L1339
N1201    +000C1191 -060L1277
N1209    +001C1287 +030C1262 +056C1242 -029L1311
N1232    -097C1360 -007C1084 +014G1059
N1270    -009C1453
N1272    -017C1439 -002H1438 +016H1355 +038H1288
N1273    -005C1477 +008H1462 +026H1437
N1275    -039A1349 -005C1327
N1277    -011A1482 +002C1479
N1278    -023A1450 -010C1437
N1281    -016A1504
N1282    0.68C1456
N1293    -007C1471
N1294    -007C1466
N1300    -122C1470 +003C1133 +009G1123
N1302    -032C1212
N1316    -002C0994


N1317    -065C1303 -015C1218
N1325    +025G1233
N1325A   +008G1346
N1331    +007C1502
N1332    -065C1275 +025C1132 -051L1337
N1337    +011G1239
N1359    +033C1259
N1365    -025E1058
N1380    -019C1156 -056L1222
N1385    +003C1177
N1395    -015C1188
N1398    -118C1282 -008C1086
N1399    -063C1224 -013C1139 -049L1177 -073L1202
N1400    -021A1249 -002A1213 +001C1255 +031C1224 +056C1213
N1404    -051C1208 +000C1136 -037L1192*
N1407    -032A1209 -013A1167 +017A1105 +027A1092 -054C1329 +019C1119
N1426    -051C1384 +004C1275 +034C1254 +059C1238
N1439    -005C1298
N1441    +012C1399
N1449    +022C1461
N1451    +032C1446
N1453    +003C1301 -027L1353
N1515    -050M1293 -020M1236
N1518    +026C1236
N1533    -039M1261 -009M1205
N1543    -070M1290 -044M1240 -014M1190
N1546    -024M1313 +006M1259
N1549    -069M1230 -043M1179 -013M1119
N1553    -071M1211 -045M1138 -015M1074
N1559    -011M1121
N1560    +008G1230
N1566    -141M1305 -114M1265 -088M1195 -058M1127
N1569    +009C1189 +044G1186
N1574    -015M1193 +015M1135
N1587    -008C1357
N1596    -023M1257 +007M1220
N1600    -024A1303 -005A1249 +025A1218 +035A1203 -002C1294 +030C1229 +044C1216 -024L1286 -048L1330
N1601    +004C1505 -021L1507
N1617    -074M1302 -048M1216 -018M1166
N1637    -072A1329 -053A1269 -023A1194 -013A1157 -020C1206 +005C1174 +030G1138
N1640    -076C1443 +009C1257
N1659    +022C1323
N1700    -030A1270 -011A1240 +019A1213 +029A1217 -008C1269 +024C1202 +038C1196
N1744    -002C1210
N1784    +023G1251
```

```
N1832     -082C1417 +003C1217
N1888.    2.27C1283 4.07C1264
N1889     -014C1450
N1961     -016C1252 +009C1211 +033G1179
N1964     +021C1156 +020G1171
N2139     +011C1229
N2146     +014B1167 +014C1144 +051F0977 +046F1004 +040F1077 +021G1138
N2207     -100C1422 +010C1145
N2217     -016C1193
N2268     -085C1443 +025C1224 +022G1229
N2276     +039C1194 +024G1205
N2300     +028B1257 +006C1231 +045G1231
N2314     +008B1337 +006C1333
N2336     -123C1457 +002C1139 +020G1115
N2339     -082C1361 -027C1331*+003C1255
N2347     -060C1444 -004C1323
N2366     -123C1385 +002C1167 +016G1156
N2379     -011B1477 +004C1476 +025C1462
N2389     -010C1372 +013C1335
N2403     -126C1276 -018C0928 +020F0877 +013F0901 +023G0895
N2441     +013C1307
N2442     -081M1355 -051M1264
N2460     -010B1277 -095C1419 -010C1279
N2500     -004C1242 +018G1226
N2523     -048C1413 +027C1268
N2525     +005C1228 +025G1241
N2532     +005B1307 +004C1310
N2535     +014B1347 +014C1334 +017C1328
N2536     +012B1477 +010C1476
N2537     +022B1237 -008C1248 +021C1238 +010E1257 +022E1238
N2541     +012G1202
N2545     -041C1507 -020C1397 +035C1324
N2549     +008B1227 +008C1217 +033C1215 +010H1227 +025H1232
N2551     -026C1351 +024C1314
N2562     +020C1401 +026C1394
N2563     -003C1373 -033L1397
N2608     +013C1284
N2613     -096C1408 +017C1115
N2633     -078C1410 -043C1345 +008C1294
N2639     +053B1267 +027C1253
N2642     -066C1501
N2646     -036C1432 +019C1324
N2654     +029B1267 +029C1282 +006H1295 +020H1284
N2655     +008B1117 -102C1290 +008C1108 +032G1101 +017H1090
N2672     -055C1418 -020C1349 -029L1353 -053L1392


N2673     -004C1445
N2681     -057A1206 -038A1172 -008A1136 +002A1129 -005B1147*-006C1137 +019C1116 +035F1111 +022F1115 +002F1125 +032G1143
N2681     +012H1126 +027H1111
N2683     -031C1093 +027C1062 +057F0979 +045F0992 +034F1034 +021G1061
N2685     +021B1217 -004B1241 -090C1389 -004C1231 +021C1225 +027G1214 -002H1239 +028H1243
N2693     +010B1327 -048C1444 +008C1341 +018H1312
N2694     -006B1537 -005C1538
N2693.    2.30B1287 1.80F1295 2.70F1291 2.40H1293
N2712     +006B1287 +006C1287 +008H1274 +022H1282
N2713     -077C1394 +032C1284
N2715     +012C1212 +018G1200 +021H1229
N2716     +015C1353 +044C1306
N2723     0.33L1459
N2732     -046C1395 +010C1310
N2742     +026F1208 +016F1227
N2744     +031C1387
N2748     +012C1255
N2749     +014C1358
N2763     +022G1270
N2768     +023B1127 -088C1335 +022C1121 +030F1095 +016F1125 +005F1143 +000H1152 +014H1132
N2775     -005C1172 +020C1136 +031F1113 +022F1116 +013F1155 -003H1143 +029H1121
N2776     -011C1229 -009H1230 +005H1233
N2782     +006C1277 +008H1240 +022H1243
N2784     -061L1248
N2787     +005B1207 -080C1342 -025C1226 +005C1193 +048F1155 +037F1160 +018F1190
N2798     +027B1317 -059C1406 +026C1299
N2805     +013G1182
N2811     +016C1252
N2820     +021G1330
N2830     -032L1576
N2831     -028C1506 -007C1462 -038L1515
N2832     -019C1374 -002H1323 +014H1310 -050L1425
N2841     -088A1182 -069A1134 -039A1070 -028A1050 +004C1038 +022C1001 +000F1004 -029F1081 +021G1020
N2844     +006H1405 +022H1381
N2855     +005C1265 -054L1324 -104L1496
N2859     -066A1278 -047A1249 -017A1203 -007A1203 -014C1207 +011C1185 +022F1190 +013F1188 +004F1205 -007F1208
N2865     +035C1252 +038C1236
N2880     +033B1267 +032C1263
N2903     -067A1080 -060A1068 -108C1200 -018C0995 +000C0986 -043D1022 -067D1085 -093D1153 -116D1213 -138D1265 +035F0949
N2903     +027F0954 +019F0962 +014F0986 +013G0961
N2911     +013C1361 -017L1406 -067L1512
N2914     +007C1412
N2942     +007H1385 +021H1328
N2950     +017B1197 -068C1290 -013C1212 +017C1192 +035F1213 +030F1201 +015F1186
N2955     -018H1368 -002H1357
```

```
N2964    +008C1215 +033C1206 +025G1201 +018H1242 +024H1210 +040H1207 +042H1209
N2967    +004F1215
N2968    +043G1285 +035H1295 +041H1276 +057H1266 +059H1270
N2974    -009C1250 +020C1208 +046C1177
N2976    +011B1097 +025C1105 +028F1095 +018F1081 +013F1073 -016F1127 +039G1084
N2983    -012C1302 +018C1280
N2985    +009C1137 +027F1117 +016F1127 -003F1162 +030G1122
N2986    +001C1283 +031C1225
N3003    +028C1236 +026G1219
N3027    +020G1246*
N3031    -102A1004 -177C1158 -034C0838 -127D1024 -172D1141 -136E1046 -092E0941 +003F0785 -004F0794 -052F0870 +012G0793
N3031    -020K0821 +010K0773
N3032    -002C1291
N3034    +020B0947 +002B0979 +020C0943 -038E1018 +050F0892 +038F0885 +013F0905 -059F1082 +031G0928 +014K0930 +034K0898
N3041    +011H1239 +028H1234
N3055    +020C1277 +041F1256 +031F1275 +016F1289
N3061    +018G1358*
N3065    -022C1346 +042F1165 +036F1152 +019F1175
N3066    +009C1357
N3067    +014C1272 +040C1258
N3077    -010C1128 -009E1126 +034F1071 +023F1080 -011F1123 +047G1067
N3078    +007C1243 +036C1218
N3079    +022G1122
N3098    -004H1317 +012H1301
N3115    +022B1027 +017B1042 -061C1120 +008C1027 +026C1032 +049C1022 -018D1058 -043D1092 -089D1175
N3147    +015B1137 -096C1357 -011C1175 +015C1157 +033F1121 +022F1108 -003F1135
N3158    +040B1317 +010C1353 +040C1304 +004H1352 +020H1323
N3166    -045A1198 +013B1167 -098C1318 +013C1134 +023G1158
N3169    -047A1228 +011C1129 +026G1134
N3183    +024G1271*
N3184    +014B1047 -129C1379*-004C1069 -001F1114 +018G1041
N3185    +011C1309 +029F1284 +018F1307 +027G1300
N3187    +017G1338
N3190    +035C1210 +031F1160 +013F1188 +020G1204
N3193    +018C1215 +041F1216 +025F1255 +049G1191 -042L1285
N3198    +013G1096
N3222    +011C1382
N3226    -011C1293
N3227    +006C1170
N3239    -040C1298
N3245    +014C1186 +039C1172 -046L1264
N3254    +013C1228
N3256    -067M1318 -041M1267
N3277    +019C1251 +022C1226
N3294    -006A1238


N3301    +009C1234
N3310    -009B1137 -060C1170 -009C1135
N3319    +013G1182
N3338    -084C1363 +021G1139
N3344    -126C1478 -001C1069 +020G1053
N3348    +035B1207 +053F1181 +042F1194 +025F1225
N3351    +002C1081 -023D1094 -048D1152 -073D1200 -096D1239 +005F1086 -002F1087 -011F1078 +017G1058
N3353    +025E1325
N3359    -078C1265 +030C1112 +024G1103
N3364    +011G1354*
N3367    +002C1217 +027C1205
N3368    +008C1014 -017D1055 -041D1095 -066D1150 -089D1208 +030G1014
N3377    -046A1250 -027A1214 +003A1175 +013A1166 +006C1148 +031C1126
N3379    +000C1090**025C1052**043F1035 +036F1036 +023F1056 +013F1061 -060L1170 -110L1263
N3384    -057A1160 -038A1135 -008A1089 +002A1076 +020C1099 +031F1103 +018F1083 -081L1290 -089L1292 -115L1328
N3389    +009C1233 +041F1259
N3395    +000E1248
N3396    +000E1292
N3412    -076C1298 +035C1154 +046F1158 +037F1139 +028F1192
N3414    -044A1284 -025A1251 +005A1205 +015A1203 +008C1207 +040F1209 +026F1213 +015F1241
N3423    +024G1163
N3430    +018C1223 -018E1268
N3432    +020G1174
N3486    -044A1188 -016C1122 -002C1106 +002F1117 -023F1149 +017G1114
N3489    +009C1107 +024C1109
N3504    -043A1252 -024A1208 +006A1164 +016A1148 +034C1180 +043C1158
N3510    -047D1454 -070D1511
N3512    -032A1386 -013A1304 +022C1305
N3516    +035B1257 -050C1312 +035C1272 -041E1319 +024E1265
N3521    -052A1074 -045A1058 -127C1240 -002C0982 +016C0974 -053E1084 +000F0987 -044F1031 +024G1015
N3556    +014B1077**025C1068 -033E1152 +020G1070
N3557    -032M1246 -002M1195
N3585    +023C1110 +049C1105
N3593    +006C1185
N3596    +026F1180
N3605    -042C1439 +043C1389 +057F1301
N3607    +039C1092 +027F1129 +041F1092
N3608    +025C1214 +033F1177
N3610    +048B1167 -063C1315 +023C1193 +030F1181 +041F1169 +050F1186
N3611    +015C1286
N3613    +056B1177
N3619    +012B1277
N3623    +023B1047 +024C1012 -045E1115 +054F1003 +031F1025 +021G1027
N3626    -033A1256 -014A1222 +016A1178 +026A1185 +021C1127 +026F1186 +037F1219 +046F1181
N3627    +017B0977 -001C0987 +017C0972 -051E1071 +025F0947 +048F0991 +025G0976
```

```
N3628    -063E1215 +037F0990 +013G1033
N3631    +012F1110 +020F1104 +056F1036 +068F1044 +030G1104
N3640    +017C1164
N3642    +016B1187 +027G1166
N3646    +029C1188 +018G1194
N3665    +019B1197 +021C1188
N3675    +007B1107
N3681    +014C1257 +031C1244
N3684    +032C1237
N3686    +019C1206
N3718    -004F1185 +012F1173 +015G1135
N3726    +006B1207 +037F1064 +050F1052 +017G1098
N3729    +038F1169 +053F1159 +035G1201
N3738    +021F1171 +032F1132 +046F1125 +036G1216
N3756    -001F1246 +010F1177 +020G1217
N3780    -008F1269 +012F1227 +026F1207
N3804    +018F1251
N3810    -024A1188 +004C1132 +018C1129 -007D1136 -057D1234 -102D1378 +022F1118 +014G1143
N3818    +042C1283
N3846    +028F1363
N3872    +047C1285
N3888    +034F1269
N3893    +009B1117 +002F1103 +016F1087 +035F1052
N3898    +005B1177 -013F1182 -002F1145 +012F1117 +022F1087
N3900    +013C1246 +039C1231
N3904    +030C1212
N3923    +006C1134
N3938    +001F1097 +011G1093
N3941    +031B1137
N3945    -001B1197
N3949    +030B1147 +037F1129
N3953    +011B1117*-114C1375**011C1089 -016F1113 +014F1095 +047F1046 +059F1015 +027G1083
N3962    +040C1190
N3972    +018F1355 +032F1288
N3982    +016F1243 +036F1178 +052F1149
N3990    +018B1367 +035E1352
N3991    +027E1364 +038E1350
N3992    +016B1067 -052E1215 +002F1071 +018F1021 -028F1118 +015G1072
N3994    +031E1346 +042E1325
N3995    -003E1295 +008E1293
N3998    +013B1167 -067D1270 -045D1234 -022D1202 +003D1175 +002E1183 +020F1167 +040F1146 +056F1134
N4008    +026E1334
N4026    +040B1177
N4027    +000E1192
N4030    -026E1154 -008F1227 +012F1161 +021F1122 +028F1114


N4036    +028B1177 -008E1195 +028G1157
N4038    +009B1101 -016E1152
N4038.   +000B1097
N4039    2.30E1161*
N4041    -011E1214 +025G1162
N4045    +007E1299
N4051    +001B1127 -100E1368 -035E1206 -024E1171 -026F1166 +003F1062 +019F1068 +024G1092
N4062    -017E1245
N4085    +027F1189 +019G1292
N4088    -031E1191 +020F1164 +031F1142 +010G1116 -055D1248 -078D1333 -100D1409
N4096    +038F1109 +023G1103
N4100    +028F1170
N4102    +030B1237 +018F1261 +028F1237 +041F1197
N4105    -002C1215
N4106    -002C1254
N4111    +050B1167 +036B1172 +033G1173
N4116    +015C1263 +019G1244
N4123    -020E1284 +006E1195 +018G1193
N4124    +036F1253 +040F1198
N4125    +031B1107
N4138    +049B1237
N4143    +025B1217
N4150    +019C1263
N4151    +016B1137 -009B1171 -084E1244 -020E1179 -008E1153
N4152    +031F1310 +040F1299 +049F1264
N4156    -049E1501**027E1404
N4165    +015G1455
N4168    +024B1247 -004B1286 +013E1269 +031F1242 +042F1223 +047G1239
N4178    +020G1190
N4179    +021C1190 +046C1195*
N4189    +011F1361 +022F1299 +031F1239 +036F1226 +018G1261
N4192    -004A1110 +023C1090 -046E1213 -028F1183 +005F1126 +030F1087 +014G1099
N4193    +036G1324
N4203    -025C1223 +005C1173
N4206    +019G1281
N4212    -009E1220 +020F1199 +029F1169 +030G1182
N4214    +014B1027 -120E1357 -043E1114 -020F1058 -007F1046 +024G1027
N4216    +005A1116 +032B1127 -060D1202 -106D1285 -036E1170 -018F1124 +018F1088 +040F1090 +018G1095
N4220    +034B1227
N4224    +024G1295
N4233    +030G1309
N4234    +023E1344
N4235    +019G1265
N4236    +019G1021
N4237    +019C1257 +052C1256 +030F1207
```

```
N4241    +024G1306
N4242    -011F1227 +011F1186 +027G1153
N4244    -019B1127*+010C1091 -059E1236 +040F1022 +010G1063
N4245    +013B1247 -020D1281 -045D1329 -089D1422
N4246    +016G1344
N4251    +039B1167
N4254    -044A1131 -037A1123 -004A1050 +006B1047 -034E1110 +006F1042 +013G1050 +000H1049
N4258    -018B0947*-018C0939 -151E1243 -075E1043 -035F0985 +019F0926 +011G0902
N4259    -012A1473 +025G1465
N4261    -028A1209 -005A1188 +025A1154 +005B1177 +041F1167
N4262    -028C1279 +027C1243 +034F1234 +038F1204 +027H1247 +042H1235 +005H1264
N4264    +013A1378
N4267    +026B1207 -001F1174 +028F1169 +041F1157 +003H1206 +018H1193 +018H1200 +033H1197
N4268    +001A1376 +030G1385
N4270    -004A1308 +029B1317 +030G1320
N4273    -023A1274 +009C1238 +035C1225 +022G1247
N4274    +005C1124 -005D1156 -055D1244 +004F1167 +017F1119 +022G1141
N4278    +010B1147 +024D1136 +000D1155 -025D1186 -048D1222 +008F1158 +023F1133 +033F1119 +046F1090 +053G1129
N4281    -017A1254 +016C1230 +040G1239
N4283    +015B1327 +008D1330 +032F1351 +041F1304 +043G1336
N4291    +041B1247
N4293    +017A1145 +051F1097
N4294    +027F1221 +040F1230 +020G1260
N4298    +033G1207
N4299    +023F1274 +034F1219 +028G1287
N4301    +031G1345
N4302    +025G1253
N4303    -047A1112 -040A1098 -006A1046 +003C1026 +021C1023*+003F1017 +024G1015
N4312    +031G1260
N4314    +006C1154 +021C1142
N4321    -072A1204 -046A1157 -013A1047 -119B1287*+014B0997 -003B1014 -054E1164 +000F1033 +008F1022 +033F0997 +045F0989
N4321    +019G1018 -009H1044
N4322    0.70B1569 1.30B1507
N4339    +021B1267 -007B1295
N4340    -010F1192 +015F1190 +028F1220 +009H1219
N4341    +044G1423
N4342    +035G1355
N4343    +033G1329
N4350    +019C1201 +037F1211 +055F1178 +035H1192
N4365    +012B1117 -013B1148 +000F1103 +027F1064
N4371    +027F1187 +040G1190
N4374    -054A1164 -035A1122 -005A1097 +005A1060 +037B1057 +023C1058 +038C1043 -060D1178 -013E1108 +024E1049 +040F1023
N4374    +065G1029 +032H1041
N4377    +037F1291 +048F1256
N4379    +006C1272


N4382    +006A1024 +016B1027 +012F1077 +027F1037 +047F0984 +038G1014
N4387    -008A1350 +012A1308 +045B1317 +017B1337
N4388    +034G1183 +031H1241
N4394    +010C1189 +024C1162 +012F1144 +021F1132 +014G1189
N4395    +006G1080
N4402    -011E1335 +022G1257 +034H1334 +017H1265
N4406    -063A1200 -044A1150 -014A1094 -004A1079 +029B1057 -021D1104 -069D1206 -022E1117 +015E1041 +025F1037 +048F0989
N4406    +058G1018 +023H1035
N4411A   3.30G1356
N4411B   3.60G1305
N4413    +009F1291
N4414    -008A1128 +020C1097 +034C1099
N4417    +012A1219 +022A1212 +040G1220
N4419    -041C1281 +028C1200
N4421    -013C1241 +013C1185 +001F1286 +018F1263 +029F1233
N4424    -004A1252 +006A1243 +026G1244
N4425    -014A1322 +018C1322 +017F1297 +042F1322 +027G1291
N4429    -016A1172 +014A1125 +019C1094 +038G1116
N4435    -028A1237 -013A1204 +020A1169 +030A1163 +023C1176 +012E1201 +030F1177 +036F1162 +059F1117 +043G1194 +039H1178
N4438    -085A1267 -066A1217 -036A1184 -026A1182 -008C1140 +006C1111 -045E1203 -026F1187 +003F1113 +018F1097 +038F1095
N4438    +022G1102
N4440    -037C1331 +018C1279*-005F1327 +014F1321 +032H1276
N4442    +023A1136 +034A1142 +028C1131 +036G1168
N4445    +024A1378 +034A1358 +028G1371
N4448    +025C1203
N4449    +034B0987 +017B0991 -033D1070 -104D1271 -100E1261 -023E1044 +036F0936 +042F0917 +048F0917 +038G1006
N4450    +016A1107 +002B1127*+025F1101 +050F1077 +036G1091
N4451    -003A1358 +027A1334 +006C1340
N4452    +048C1287
N4458    +000A1318 +033B1317 +021E1321 +023F1329 +046F1283 +049H1290
N4459    -018A1230 +005A1178 +035A1146 +014C1158 +022F1186 +042F1174 +051F1157
N4461    +004A1225 +014A1215 +032C1202 -004E1244 +030F1201 +043F1187 +050F1167 +024H1215 +041H1204
N4464    +013B1367
N4467    -010B1567
N4468    -001H1427 +017H1393
N4472    -080A1130 -032A1048 -022A1000 +028B0957 +011B0977 -042E1059 -022F1008 +007F0966 +055F0914 +041G0941
N4473    +006A1145 +016A1137 +009C1152 +034C1128 +032F1137 +052F1111 +043H1117
N4474    +029C1262 +034F1262
N4476    +013B1347 +030E1328 +030F1303 +039F1343 +020F1335 +003H1337 +021H1324 +043H1316
N4477    -011A1174 -001A1160 -008C1178 +019F1147 +028F1124 +026H1135
N4478    -002A1245 +028A1234 +033C1224 +020E1241 +029F1241 +044F1207 +011H1233 +033H1230
N4479    +004A1389 +034A1356 +039C1352 +026F1411 +044F1309 +017H1356 +039H1361
N4480    +012G1314
N4485    +019B1247 +019E1237 +034G1240
```

```
N4486    -073A1167 -024A1072 +009A1014 +019B0997 -007D1036 -031D1073 -056D1122 -079D1177 -102D1242 -098E1238 -074E1169
N4486    -032E1082 -021E1064 -014F1140 +019F1019 +038F0981 +046G0964 -004H1028 +023H1018
N4486B   0.70B1457 0.60C1523 0.60D1434
N4490    -028A1078 +015B1017 -025E1059 +040F0975 +051F0969 +023G1024
N4491    +025C1349
N4492    -006C1350
N4494    +033B1097 -020B1166
N4496.   5.2*G1206
N4501    -083A1262 -035A1108 -025A1114 -001A1055 -138B1417*-018D1073 -042D1125 -067D1195 -090D1268 -112D1327 -006E1052
N4501    -025F1085 -008F1050 -019F1031 +020G1018
N4517    +023G1121
N4517A   +023G1267
N4519    +011G1236
N4526    +025C1065 +043C1065
N4527    +036C1157 +017G1138
N4528    +008C1290
N4532    +030G1233
N4535    -091A1380 -042A1194 -008A1102 -032F1187 -003F1071 +022G1050
N4536    -041A1198 +009G1107
N4539    +025G1290
N4546    +017C1147
N4548    +012C1100 -014D1141 -038D1191 -063D1250 -108D1362 -002E1122 -010F1102 +008F1092 +020G1098 +006H1115
N4550    -013A1278 +045C1253
N4551    +005A1310 +038B1307 +010B1320
N4552    -027A1160 +008C1118 +023C1111 +004F1108 +033F1092 +042F1100 +038H1100
N4559    -049A1208 -046E1149 +025F1027 +014G1041
N4564    -027C1261 +028C1199 +051G1225
N4565    -100B1247*-083D1212 -129D1359 -048E1141 +044F0993 +031G1039
N4567    +034G1209
N4568    +025G1175
N4569    -039A1128 +021C1037 -010E1069 -038F1119 +007F1053 +059F1003 +022G1024
N4570    +053C1175
N4571    +015F1254 +024F1203 +024G1177
N4576    2.00G1428
N4578    +000B1257*-053C1316 +017C1234
N4579    -077A1228 -029A1112 +005A1072 -077B1217**+009B1067 -012D1079 -036D1125 -061D1176 -084D1225 -106D1271 +000E1071
N4579    +029G1042
N4586    +025G1261
N4589    +025B1217
N4594    -005B0957**+027B0927 +010B0945 -041E1028 +040G0925 +021K0928
N4596    +039G1148
N4605    -021E1144
N4606    +032G1276
N4608    +037G1210
N4618    -025E1208 -013E1170 +013F1174 +022F1139 +027G1124


N4621    -030A1173 +028C1090 +039F1090
N4625    +008E1312 +019E1308 +031G1296
N4627    +014C1328 -044D1462 +015E1306 +034G1314
N4631    -054A1168 +007C1000 -050E1132 +033F0935 +016G0985
N4633    +018G1381
N4634    +021G1320
N4636    +016B1087
N4638    +004A1237 +036C1216
N4639    +035G1222
N4643    -009D1177 -059D1244 -102D1350
N4647    -033A1270 +000C1241 +025G1219
N4649    -047A1110 +011B1027 +011C1006 +048G0995
N4647.   8.90F1001 11.8F0982 13.1F0965 15.9F0950
N4651    -024F1189 +024F1151 +025G1134
N4653    +029G1283
N4654    -003F1136 +011F1106 +020F1092 +027G1115
N4656    -040E1206 +055F0943 +018G1090
N4660    -006A1234 +027C1201
N4666    -008A1178 -056C1364 +029C1156 +028G1152 -040D1228 -085D1338
N4668    +029G1359
N4670    +024E1315 +035E1313
N4677    -012M1415
N4683    +003M1430
N4689    +032G1160
N4691    -009E1195
N4696    -034M1311 -004M1231
N4697    +013C1044
N4698    +016C1165 +014D1158 -011D1192 -036D1236 -057D1277 -081D1323 +039G1164
N4699    -082C1170 -006C1063 +006D1054 -018D1089 -044D1110 -067D1151 -089D1197
N4706    -005M1417
N4709    -022M1353
N4710    +028A1195 +033C1189
N4712    +014G1359
N4713    -006D1229 -031D1282
N4725    +004B1017 +012F1004 +023F0975 +031F0994 +016G1018
N4736    -007R0907 -058E0955 -029F0919 -011F0902 +012F0876 +037F0836 +033G0902 +005K0897
N4742    +034C1242
N4744    0.86M1413
N4747    +020G1302
N4753    -089C1276 +001C1093 -027E1151
N4754    +023C1153
N4762    +035C1119 -063D1256
N4789    +050C1310
N4793    -043C1392 +045C1230
N4798    +034C1421
```

```
N4800      +027B1237
N4814      +031B1287
N4826      +016R0947 -001B0954 -052E1048 +030F0926 +030F0926 +025G0936 +031K0946
N4827      +048C1389
N4841.     3.36C1356
N4850      -007C1526 +023C1530
N4853      -007C1445 +022C1439
N4856      +003C1159 +017C1159
N4860      -038C1525 -017C1481
N4861      -075C1392 +000C1318
N4865      +018C1489 +025C1443 -010D1485 -054D1527
N4864      0.68C1476
N4866      +023C1212
N4867      0.68C1555
N4869      0.68C1489 1.34C1483
N4872      -033B1517*-055C1546 -034C1529
N4874      -002A1388**+018A1358**+026B1357*-001C1433 +022C1366 +028C1373 +019D1389 -007D1429 -030D1480 -077E1609 -057E1561
N4874      -045E1516 -027E1467 -005E1391 +025E1361 +013H1365 +031H1337
N4881      +023C1466 -056D1565 -012D1499
N4886      -004C1512
N4889      -026A1358*-007A1308**+001B1327 -026B1365 -027C1380 -004C1312 +025C1272 -033D1377 -076D1473 -012H1337 +006H1305
N4895      -020C1456 +010C1427
N4896      0.68C1510
N4898.     0.68C1459
N4900      +009C1211 +014F1191 +024F1183 +039F1199
N4902      -079C1389 -003C1192
N4904      +000E1284
N4907      +008C1459 -001D1449 -027D1487 -050D1552 -070D1605
N4908      -007C1498
N4911      +006C1383 +046C1349 -029D1433 -072D1578
N4915      +012C1315 +042C1296
N4921      +014C1357 -011D1356 -035D1417 -060D1481 -084D1528
N4926      +013C1425 +038C1403
N4931      +027C1451
N4941      +022C1194
N4957      +055C1410
N4958      +010C1156 +035C1150
N4961      +038C1396
N4976      -069M1268 -043M1214 -013M1162
N4995      -064C1370 +012C1199
N5005      -018A1128 +025B1047 -089C1251 +019C1065 -025D1111 -026E1127 +030G1063 -050D1146 -073D1193 -095D1245
N5018      +030C1217
N5033      -058A1178 +003C1086*-066E1197 -057F1155 -042F1149 -019F1137 +005G1074
N5049      +018C1373 +043C1384*
N5055      +001B0937 -067E1084 -020F0989 +009F0945 +028F0937 +036F0936 +021G0937


N5077      +017C1248
N5087      +036C1213
N5112      -026E1316
N5128      +044G0794
N5173      +038B1377
N5194      -002B0907*-145C1287 -002C0899 -069D1066 -094D1120 -117D1178 -140D1248 -059E1052 +013G0900
N5195      +016B1067 -095C1244 +015C1071 -045D1184 -009E1112 +046G1053
N5198      +036B1297
N5204      +003C1199 +022G1178
N5236      -115C1094 -007C0839 -140E1133 -075E1037 +028F0780
N5248      -038A1148 -015A1104 +004C1102 +022C1104 -021D1118 -045D1164 -070D1231 -093D1285 -046E1182 -037F1137 -008F1115
N5248      +001F1098 +014G1049
N5253      -002E1119
N5273      +008B1267 -003E1276
N5297      -017F1316 -009F1279 +000F1268 +006F1248
N5308      +024B1257 +024C1234 +049C1228
N5322      +026B1117 +001B1152 +001C1101 +026C1099 -010E1167 -001F1152 +019F1164 +037F1150
N5328      +013C1310
N5353      +032C1206
N5354      +043C1244
N5363      -028A1198 -005A1146 +025A1102 +005B1147 -048C1260 +007C1128 -030D1188 +043G1121
N5364      -041A1208 -008A1142 +001C1123 -031F1110 -002F1084 +016G1116
N5371      +006C1163 -012F1174 +017F1116
N5377      +012C1239 +026C1206
N5383      -027E1260
N5394      +023C1355 +001E1389
N5395      +003C1224 -007E1275
N5426      -051C1427 -022C1313 -010E1301 +016G1283
N5427      -055C1438 +000C1196 -013E1225 +021G1210
N5448      +040B1217
N5457      -045C0924 -161D1312 -114E1167 -008F0834 +006G0835 -001K0881
N5473      -008C1272 +022C1237 +011E1263
N5474      -021C1260 -034E1249 +013F1165 +028F1135 +026G1137
N5485      +030B1247 +029C1254
N5493      +008C1256 +038C1233
N5533      +030B1267 +022C1278
N5548      +036B1337 +038C1299
N5557      +033B1227 +035C1227
N5560      -019D1368 +042E1322
N5566      +023C1150 -026D1194 -074D1266 -097D1296 -016E1193 +010E1141 -107L1324
N5574      +041C1334 +030E1324 -043L1409
N5576      +025C1200 -015D1234 +009E1206 -040L1257 -090L1340
N5585      +007C1163 +023G1139
N5600      +023E1321
N5614      +007B1267
```

```
N5631    +029B1257
N5633    -063C1466 -007C1317 -012D1318 -058D1420
N5638    +024C1242
N5645    +008A1293
N5660    -012E1263
N5668    -087C1447 +004C1228
N5672    +018B1427 -030C1478 +020C1407
N5676    -094C1451 -009C1187 +017C1197*
N5687    +066C1261
N5689    +038C1279
N5690    +015A1255
N5701    -019A1238 -108L1406
N5713    +000C1202 -010E1215 +001E1209 +019F1167 +028F1162 +037F1143
N5728    -026A1258
N5740    +009A1273 +037C1254 -009E1301 +024G1265
N5746    -072C1292 +037C1143 -032E1237 +011G1164
N5757    -030A1344
N5774    +014G1284
N5775    +024G1225
N5791    -021A1314
N5806    +032C1237
N5812    +042C1249
N5813    +010B1207 -063C1338 +010C1191 +012C1201*
N5820    +042B1347 +041C1298
N5831    +038B1277 +037C1254 +038E1273
N5838    +029B1177 +029C1182 +004E1217
N5839    -004A1395
N5845    -001A1347
N5846    -045A1265 +042G1124
N5846.   -004A1175 +026A1158 +031B1127 +031C1122 +006E1174 +032E1148 +024F1183 +033F1145 +041F1124
N5846A   +048B1377 +014C1454 +049C1396
N5850    +012C1218 +021C1191 +026C1178 -046D1323 -095D1405 -013E1266 +013E1193 +010F1239 +029G1167
N5854    +025C1267
N5857    +045C1386
N5857.   5.69C1290
N5859    +035C1330 +041C1327
N5866    +025B1097 +025C1088 +000E1122
N5878    +023C1236
N5879    +033B1227 +019B1227 +019C1204 +033C1205 -017E1251
N5898    +016A1265 +049C1253
N5899    +038B1257 +038C1248
N5903    +008A1275 +041C1258
N5907    +024C1118 -091D1362 -045E1247 +013G1115
N5921    +002B1177*-021C1187 +002C1163
N5936    -006A1353 +024A1295


N5962    +029B1197 +029C1220 +011F1237 +022F1217
N5970    +028B1247 +037C1225 +021F1202 +038F1146
N5976    +015C1587
N5981    +020B1397 -010C1416
N5982    +031B1237 +031C1229 +020E1244 +027F1225
N5985    +017B1197 +003B1207 -033E1271
N6015    +005B1177 -020B1191 +005C1171 -031E1235 +010G1182
N6027A   0.42C1572
N6027D   0.42C1487 0.68C1473
N6052    +024E1343
N6070    +011C1248 -016E1292
N6106    -024A1350 +006A1277
N6118    -045A1364
N6181    +015C1255 +029C1250 +039F1197
N6207    +006B1237 +008C1221*-005E1229 +029F1175
N6217    +032B1187 +031C1188 -005E1230 +005F1250 +034F1187
N6239    +030C1308 +040C1274 -005D1302 -030D1327 -075D1441
N6314    -033C1512 +023C1410
N6340    -004C1228 +021C1200
N6359    +007A1348 +030C1373
N6384    -068A1304 -018C1191 +005C1149 -046E1248 +012G1134
N6412    +028C1244 +023G1233
N6482    +007A1246 +017C1312
N6503    +008B1107**+004C1091 -031D1142 -079D1280 -032E1158 +021F1106 +030G1089
N6574    -019A1318 -001A1285 +007B1287 +002C1298 +032C1287 -026D1308 -048D1359
N6615    -048A1482
N6627    -045A1559 +028C1440
N6635    -030A1496 -028C1490
N6643    -094C1502 +016C1190 +015G1173
N6654    -079C1551 +006C1275
N6658    -030A1444 -028C1463 +016C1430 +022C1405 +023F1371 +051F1367
N6661    -043A1409 -041C1413 +032C1302 +035C1311**+044F1279 +064F1253
N6674    -079C1457 +020C1295
N6702    -002C1427 +019C1388
N6703    -010C1297
N6710    1.15C1450 1.34C1410
N6769    -032M1328
N6770    -037M1371
N6771    -005M1390
N6814    -049A1357 -031A1303 -071C1411 +002C1236 +027C1214
N6822    +014G0935*
N6824    +003C1304
N6835    +005A1356
N6851    -003M1322
N6861    -015M1264
```

```
N6861D    -018M1381
N6868     -021M1261
N6870     -019M1368
N6875     -007M1331
N6878     -016M1438
N6893     -024M1320
N6907     -038A1281
N6909     -004M1336
N6921     +023A1437 +051C1452
N6927     -005C1549
N6928     -041C1434 +032C1374 +035C1365
N6930     +017C1410
N6944     -003C1470 -032D1484
N6946     -044A1108 -024C1033 -005F1058 +014G0977
N6951     -042A1313 -099C1462 -014C1279 +027G1193
N6954     +006C1411
N6962     -072C1424 +002C1309
N6963     0.32C1582 0.71C1508
N6964     -031C1412 +012C1426 +019C1399 -038D1458
N7013     -018A1330
N7137     +024C1326 +038C1303 +047C1318*-016H1383 +024H1304
N7171     -067C1504 +006C1322
N7177     -030A1232 +005B1207*-071C1313 +003C1202 +020C1208 +013H1194 +035H1174
N7213     -046M1231
N7217     -041A1214 +009B1107 -032B1177*-038C1181 +017C1104 +040G1109 +007H1120 +024H1108
N7240     -034C1560 -022C1539
N7242     +007C1459
N7252     +000C1323
N7302     -029C1385 +045C1311
N7314     +015C1169 +029C1165
N7317     -031C1556 +004C1517
N7318A    -021C1535 -009C1511 +011C1468
N7318B    -067C1529 -033C1493
N7318.    1.15C1389 1.34C1388
N7319     -007C1367
N7331     -152C1340 -118C1248 +013C1052 +021F1033 +027F1004 +022G1037 -079D1146 -102D1192 -124D1247
N7332     +013B1187 -075C1304 +011C1205 -041L1239 -065L1272 -080L1293 -103L1325
N7339     +016B1307 +014C1322
N7343     +011C1438 -046D1502
N7377     -064C1383 +021C1231
N7385     -010C1424
N7386     +001C1457
N7392     +019C1263
N7410     -069M1408 -014M1180
N7412     -024M1239


N7418     -077M1469 -022M1237
N7421     -057M1518 -002M1288
N7424     -060M1270
N7448     -022A1253 +013B1197 +011C1221 +036C1208
N7457     -030A1278 -021B1267*-027C1273 +005H1232 +019H1177 +035H1182
N7469     -004A1299 +029C1288
N7479     -020A1230 -103C1677 +008C1176 -052D1290 -097D1411
N7496     -019M1235
N7499     -004C1508
N7501     -004C1525
N7503     +019C1495 +025C1453
N7507     +001C1188 +030C1156
N7531     -023M1237
N7537     +023C1392
N7541     +001A1272 +029C1259
N7552     -071M1273 -070M1266 -045M1218 -015M1164
N7562     -035C1377 -014C1333 +015C1323 +041C1277
N7576     +016C1390
N7582     -070M1352 -045M1276 -015M1196
N7585     -010C1289
N7590     -054M1336 -029M1265 +001M1219
N7599     -072M1429 -047M1327*-017M1245
N7600     +036C1286
N7606     -092C1200 +007C1177
N7611     -027C1414 +017C1388 +024C1359 -029L1411 -037L1450
N7617     +025C1492 -028L1524 -036L1554
N7619     -021A1318 -003A1276 +027A1230 +037A1220 -043C1355 +000C1302 +007C1271 +030C1235 +047C1231 -022L1292 -046L1330
N7619     -054L1376 -050D1353
N7623     -007C1428 +043C1383 +014L1398 -010L1413 -014D1434
N7625     +027C1317
N7626     -018A1312 +001A1277 +031A1234 +041A1217 -040C1360 +004C1298 +011C1292 +033C1260 +036C1258 +050C1227 -018L1299
N7626     -042L1340 -046D1373
N7640     -001C1189 +014G1146
N7671     -006C1399
N7678     -075C1521 +010C1258
N7679     +003A1346 +006C1331
N7682     +000C1440 +029C1393
N7716     +018A1308 -053C1422 +020C1294 +023H1302 +037H1297
N7723     -036A1256 -077C1425 -004C1209 +022C1200
N7727     -048A1218 -089C1325 -016C1190 +010C1164
N7741     -088C1469 -015C1265 +002C1252 +025G1177 +002H1224 +018H1164
N7742     -011C1243 +019C1231
N7743     -003A1256 +000C1242
N7769     -056C1520 -012C1295
N7770     -004C1459
```

```
N7771    +021C1317
N7782    +007A1320
N7785    -002A1318 +008C1318
N7793    -052A1133 -047C1142
N7814    -052A1259 -022A1190 -093C1401 +006C1169
I0010    -019C1364
I0239    +020G1194
I0342    1.19A1281 2.27C1251 18.1C1068*
I0356    1.19A1336
I0391    +034C1301
I0529    5.50G1268*
I0775    +028H1439 +050H1418
I0783    0.70B1527*
I0783A   0.70B1637*
I1183    0.70B1497 0.68C1563
I1185    0.71C1487 1.15C1473
I1194    0.71C1546 1.15C1525
I1302    0.71C1424
I1303    -016A1559
I1308    1.15C1412
I1317    0.32C1471 0.71C1464
I1459    0.49M1237 1.76M1144
I1460    0.71C1526 1.15C1510
I1613    +013C1091 +034G1014
I1727    -007C1274 +022G1225
I1784    3.10G1406
I2233    +030G1313
I2574    +014G1106
I3061    +021G1437
I3115    +003G1378
I3259    +032G1435
I3267    +037G1433
I3475    +025E1475 +036E1449
I3476    +001H1359 +023H1344
I3896    -013M1324
I3946    0.68C1524 1.34C1513
I4011    0.12E1708 0.19E1675 0.25E1685 0.38E1633 0.63E1609
I4012    1.34C1609
I4021    0.68C1595 1.34C1553
I4045    0.68C1525
I4051    0.68C1488 0.35D1524 1.08D1464
I5267    -078M1311 -053M1257 -023M1196
I5273    -014M1210
A0235    0.71C1456
A0438    0.71C1509


A0814    +015G1129
A0909    +025G1309*
A0936    5.30G1342
A0947    0.60D1260
A0956    7.00G1311
A0957    2.40C1305 7.70G1197
A1006    12.0G1135
A1009    +023C1324 +026G1171
A1101    +065E1517 +054E1509
A1111    11.0G1293
A1232    2.50G1473
A1248A   0.88M1489
A1248B   0.88M1468
A1248C   0.88M1421
A1248D   0.88M1399
A1255    1.34C1525
A1311    3.20G1363
A1339    3.50G1337
A1353    6.50G1310*
A1955A   0.42C1498
A1955B   0.42C1638
A2058    0.71C1524
A2059A   0.71C1615
A2059B   0.71C1651
A2144    -015C1259
A2326    +037G1263
A2359    5.08C1205 8.61C1164 12.6G1129
```

APPENDIX II

Integrated Colors in (B-V) System

$X = \log A/D(0)$, Source, (B-V) (X)

```
N0016      +008C0096 +038C0094
N0023      -046C0084 +028C0083 +030C0080
N0068      -037C0089
N0069      -004C0100
N0071      -028C0112 -007C0100
N0072      -010C0113 +020C0101
N0072A     0.61C0098
N0080      -015C0101
N0083      -011C0107
N0105      2.27C0072
N0125      -006L0084 -030L0087 +023C0099 +048C0095
N0127      -001L0103 -025L0094
N0128      +017C0101 +020C0099 -034L0101 -058L0102
N0130      0.68L0077 0.40L0082
N0147      +024B0096 -032B0093 -034C0069 -009C0087 +049G0094
N0151      -076C0109 +015C0085
N0157      -097C0087 -012C0056 +014C0060 +028C0059 +017G0083
N0160      -065C0106 +010C0097
N0178      +020C0058
N0182      +003C0085
N0185      -009B0101 -032B0093 -009C0086 +042G0096 -012H0089 -002H0091 +002H0089 -086L0095
N0194      +017C0100 +047C0088
N0205      -027B0085 -050B0076 -053C0074 -028C0076 -013C0079 -088D0070 -133D0059 -027E0078 +045G0084 -104L0070
N0210      -110C0095 -025C0083 +015C0075
N0214      -064C0085 +021C0072
N0221      -049A0094 +010B0096 -067B0094 -066C0091 +010C0089 -050D0093 -095D0095 -026E0094 +050G0099 -067L0097
N0224      -216A0101 -140B0105 -171B0105 -216B0103 -252D0103 -222D0101 -200D0101 -175D0099 -166E0102 -139E0102 -139E0102
N0224        *E0092 +028G0096
N0227      +003C0092
N0247      -019C0072
N0255      -076C0069 +033C0061
N0278      -068C0071 +017C0065 +020H0069 +035H0067
N0357      -017C0106 -010C0107
N0375      -002C0102
N0379      -000C0103 +020C0103 +027C0103 -002L0102 -026L0106
N0380      -005C0101 +016C0103 +022C0106 -006L0097 -030L0105
N0382      +003L0102 -021L0095
N0383      +016C0102 -030L0104
N0384      +019C0089 -004L0094 -028L0100
N0385      +019C0092 +025C0103 -004L0092 -028L0102
N0386      +001C0104 -001L0080 -025L0104
N0388      +001C0105 +022C0085 +028C0092 -001L0117 -025L0114
N0404      +008C0088 +046G0101 -012H0087 +010H0091
N0428      +010C0050 +015C0051 +007G0048
N0470      -046L0074 -070L0079 -085L0089


N0474      -060C0091 -039C0088 -061L0090
N0488      -106C0098 -094C0097 -021C0086 +027G0095 -004H0089 +016H0081
N0499      -028L0106
N0507      -032L0101
N0514      +034C0067
N0520      -084C0064 +027C0078 +041C0077 +049G0091 -050L0070
N0524      +053A0104 -057C0107 -013C0100 +016C0092 -035L0106 -043L0107 -059L0110 -093L0111
N0560      +046C0100 +048C0095 -014L0091
N0564      -009C0097
N0578      -074C0067 +002C0066 +016C0060 +019G0054
N0584      +056A0094 -017C0086
N0596      -012C0086
N0598      -168A0073 -109B0073 -134E0059 +013G0056      *E0055
N0613      +028C0077
N0628      -026C0072 -147C0086 -022C0063 -004C0063 +011G0057
N0636      +026C0094
N0660      -002G0084
N0672      +014C0060 +026G0058
N0681      -068C0091 +017C0089
N0718      -075C0086 +010C0083
N0720      -026A0100 +006C0091
N0721      -009C0070
N0736      -004C0097 +017C0092
N0741      -008C0104 -001C0101
N0750      -006C0104 -031L0105 -039L0101
N0751      -002C0092 -028L0104 -036L0102
N0750.     1.15C0094 2.27C0109 0.96H0099 1.43H0102
N0753      +009C0067 +029G0064 -014H0077 +009H0070
N0770      -014C0115
N0772      -003C0079 +030G0079
N0779      +040C0086 -045C0092 +031C0084
N0784      +021G0051
N0788      +000C0074
N0803      +034G0066
N0821      -047C0110 -004C0096 +026C0096 +028C0101 +051C0094
N0864      -106C0069 -050C0069 +005C0061
N0871      +024C0063
N0877      +008C0069
N0890      -001C0096 -009H0097 +021H0098 -031L0098
N0891      +016C0092 +016G0092
N0908      -072C0077 +019C0069 +025G0069
N0922      +010C0070
N0925      -012C0060 -098C0058 -022C0061 +011C0063 +024G0056
N0936      -054A0101 +004C0092 +021G0098
N0941      +023G0055
```

```
N0949      +009H0057 +031H0068
N0972      +003C0085
N1003      +013C0056 +027G0058
N1023      -053A0103 +006C0094 +034G0105
N1042      -105C0080 +026G0057
N1048.     0.43C0098
N1052      +021C0093 +043G0091
N1055      +028G0089
N1058      -002C0054 +040G0068 +000H0064 +015H0063
N1068      -067A0079 -107C0088 -034C0069 -008C0072 +027G0084
N1073      -011C0054 +014G0057
N1079      +003C0095
N1084      -027A0064 -067C0082 +032C0065
N1087      +012C0065 -078C0060 +021C0060 +030G0058
N1090      +031G0067
N1097      -031C0099 -013C0065
N1097A     0.68C0096
N1140      +042C0043 -034L0039
N1156      +001C0049 +027C0060 +043G0054 -058L0056
N1169      -044H0097 -014H0090
N1175      +001H0101 +031H0098
N1199      -030L0102
N1201      -000C0089 -060L0102
N1209      +001C0092 +030C0100 +056C0097 -029L0098
N1232      -097C0110 -007C0076 +014G0061
N1270      -009C0113
N1272      -017C0116 -002H0117 +016H0109 +038H0100
N1273      -005C0112 +008H0114 +026H0120
N1275      -039A0091 -005C0080
N1277      -010A0109 +002C0108
N1278      -023A0100 -010C0106
N1281      -015A0111
N1282      0.68C0115
N1293      -007C0104
N1294      -007C0110
N1300      -122C0085 +003C0072 +009G0067
N1302      -032C0070
N1316      -002C0082
N1317      -065C0076 -015C0067
N1325      +025G0078
N1325A     +008G0062
N1331      +007C0077
N1332      -065C0106 +025C0090 -051L0105
N1337      +011G0058
N1359      +033C0039


N1365      -025E0070
N1380      -019C0079 -056L0107
N1385      +003C0066
N1395      -015C0092
N1398      -118C0094 -008C0097
N1399      -063C0089 -013C0076 -049L0095 -073L0095
N1400      -002A0080 +001C0093 +031C0095 +056C0093
N1404      -051C0091 -000C0085 -037L0112*
N1407      -014A0106 -054C0107 +019C0096
N1426      -051C0090 +004C0080 +034C0091 +059C0086
N1439      -005C0088
N1441      +012C0100
N1449      +022C0089
N1451      +032C0106
N1453      +003C0104 -027L0109
N1515      -050M0097 -020M0085
N1518      +026C0062
N1533      -039M0099 -009M0093
N1543      -070M0100 -044M0099 -014M0096
N1546      -024M0094 +006M0087
N1549      -069M0093 -043M0097 -013M0088
N1553      -071M0099 -045M0097 -015M0090
N1559      -011M0045
N1560      +008G0073
N1566      -141M0072 -114M0080 -088M0074 -058M0087
N1569      +009C0081 +044G0071
N1574      -015M0093 +015M0078
N1587      -008C0096
N1596      -023M0094 +007M0092
N1600      -006A0131 -002C0097 +030C0095 +044C0096 -024L0101 -048L0104
N1601      +004C0095 -021L0096
N1617      -074M0102 -048M0099 -018M0093
N1637      -053A0085 -020C0058 +005C0066 +030G0065
N1640      -076C0089 +009C0074
N1659      +022C0066
N1700      -012A0110 -008C0080 +024C0088 +038C0097
N1744      -002C0051
N1784      +023G0071
N1832      -082C0089 +003C0081
N1888.     2.27C0088 4.07C0092
N1889      -014C0092
N1961      -016C0078 +009C0074 +033G0075
N1964      +021C0078 +020G0080
N2139      +011C0028
N2146      +014C0080 +021G0071
```

```
N2207     -100C0093 +010C0071
N2217     -016C0088
N2268     -085C0100 +025C0073 +022G0074
N2276     +039C0068 +024G0053
N2300     +028B0102 +027C0096 +045G0111
N2314     +008B0099 +006C0095
N2336     -123C0087 +002C0072 +020G0065
N2339     -082C0092 -027C0085 +003C0073
N2347     -060C0091 -004C0079
N2366     -123C0085 +002C0063 +016G0051
N2379     +004C0089 +025C0101
N2389     -010C0051 +013C0057
N2403     -075B0062 -126C0067 -018C0057 +023G0049
N2441     +013C0082
N2442     -081M0106 -051M0100
N2460     -095C0094 -010C0088
N2500     -004C0060 +018G0061
N2523     -048C0097 +027C0069
N2525     +005C0060 +025G0076
N2532     +004C0064
N2535     +014C0049 +017C0060
N2536     +010C0060
N2537     -008C0063 +021C0066 +010E0061 +022E0066
N2541     +012G0055
N2545     -041C0089 -020C0092 +035C0080
N2549     +008C0092 +033C0094 +010H0096 +025H0099
N2551     -026C0098 +024C0103
N2562     +020C0107 +026C0101
N2563     -003C0097 -033L0101
N2608     +013C0075
N2613     -096C0097 +017C0052
N2633     -078C0060 -043C0080 +008C0097
N2639     +027C0088
N2642     -066C0105
N2646     -036C0104 +019C0100
N2654     +029C0091 +006H0096 +021H0102
N2655     +008B0087 -102C0091 +008C0086 +032G0087 +017H0085
N2672     -055C0100 -020C0104 -029L0101 -053L0104
N2673     -004C0078
N2681     -039A0082 -005B0075 -006C0082 +019C0082 +032G0080 +012H0079 +027H0081
N2683     -031C0097 +027C0087 +021G0091
N2685     -090C0107 -004C0083 +021C0085 +027G0078 -002H0087 +028H0093
N2693     -048C0118 +008C0100 +018H0100
N2694     -005C0103
N2693.    2.40H0099


N2712     +006C0072 +008H0069 +023H0067
N2713     -077C0106 +032C0097
N2715     +012C0067 +018G0060 +021H0050
N2716     +015C0086 +044C0085
N2723     0.33L0100
N2732     -046C0097 +010C0098
N2744     +031C0045
N2748     +012C0076
N2749     +014C0100
N2763     +022G0063
N2768     -088C0134 +022C0094 +000H0095 +015H0093
N2775     -005C0089 +020C0085 -003H0092 +029H0090
N2776     -011C0064 -009H0056 +006H0057
N2782     +006C0070 +008H0061 +023H0064
N2784     -061L0122
N2787     -080C0102 -025C0102 +005C0100
N2798     -059C0070 +026C0074
N2805     +013G0052
N2811     +016C0073
N2820     +021G0051
N2830     -032L0090
N2831     -028C0100 -007C0105 -038L0097
N2832     -019C0098 -002H0096 +014H0103 -050L0103
N2841     -069A0095 +004C0089 +022C0083 +021G0084
N2844     +006H0082 +022H0079
N2855     +005C0088 -054L0101 -104L0101
N2859     -047A0095 -014C0091 +011C0096
N2865     +035C0067 +038C0083
N2880     +032C0088
N2903     -067A0067 -108C0080 -018C0073 +000C0069 -043D0071 -067D0072 -093D0074 -116D0070 -138D0066 +013G0060
N2911     +013C0104 -017L0108 -067L0120
N2914     +007C0093
N2942     +007H0054 +022H0060
N2950     -011B0093 -068C0095 -013C0089 +017C0092
N2955     -018H0066 -002H0068
N2964     +008C0067 +033C0080 +025G0065 +018H0081 +025H0070 +040H0071 +042H0075
N2968     +043G0109 +035H0099 +042H0106 +057H0092 +059H0104
N2974     -009C0092 +020C0097 +046C0101
N2976     -014B0063 +025C0066 +039G0077
N2983     -012C0094 +018C0093
N2985     +009C0076 +030G0075
N2986     +001C0091 +031C0092
N3003     +028C0053 +026G0047
N3031     -102A0097 -092B0097 -177C0100 -034C0095 -127D0102 -172D0107 -136E0109 -092E0102 +012G0095
N3032     -002C0074
```

```
N3034    -012B0081 +020C0085 -038E0091 +031G0091
N3041    +011H0071 +028H0093
N3055    +020C0063
N3065    -022C0095
N3066    +009C0077
N3067    +014C0066 +040C0058
N3077    -010C0080 -009E0070 +047G0080
N3078    +007C0086 +036C0080
N3079    +022G0065
N3098    -004H0089 +012H0089
N3115    +017B0095 +026C0097 -061C0102 +008C0100 +049C0094 -018D0096 -043D0098 -089D0100
N3147    -096C0092 -011C0082 +015C0082
N3158    +040B0096 +010C0100 +040C0100 +004H0102 +020H0098
N3166    -045A0091 -040B0092 -098C0104 +013C0092 +023G0090
N3169    -047A0092 +011C0080 +026G0082
N3184    -129C0083 -004C0071 +018G0059
N3185    +011C0080 +027G0082
N3187    +017G0051
N3190    +035C0097 +020G0096
N3193    +018C0092 +049G0091 -042L0093
N3198    +013G0055
N3222    +011C0094
N3226    -011C0091
N3227    +006C0080
N3239    -040C0046
N3245    +014C0090 +039C0087 -046L0093
N3254    +013C0069
N3256    -067M0066 -041M0063
N3277    +019C0085 +022C0085
N3294    -006A0055
N3301    +009C0089
N3310    -060C0045 -009C0041
N3319    +013G0046
N3338    -084C0092 +021G0057
N3344    -126C0118 -001C0070 +020G0048
N3351    +002C0079 -023D0082 -048D0088 -073D0086 -096D0082 +017G0084
N3353    +025E0050
N3359    -078C0086 +030C0060 +024G0054
N3367    +002C0063 +027C0055
N3368    +008C0089 -017D0089 -041D0093 -066D0096 -089D0100 +030G0087
N3377    -027A0097 +006C0078 +031C0086
N3379    -000C0052 +025C0092 -060L0097 -110L0098
N3384    -038A0104 +020C0086 -081L0093 -089L0087 -115L0089
N3389    +009C0054
N3395    -000E0031


N3396    +000E0041
N3412    -076C0093 +035C0089
N3414    -025A0114 +008C0092
N3423    +024G0046
N3430    +018C0072 -018E0059
N3432    +020G0048
N3486    -044A0060 -016C0060 -002C0048 +017G0055
N3489    +009C0062 +024C0057
N3504    -025A0085 +034C0061 +043C0080
N3510    -047D0042 -070D0048
N3512    +022C0066
N3516    -050C0107 +035C0083 -041E0078 +024E0082
N3521    -052A0082 -127C0094 -002C0083 +016C0083 -053E0086 +024G0093
N3556    +014B0062 +025C0063 -033E0068 +020G0060
N3557    -032M0110 -002M0098
N3585    +023C0097 +049C0095
N3593    +006C0076
N3605    -042C0091 +043C0097
N3607    +039C0092
N3608    +025C0089
N3610    -063C0093 +023C0085
N3611    +015C0057
N3623    -062B0103 +024C0074 -045E0099 +021G0091
N3626    -014A0085 +021C0066
N3627    -092B0093 -001C0066 +017C0066 -051E0079 +025G0076
N3628    -063E0089 +013G0082
N3631    +030G0061
N3640    +017C0092
N3642    +027G0051
N3646    +029C0068 +018G0068
N3665    +021C0095
N3681    +014C0063 +031C0078
N3684    +032C0066
N3686    +019C0060
N3718    +015G0074
N3726    +006B0055 +017G0052
N3729    +035G0062
N3738    +036G0044
N3756    +020G0065
N3810    -025A0076 +004C0049 +018C0054 -007D0062 -057D0068 -102D0082 +014G0064
N3818    +042C0089
N3872    +047C0095
N3898    +005B0090
N3900    +013C0081 +039C0084
N3904    +030C0101
```

```
N3923   +006C0100
N3938   +011G0053
N3949   +031B0046
N3953   +011C0074 +027G0071
N3962   +040C0097
N3990   +035E0C86
N3991   +027E0043 +038E0031
N3992   -052E0094 +015G0082
N3994   +031E0071 +042E0051
N3995   -003E0031 +008E0016
N3998   +013B0091 +003D0096 -022D0096 -045D0098 -067D0100 +002E0096
N4008   +026E0091
N4027   -000E0055
N4030   -026E0071
N4036   +029B0089 -008E0096 +028G0089
N4038   +009B0063 -016E0059
N4039   2.30E0066
N4041   -011E0061 +025G0055
N4045   +007E0084
N4051   -100E0075 -035E0071 -024E0064 +024G0074
N4062   -017E0081
N4085   +019G0060
N4088   -031E0067 +010G0060 -055D0076 -078D0084 -100D0089
N4096   +023G0045
N4105   -002C0098
N4106   -002C0097
N4111   +033G0084
N4116   +015C0063 +019G0047
N4123   -020E0068 +006E0074 +018G0053
N4125   +006B0089
N4150   +019C0079
N4151   -084E0066 -020E0079 -008E0071
N4156   -049E0069 +027E0089
N4165   +015G0084
N4168   -004B0087 +013E0097 +047G0102
N4178   +020G0050
N4179   +021C0090 +046C0092
N4189   +018G0078
N4192   +004A0089 +023C0076 -046E0092 +014G0081
N4193   +036G0088
N4203   -025C0091 +005C0087
N4206   +019G0069
N4212   -009E0063 +030G0076
N4214   -018B0046 -120E0033 -043E0043 +024G0044
N4216   -077B0105 -060D0103 -106D0110 -036E0100 +018G0103


N4224   +024G0111
N4233   +030G0109
N4234   +023E0063
N4235   +019G0104
N4236   +019G0041
N4237   +019C0090 +052C0083
N4241   +024G0105
N4242   +027G0053
N4244   -018B0056 +010C0049 -059E0064 +010G0045
N4245   -020D0091 -045D0093 -089D0092
N4246   +016G0074
N4248   +043G0061
N4254   -044A0070 +005B0057 -034E0058 +013G0062 +000H0061
N4258   -018C0077 -151E0077 -075E0082 +011G0066
N4259   +025G0100
N4261   -029A0098
N4262   -028C0104 +027C0103 +027H0093 +042H0090 +005H0094
N4267   +003H0092 +018H0093 +018H0099 +033H0096
N4268   +030G0110
N4270   +004A0082 +030G0098
N4273   -023A0041 +009C0043 +035C0047 +022G0064
N4274   +005C0086 -005D0096 -055D0099 +022G0095
N4277   +037G0103
N4278   +010B0093 +024D0094 +000D0093 -025D0095 -048D0096 +053G0088
N4281   +017A0095 +016C0087 +040G0104
N4283   +015B0089 +008D0094 +043G0091
N4294   +020G0054
N4298   +033G0071
N4299   +028G0042
N4301   +031G0044
N4302   +025G0091
N4303   +047A0064 +003C0049 +021C0064 +024G0053
N4312   +031G0082
N4314   +006C0083 +021C0087
N4321   -072A0075 -004B0068 -119B0064 -054E0071 +019G0075 -009H0070
N4322   0.70B0082
N4339   -007B0090
N4340   +009H0099
N4341   +044G0097
N4342   +035G0098
N4343   +033G0102
N4350   +019C0085 +036H0093
N4365   -013B0095
N4371   +040G0101
N4374   -035A0101 +038B0098 +023C0098 +038C0096 -060D0101 -013E0097 +024E0100 +065G0095 +032H0096
```

```
N4379      +006C0098
N4382      +015B0088 +038G0089
N4387      +017B0092
N4388      +034G0079 +031H0062
N4394      +010C0084 +024C0073 +014G0092
N4395      +006G0053
N4402      -011E0081 +022G0081 +034H0088
N4406      -045A0095 +029B0099 -021D0093 -069D0096 -022E0094 +015E0090 +058G0095 +023H0092
N4410.     +028G0103
N4411A     3.30G0072
N4411B     3.60G0064
N4414      -008A0076 +020C0070 +034C0070
N4417      +040G0089
N4419      -041C0103 +028C0101
N4421      -013C0082 +013C0085
N4424      +026G0071
N4425      +018C0097 +027G0098
N4429      +019C0092 +038G0103
N4435      -010A0095 +023C0092 +012E0089 +043G0093 +040H0095
N4438      -067A0089 -008C0085 +006C0086 -045E0097 +022G0084
N4440      -037C0098 +018C0102 +033H0090
N4442      +028C0091 +036G0097
N4445      +028G0084
N4448      +025C0093
N4449      +016B0039 -033D0034 -104D0031 -100E0031 -023E0037 +038G0040
N4450      +002B0085 +036G0082
N4451      +006C0080
N4452      +048C0110
N4458      +005B0086 +021E0086 +050H0104
N4459      +014C0086
N4461      +032C0079 -004E0094 +024H0089 +041H0088
N4464      +013B0097
N4467      -010B0093
N4468      -001H0084 +017H0080
N4472      -080A0098 +011B0095 -040E0097 +041G0094
N4473      +006A0088 +009C0085 +034C0083 +043H0096
N4474      +029C0095
N4476      +013B0085 +030E0085 +003H0080 +021H0080 +043H0083
N4477      -011A0095 -008C0085 +026H0099
N4478      -002A0097 +033C0088 +020E0094 +011H0087 +033H0089
N4479      +004A0098 +039C0094 +017H0091 +039H0096
N4480      +012G0073
N4485      +019E0034 +034G0040
N4486      -073A0106 +018B0095 -007D0097 -031D0098 -056D0099 -079D0100 -102D0101 -098E0103 -074E0092 -032E0098 -021E0097
N4486      +046G0092 -004H0092 +013H0095


N4486B     0.70B0099 0.60C0104 0.60D0106
N4490      -028A0082 +015B0042 -025E0038 +023G0045
N4491      +025C0092
N4492      -006C0066
N4494      -021B0094
N4496.     5.2*G0061
N4501      -083A0086 -138B0107 -018D0086 -042D0091 -067D0098 -090D0105 -112D0107 -006E0080 +020G0072
N4517      +023G0074
N4517A     +023G0048
N4519      +011G0054
N4526      +025C0093 +043C0095
N4527      +036C0074 +017G0089
N4528      +008C0100
N4532      +030G0041
N4535      -091A0079 +022G0065
N4536      -041A0058 +009G0061
N4539      +025G0086
N4546      +017C0098
N4548      +012C0092 -014D0092 -038D0086 -063D0097 -108D0097 -002E0080 +020G0068 +006H0083
N4550      -013A0092 +045C0094
N4551      +010B0093
N4552      -027A0106 +008C0080 +023C0082 +038H0105
N4559      -049A0057 -046E0048 +014G0046
N4564      -027C0103 +028C0100 +051G0094
N4565      -100B0104 -083D0105 -129D0118 -048E0098 +031G0085
N4567      +034G0077
N4568      +025G0088
N4569      -040A0076 +021C0086 -010E0080 +022G0064
N4570      +053C0095
N4571      +024G0053
N4576      2.00G0078
N4578      +000B0085 -053C0099 +017C0101
N4579      -077A0091 +009B0087 -077B0098 -012D0087 -036D0085 -061D0095 -084D0096 -106D0099 -000E0088 +029G0083
N4586      +025G1001
N4594      +010B0098 -005B0098 -041E0102 +040G0098
N4596      +039G0099
N4605      -021E0050
N4606      +032G0084
N4607      +016G0093
N4608      +037G0096
N4618      -025E0050 -013E0046 +027G0043
N4621      -030A0103 +028C0095
N4625      +008E0057 +019E0066 +031G0053
N4627      +014C0080 -044D0059 +015E0063 +034G0063
N4631      -054A0052 +007C0053 -050E0059 +016G0057
```

```
N4633      +018G0065
N4634      +021G0078
N4636      +016B0092
N4638      +004A0098 +036C0077
N4639      +035G0071
N4643      -009D0096 -059D0098 -102D0101
N4647      -033A0088 -000C0073 +025G0057
N4649      -047A0107 +011B0097 +011C0094 +048G0100
N4651      +025G0058
N4653      +029G0054
N4654      +027G0067
N4656      -040E0025 +018G0042
N4660      -006A0101 +027C0094
N4666      -008A0069 -056C0097 +029C0084 +028G0071 -040D0088 -085D0101
N4668      +029G0048
N4670      +024E0043 +035E0035
N4677      -012M0105
N4683      +003M0111
N4689      +032G0067
N4691      -009E0055
N4692      +021E0083
N4696      -034M0107 -004M0106
N4697      +013C0089
N4698      +016C0078 +014D0090 -011D0093 -036D0093 -057D0094 -081D0097 +039G0093
N4699      -082C0092 -006C0093 +006D0088 -018D0090 -044D0093 -067D0094 -089D0095
N4706      -005M0107
N4709      -022M0115
N4710      +033C0084
N4712      +014G0058
N4713      -006D0045 -031D0044
N4725      -081B0099 +016G0074
N4736      -007B0075 -058E0078 +033G0076
N4742      +034C0101
N4744      0.86M0107
N4747      +020G0064
N4753      -089C0104 +001C0093 -027E0095
N4754      +023C0095
N4762      +035C0073 -063D0088
N4789      +050C0107
N4793      -043C0075 +045C0067
N4798      +034C0106
N4826      -001B0085 -052E0086 +025G0087
N4827      +048C0095
N4841.     3.36C0104
N4850      -007C0106 +023C0097


N4853      -007C0091 +022C0089
N4856      +003C0097 +017C0098
N4860      -038C0092 -017C0112
N4861      -075C0049 +000C0057
N4864      0.68C0094
N4865      +018C0103 +025C0083 -010D0098 -054D0096
N4866      +023C0086
N4867      0.68C0095
N4869      0.68C0101 1.34C0104
N4872      -033B0101 -055C0098 -034C0103
N4874      +000B0101 +028C0107 -001C0106 +022C0112 +019D0100 -007D0101 -030D0104 -077E0106 -057E0105 -045E0102 -027E0105
N4874      -005E0101 +025E0102 +013H0100 +031H0101
N4881      +023C0106 -056D0096 -012D0099
N4886      -004C0095
N4889      -026B0109 -027C0115 -004C0113 +025C0112 -033D0102 -076D0104 -012H0104 +006H0106
N4895      -020C0104 +010C0101
N4896      0.68C0097
N4898      0.68C0102
N4900      +009C0066
N4902      -079C0107 -003C0074
N4904      -000E0066
N4907      +008C0122 -001D0089 -027D0088 -050D0099 -070D0102
N4908      -007C0104
N4911      +006C0106 +046C0081 -029D0079 -072D0102
N4915      +012C0089 +042C0089
N4921      +014C0100 -011D0088 -035D0096 -060D0099 -084D0101
N4926      +013C0112 +038C0107
N4931      +027C0104
N4941      +022C0086
N4957      +055C0106
N4958      +010C0085 +035C0089
N4961      +038C0046
N4976      -069M0098 -043M0100 -013M0096
N4995      -064C0089 +012C0088
N5005      -018A0089 -089C0103 +019C0095 -025D0086 -026E0088 +030G0076 -050D0088 -073D0090 -095D0094
N5018      +030C0105
N5033      -058A0076 +003C0056 -066E0088 +005G0058
N5049      +018C0070 +043C0069
N5055      -055B0067 -067E0084 +021G0074
N5077      +017C0107
N5087      +036C0103
N5112      -026E0050
N5128      +044G0098
N5194      -002B0059 -145C0057 -002C0050 -069D0072 -094D0075 -117D0080 -140D0082 -059E0073 +013G0067
N5195      +016B0085 -095C0098 +015C0079 -045D0105 -009E0098 +046G0106
```

```
N5204    +003C0052 +022G0044
N5236    -115C0066 -007C0072 -140E0052 -075E0070
N5248    -038A0080 +004C0069 +022C0061 -021D0069 -045D0072 -070D0078 -093D0079 -046E0072 +014G0058
N5253    -002E0044
N5273    -003E0084
N5308    +024B0095 +024C0082 +049C0092
N5322    +026B0088 +001C0091 +026C0086 -010E0090
N5328    +013C0086
N5353    +032C01C0
N5354    +043C0092
N5363    -028A0104 +005B0100 -048C0106 +007C0100 -030D0098 +043G0096
N5364    -042A0080 +001C0066 +016G0067
N5371    +006C0067
N5377    +012C0092 +026C0075
N5383    -027E0071
N5394    +023C0068 +001E0069
N5395    +003C0078 -007E0074
N5426    -051C0072 -022C0069 -010E0047 +016G0064
N5427    -055C0082 -000C0063 -013E0064 +021G0066
N5457    -045C0059 -161D0076 -114E0075 +006G0047
N5473    -008C0083 +022C0085 +011E0095
N5474    -021C0067 -034E0052 +026G0048
N5485    +029C0091
N5493    +008C0086 +038C0093
N5533    +022C0089
N5548    +038C0060
N5557    +035C0095
N5560    -019D0078 +042E0086
N5566    +023C0080 -026D0091 -074D0097 -097D0099 -016E0094 +010E0092 -107L0104
N5574    +041C0083 +030E0084 -043L0085
N5576    +020C0081 -015D0092 +009E0090 -040L0091 -090L0096
N5585    +007C0052 +023G0051
N5600    +023E0049
N5633    -063C0088 -007C0056 -012D0063 -058D0070
N5638    +024C0086
N5660    -012E0049
N5668    -087C0074 +004C0068
N5672    +019B0058 -030C0072 +020C0071
N5676    -094C0110 -009C0074 +017C0067
N5687    +066C0085
N5689    +038C0094
N5701    -108L0101
N5713    +000C0069 -010E0063 +001E0064
N5728    -026A0079
N5740    +037C0061 -009E0073 +024G0078


N5746    -072C0106 +037C0091 -032E0108 +011G0103
N5757    -030A0098
N5774    +014G0063
N5775    +024G0083
N5791    -021A0098
N5806    +032C0072
N5812    +042C0098
N5813    -063C0101 +010C0099 +012C0098
N5820    +042B0117 +041C0094
N5831    +037C0081 +038E0095
N5838    +029C0095 +004E0096
N5845    +000A0086
N5846    -045A0079 +042G0096
N5846.   +031C0091 +006E0105 +032E0108
N5846A   +014C0099 +049C0099
N5850    +021C0086 +012C0083 +026C0086 -046D0097 -095D0101 -013E0087 +013E0083 +029G0071
N5854    +025C0085
N5857    +045C0071
N5859    +035C0089 +041C0082
N5857.   5.69C0080
N5866    +000B0086 +025C0083 +000E0090
N5878    +023C0082
N5879    +019C0061 +033C0061 -017E0070
N5898    +016A0094 +049C0073
N5899    +038C0077
N5903    +008A0104 +041C0082
N5907    +024C0083 -091D0098 -045E0088 +013G0076
N5921    -021C0091 +002C0067
N5962    +029C0066
N5970    +037C0074
N5976    +015C0103
N5981    -010C0091
N5982    +031B0092 +031C0092 +020E0094
N5985    -033E0087
N6015    -020B0057 +005C0062 -031E0059 +010G0060
N6027A   0.42C0080
N6027D   0.42C0098 0.68C0090
N6052    +024E0044
N6070    +011C0068 -016E0074
N6106    -024A0083
N6118    -045A0091
N6181    +015C0061 +029C0064
N6207    +008C0055 -005E0055
N6217    +031C0065 -005E0067
N6239    +030C0056 +040C0067 -005D0047 -030D0049 -075D0051
```

```
N6314      -033C0085 +023C0080
N6340      -004C0086 +021C0086
N6359      +030C0089
N6384      -068A0094 -018C0069 +005C0072 -046E0091 +012G0077
N6412      +028C0055 +023G0055
N6482      +007A0091 +017C01C1
N6503      +008B0068 +004C0069 -031D0072 -079D0074 -032E0071 +030G0067
N6574      -001A0086 +007B0084 +002C0083 +032C0083 -026D0084 -048D0087
N6615      -048A0097
N6627      -045A0110 +028C0101
N6635      -030A0101 -028C0102
N6643      -094C0077 +016C0073 +015G0066
N6654      -079C0091 +006C0092
N6658      +030A0104 -028C0107 +016C0115 +022C0103
N6661      -043A0097 -041C0107 +032C0104 +035C0101
N6674      -079C0110 +020C0082
N67O2      -002C0103 +019C0099
N6703      -010C0092
N6710      1.15C0100 1.34C0104
N6769      -032M0083
N6770      -037M0097
N6771      -005M0105
N6814      -031A0091 -071C0109 +002C0087 +027C0088
N6824      +003C0083
N6835      +005A0088
N6851      -003M0094
N6861      -015M0106
N6861D     -018M0101
N6868      -021M0103
N6870      -019M0101
N6875      -007M0099
N6878      -016M0072
N6893      -024M0106
N6907      -038A0072
N6909      -004M0090
N6921      +023A0091 +051C0111
N6927      -005C0099
N6928      -041C0108 +032C0105 +035C0098
N6930      +017C0089
N6944      -003C0109 -032D0102
N6946      -044A0088 -024C0080 +014G0083
N6951      -042A0103 -099C0112 -014C0104 +027G0086
N6954      +006C0089
N6962      -072C0112 +002C0087
N6963      0.32C0097 0.71C0088


N6964      -031C0103 +012C0106 +019C0100 -038D0101
N7013      -018A0098
N7137      +024C0066 +038C0070 +047C0076 -016H0071 +024H0072
N7171      -067C0092 +006C0073
N7177      -030A0083 +005B0080 -071C0098 +003C0083 +020C0088 +013H0078 +035H0083
N7213      -046M0090
N7217      -041A0100 +009B0093 -032B0098 -038C0096 +017C0094 +040G0091 +009H0094 +024H0092
N7240      -034C0109 -022C0107
N7242      +007C0100
N7252      +000C0078
N7302      -029C0096 +045C0085
N7314      +015C0070 +029C0073
N7317      -031C0095 +004C0090
N7318A     -021C0107 -009C0105 +011C0100
N7318B     -067C0111 -033C0101
N7319.     1.15C0097 1.34C0092
N7319      -007C0073
N7331      -152C0109 -118C0107 +013C0089 +022G0083 -079D0100 -102D0103 -124D0108
N7332      +013B0092 -075C0091 +011C0086 -041L0090 -065L0092 -080L0091 -103L0092
N7339      +016B0091 +014C0085
N7343      +011C0089 -046D0081
N7377      -064C0106 +021C0082
N7385      -010C0103
N7386      +001C0106
N7392      +019C0095
N7410      -069M0096 -014M0093
N7412      -024M0058
N7418      -077M0075 -022M0060
N7421      -057M0083 -002M0070
N7424      -060M0C61
N7448      -022A0C64 +013B0052 +011C0051 +036C0052
N7457      -030A0091 -021B0091 -027C0092 +005H0087 +020H0089 +035H0097
N7469      +029C0067
N7479      -103C0106 +008C0069 -052D0086 -097D0093
N7496      -019M0058
N7499      -004C0106
N7501      -004C0115
N7503      +019C0104 +025C0111
N7507      +001C0089 +030C0088
N7531      -023M0076
N7537      +023C0063
N7541      +029C0076
N7552      -071M0073 -070M0070 -045M0072 -015M0072
N7562      -035C0110 -014C0104 +015C0110 +041C0106
N7576      +016C0082
```

```
N7582      -070M0090 -045M0083 -015M0081
N7585      -010C0092
N7590      -054M0075 -029M0070 +001M0061
N7599      -072M0070 -047M0068*-017M0065
N7600      +036C0092
N7606      -092C0096 +007C0076
N7611      -027C0092 +017C0093 +024C0097 -029L0105 -037L0087
N7617      +025C0092 -028L0097 -036L0106
N7619      +039A0103 -043C0103 +000C0109 +007C0101 +030C0100 +047C0104
N7623      -007C0100 +043C0103 +014L0109 -010L0105 -014D0098
N7625      +027C0073
N7626      +000A0094 +004C0102 +011C0092 -040C0102 +050C0101 +033C0101 +036C0103 -018L0106 -042L0104 -046D0104
N7640      -001C0067 +014G0048
N7671      -006C0092
N7678      -075C0086 +010C0069
N7679      +006C0057
N7682      -000C0094 +029C0100
N7716      -053C0063 +020C0073 +023H0076 +038H0076
N7723      -036A0079 -077C0074 -004C0066 +022C0071
N7727      -049A0100 -089C0072 -016C0086 +010C0085
N7741      -015C0066 -088C0057 +002C0066 +025G0057 +003H0062 +018H0079
N7742      -011C0072 +019C0073
N7743      -000C0099
N7769      -056C0091 -012C0060
N7770      -004C0060
N7771      +021C0085
N7785      +008C0104
N7793      -052A0072 -047C0066
N7814      -052A0086 -093C0098 +006C0097
```

```
I0010      -019C0089
I0239      +020G0072
I0342      1.19A0095 2.27C0094
I0356      1.19A0142
I0391      +034C0033
I0775      +028H0093 +050H0107
I0783      0.70B0086
I0783A     0.40B0086
I1183      0.68C0112
I1185      0.71C0089 1.15C0092
I1194      0.71C0092 1.15C0105
I1302      0.71C0077
I1303      -016A0091
I1308      1.15C0074
I1317      0.32C0077 0.71C0090
I1459      0.49M0101 1.76M0097
I1460      0.71C0067 1.15C0086
I1613      +013C0066 +034G0055
I1727      -007C0066 +022G0048
I1784      3.10G0091
I2233      +030G0051
I2389      +002C0067
I2574      +014G0046
I3061      +021G0078
I3115      +003G0070
I3259      +032G0076
I3267      +037G0078
I3475      +026E0064 +036E0069
I3476      +001H0039 +023H0050
I3896      -013M0103
I3946      0.68C0115 1.34C0100
I4011      0.12E0098 0.19E0097 0.25E0100 0.38E0097 0.63E0080
I4012      1.34C0115
I4021      0.68C0081 1.34C0077
I4045      0.68C0102
I4051      0.68C0100 0.35D0101 1.08D0097
I5267      -078M0098 -053M0097 -023M0094
I5273      -014M0048
```

```
A0235    0.71C0074
A0438    0.71C0089*
A0814    +015G0051
A0936    5.30G0046
A0947    0.60D0034
A0956    7.00G0044
A0957    2.40C0053  7.70G0050
A1006    12.0G0097
A1009    +024C0055  +026G0041
A1101    +053E0055  +064E0088
A1111    11.0G0091
A1232    2.50G0053
A1248A   0.88M0112
A1248B   0.88M0085
A1248C   0.88M0101
A1248D   0.88M0110
A1255    1.34C0028
A1311    3.20G0037
A1955A   0.42C0122
A1955B   0.42C0097
A2058    0.71C0108
A2059A   0.71C0069
A2059B   0.71C0066
A2144    -016C0091
A2326    +037G0059
A2359    5.08C0043  8.61C0034  12.6G0044
```

APPENDIX III

Integrated Colors in (U-B) System

$X = \log A/D(0)$, Source, (U-B) (X)

```
N0125      -006L0037 -030L0036
N0127      -001L0046 -025L0041
N0128      -034L0061 -058L0062
N0130      0.40L0001
N0185      -086L0037
N0205      -104L0017 -133D0010 -088D0015 -027E0018
N0221      -067L0049 -095D0050 -050D0050 -026E0059
N0224      -252D0068 -222D0066 -200D0067 -174D0066 -164E0066 -151D0064 -139E0066 -139E0062      *E0050
N0379      -002L0054 -026L0057
N0380      -006L0063 -030L0060
N0382      +003L0056 -021L0051
N0383      -030L0062
N0384      -004L0059 -028L0055
N0385      -004L0056 -028L0050
N0386      -001L0065 -025L0056
N0388      -001L0042 -025L0056
N0470      -046L0002 -070L0015 -085L0015
N0474      -061L0046
N0499      -028L0064
N0507      -032L0060
N0520      -050L0021
N0524      -035L0061 -043L0068 -059L0068 -093L0075
N0560      -014L0051
N0598      -134E0001      *E-010
N0750      -031L0056 -039L0066
N0751      -028L0056 -036L0094
N0890      -031L0054
N1201      -060L0056
N1209      -029L0063
N1332      -051L0088
N1365      -025E0017
N1380      -056L0044
N1399      -049L0049
N1404      -037L0051*
N1453      -027L0067
N1515      -050M0035 -020M0022
N1533      -039M0048 -009M0063
N1543      -070M0043*-044M0050 -014M0050
N1546      -024M0025 +006M0027
N1549      -069M0053 -043M0050 -013M0050
N1553      -071M0052 -045M0049 -015M0053
N1559      -011M-005
N1566      -141M-010*-114M-004 -088M0000 -058M0003
N1574      -015M0045 +015M0034
N1596      -023M0039*+007M0042*


N1600      -024L0060
N1601      -021L0050
N1617      -074M0055*-048M0051 -018M0045
N2442      -081M0028 -051M0032
N2537      +010E-005 +022E-016
N2563      -033L0068
N2672      -029L0057 -053L0036
N2723      0.33L0053
N2784      -061L0069
N2830      -032L0030
N2831      -038L0048
N2832      -050L0064
N2855      -054L0052
N2903      -138D-004 -116D0005 -093D0008 -067D0012 -043D0011
N2911      -017L0065
N3031      -172D0068 -136E0076*-127D0060 -092E0064
N3034      -038E0038
N3077      -009E0010
N3115      -089D0062 -043D0054 -018D0056
N3193      -042L0058
N3245      -046L0051
N3256      -067M-032*-041M-015*
N3351      -096D0016 -073D0026 -048D0029 -023D0024
N3353      +025E-030
N3368      -089D0052 -066D0048 -041D0041 -017D0037
N3379      -060L0063
N3384      -081L0070 -089L0047 -115L0058
N3395      +000E-025
N3396      +000E-021
N3430      -018E0008
N3510      -070D-020 -047D-019
N3516      -041E-012 +024E-002
N3521      -053E0033
N3556      -033E0004
N3557      -032M0066 -002M0060
N3623      -045E0056
N3627      -051E0022
N3628      -063E0052
N3810      -102D0021 -057D0003 -007D-005
N3990      +035E0039
N3991      +027E-050 +038E-014
N3992      -052E0049
N3994      +031E-013 +042E-012
N3995      -003E-031 +008E-045
N3998      -067D0058 -045D0056 -022D0054 +003D0052 +002E0054
```

```
N4008    +026E0025
N4027    +000E-006
N4030    -026E0003
N4036    -008E0058
N4038    -016E-023
N4039    2.30E-006
N4041    -011E-004
N4045    +007E0026
N4051    -100E-006 -035E0003 -024E0010
N4062    -017E0011
N4088    -055D0011 -078D0020 -100D0028 -031E0008
N4123    -020E-004 +006E-002
N4151    -084E-031 -020E-006 -008E-006
N4156    -049E-020 +027E0026
N4168    +013E0040
N4192    -046E0048
N4212    -009E0012
N4214    -120E-038 -043E-034
N4216    -106D0072 -060D0062 -036E0060
N4234    +023E-016
N4244    -059E0004
N4245    -089D0040 -045D0045 -020D0045 +003D0039*
N4254    -034E0004
N4258    -151E0030 -075E0024
N4274    -055D0052 -005D0046
N4278    -048D0054 -025D0050 +000D0048 +024D0050
N4283    +008D0056
N4321    -054E0010
N4374    -060D0060 -013E0057 +024E0060
N4402    -011E0016
N4406    -069D0059 -022E0059 -021D0054 +015E0045
N4435    +012E0049
N4438    -045E0047
N4449    -104D-036 -100E-034 -033D-032 -023E-032
N4458    +021E0036
N4461    -004E0053
N4472    -040E0064
N4476    +030E0027
N4478    +020E0034
N4485    +019E-023
N4486    -102D0057 -098E0061 -079D0055 -074E0062 -056D0058 -032E0059 -031D0057 -021E0060 -007D0054
N4486B   0.60D0046
N4490    -025E-016
N4501    -112D0065 -090D0058 -067D0048 -042D0037 -018D0029 -006E0032
N4548    -108D0054 -063D0050 -038D0042 -014D0034 -003E0035


N4559    -046E-001
N4565    -129D0074 -083D0058 -048E0058
N4569    -010E0031
N4579    -106D0050 -084D0048 -061D0047 -036D0040 -012D0037 +000E0034
N4594    -041E0064
N4605    -021E-007
N4618    -025E-010 -013E-016
N4625    +008E-007 +019E-022
N4627    -044D0008 +015E0012
N4631    -050E-006
N4643    -102D0059 -059D0058 -009D0052
N4656    -040E-029
N4666    -040D0027 -085D0044
N4670    +024E-040 +035E-056
N4677    -012M0048
N4683    +003M0063
N4691    -009E-008
N4692    +021E0064
N4696    -034M0061 -004M0071
N4698    -081D0052 -057D0052 -036D0052 -011D0046 +014D0044
N4699    -081D0052 -057D0048 -036D0045 -011D0040 +014D0035
N4706    -005M0054*
N4709    -022M0064
N4713    -031D-024 -006D-025
N4736    -058E0022
N4753    -027E0053
N4762    -063D0050
N4826    -052E0036
N4865    -054D0052 -010D0052
N4874    -074E0062 -057E0064 -045E0063 -030D0060 -027E0059 -007D0056 -005E0058 +019D0056 +025E0058
N4881    -056D0058 -012D0044
N4889    -076D0064 -033D0060
N4904    -000E-004
N4907    -070D0057 -050D0053 -027D0038 -001D0037
N4911    -072D0042 -029D0022
N4921    -084D0056 -060D0052 -035D0047 -011D0040
N4976    -069M0047 -043M0038 -013M0036
N5005    -026E0040 -025D0035 -050D0042 -073D0044 -095D0051
N5033    -066E0026
N5055    -067E0020
N5112    -026E-023
N5194    -140D0031 -117D0024 -094D0014 -069D0011 -059E0006
N5195    -045D0056 -009E0044
N5236    -140E-018 -075E0006
N5248    -093D0015 -070D0015 -046E0012 -045D0011 -021D0006
```

```
N5253     -002E-019
N5273     -003E0041
N5322     -010E0049
N5363     -030D0058
N5383     -027E0012
N5394     +001E0016
N5395     -007E0011
N5426     -010E-001
N5427     -013E-006
N5457     -161D0017 -114E0021
N5473     +011E0054
N5474     -034E-006
N5560     -019D0015 +042E0021*
N5566     -107L0063 -097D0056 -074D0053 -026D0046 -016E0051 +010E0042
N5574     -043L0036 +030E0028
N5576     -040L0043 -015D0046 +009E0048 -090L0050
N5600     +023E-009
N5633     -058D0008 -012D0000
N5660     -012E-014
N5701     -108L0105
N5713     -010E0002 -001E0005
N5740     -009E0018
N5746     -032E0058
N5831     +038E0060
N5838     +004E0068
N5846     +006E0060 +032E0058
N5850     -095D0060 -046D0056 +013E0026
N5866     +000E0038
N5879     -017E0010
N5907     -091D0048 -045E0036
N5982     +020E0053
N5985     -033E0029
N6015     -031E0004
N6052     +024E-030
N6070     -016E0020
N6207     -005E-021
N6217     -005E-010
N6239     -075D-022 -030D-016 -005D-017
N6384     -046E0042
N6503     -079D0022 -032E-003 -031D0008
N6574     -026D0022 -048D0022
N6769     -032M0028
N6770     -037M002 *
N6771     -005M003 *
N6851     -003M0048


N6861     -015M0055
N6861D    -018M0053
N6868     -021M0061
N6870     -019M006 *
N6875     -007M0046
N6878     -016M0024
N6893     -024M006 *
N6909     -004M004 *
N6944     -032D0069
N6964     -038D0068
N7213     -046M0043
N7331     -079D0053 -102D0057 -124D0068
N7332     -041L0038 -065L0045 -080L0049 -103L0049
N7343     -046D0027
N7410     -069M0056 -014M0052
N7412     -024M0005
N7418     -077M0010 -022M-005
N7421     -057M0028 -002M0010
N7424     -060M0001
N7479     -052D0032 -097D0044
N7496     -019M0000
N7531     -023M0002
N7552     -071M0009 -070M0002 -045M0015 -015M0013
N7582     -070M0028 -045M0030 -015M0022
N7590     -054M0008 -029M0004 +001M0005
N7599     -072M0009 -047M-002*-017M-001
N7611     -029L0063 -037L0076
N7617     -028L0036 -036L0078
N7619     -022L0062 -046L0065 -054L0066 -050D0074
N7623     +014L0051 -010L0067 -014D0065
N7626     -018L0060 -042L0056 -046D0072
I1459     0.49M0065 1.76M0055
I3475     +026E0017 +036E0009
I3896     -013M0091*
I4011     0.12E0049 0.19E0047 0.25E0040 0.38E0052 0.63E0055
I4051     0.35D0056 1.08D0055
I5267     -078M0060 -053M0055 -023M0044
I5273     -014M0002
A0947     0.60D-029
A1101     +053E-025 +064E-008
A1248A    0.88M0046
A1248B    0.88M0055
A1248C    0.88M0065
A1248D    0.88M0048
```

APPENDIX IV

Listing by Right Ascension

NGC, I or A, RA, D (1950)

NGC	RA (1950)	D	NGC	RA (1950)	D	NGC	RA (1950)	D	NGC	RA (1950)	D	NGC	RA (1950)	D
I5381	0 0.6	15 40	N0275	0 48.5	-7 20	N0684	1 47.4	27 24	N1055	2 39.2	0 16	N1375	3 33.3	-35 26
N7814	0 0.7	15 51	N0278	0 49.2	47 18	I1731	1 47.4	26 57	N1063	2 39.7	-5 47	N1374	3 33.4	-35 24
N7817	0 1.4	20 28	N0289	0 50.4	-31 29	N0691	1 47.9	21 31	N1068	2 40.1	-0 14	N1379	3 34.2	-35 37
N0001	0 4.7	27 26	A0051	0 51.0	-73 6	N0693	1 47.9	5 54	N1058	2 40.2	37 8	N1380	3 34.6	-35 9
N0002	0 4.7	27 24	N0300	0 52.6	-37 58	N0694	1 48.3	21 44	N1072	2 41.0	0 5	N1376	3 34.7	-5 12
I1530	0 4.8	32 19	N0309	0 54.0	-10 13	I0167	1 48.3	21 38	N1073	2 41.2	1 10	N1381	3 34.7	-35 28
N0007	0 5.8	-30 11	A0055	0 54.6	-4 16	N0695	1 48.4	22 20	N1079	2 41.6	-29 13	N1380A	3 34.8	-34 53
N0008	0 6.1	23 34	N0315	0 55.1	30 5	N0697	1 48.5	22 6	N1084	2 43.5	-7 47	I1970	3 34.8	-44 7
N0010	0 6.1	-34 9	N0327	0 55.4	-5 24	N0701	1 48.6	-9 57	N1087	2 43.9	-0 42	N1386	3 35.0	-36 10
N0012	0 6.1	4 20	N0329	0 55.5	-5 20	I1738	1 48.7	-10 2	N1090	2 44.0	-0 27	N1380B	3 35.1	-35 21
N0013	0 6.2	33 9	N0337	0 57.3	-7 51	N0702	1 48.8	-4 18	N1097	2 44.3	-30 29	N1387	3 35.1	-35 41
N0009	0 6.3	23 33	A0058	0 57.6	-33 58	N0706	1 49.2	6 4	N1097A	2 44.3	-30 29	N1385	3 35.2	-24 40
N0016	0 6.5	27 27	N0337A	0 59.2	-7 52	N0720	1 50.6	-13 59	N1094	2 44.8	-0 28	N1389	3 35.3	-35 55
N0020	0 7.0	33 1	N0352	0 59.6	-4 31	N0718	1 50.7	3 57	N1104	2 46.0	-0 29	N1395	3 36.3	-23 11
N0023	0 7.3	25 39	N0357	1 0.8	-6 37	N0721	1 51.9	39 8	I1856	2 46.2	-0 56	N1393	3 36.4	-18 36
N0024	0 7.4	-25 15	I1613	1 2.5	1 52	N0731	1 52.5	-9 15	N1136	2 49.4	-55 16	N1399	3 36.6	-35 37
N0021	0 7.8	32 51	A0103	1 2.6	-6 29	N0736	1 53.8	32 48	N1140	2 52.2	-10 14	N1398	3 36.8	-26 30
N0026	0 7.8	25 34	N0375	1 4.3	32 5	N0741	1 53.8	5 23	N1143	2 52.6	-0 22	N1394	3 36.9	-18 27
N0029	0 8.2	33 4	N0379	1 4.5	32 15	N0755	1 53.8	-9 18	N1144	2 52.6	-0 22	N1404	3 37.0	-35 45
N0045	0 11.4	-23 27	N0380	1 4.5	32 13	N0740	1 54.0	32 47	A0255	2 55.1	-54 48	N1411	3 37.1	-44 15
N0048	0 11.5	47 58	N0382	1 4.6	32 8	N0750	1 54.6	32 58	N1156	2 56.7	25 3	N1400	3 37.2	-18 51
N0051	0 12.0	47 59	N0383	1 4.6	32 9	N0751	1 54.6	32 58	N1172	2 59.3	-15 2	N1401	3 37.2	-22 53
N0055	0 12.5	-39 30	N0384	1 4.6	32 2	N0753	1 54.6	35 41	N1179	2 59.7	-19 6	N1406	3 37.5	-31 28
N0067	0 15.7	29 48	N0385	1 4.7	32 3	N0759	1 54.8	36 6	N1169	3 0.1	46 12	N1427A	3 37.7	-35 47
N0068	0 15.8	29 48	N0386	1 4.7	32 5	N0761	1 54.9	33 9	N1187	3 0.4	-23 4	N1407	3 37.9	-18 44
N0069	0 15.8	29 46	N0388	1 5.0	32 2	N0782	1 56.1	-58 1	N1175	3 1.3	42 8	I0343	3 37.9	-18 36
N0070	0 15.9	29 49	N0406	1 5.8	-70 9	N0770	1 56.5	18 43	N1199	3 1.3	-15 48	N1415	3 38.7	-22 43
N0071	0 15.9	29 48	N0403	1 6.4	32 29	N0772	1 56.6	18 46	N1201	3 2.0	-26 15	N1416	3 38.8	-22 56
N0072	0 15.9	29 46	I0079	1 6.4	-16 13	N0779	1 57.2	-6 12	N1185	3 2.3	42 38	N1422	3 39.3	-21 51
N0072A	0 16.0	29 45	N0404	1 6.6	35 27	N0777	1 57.3	31 12	N1209	3 3.8	-15 48	N1417	3 39.5	-4 52
I0010	0 17.6	59 2	N0407	1 7.8	32 52	N0784	1 58.4	28 36	N1232	3 7.5	-20 46	I0346	3 39.5	-18 25
N0080	0 18.6	22 5	N0410	1 8.2	32 53	N0788	1 58.6	-7 3	N1232A	3 8.0	-20 47	N1418	3 39.8	-4 53
N0083	0 18.8	22 9	N0434	1 10.2	-58 31	N0803	2 1.0	15 47	N1249	3 8.6	-53 32	N1425	3 40.1	-30 4
N0095	0 19.6	10 12	N0428	1 10.4	0 43	N0808	2 1.6	-23 32	N1241	3 8.8	-9 7	N1421	3 40.2	-13 40
N0100	0 21.4	16 13	N0434A	1 10.5	-58 29	N0821	2 5.6	10 46	N1242	3 8.9	-9 6	N1427	3 40.4	-35 34
N0105	0 22.7	12 37	N0440	1 10.9	-58 33	N0818	2 5.7	38 32	N1313A	3 9.4	-66 52	N1433	3 40.4	-47 24
N0120	0 25.0	-1 47	N0439	1 11.5	-32 0	N0829	2 6.2	-8 2	N1248	3 10.3	-5 25	N1428	3 40.5	-35 19
N0124	0 25.4	-2 5	N0442	1 11.9	-1 17	N0833	2 7.0	-10 22	N1255	3 11.4	-25 58	N1426	3 40.6	-22 16
A0026	0 26.1	2 39	N0450	1 13.0	-1 7	N0835	2 7.0	-10 22	N1288	3 15.3	-32 46	N1424	3 40.8	-4 53
N0125	0 26.3	2 33	N0467	1 16.6	3 3	N0838	2 7.2	-10 23	N1291	3 15.5	-41 17	N1437	3 41.7	-36 1
N0127	0 26.6	2 36	N0470	1 17.1	3 9	N0839	2 7.3	-10 26	N1270	3 15.6	41 18	I0342	3 41.9	67 57
N0128	0 26.7	2 35	N0473	1 17.5	16 14	N0842	2 7.4	-8 0	N1272	3 15.7	41 16	N1439	3 42.6	-22 5
N0131	0 27.1	-33 33	N0474	1 17.5	3 10	I1783	2 7.8	-33 13	N1292	3 16.0	-27 48	N1440	3 42.8	-18 27
N0132	0 27.7	1 49	N0491A	1 17.6	-34 8	N0848	2 8.2	-10 34	N1273	3 16.1	41 22	N1448	3 42.9	-44 48
N0134	0 27.9	-33 32	A0118	1 18.4	15 26	N0864	2 12.8	5 45	N1274	3 16.4	41 22	N1452	3 43.1	-18 47

NGC	RA (1950)	D	NGC	RA (1950)	D	NGC	RA (1950)	D	NGC	RA (1950)	D	NGC	RA (1950)	D
N0145	0 29.2	-5 26	N0488	1 19.1	5 0	I1784	2 13.2	32 24	N1275	3 16.5	41 20	N1441	3 43.2	-4 15
N0147	0 30.4	48 14	N0491	1 19.1	-34 19	I1788	2 13.4	-31 26	N1277	3 16.5	41 24	N1449	3 43.5	-4 18
I1554	0 30.7	-32 32	N0495	1 20.1	33 12	N0871	2 14.5	14 19	N1278	3 16.5	41 23	N1451	3 43.6	-4 14
N0151	0 31.6	-9 58	N0499	1 20.4	33 11	N0876	2 15.2	14 18	N1282	3 16.6	41 8	N1453	3 44.0	-4 8
N0148	0 31.8	-32 4	N0507	1 20.7	9 10	N0877	2 15.3	14 19	N1281	3 16.7	41 27	N1461	3 46.1	-16 32
N0150	0 31.8	-28 5	N0509	1 20.8	32 59	A0218A	2 18.5	39 9	N1297	3 17.0	-19 16	N1483	3 51.2	-47 38
N0157	0 32.3	-8 40	N0514	1 21.3	12 39	A0218B	2 18.5	39 9	N1300	3 17.5	-19 35	I2006	3 52.2	-36 8
N0160	0 33.4	23 41	N0516	1 21.5	9 18	N0890	2 19.1	33 2	I1913	3 17.5	-32 39	N1482	3 52.5	-20 39
N0163	0 33.5	-10 24	N0518	1 21.6	9 3	N0895	2 19.1	-5 45	N1313	3 17.6	-66 40	N2573	3 54.0	-89 52
N0165	0 33.9	-10 24	N0520	1 22.0	3 32	N0891	2 19.3	42 7	N1302	3 17.7	-26 14	N1487	3 54.1	-42 31
N0169	0 34.3	23 43	N0521	1 22.0	1 28	N0907	2 20.7	-20 56	N1293	3 17.9	41 10	N1469	3 54.2	68 29
I1559	0 34.3	23 43	N0522	1 22.1	9 44	N0908	2 20.8	-21 27	N1294	3 18.0	41 8	N1493	3 55.9	-46 21
N0175	0 34.9	-20 12	N0524	1 22.1	9 16	N0898	2 20.9	41 43	N1305	3 18.8	-2 30	N1494	3 56.2	-49 3
A0035	0 35.0	-34 1	N0532	1 22.7	9 0	N0922	2 22.9	-25 1	N1310	3 19.1	-37 19	N1511	3 59.3	-67 46
N0182	0 35.7	2 28	N0533	1 22.9	1 30	N0918	2 23.2	18 17	N1309	3 19.8	-15 35	N1485	3 59.5	70 55
N0185	0 36.1	48 4	N0545	1 23.4	-1 36	N0926	2 23.5	-0 37	N1316	3 20.7	-37 25	N1511A	4 0.1	-67 56
N0191	0 36.4	-9 17	N0547	1 23.4	-1 36	N0925	2 24.3	35 22	N1317	3 20.8	-37 17	N1511B	4 0.7	-67 45
N0178	0 36.6	-14 27	N0550	1 24.1	1 46	N0936	2 25.1	-1 22	N1315	3 20.9	-21 33	N1507	4 1.8	-2 20
I1563	0 36.6	-9 17	N0560	1 24.9	-2 11	N0941	2 26.0	-1 22	N1319	3 21.7	-21 41	N1510	4 1.9	-43 33
N0194	0 36.8	2 46	N0564	1 25.2	-2 9	N0945	2 26.2	-10 45	N1316A	3 22.0	-36 39	N1512	4 2.3	-43 29
N0198	0 36.9	2 32	I0127	1 27.3	-7 14	N0948	2 26.3	-10 44	N1325	3 22.3	-21 43	N1515A	4 2.5	-54 14
N0195	0 37.1	-9 28	N0578	1 28.0	-22 56	N0942	2 26.6	-11 3	N1325A	3 22.7	-21 31	I0356	4 2.5	69 41
N0200	0 37.1	2 37	N0584	1 28.8	-7 7	N0943	2 26.6	-11 3	N1316C	3 23.0	-37 12	N1515	4 2.7	-54 14
N0205	0 37.6	41 25	N0586	1 29.1	-7 9	N0949	2 27.6	36 56	N1326A	3 23.1	-36 31	N1518	4 4.7	-21 18
N0210	0 38.0	-14 9	N0596	1 30.3	-7 17	N0955	2 28.0	-1 19	N1326B	3 23.3	-36 31	I2033	4 6.1	-53 48
N0214	0 38.7	25 14	N0600	1 30.8	-7 35	N0958	2 28.1	-3 9	N1331	3 23.9	-21 32	N1521	4 6.2	-21 11
N0221	0 40.0	40 36	N0598	1 31.1	30 24	N0986A	2 30.7	-39 32	N1332	3 24.1	-21 31	N1527	4 6.9	-48 1
N0224	0 40.0	41 0	N0613	1 32.0	-29 40	N0976	2 31.2	20 44	I1933	3 24.3	-52 57	I2035	4 7.6	-45 38
N0227	0 40.1	-1 48	N0615	1 32.6	-7 35	N0972	2 31.3	29 6	N1337	3 25.6	-8 34	I2038	4 7.7	-56 7
N0237	0 40.9	-0 24	N0625	1 32.9	-41 41	N0986	2 31.6	-39 15	N1339	3 26.1	-32 27	N1533	4 8.8	-56 15
N0244	0 43.2	-15 51	N0628	1 34.0	15 32	N0991	2 33.2	-7 22	N1341	3 26.1	-37 19	N1536	4 10.0	-56 36
N0245	0 43.7	-1 59	N0636	1 36.6	-7 45	I0239	2 33.5	38 45	N1344	3 26.7	-31 14	N1531	4 10.1	-32 59
N0247	0 44.6	-21 1	N0643B	1 38.4	-75 16	A0235	2 34.6	34 12	N1351A	3 26.9	-35 21	N1532	4 10.2	-33 0
A0045A	0 45.0	-20 42	N0660	1 40.2	13 21	N1003	2 36.1	40 40	N1351	3 28.5	-35 2	N1543	4 11.7	-57 52
A0045B	0 45.0	-20 42	N0643C	1 41.2	-75 31	N1022	2 36.1	-6 53	N1350	3 29.1	-33 47	N1537	4 11.8	-31 41
N0253	0 45.1	-25 34	N0661	1 41.4	28 25	A0236	2 36.4	18 9	N1353	3 29.3	-21 0	N1546	4 13.6	-56 11
N0254	0 45.2	-31 42	A0143	1 43.0	-43 51	N1035	2 37.0	-8 20	I1954	3 30.2	-52 5	N1549	4 14.7	-55 42
N0255	0 45.2	-11 45	N0670	1 44.5	27 38	I1830	2 37.0	-27 39	N1355	3 30.9	-5 10	N1553	4 15.2	-55 54
N0252	0 45.4	27 20	I1727	1 44.7	27 5	N1023	2 37.2	38 52	N1357	3 30.9	-13 50	I2056	4 15.6	-60 20
N0259	0 45.5	-3 3	N0672	1 45.0	27 11	A0237	2 37.5	-34 44	N1358	3 31.2	-5 16	I2058	4 16.8	-56 3
N0260	0 45.9	27 24	N0685	1 45.9	-53 2	I1953	2 37.7	-21 39	N1365	3 31.5	-19 41	N1530	4 16.9	75 11
A0046	0 46.0	-13 5	N0676	1 46.3	5 40	N1042	2 38.0	-8 40	N1366	3 31.8	-36 18	N1559	4 17.0	-62 55
N0268	0 47.6	-5 28	N0678	1 46.6	21 46	N1047	2 38.2	-8 23	N1371	3 32.0	-31 23	N1558	4 17.7	-45 9
N0273	0 48.3	-7 10	N0681	1 46.7	-10 40	N1048A	2 38.2	-8 46	N1371	3 32.8	-25 6	N1566	4 18.9	-55 4
N0274	0 48.5	-7 20	N0680	1 47.0	21 44	N1048B	2 38.2	-8 46				N1574	4 21.0	-57 5
						N1052	2 38.6	-8 28						

NGC	RA (1950)	D	NGC	RA (1950)	D	NGC	RA (1950)	D	NGC	RA (1950)	D	NGC	RA (1950)	D
N1569	4 26.0	64 45	N2276	7 11.0	85 52	N2683	8 49.6	33 38	A0937D	9 36.3	-4 37	N3165	10 10.9	3 37
N1560	4 26.1	71 48	N2347	7 11.6	64 54	N2681	8 50.0	51 31	N2955	9 38.3	36 7	N3159	10 11.0	38 54
N1596	4 26.6	-55 7	N2369	7 16.0	-62 16	I2421	8 51.3	32 53	N2962	9 38.3	5 24	N3161	10 11.0	38 54
N1602	4 26.8	-55 10	N2336	7 16.2	80 20	N2685	8 52.2	58 59	N2977	9 38.8	75 6	N3163	10 11.2	38 53
I2082	4 28.0	-53 56	N2300	7 16.5	85 50	N2698	8 53.1	-2 59	N2950	9 39.1	59 5	N3166	10 11.2	3 40
N1587	4 28.1	0 33	N2369A	7 18.3	-62 49	N2692	8 53.4	52 16	N2967	9 39.5	0 34	N3144	10 11.4	74 28
N1599	4 29.2	-4 41	I0467	7 19.3	80 1	N2693	8 53.5	51 33	N2964	9 40.0	32 5	N3169	10 11.7	3 43
N1600	4 29.2	-5 10	N2369B	7 19.8	-61 57	N2694	8 53.5	51 32	N2974	9 40.0	-3 29	N3175	10 12.4	-28 38
N1601	4 29.2	-5 10	N2397A	7 21.4	-68 45	N2708	8 53.6	-3 9	N2968	9 40.3	32 10	N3147	10 12.8	73 39
N1606	4 29.5	-5 9	N2397	7 21.5	-68 54	N2713	8 54.8	3 8	N2970	9 40.6	32 13	N3177	10 13.9	21 22
I2085	4 30.3	-54 32	N2366	7 23.6	69 8	N2716	8 55.0	3 17	N2980	9 40.8	-9 23	N3185	10 14.9	21 56
N1617	4 30.6	-54 42	N2379	7 24.2	33 55	N2701	8 55.5	53 59	N2978	9 40.9	-9 33	N3187	10 15.0	22 8
N1614	4 31.9	-8 41	N2389	7 25.8	33 58	N2712	8 56.2	45 7	N2959	9 41.1	68 49	N3184	10 15.2	41 40
N1615	4 33.1	19 51	I2200A	7 27.4	-62 10	N2722	8 57.0	-3 32	N2961	9 41.3	68 50	N3190	10 15.4	22 5
N1618	4 33.7	-3 15	I2200	7 27.7	-62 14	N2719	8 57.1	35 55	N2983	9 41.3	-20 15	N3193	10 15.7	22 9
N1620	4 34.0	-0 14	N2417	7 29.5	-62 09	N2719A	8 57.1	35 55	N2957	9 41.8	73 13	N3182	10 15.9	58 28
N1622	4 34.1	-3 17	N2403	7 32.0	65 43	N2723	8 57.7	3 23	N2986	9 42.0	-21 3	N3200	10 16.2	-17 44
N1625	4 34.6	-3 24	A0733	7 33.0	63 4	N2726	9 1.1	60 10	N2989	9 43.1	-18 9	N3203	10 16.3	-26 27
N1635	4 37.6	-0 38	N2415	7 33.7	35 20	N2744	9 1.8	18 40	N2976	9 43.2	68 8	N3198	10 16.7	45 49
A0438	4 38.1	4 8	N2434	7 35.0	-69 10	N2715	9 2.0	78 16	N2992	9 43.3	-14 6	N3183	10 17.8	74 26
N1530A	4 38.2	75 37	N2427	7 35.1	-47 30	N2749	9 2.5	18 31	N2993	9 43.4	-14 8	N3206	10 18.5	57 11
N1637	4 38.9	-2 56	N2442	7 36.5	-69 25	N2752	9 2.9	18 31	N2997	9 43.5	-30 58	N3213	10 18.6	19 55
N1638	4 39.1	-1 53	N2424	7 37.3	39 21	N2742	9 3.7	60 41	I0562	9 43.5	-3 44	N3223	10 19.4	-34 0
N1640	4 40.1	-20 32	I0469	7 42.5	85 23	N2763	9 4.5	-15 17	N2990	9 43.6	5 57	N3221	10 19.6	21 51
N1642	4 40.3	0 31	N2444	7 43.5	39 9	N2764	9 5.4	21 39	A0944A	9 43.8	3 17	N3214	10 19.8	57 18
N1659	4 44.0	-4 53	N2445	7 43.5	39 8	N2742A	9 6.0	62 22	A0944B	9 43.8	3 15	N3222	10 19.8	20 8
N1672	4 44.9	-59 20	N2466	7 45.6	-71 17	N2770	9 6.5	33 20	N3001	9 44.1	-30 13	N3220	10 20.4	57 17
N1666	4 46.0	-6 39	N2441	7 47.1	73 6	N2732	9 7.3	79 24	N3003	9 45.6	33 39	N3226	10 20.7	20 9
N1667	4 46.2	-6 24	I2209	7 52.0	60 27	N2775	9 7.7	7 15	N2998	9 45.8	44 19	N3227	10 20.7	20 7
N1688	4 47.6	-59 53	N2460	7 52.7	60 31	N2768	9 7.8	60 16	N2985	9 46.0	72 31	N3241	10 22.1	-32 13
I0391	4 49.8	78 6	N2468	7 54.0	56 30	N2777	9 8.1	7 25	N3023	9 47.3	0 51	N3239	10 22.4	17 25
N1703	4 52.1	-59 49	N2469	7 54.0	56 50	N2748	9 8.2	76 41	N3020	9 47.4	13 3	N3244	10 23.3	-39 35
N1705	4 53.2	-53 26	N2475	7 54.2	53 00	N2788	9 8.3	-67 44	A0947	9 47.4	28 12	N3238	10 23.4	57 28
N1699	4 54.5	-4 50	N2500	7 58.2	50 54	N2776	9 8.9	45 11	N3024	9 47.8	12 59	N3256A	10 23.6	-43 32
N1700	4 54.5	-4 56	N2523A	7 58.4	74 14	N2781	9 9.1	-14 36	N3021	9 48.0	33 47	I0610	10 23.6	20 29
I0398	4 55.8	-7 49	N2507	7 58.7	15 50	A0909	9 9.5	74 28	N3032	9 49.2	29 28	N3245A	10 24.2	28 54
N1720	4 56.5	-7 55	N2514	8 0.0	15 56	N2784	9 10.1	-23 58	N3038	9 49.2	-32 32	N3250	10 24.3	-39 41
N1726	4 57.3	-7 49	I0492	8 2.6	26 18	N2782	9 10.9	40 19	N3059	9 49.5	-73 41	N3245	10 24.5	28 46
N1744	4 57.9	-26 6	N2525	8 3.3	-11 17	N2836	9 13.1	-69 8	N3039	9 49.9	2 22	I2574	10 25.0	68 43
N1771	4 58.5	-63 13	N2521	8 4.9	57 55	N2822	9 13.4	-69 26	N3041	9 50.3	16 55	N3250A	10 25.6	-39 49
N1741	4 59.1	-4 20	N2532	8 7.0	34 8	I0529	9 13.4	73 57	N3044	9 51.0	1 49	N3250B	10 25.6	-40 10
N1752	4 59.8	-8 18	N2523B	8 7.1	73 44	N2793	9 13.7	34 39	N3027	9 51.3	72 26	N3250C	10 25.7	-39 45
N1796	5 2.1	-61 12	N2535	8 8.2	25 21	N2811	9 13.9	-16 6	N3061	9 51.3	76 6	N3256	10 25.7	-43 38
N1779	5 2.9	-9 13	N2536	8 8.3	25 20	N2815	9 14.1	-23 24	N3031	9 51.5	69 18	N3250D	10 25.8	-39 33
N1784	5 3.2	-11 56	N2534	8 9.1	55 50	N2798	9 14.4	42 10	N3034	9 51.9	69 56	N3260	10 25.9	-35 18
N1792	5 3.5	-38 4	N2523	8 9.2	73 45	N2799	9 14.6	42 10	N3052	9 52.0	-18 24	N3258A	10 26.1	-35 13
N1796A	5 4.6	-61 15	N2537	8 9.7	46 9	N2787	9 14.9	69 25	N3054	9 52.1	-25 28	N3254	10 26.5	29 45
N1800	5 4.6	-32 1	N2543	8 9.7	36 25	N2835	9 15.7	-22 8	N3056	9 52.3	-28 4	N3257	10 26.5	-35 25
N1808	5 5.9	-37 34	N2537A	8 10.1	46 10	A0916	9 15.7	-11 53	N3055	9 52.7	4 31	N3258	10 26.6	-35 20
N1796B	5 7.3	-61 31	I2233	8 10.4	45 54	N2825	9 16.4	33 57	N3043	9 52.8	59 32	N3261	10 26.8	-44 23
A0509	5 9.5	-14 50	N2541	8 11.1	49 15	N2826	9 16.4	33 50	A0953	9 52.8	8 36	N3250E	10 26.9	-39 50
N1832	5 10.0	-15 47	N2545	8 11.3	21 30	N2805	9 16.5	64 19	I2522	9 53.1	-32 54	N3256B	10 26.9	-44 8
N1888	5 20.2	-11 32	N2523C	8 12.0	73 30	N2831	9 16.7	33 59	I2523	9 53.1	-32 59	N3256C	10 26.9	-43 36
N1889	5 20.2	-11 32	A0814	8 14.1	70 52	N2830	9 16.8	33 58	N3067	9 55.4	32 37	N3262	10 27.1	-43 55
A0524	5 24.0	-69 48	N2549	8 14.9	57 58	N2832	9 16.8	33 59	A0955A	9 55.8	29 6	N3263	10 27.2	-43 53
N1947	5 26.0	-63 49	N2552	8 15.4	50 11	N2814	9 17.3	64 28	A0955B	9 55.8	29 6	N3267	10 27.5	-35 3
N1954	5 30.6	-14 6	N2544	8 15.7	74 8	N2820A	9 17.6	64 25	N3078	9 56.2	-26 41	I2584	10 27.6	-34 39
N1964	5 31.2	-21 59	N2565	8 16.9	22 10	N2848	9 17.8	-16 18	A0956	9 56.5	30 59	N3268	10 27.7	-35 04
N1961	5 36.8	69 24	N2562	8 17.5	21 17	N2820	9 17.9	64 27	N3081	9 56.8	-22 33	N3269	10 27.8	-34 57
N2082	5 41.6	-64 20	N2563	8 17.7	21 14	N2841	9 18.6	51 12	N3087	9 57.0	-33 59	N3258B	10 28.1	-35 18
N2090	5 45.2	-34 15	N2550	8 18.7	74 10	N2844	9 18.6	40 22	N3089	9 57.3	-28 4	N3271	10 28.2	-35 6
N2139	5 59.0	-23 40	N2551	8 18.8	73 35	N2855	9 19.1	-11 41	A0957	9 57.3	5 34	N3273	10 28.2	-35 21
N2179	6 5.9	-21 44	N2578	8 19.0	-13 9	N2852	9 20.1	40 21	N3073	9 57.4	55 51	N3265	10 28.4	29 3
N2188	6 8.3	-34 5	I2363	8 22.9	19 37	N2853	9 20.2	40 23	N3065	9 57.7	72 25	N3275	10 28.6	-36 28
N2196	6 10.1	-21 47	N2550A	8 23.6	74 4	N2865	9 21.2	-22 58	N3066	9 57.8	72 22	I2587	10 28.7	-34 18
N2146	6 10.7	78 23	N2595	8 24.9	21 38	N2859	9 21.3	34 44	N3091	9 57.8	-19 23	N3258C	10 29.1	-34 57
N2207	6 14.3	-21 21	N2601	8 25.2	-67 57	N2872	9 23.1	11 39	N3095	9 57.9	-31 18	N3259	10 29.2	65 18
I2163	6 14.4	-21 21	N2598	8 27.2	21 40	N2874	9 23.2	11 39	N3100	9 58.4	-31 25	N3258D	10 29.6	-35 9
N2146A	6 16.0	78 35	N2591	8 30.9	78 12	N2884	9 24.0	-11 20	N3079	9 58.6	55 57	N3274	10 29.6	27 56
N2217	6 19.7	-27 14	N2613	8 31.1	-22 48	N2888	9 24.2	-27 48	N3077	9 59.4	68 58	N3281	10 29.7	-34 36
N2223	6 22.5	-22 49	N2608	8 32.2	28 38	N2889	9 24.8	-11 25	N3098	9 59.5	24 58	N3266	10 29.9	65 1
I0449	6 40.0	71 25	N2623	8 35.4	25 56	N2880	9 25.7	62 44	N3109	10 0.8	-25 55	N3258E	10 30.0	-34 45
N2256	6 40.8	74 17	I0511	8 35.6	73 41	N2915	9 26.5	-76 25	I2537	10 1.7	-27 19	N3277	10 30.2	28 46
N2273B	6 42.2	60 24	N2614	8 37.4	73 10	I2487	9 27.3	20 18	N3136A	10 2.1	-67 13	N3252	10 30.5	74 2
N2258	6 42.4	74 33	N2642	8 38.3	-3 57	N2902	9 28.5	-14 30	N3113	10 2.2	-28 12	N3285A	10 30.6	-27 15
N2280	6 42.8	-27 35	N2639	8 40.1	50 24	N2892	9 28.9	67 51	N3115	10 2.8	-7 28	N3281C	10 30.7	-34 39
I0451	6 46.6	74 34	N2649	8 41.1	34 56	N2903	9 29.3	21 44	N3124	10 4.2	-19 0	N3285	10 31.3	-27 12
N2290	6 47.5	33 25	N2629	8 41.9	73 10	N2907	9 29.3	-16 32	N3125	10 4.2	-29 41	N3289	10 31.9	-35 4
N2291	6 47.5	33 31	I2389	8 42.6	73 44	N2911	9 31.0	10 22	N3136	10 4.5	-67 8	N3281D	10 32.0	-34 8
N2294	6 47.7	33 31	N2633	8 42.7	74 18	N2914	9 31.3	10 20	A1006	10 5.8	12 33	N3287	10 32.1	21 55
N2310	6 52.4	-40 48	N2634	8 42.8	74 10	N2916	9 32.0	21 56	I2554	10 7.5	-66 48	N3285B	10 32.3	-27 24
N2325	7 0.7	-28 38	N2634A	8 43.0	74 8	N2919	9 32.3	10 30	N3143	10 7.6	-12 20	N3288	10 33.1	58 49
N2268	7 1.3	84 30	N2636	8 43.1	73 51	N2924	9 32.8	-16 11	N3145	10 7.7	-12 10	N3318A	10 33.3	-41 29
I2174	7 2.5	75 26	N2654	8 44.3	60 28	N2935	9 34.5	-20 54	A1009	10 8.8	-4 28	N3294	10 33.4	37 35
N2314	7 3.8	75 19	N2646	8 44.6	73 40	N2942	9 36.2	34 14	N3136B	10 9.9	-66 44	N3299	10 33.7	12 58
N2326A	7 4.9	50 44	N2650	8 45.2	70 29	N2944	9 36.2	32 32	N3156	10 10.1	3 22	N3307	10 33.9	-27 16
N2339	7 5.4	18 52	N2672	8 46.6	19 16	A0936	9 36.2	71 26	N3151	10 10.6	38 51	N3300	10 34.0	14 26
A0708	7 8.3	73 34	N2673	8 46.6	19 16	A0937A	9 36.3	-4 37	N3152	10 10.7	39 5	N3308	10 34.0	-27 11
N2344	7 8.5	47 17	I0520	8 48.4	73 41	A0937B	9 36.3	-4 37	N3162	10 10.7	22 59	N3301	10 34.3	22 8
I2179	7 10.8	65 3	N2655	8 49.4	78 25	A0937C	9 36.3	-4 37	N3158	10 10.9	39 0	N3309	10 34.3	-27 16

NGC	RA (1950)		D	
N3311	10	34.4	-27	17
N3306	10	34.5	12	53
N3304	10	34.7	37	43
N3312	10	34.8	-27	20
N3314	10	34.9	-27	25
N3318	10	35.1	-41	22
N3316	10	35.2	-27	21
N3318B	10	35.5	-41	12
N3310	10	35.7	53	46
N3319	10	36.4	41	56
N3320	10	36.7	47	40
N3333	10	37.6	-35	47
N3347A	10	38.1	-36	10
N3347C	10	38.5	-36	2
N3338	10	39.5	14	0
N3347B	10	39.6	-36	40
N3347	10	40.5	-36	6
N3329	10	40.6	77	5
N3344	10	40.7	25	11
N3346	10	41.0	15	9
N3351	10	41.3	11	58
N3358	10	41.3	-36	7
N3357	10	41.7	14	20
N3353	10	42.3	56	14
N3359	10	43.4	63	30
N3348	10	43.5	73	7
N3367	10	44.0	14	1
N3368	10	44.2	12	5
N3370	10	44.5	17	32
N3377A	10	44.7	14	20
N3364	10	44.9	72	42
N3377	10	45.1	14	15
N3379	10	45.2	12	51
N3380	10	45.4	28	52
N3450	10	45.6	-20	35
N3384	10	45.7	12	54
N3389	10	45.8	12	48
N3390	10	45.8	-31	17
I2604	10	46.6	33	3
N3395	10	47.1	33	15
N3396	10	47.2	33	16
N3404	10	47.8	-11	51
N3400	10	48.0	28	44
N3412	10	48.3	13	41
N3398	10	48.5	55	41
N3413	10	48.6	33	2
N3414	10	48.6	28	15
N3418	10	48.7	28	22
N3419	10	48.7	14	13
N3419A	10	48.7	14	18
N3423	10	48.7	6	7
N3415	10	48.9	43	59
N3424	10	49.0	33	10
N3408	10	49.1	58	41
N3433	10	49.4	10	26
N3430	10	49.5	33	14
N3432	10	49.7	36	54
N3437	10	49.9	23	11
N3403	10	50.1	73	57
N3444	10	50.4	10	27
N3449	10	50.6	-32	40
N3440	10	50.8	57	23
N3447	10	50.8	17	2
N3447A	10	50.8	17	2
N3445	10	51.6	57	15
N3448	10	51.7	54	34
N3456	10	51.7	-15	46
N3454	10	51.8	17	36
N3455	10	51.8	17	33
N3464	10	52.2	-20	49
N3458	10	53.0	57	22
N3466	10	53.6	10	1
N3470	10	55.7	59	46
N3478	10	56.5	46	23
N3485	10	57.4	15	6
N3489	10	57.7	14	10
N3486	10	57.8	29	15
N3488	10	58.4	57	56
N3495	10	58.6	3	53
N3499	11	0.2	56	29
N3504	11	0.5	28	15
N3506	11	0.6	11	21
N3511	11	0.8	-22	50
N3510	11	1.0	29	9
N3513	11	1.1	-22	58
A1101	11	1.2	41	7
N3512	11	1.3	28	18
N3509	11	1.6	5	6
N3515	11	2.0	28	30
N3517	11	2.6	56	48
N3521	11	3.2	0	14
N3516	11	3.4	72	50
A1105A	11	4.7	18	42
A1105B	11	4.7	18	42
N3557A	11	4.8	-36	56
A1107A	11	7.2	24	32
N3547	11	7.3	11	0
N3557B	11	7.3	-37	5
A1107B	11	7.3	24	32
N3557	11	7.5	-37	16
I2627	11	7.5	-23	28
A1108A	11	8.1	29	2
A1108B	11	8.1	29	2
A1108C	11	8.1	29	2
N3549	11	8.2	53	39
N3564	11	8.2	-37	16
N3568	11	8.5	-37	11
N3556	11	8.7	55	57
N3571	11	8.9	-18	1
A1111	11	10.8	22	26
N3585	11	10.9	-26	29
N3577	11	11.0	48	38
N3583	11	11.4	48	39
N3593	11	12.0	13	6
N3596	11	12.4	15	4
N3599	11	12.8	18	23
N3605	11	14.2	18	18
N3607	11	14.3	18	20
N3608	11	14.4	18	26
N3611	11	14.9	4	50
N3614A	11	15.5	46	0
N3610	11	15.6	59	4
N3614	11	15.6	46	2
N3613	11	15.7	58	17
N3621	11	15.9	-32	32
N3623	11	16.3	13	23
N3619	11	16.5	58	2
N3626	11	17.5	18	38
N3627	11	17.6	13	17
N3625	11	17.7	58	3
N3628	11	17.7	13	53
N3630	11	17.7	3	15
N3629	11	17.9	27	15
N3633	11	17.9	3	51
N3636	11	17.9	-10	1
N3637	11	18.1	-9	58
N3631	11	18.3	53	28
N3640	11	18.5	3	31
N3641	11	18.6	3	28
N3643	11	19.0	3	13
N3646	11	19.2	20	27
N3642	11	19.6	59	21
N3649	11	19.7	20	28
N3650	11	19.7	20	59
N3655	11	20.3	16	51
N3656	11	20.8	54	7
N3657	11	21.1	53	11
N3659	11	21.1	18	5
N3658	11	21.3	38	49
N3662	11	21.3	-0	49
N3664	11	21.7	3	35
N3664A	11	21.8	3	30
N3666	11	21.9	11	37
N3665	11	22.1	39	2
N3672	11	22.5	-9	32
N3669	11	22.6	57	59
N3673	11	22.8	-26	28
N3675	11	23.5	43	52
N3674	11	23.6	57	19
N3677	11	23.6	47	16
N3681	11	23.9	17	9
N3684	11	24.5	17	18
N3682	11	24.8	66	52
N3683	11	24.8	57	9
N3686	11	25.1	17	30
N3687	11	25.3	29	47
N3689	11	25.5	25	56
N3691	11	25.5	17	11
N3690	11	26.0	58	49
I0694	11	26.0	58	49
N3683A	11	27.0	57	23
N3706	11	27.3	-36	8
N3705	11	27.6	9	33
N3717	11	29.0	-29	59
A1129	11	29.2	71	5
N3719	11	29.7	1	6
N3720	11	29.8	1	5
A1130A	11	29.8	53	12
A1130B	11	29.8	53	12
N3718	11	29.9	53	21
N3726	11	30.7	47	19
N3729	11	31.0	53	24
N3732	11	31.7	-9	34
N3733	11	32.3	55	7
N3737	11	32.9	55	14
N3735	11	33.1	70	48
N3738	11	33.1	54	48
N3755	11	33.9	36	41
I2943	11	34.0	55	7
N3756	11	34.1	54	34
N3759A	11	34.2	55	26
N3759	11	34.3	55	6
N3769	11	35.1	48	11
N3769A	11	35.1	48	11
N3773	11	35.6	12	23
N3783	11	36.5	-37	28
N3780	11	36.7	56	33
N3782	11	36.9	46	44
N3786	11	37.1	32	11
N3788	11	37.2	32	13
N3799	11	37.6	15	36
N3800	11	37.6	15	37
N3804	11	38.1	56	29
N3810	11	38.4	11	45
N3813	11	38.7	36	49
N3818	11	39.4	-5	53
N3824	11	40.1	53	3
N3829	11	40.8	53	0
N3835	11	41.4	60	23
N3838	11	41.6	58	14
N3846	11	41.8	55	55
N3846A	11	42.0	55	18
N3850	11	42.0	56	10
N3865	11	42.7	-8	56
N3872	11	43.2	14	3
N3877	11	43.5	47	46
N3885	11	44.3	-27	39
A1145A	11	44.5	-3	33
N3887	11	44.6	-16	35
A1145B	11	44.7	-3	33
A1145C	11	44.8	-3	34
N3888	11	45.0	56	15
N3892	11	45.5	-10	41
N3893	11	46.1	49	0
N3894	11	46.2	59	42
N3895	11	46.4	59	42
N3896	11	46.4	48	58
N3905	11	46.5	-9	29
N3900	11	46.6	27	17
N3898	11	46.7	56	22
N3902	11	46.7	26	24
N3904	11	46.7	-29	2
N3906	11	47.1	48	42
N3912	11	47.5	26	46
N3913	11	47.8	55	37
N3916	11	48.2	55	25
N3917	11	48.3	52	6
N3921	11	48.5	55	22
N3923	11	48.5	-28	33
N3931	11	48.6	52	17
N3928	11	49.2	48	58
N3930	11	49.2	38	17
N3936	11	49.9	-26	37
N3938	11	50.2	44	24
N3941	11	50.3	37	16
N3945	11	50.6	60	57
N3949	11	51.1	48	8
N3952	11	51.1	-3	43
N3953	11	51.2	52	37
N3955	11	51.5	-22	54
N3956	11	51.6	-20	18
N3957	11	51.6	-19	17
N3958	11	52.0	58	38
N3962	11	52.2	-13	42
N3963	11	52.4	58	46
N3972	11	53.2	55	35
N3975	11	53.3	60	48
N3976	11	53.4	7	2
N3977	11	53.5	55	40
N3978	11	53.6	60	48
N3981	11	53.7	-19	37
N3982	11	53.9	55	24
N3985	11	54.1	48	37
N3986	11	54.2	32	18
N3990	11	55.0	55	44
N3991	11	55.0	32	38
N3992	11	55.0	53	39
N3993	11	55.1	25	31
N3994	11	55.1	32	34
N3995	11	55.2	32	35
N3997	11	55.3	25	33
N3998	11	55.3	55	44
N4008	11	55.7	28	28
N4013	11	56.0	44	13
N4024	11	56.0	-18	5
I0749	11	56.0	43	1
N4010	11	56.1	47	31
I0750	11	56.3	43	0
I0751	11	56.3	42	51
N4020	11	56.4	30	42
N4025	11	56.6	38	5
N4026	11	56.9	51	14
N4027	11	57.0	-18	59
A1157	11	57.2	37	48
N4030	11	57.8	-0	49
N4032	11	58.0	20	21
N4033	11	58.0	-17	34
N4035	11	58.5	-15	41
N4037	11	58.8	13	41
N4036	11	58.9	62	10
N4038	11	59.3	-18	35
N4039	11	59.3	-18	35
N4041	11	59.7	62	25
N4045	12	0.2	2	15
N4047	12	0.2	48	55
N4050	12	0.4	-16	6
N4051	12	0.6	44	48
I0757	12	0.9	62	56
N4062	12	1.5	32	10
N4064	12	1.6	18	43
N4067	12	1.6	11	8
N4068	12	1.7	52	50
N4073	12	1.9	2	11
N4081	12	2.2	64	42
N4079	12	2.3	-2	6
N4085	12	2.3	50	38
N4088	12	3.0	50	49
I2995	12	3.0	-27	39
A1203A	12	3.2	31	21
A1203B	12	3.2	31	21
N4094	12	3.3	-14	16
N4108A	12	3.3	67	32
N4096	12	3.5	47	45
N4100	12	3.6	49	51
N4102	12	3.8	52	59
N4105	12	4.1	-29	30
N4106	12	4.2	-29	31
N4108	12	4.3	67	26
N4109	12	4.5	43	15
N4111	12	4.5	43	21
A1205	12	4.6	17	16
N4114	12	4.7	-13	55
N4108B	12	4.8	67	30
N4116	12	5.1	2	58
N4117	12	5.2	43	24
N4118	12	5.2	43	24
N4120	12	5.5	69	52
N4121	12	5.5	65	24
N4123	12	5.6	3	9
N4124	12	5.6	10	40
N4125	12	5.7	65	27
N4128	12	6.1	69	3
N4129	12	6.3	-8	45
N4135	12	6.6	44	17
N4136	12	6.7	30	12
N4137	12	6.8	44	22
N4138	12	7.0	43	58
N4142	12	7.1	53	24
N4143	12	7.1	42	49
N4144	12	7.5	46	44
N4145	12	7.5	40	10
N4146	12	7.6	26	42
I0764	12	7.6	-29	28
N4150	12	8.0	30	41
N4151	12	8.0	39	41
N4152	12	8.1	16	19
N4156	12	8.4	39	45
N4157	12	8.6	50	46
N4158	12	8.6	20	27
N4162	12	9.4	24	24
N4163	12	9.5	36	28
N4165	12	9.7	13	31
N4168	12	9.8	13	29
N4178	12	10.2	11	9
N4179	12	10.3	1	35
I3044	12	10.3	14	15
N4180	12	10.6	7	19
N4183	12	10.8	43	57
N4190	12	11.1	36	54
N4189	12	11.2	13	42
N4192	12	11.3	15	11
N4193	12	11.3	13	27
N4186	12	11.6	15	1
N4194	12	11.7	54	49
N4203	12	12.5	33	29
I3061	12	12.5	14	18
N4206	12	12.8	13	20
N4210	12	12.8	66	16
A1213	12	12.9	6	5
N4212	12	13.1	14	11
N4214	12	13.1	36	36
N4217	12	13.3	47	22
N4215	12	13.4	6	41
N4216	12	13.4	13	25
N4218	12	13.5	48	25
N4220	12	13.7	48	10
N4221	12	13.7	66	31
N4219	12	13.8	-43	3
N4222	12	13.8	13	34
A1214A	12	13.8	28	25
A1214B	12	13.8	28	25
N4224	12	14.0	7	44
N4226	12	14.0	47	18
N4236	12	14.3	69	45
N4231	12	14.5	47	46
N4232	12	14.5	47	45
N4233	12	14.6	7	54
N4234	12	14.6	3	58
N4235	12	14.6	7	28
N4237	12	14.7	15	36
N4241	12	14.9	6	57
N4242	12	14.9	45	54
N4244	12	15.0	38	5
N4245	12	15.2	29	53
N4250	12	15.2	71	5
N4219A	12	15.3	-43	14
N4246	12	15.3	7	28
N4247	12	15.3	7	34
N4248	12	15.3	47	42
I0773	12	15.4	6	25
I3115	12	15.4	6	56
N4251	12	15.7	28	27
N4252	12	15.9	5	51
N4253	12	16.0	30	7
N4254	12	16.3	14	42
I0775	12	16.3	13	10
N4256	12	16.4	66	11
I3136	12	16.4	6	28
N4258	12	16.5	47	35
N4257	12	16.6	6	1
N4259	12	16.8	5	39
N4260	12	16.8	6	23
N4261	12	16.8	6	6
A1217	12	16.8	4	8
N4262	12	17.0	15	9
N4264	12	17.0	6	7
N4266	12	17.1	5	50
N4267	12	17.2	13	3
N4268	12	17.2	5	34
N4269	12	17.3	6	18
N4270	12	17.3	5	44
I3155	12	17.3	6	18
N4273	12	17.4	5	37
N4274	12	17.4	29	53
N4277	12	17.6	5	37
N4278	12	17.7	29	34
N4281	12	17.8	5	40
N4283	12	17.9	29	35
N4291	12	18.1	75	40
N4286	12	18.2	29	38
N4288	12	18.2	46	34
N4290	12	18.5	58	22
N4292	12	18.7	4	52
N4293	12	18.7	18	40
N4294	12	18.7	11	47
N4298	12	19.0	14	53
N4299	12	19.2	11	47
N4302	12	19.2	14	53
I0783	12	19.2	16	0
N4303	12	19.4	4	45
N4305	12	19.5	13	1
N4306	12	19.5	13	4
N4307	12	19.5	9	20
N4304	12	19.6	-33	12
N4309	12	19.7	7	25
N4319	12	19.8	75	36
N4301	12	19.9	4	50
I0783A	12	19.9	15	59
N4310	12	20.0	29	29
N4312	12	20.0	15	49

NGC	RA (1950)	D	NGC	RA (1950)	D	NGC	RA (1950)	D	NGC	RA (1950)	D	NGC	RA (1950)	D
N4314	12 20.0	30 10	I3381	12 25.8	12 0	N4555	12 33.2	26 48	N4679	12 44.8	-39 18	I3896A	12 52.6	-49 49
N4313	12 20.1	12 4	N4450	12 25.9	17 21	N4562	12 33.2	26 7	N4683	12 44.9	-41 14	A1253	12 52.6	0 23
N4321	12 20.4	16 6	N4451	12 26.1	9 32	I3546	12 33.3	26 29	N4687	12 45.0	35 38	N4802	12 53.2	-11 47
N4322	12 20.4	16 10	I3392	12 26.1	15 16	N4553	12 33.4	-39 10	N4696A	12 45.0	-41 12	I3900	12 53.2	27 32
N4332	12 20.5	66 8	N4452	12 26.2	12 2	I3547	12 33.4	26 36	A1245	12 45.1	27 15	N4808	12 53.3	4 35
N4324	12 20.6	5 31	N4455	12 26.2	23 6	N4559	12 33.5	28 14	N4689	12 45.2	14 1	N4814	12 53.3	58 37
N4326	12 20.6	6 21	N4454	12 26.3	-1 40	N4561	12 33.6	19 36	N4688	12 45.3	4 36	I3896	12 53.7	-50 3
N4329	12 20.8	-12 15	I3393	12 26.3	13 11	N4565	12 33.9	26 16	N4692	12 45.5	27 29	N4819	12 54.0	27 15
N4333	12 20.8	6 19	N4457	12 26.4	3 51	N4564	12 34.0	11 43	N4696B	12 45.5	-40 58	N4821	12 54.1	27 13
N4334	12 20.8	7 45	N4458	12 26.4	13 31	N4567	12 34.0	11 32	N4691	12 45.6	-3 4	N4835A	12 54.2	-46 7
N4339	12 21.0	6 22	N4460	12 26.4	45 8	N4568	12 34.1	11 31	N4694	12 45.7	11 15	N4818	12 54.3	-8 15
N4340	12 21.0	17 0	N4459	12 26.5	14 15	I3583	12 34.2	13 32	N4698	12 45.8	8 45	N4826	12 54.3	21 57
N4346	12 21.0	47 16	N4461	12 26.6	13 28	N4569	12 34.3	13 26	A1246A	12 45.8	27 8	N4827	12 54.3	27 27
N4342	12 21.1	7 22	N4462	12 26.7	-22 54	N4571	12 34.3	14 28	N4697	12 46.0	-5 32	I3917	12 54.4	22 16
N4343	12 21.1	7 16	N4464	12 26.8	8 26	N4570	12 34.4	7 31	N4696	12 46.1	-41 2	N4825	12 54.5	-13 24
N4344	12 21.1	17 49	N4466	12 27.0	7 58	I3598	12 34.9	28 28	N4696C	12 46.2	-40 32	A1255	12 54.5	32 42
I3253	12 21.1	-34 21	N4467	12 27.0	8 16	N4576	12 35.0	4 38	N4704	12 46.4	42 11	N4839	12 55.0	27 45
I3258	12 21.2	12 44	N4468	12 27.0	14 19	N4578	12 35.0	9 50	I3804	12 46.4	35 36	N4841A	12 55.2	28 45
N4341	12 21.3	7 23	N4469	12 27.0	9 2	N4575	12 35.1	-40 16	N4696D	12 46.5	-41 26	N4841B	12 55.2	28 45
N4348	12 21.3	-3 10	N4470	12 27.1	8 6	N4579	12 35.1	12 5	N4699	12 46.5	-8 24	N4842	12 55.2	27 46
N4363	12 21.3	75 13	I3418	12 27.2	11 41	N4580	12 35.3	5 38	N4700	12 46.5	-11 8	N4835	12 55.3	-45 59
I3259	12 21.3	7 28	N4472	12 27.3	8 16	N4589	12 35.6	74 28	N4696E	12 46.6	-40 39	N4845	12 55.5	1 51
N4350	12 21.4	16 58	N4473	12 27.3	13 42	N4584	12 35.8	13 23	N4701	12 46.6	3 39	N4848	12 55.7	28 30
N4351	12 21.5	12 29	N4474	12 27.4	14 21	N4586	12 35.9	4 35	I3806	12 46.6	15 10	N4850	12 55.8	28 14
N4352	12 21.5	11 29	N4476	12 27.5	12 37	N4592	12 36.7	-0 16	A1248A	12 46.7	-41 11	N4849	12 55.9	26 40
N4353	12 21.6	8 5	N4477	12 27.6	13 55	N4603A	12 36.9	-40 26	N4703	12 46.8	-8 51	N4853	12 56.2	27 53
I3267	12 21.6	7 19	N4478	12 27.8	12 36	N4593	12 37.0	-5 4	A1247	12 46.8	-9 51	I3946	12 56.4	28 5
N4359	12 21.7	31 47	N4479	12 27.8	13 51	N4594	12 37.3	-11 21	A1248B	12 46.8	-41 6	N4858	12 56.5	28 23
N4361	12 22.0	-18 30	N4480	12 27.9	4 31	N4595	12 37.3	15 34	N4705	12 46.9	-4 55	N4860	12 56.5	28 24
N4365	12 22.0	7 36	N4486B	12 28.0	12 46	N4596	12 37.4	10 27	N4708	12 47.1	-10 49	I3949	12 56.6	28 7
N4369	12 22.1	39 39	N4483	12 28.2	9 17	N4597	12 37.5	-5 32	N4710	12 47.1	15 26	N4856	12 56.7	-14 46
N4375	12 22.2	28 50	N4485	12 28.2	41 58	N4603B	12 37.7	-40 28	N4706	12 47.2	-40 59	N4861	12 56.7	35 8
N4370	12 22.4	7 43	N4486	12 28.3	12 40	N4605	12 37.8	61 53	N4712	12 47.2	25 44	I3960A	12 56.7	28 8
N4371	12 22.4	11 59	N4487	12 28.3	-7 48	N4602	12 38.0	-4 52	A1246B	12 47.2	27 10	N4864	12 56.8	28 15
N4386	12 22.4	75 48	N4488	12 28.3	8 38	N4603C	12 38.0	-40 29	N4709	12 47.3	-41 6	N4865	12 56.8	28 22
I3290	12 22.5	-39 30	N4490	12 28.3	41 55	N4601	12 38.2	-40 39	A1248C	12 47.4	-41 14	N4868	12 56.8	37 35
N4374	12 22.6	13 10	N4491	12 28.4	11 45	N4603	12 38.3	-40 42	N4713	12 47.5	5 35	N4867	12 56.9	28 16
N4373	12 22.7	-39 28	N4492	12 28.4	8 21	N4606	12 38.4	12 10	N4718	12 48.0	-5 0	N4866	12 57.0	14 27
N4377	12 22.7	15 2	N4494	12 28.9	26 3	N4607	12 38.7	12 10	N4728	12 48.0	27 42	N4869	12 57.0	28 11
N4373A	12 22.8	-39 2	N4496A	12 29.1	4 12	N4608	12 38.7	10 26	N4725	12 48.1	25 46	N4872	12 57.2	28 14
N4378	12 22.8	5 12	N4496B	12 29.1	4 12	N4612	12 39.0	7 35	N4724	12 48.3	-14 4	N4874	12 57.2	28 14
N4379	12 22.8	15 53	N4497	12 29.1	11 53	N4618	12 39.2	41 25	N4727	12 48.3	-14 4	N4881	12 57.5	28 31
N4382	12 22.8	18 28	N4500	12 29.1	58 14	N4619	12 39.4	35 20	N4749	12 48.3	71 53	N4886	12 57.6	28 15
I3303	12 22.8	13 0	N4498	12 29.2	17 8	N4603D	12 39.5	-40 33	N4731	12 48.4	-6 8	N4880	12 57.7	12 45
N4380	12 22.9	10 17	I3442	12 29.4	14 23	N4616	12 39.5	-40 22	N4750	12 48.4	73 9	N4889	12 57.7	28 15
N4383	12 23.0	16 45	I3457	12 29.4	12 56	N4621	12 39.5	11 55	A1249	12 48.5	28 7	N4895A	12 57.7	28 26
N4391	12 23.0	65 13	N4501	12 29.5	14 42	N4625	12 39.5	41 33	N4733	12 48.6	11 10	I4011	12 57.7	28 16
N4385	12 23.1	0 50	N4503	12 29.6	11 27	N4623	12 39.6	7 56	N4736	12 48.6	41 23	I4012	12 57.7	28 21
N4389	12 23.1	45 58	N4504	12 29.7	-7 17	N4627	12 39.7	32 51	N4734	12 48.7	5 7	N4877	12 57.8	-15 1
I3322A	12 23.1	7 30	N4506	12 29.7	13 42	N4631	12 39.8	32 49	A1248D	12 48.9	-40 51	N4895	12 57.8	28 29
N4387	12 23.2	13 5	N4517A	12 29.9	0 38	N4622	12 39.9	-40 28	N4739	12 49.0	-8 8	I4021	12 57.8	28 19
N4388	12 23.3	12 56	I3474	12 30.1	2 56	N4648	12 39.9	74 41	N4742	12 49.2	-10 12	N4896	12 57.9	28 35
N4390	12 23.3	10 44	A1230	12 30.1	9 27	N4630	12 40.0	4 14	N4747	12 49.4	26 1	N4898	12 57.9	28 13
I3322	12 23.3	7 50	N4517	12 30.2	0 23	N4632	12 40.0	0 11	N4746	12 49.5	12 21	N4891	12 58.1	-13 9
N4394	12 23.4	18 29	I3475	12 30.2	13 3	N4633	12 40.0	14 38	N4744	12 49.6	-40 46	N4900	12 58.2	2 46
N4395	12 23.4	33 49	I3476	12 30.2	14 19	N4634	12 40.2	14 34	N4754	12 49.7	11 35	I4040	12 58.2	28 20
N4396	12 23.5	15 57	I3478	12 30.3	14 28	N4635	12 40.2	20 12	N4753	12 49.8	-0 55	N4899	12 58.3	-13 41
I3330	12 23.5	31 7	I3481	12 30.3	11 40	N4638	12 40.2	11 43	N4756	12 50.3	-15 8	N4902	12 58.3	-14 15
N4402	12 23.6	13 24	I3481A	12 30.5	11 40	N4636	12 40.3	2 57	N4757	12 50.3	-10 2	N4904	12 58.4	0 15
N4405	12 23.6	16 27	N4516	12 30.6	14 51	N4637	12 40.3	11 43	N4758	12 50.3	16 7	N4907	12 58.4	28 25
N4406	12 23.7	13 13	I3483	12 30.6	11 37	N4639	12 40.3	13 31	N4767A	12 50.3	-39 35	N4908	12 58.4	28 18
N4410A	12 23.9	9 18	N4509	12 30.7	32 22	N4645A	12 40.3	-41 5	N4762	12 50.4	11 31	N4914	12 58.4	37 35
N4410B	12 23.9	9 18	N4519	12 31.0	8 56	N4642	12 40.7	-0 23	N4760	12 50.5	-10 13	I4045	12 58.4	28 21
N4373B	12 24.0	-38 51	N4520	12 31.1	-7 7	N4643	12 40.8	2 15	N4766	12 50.5	-10 6	I4051	12 58.4	28 17
N4411A	12 24.0	9 9	N4523	12 31.1	15 26	N4645B	12 40.8	-41 5	N4763	12 50.6	-16 43	N4911	12 58.6	28 3
N4412	12 24.0	4 14	N4522	12 31.2	9 27	N4647	12 41.0	11 51	N4765	12 50.7	4 45	N4915	12 58.8	-4 16
N4413	12 24.0	12 53	I0800	12 31.4	15 38	N4649	12 41.1	11 49	N4771	12 50.8	1 33	N4922	12 59.0	29 35
N4414	12 24.0	31 30	N4528	12 31.5	11 35	N4651	12 41.2	16 40	N4772	12 51.0	2 27	N4921	12 59.3	28 9
N4411B	12 24.3	9 9	N4526	12 31.6	7 58	N4645	12 41.3	-41 29	N4773	12 51.0	-8 24	N4926	12 59.5	27 53
N4417	12 24.3	9 52	N4527	12 31.6	2 56	N4653	12 41.4	-0 18	N4775	12 51.1	-6 21	N4924	12 59.6	-14 42
N4419	12 24.4	15 19	N4531	12 31.7	13 21	N4654	12 41.4	13 23	N4767	12 51.2	-39 27	N4926A	12 59.7	27 54
N4420	12 24.4	2 46	N4534	12 31.7	35 48	N4656	12 41.6	32 26	N4777	12 51.4	-8 28	N4928	13 0.3	-7 49
N4421	12 24.5	15 44	N4532	12 31.8	6 44	N4657	12 41.7	32 29	N4780	12 51.5	-8 21	I0844	13 0.5	-30 15
N4424	12 24.6	9 42	N4533	12 31.8	2 36	N4660	12 42.0	11 26	N4789A	12 51.7	27 25	N4931	13 0.6	28 18
N4425	12 24.7	13 1	N4535	12 31.8	8 28	N4658	12 42.1	-9 49	N4781	12 51.8	-10 16	N4933A	13 1.2	-11 14
N4428	12 24.9	-7 54	N4536	12 31.9	2 28	I3720	12 42.2	12 21	N4789	12 51.9	27 20	N4933B	13 1.2	-11 14
N4429	12 24.9	11 23	N4539	12 32.1	18 29	N4663	12 42.4	-9 54	N4767B	12 52.0	-39 35	N4936	13 1.5	-30 15
N4431	12 24.9	12 34	I3522	12 32.1	15 28	N4665	12 42.6	3 19	N4782	12 52.0	-12 19	N4944	13 1.5	28 28
N4433	12 25.0	-8 1	A1232	12 32.2	6 34	N4666	12 42.6	-0 12	N4783	12 52.0	-12 18	N4947A	13 1.5	-34 58
I3370	12 25.0	-39 4	N4540	12 32.3	15 50	N4670	12 42.8	27 23	N4784	12 52.0	-10 21	N4941	13 1.6	-5 17
N4441	12 25.1	65 5	I3528	12 32.3	15 49	N4668	12 43.0	-0 17	N4786	12 52.0	-6 35	N4939	13 1.7	-10 5
N4435	12 25.2	13 21	N4545	12 32.4	63 47	N4673	12 43.2	27 20	N4790	12 52.2	-9 58	N4942	13 1.7	-7 24
N4436	12 25.2	12 36	N4541	12 32.6	0 2	N4674	12 43.4	-8 23	N4793	12 52.3	29 13	A1302	13 2.0	-3 18
N4438	12 25.3	13 17	N4507	12 32.9	-39 38	N4672	12 43.5	-41 27	N4809	12 52.3	2 56	N4948	13 2.3	-7 41
N4440	12 25.4	12 34	N4546	12 32.9	-3 31	N4676A	12 43.7	31 0	N4810	12 52.3	2 55	N4945	13 2.4	-49 13
N4442	12 25.6	10 5	N4548	12 32.9	14 46	N4676B	12 43.7	31 0	N4792	12 52.4	-12 16	N4948A	13 2.5	-7 53
I0794	12 25.6	12 22	N4550	12 32.9	12 30	N4677	12 44.2	-41 19	N4798	12 52.4	27 42	N4951	13 2.5	-6 14
N4445	12 25.7	9 42	N4544	12 33.0	3 18	A1244	12 44.2	26 50	N4800	12 52.4	46 48	N4947	13 2.6	-35 4
N4448	12 25.8	28 54	N4551	12 33.1	12 33	N4682	12 44.7	-9 48	N4795	12 52.5	8 20	N4952	13 2.7	29 24
N4449	12 25.8	44 22	N4552	12 33.1	12 50	N4684	12 44.7	-2 28	N4794	12 52.6	-12 21	N4957	13 2.8	27 50

NGC	RA (1950)	D
N4958	13 3.1	-7 45
N4961	13 3.4	28 0
I4182	13 3.5	37 52
N4945A	13 3.7	-49 24
N4965	13 4.5	-27 57
N4976	13 5.9	-49 14
N4981	13 6.1	-6 31
N4980	13 6.4	-28 23
N4984	13 6.4	-15 15
N4995	13 7.0	-7 34
N4999	13 7.2	1 55
A1306	13 7.4	-15 29
I4209	13 8.0	-6 54
N5005	13 8.5	37 19
A1309	13 8.8	3 40
N5003	13 9.1	42 28
N5014	13 9.2	36 33
N5012	13 9.3	23 11
N5011A	13 9.4	-43 3
N5016	13 9.7	24 21
N5011	13 10.0	-42 50
N5023	13 10.0	44 18
A1310	13 10.2	-32 25
N5017	13 10.3	-16 30
N5018	13 10.3	-19 15
N5022	13 10.7	-19 15
A1311	13 11.0	36 28
N5028	13 11.1	-12 47
N5030	13 11.2	-16 14
N5033	13 11.2	36 51
N5026	13 11.3	-42 42
N5035	13 12.1	-16 15
N5037	13 12.4	-16 20
N5042	13 12.8	-23 43
N5044	13 12.8	-16 8
N5046	13 13.0	-16 4
N5047	13 13.1	-16 14
N5049	13 13.3	-16 8
N5055	13 13.5	42 17
N5054	13 14.3	-16 23
N5061	13 15.3	-26 36
N5064	13 16.0	-47 39
N5068	13 16.2	-20 47
N5074	13 16.2	31 44
N5090A	13 16.4	-43 24
N5077	13 16.9	-12 24
N5079	13 17.0	-12 27
N5078	13 17.1	-27 9
N5090B	13 17.3	-43 36
N5084	13 17.5	-21 34
N5085	13 17.6	-24 9
N5087	13 17.7	-20 21
N5088	13 17.7	-12 19
N5082	13 18.0	-43 26
N5091	13 18.2	-43 28
N5090	13 18.3	-43 28
N5101	13 19.0	-27 11
N5102	13 19.1	-36 23
N5107	13 19.1	38 49
N5112	13 19.6	39 0
N5116	13 20.5	27 14
N5127	13 21.4	31 49
N5144	13 21.5	70 46
I4237	13 21.8	-20 53
N5121	13 21.9	-37 25
N5121A	13 22.4	-37 6
N5128	13 22.4	-42 45
N5134	13 22.6	-20 51
N5135	13 22.9	-29 34
N5147	13 23.7	2 22
N5148	13 24.0	2 34
N5150	13 24.9	-29 18
N5156	13 25.7	-48 39
N5169	13 26.0	46 53
N5161	13 26.3	-32 54
N5173	13 26.3	46 51
I4263	13 26.5	47 10
N5172	13 26.9	17 19
N5170	13 27.1	-17 42
N5194	13 27.8	47 27
N5195	13 27.9	47 31
N5198	13 28.2	46 56
N5204	13 28.3	58 40
I4278	13 28.3	47 29
N5188	13 28.6	-34 32
N5193	13 29.1	-32 58
N5216	13 30.4	62 58
N5218	13 30.5	63 2
N5229	13 32.1	48 9
N5230	13 33.0	13 56

NGC	RA (1950)	D
I4296	13 33.8	-33 43
N5236	13 34.3	-29 37
N5248	13 35.1	9 8
N5247	13 35.3	-17 38
N5254	13 36.9	-11 14
N5253	13 37.1	-31 24
N5257	13 37.3	1 6
N5266A	13 37.3	-48 6
N5258	13 37.4	1 5
A1339	13 38.8	54 35
N5278	13 39.8	55 55
N5279	13 39.8	55 55
N5266	13 39.9	-47 56
N5273	13 39.9	35 55
N5276	13 40.1	35 53
N5289	13 43.0	41 45
N5290	13 43.2	41 58
N5296	13 43.7	44 5
N5293	13 44.3	16 34
N5297	13 44.3	44 5
N5291	13 44.5	-30 8
A1345B	13 44.8	34 7
A1345A	13 44.9	34 6
N5301	13 45.0	46 24
N5298	13 45.4	-30 11
N5308	13 45.4	61 14
N5300	13 45.7	4 11
I4327	13 45.8	-29 59
N5302	13 46.0	-30 14
I4329	13 46.2	-30 3
N5304	13 47.1	-30 19
N5322	13 47.6	60 26
N5313	13 47.7	40 13
N5320	13 48.3	41 35
N5326	13 48.7	39 49
N5324	13 49.4	-5 48
N5328	13 50.0	-28 14
N5334	13 50.4	-0 53
N5347	13 51.1	33 43
N5350	13 51.2	40 37
N5351	13 51.2	38 9
N5353	13 51.3	40 31
N5354	13 51.4	40 33
N5348	13 51.8	5 29
N5356	13 52.5	5 34
N5368	13 52.7	54 35
N5362	13 52.8	41 30
A1353	13 53.0	54 8
N5357	13 53.1	-30 6
N5360	13 53.1	5 16
N5365A	13 53.3	-43 45
N5363	13 53.6	5 29
N5371	13 53.6	40 43
N5376	13 53.6	59 45
N5364	13 53.7	5 15
N5379	13 53.9	59 59
N5377	13 54.3	47 27
N5389	13 54.5	59 59
N5378	13 54.6	38 1
N5365	13 54.8	-43 42
N5380	13 54.8	37 51
I4351	13 54.9	-29 5
N5374	13 55.0	6 20
N5383	13 55.0	42 5
N5365B	13 55.4	-43 44
N5387	13 56.0	6 18
N5394	13 56.5	37 41
N5395	13 56.5	37 39
N5396	13 56.6	29 21
N5403	13 57.7	38 25
A1358	13 57.7	-45 10
N5406	13 58.2	39 9
N5398	13 58.3	-32 50
N5422	13 59.0	55 24
N5430	13 59.1	59 34
N5443	14 0.4	56 3
N5419	14 0.7	-33 44
N5426	14 0.8	-5 49
N5427	14 0.8	-5 47
N5448	14 0.9	49 25
N5444	14 1.2	35 22
N5457	14 1.4	54 35
N5480	14 2.4	50 57
N5481	14 2.6	50 57
N5473	14 3.0	55 8
N5474	14 3.2	53 54
N5475	14 3.5	55 59
N5477	14 3.7	54 41
N5468	14 4.0	-5 14
N5464	14 4.2	-29 46

NGC	RA (1950)	D
N5472	14 4.3	-5 14
N5484	14 5.1	55 16
N5485	14 5.5	55 14
N5486	14 5.7	55 20
N5483	14 7.4	-43 5
N5490	14 7.6	17 46
I0982	14 7.6	17 55
N5490C	14 7.7	17 51
I0983	14 7.7	17 57
N5493	14 8.9	-4 49
N5496	14 9.0	-0 56
N5494	14 9.5	-30 26
A1410	14 9.7	52 34
N5506	14 10.7	-2 58
N5507	14 10.8	-2 55
N5523	14 12.6	25 34
N5529	14 13.4	36 27
N5533	14 14.1	35 35
N5534	14 15.0	-7 11
N5544	14 15.0	36 48
N5545	14 15.0	36 48
N5530	14 15.4	-43 9
N5548	14 15.7	25 22
N5557	14 16.4	36 43
N5556	14 17.6	-29 1
N5560	14 17.6	4 13
N5566	14 17.8	4 11
N5585	14 18.0	56 57
N5569	14 18.1	4 13
N5574	14 18.4	3 28
N5576	14 18.5	3 30
N5577	14 18.7	3 40
N5584	14 19.8	-0 10
N5592	14 21.0	-28 27
N5600	14 21.4	14 52
N5595	14 21.5	-16 30
N5597	14 21.7	-16 33
N5613	14 22.0	35 7
N5614	14 22.0	35 5
N5605	14 22.3	-12 57
N5631	14 25.1	56 48
N5633	14 25.6	46 22
N5636	14 27.1	3 30
N5638	14 27.1	3 27
N5641	14 27.1	29 2
N5653	14 28.0	31 25
N5645	14 28.1	7 29
N5660	14 28.1	49 50
N5612	14 28.2	-78 11
I4444	14 28.5	-43 12
N5643	14 29.4	-43 59
N5673	14 29.8	50 10
N5665	14 29.9	8 18
N5669	14 30.3	10 8
N5672	14 30.5	31 53
N5678	14 30.7	58 8
I1029	14 30.7	50 8
N5668	14 30.9	4 40
N5676	14 31.0	49 41
N5682	14 32.8	48 53
N5683	14 33.0	48 53
N5687	14 33.3	54 42
N5689	14 33.7	48 57
I4448	14 34.2	-78 36
N5693	14 34.6	48 45
N5690	14 35.2	2 30
N5691	14 35.3	-0 11
N5707	14 35.8	51 47
N5701	14 36.7	5 34
N5705	14 37.3	-0 31
N5713	14 37.6	-0 5
N5716	14 38.3	-17 15
N5719	14 38.3	-0 5
N5728	14 39.6	-17 3
N5733	14 40.2	-0 9
N5739	14 40.6	42 3
N5740	14 41.9	1 54
N5746	14 42.3	2 10
N5750	14 43.6	-0 1
A1444	14 43.8	8 42
N5756	14 44.9	-14 39
N5757	14 45.0	-18 53
A1447	14 46.8	-9 57
N5768	14 49.6	-2 20
N5772	14 49.8	40 48
I1067	14 50.5	3 32
N5774	14 51.3	3 47
N5775	14 51.5	3 45
N5783	14 51.8	52 18
N5792	14 55.8	-0 54

NGC	RA (1950)	D
N5791	14 56.0	-19 4
N5793	14 56.6	-16 30
N5796	14 56.6	-16 26
N5820	14 57.2	54 5
N5806	14 57.5	2 5
N5832	14 57.8	71 53
N5811	14 57.9	1 50
N5812	14 58.2	-7 16
N5813	14 58.7	1 54
N5829	15 0.5	23 32
N5831	15 1.6	1 24
N5838	15 2.9	2 18
N5839	15 2.9	1 49
N5845	15 3.5	1 49
N5846	15 4.0	1 48
N5846A	15 4.0	1 48
N5850	15 4.6	1 44
N5866	15 5.1	55 57
N5857	15 5.2	19 47
N5854	15 5.3	2 45
N5859	15 5.3	19 46
I1091	15 5.6	-10 57
I1099	15 5.8	56 41
N5658	15 6.1	-11 1
N5861	15 6.4	-11 8
N5874	15 6.4	54 57
N5864	15 7.0	3 14
N5875	15 7.7	52 43
N5876	15 8.0	54 42
N5879	15 8.4	57 12
N5866B	15 10.9	55 58
N5878	15 11.0	-14 5
A1511	15 11.0	-15 18
N5889	15 11.6	41 31
N5893	15 11.8	42 8
N5885	15 12.4	-9 53
N5899	15 13.2	42 14
N5900	15 13.3	42 23
N5905	15 14.1	55 42
N5907	15 14.6	56 31
N5898	15 15.2	-23 55
N5908	15 15.4	55 36
N5903	15 15.6	-23 51
A1516	15 16.3	43 3
N5916A	15 18.5	-12 55
N5915	15 18.8	-12 55
N5916	15 18.9	-12 59
N5921	15 19.5	5 15
N5929	15 24.3	41 50
N5930	15 24.4	41 51
N5949	15 27.2	64 55
N5936	15 27.6	13 9
N5951	15 31.4	15 10
N5953	15 32.3	15 22
N5954	15 32.3	15 22
N5957	15 33.0	12 13
N5962	15 34.2	16 46
N5964	15 35.1	6 8
N5976	15 35.8	59 36
N5970	15 36.1	12 20
I1131	15 36.5	12 15
N5968	15 36.9	-30 24
N5981	15 36.9	59 33
N5982	15 37.6	59 32
N5985	15 38.6	59 30
N5967A	15 40.5	-75 38
N5984	15 40.6	14 22
N5967	15 41.9	-75 31
N6015	15 50.7	62 28
N6027A	15 57.0	20 55
N6027D	15 57.0	20 55
N6068A	15 57.4	79 6
N6068	15 58.1	79 6
N6041	16 2.4	17 49
N6044	16 2.7	18 0
N6045	16 2.8	17 53
N6047	16 2.9	17 51
I1173	16 2.9	17 32
N6052	16 3.1	20 41
N6055	16 3.3	18 15
I1181A	16 3.3	17 42
I1181B	16 3.3	17 42
I1182	16 3.3	17 56
I1183	16 3.3	17 54
N6056	16 3.4	18 3
I1185	16 3.4	17 51
I1186	16 3.5	17 28
N6061	16 4.0	18 22
I1194	16 4.3	17 55
N6070	16 7.4	0 50

NGC	RA (1950)	D
N6106	16 16.3	7 31
N6140	16 19.0	65 29
N6118	16 19.3	-2 11
N6143	16 20.6	55 12
N6166	16 26.9	39 40
N6166A	16 26.9	39 40
N6166B	16 26.9	39 40
N6166C	16 26.9	39 40
N6181	16 30.1	19 56
N6217	16 34.8	78 18
N6196	16 35.5	36 12
N6211	16 40.6	57 54
N6207	16 41.3	36 56
N6215	16 46.8	-58 55
N6246A	16 48.0	55 47
A1648A	16 48.0	45 35
A1648B	16 48.0	45 35
A1648C	16 48.0	45 35
N6215A	16 48.3	-58 51
N6239	16 48.4	42 50
N6221	16 48.5	-59 8
N6246	16 48.7	55 38
N6240	16 50.7	2 28
I1237	16 55.2	55 8
N6296	17 6.2	4 0
N6306	17 7.0	60 47
N6307	17 7.1	60 49
N6310	17 7.3	61 3
N6308	17 9.9	23 26
N6314	17 10.5	23 20
N6315	17 10.6	23 17
I1248	17 10.7	59 56
N6340	17 11.1	72 22
N6300	17 12.3	-62 46
N6359	17 17.4	61 50
A1718A	17 18.1	49 8
A1718B	17 18.1	49 8
A1719	17 19.4	57 58
I4653	17 22.3	-60 52
N6381	17 26.6	60 3
N6384	17 29.9	7 6
N6412	17 30.8	75 45
I4662	17 42.1	-64 39
I4662A	17 46.2	-64 58
N6478	17 48.3	51 10
N6493A	17 49.3	61 30
N6482	17 49.8	23 5
N6503	17 49.9	70 10
N6500	17 53.8	18 21
N6501	17 54.1	18 23
N6555	18 5.6	17 30
N6570	18 8.9	14 4
N6438	18 9.4	-85 26
N6574	18 9.5	14 58
N6438A	18 9.9	-85 26
N6587	18 11.7	18 48
N6621	18 13.5	68 18
N6615	18 16.3	13 13
N6627	18 20.5	15 39
N6643	18 21.2	74 33
I4710	18 23.5	-67 1
N6651	18 24.7	71 34
I4713	18 24.7	-67 16
N6654	18 25.2	73 9
N6635	18 25.3	14 44
I4714	18 25.7	-66 42
I4717	18 28.9	-58 0
I4719	18 29.0	-56 46
I4720	18 29.2	-58 26
I4721	18 30.1	-58 32
N6667	18 30.6	67 57
N6658	18 31.9	22 50
N6661	18 32.5	22 52
N6690	18 35.4	70 29
N6674	18 36.5	25 20
N6654A	18 41.0	73 30
N6684	18 44.1	-65 14
N6702	18 45.5	45 39
N6703	18 45.9	45 30
N6684A	18 47.1	-64 55
N6699	18 47.8	-57 23
N6710	18 48.6	26 47
N6707	18 51.3	-53 53
I4796	18 52.3	-54 17
I4797	18 52.3	-54 22
A1853	18 52.9	-54 36
N6721	18 56.5	-57 51
I4806	18 57.2	-57 36
I4810	18 58.8	-56 14
I4820	19 4.5	-63 32

NGC	RA (1950)	D
N6744	19 5.0	-63 56
N6764	19 6.9	50 51
N6753	19 7.2	-57 8
N6754	19 7.5	-50 44
I4829	19 8.6	-56 38
N6758	19 9.8	-56 24
I4832	19 9.8	-56 43
I4837A	19 11.2	-54 13
I4837	19 11.3	-54 46
N6761	19 11.4	-50 45
I4839	19 11.5	-54 43
I4836	19 11.7	-60 17
I4840	19 11.7	-56 19
N6769	19 13.9	-60 35
N6770	19 14.2	-60 36
N6771	19 14.4	-60 41
I4842	19 15.0	-60 44
I4845	19 16.0	-60 31
N6780	19 18.7	-55 53
N6782	19 19.5	-60 2
N6776A	19 20.4	-63 48
N6796	19 20.6	61 2
N6776	19 20.7	-63 59
I4852	19 22.0	-60 28
I1302	19 29.0	35 39
I1303	19 29.5	35 45
N6808	19 38.5	-70 46
N6810	19 39.4	-58 47
N6814	19 39.9	-10 25
I4889	19 41.3	-54 29
N6821	19 41.7	-6 57
N6822	19 42.1	-14 53
I1308	19 42.3	-14 51
N6824	19 42.6	55 59
I4892	19 44.1	-70 22
N6835	19 51.8	-12 42
N6836	19 51.9	-12 49
A1955A	19 55.1	40 17
A1955B	19 55.1	40 17
N6850	19 59.6	-54 59
N6851	19 59.9	-48 25
N6854	20 1.8	-54 32
N6851A	20 2.3	-48 8
N6851B	20 2.3	-48 8
I4943	20 2.9	-48 32
N6861	20 3.7	-48 31
N6861D	20 4.7	-48 23
N6868	20 6.3	-48 31
N6870	20 6.5	-48 26
N6861E	20 7.3	-48 48
N6861F	20 7.6	-48 26
N6875A	20 8.3	-46 19
N6875	20 9.6	-46 19
N6878A	20 10.0	-44 59
I4960	20 10.1	-70 42
N6878	20 10.3	-44 41
N6872	20 11.7	-70 55
I4970	20 11.7	-70 55
I4972	20 12.5	-71 4
N6876	20 13.1	-71 1
N6877	20 13.4	-71 0
N6887	20 13.4	-52 56
N6880	20 14.3	-71 1
I4981	20 14.5	-71 0
N6890	20 14.8	-44 58
N6893	20 17.2	-48 25
N6902A	20 19.4	-44 27
I5000	20 19.9	6 17
A2021	20 20.6	-44 10
I1317	20 20.7	0 30
N6906	20 21.1	6 18
N6902	20 21.2	-43 50
N6902B	20 21.6	-44 2
N6907	20 22.1	-24 58
N6909	20 24.1	-47 12
N6915	20 25.1	-3 13
N6921	20 26.4	25 33
I5020	20 27.8	-33 42
N6923	20 28.6	-31 1
N6927	20 30.2	9 43
N6927A	20 30.2	9 41
N6928	20 30.4	9 45
N6930	20 30.5	9 41
N6925	20 31.2	-32 9
N6946	20 33.9	59 58
N6935	20 34.7	-52 17
N6937	20 35.1	-52 20
N6944A	20 35.7	6 43
N6944	20 35.9	6 48
N6951	20 36.5	65 56
N6942	20 37.0	-54 30
N6943	20 39.8	-68 55
I5039	20 40.2	-30 3
N6954	20 41.5	3 1
N6962	20 44.7	0 8
N6963	20 44.8	0 20
N6964	20 44.8	0 7
N6958	20 45.4	-38 11
I5052	20 47.5	-69 25
I5063	20 48.2	-57 16
N6970	20 48.6	-48 59
N6982	20 53.8	-52 3
N6984	20 54.3	-52 4
A2058	20 58.5	16 6
A2059A	20 58.8	15 55
A2059B	20 59.6	15 55
N7013	21 1.4	29 42
N7007	21 1.9	-52 45
N7014	21 4.5	-47 24
N7020	21 7.3	-64 15
N7029	21 8.4	-49 30
N7038	21 11.7	-47 26
I5092	21 12.1	-64 41
N7046	21 12.5	2 38
N7041	21 13.0	-48 35
N7049	21 15.6	-48 47
A2119	21 19.5	-46 13
A2120	21 20.0	-46 0
I5105	21 21.2	-40 50
I5105A	21 22.6	-40 29
I5105B	21 22.9	-41 3
N7059	21 23.6	-60 14
N7065	21 24.1	-7 14
N7065A	21 24.3	-7 16
N7064	21 25.5	-53 0
N7070	21 27.3	-43 19
N7072	21 27.4	-43 22
N7072A	21 27.4	-43 26
N7070A	21 27.6	-43 1
N7079	21 29.3	-44 18
N7083	21 31.8	-64 7
N7090	21 32.9	-54 47
N7097	21 37.1	-42 46
N7102	21 37.2	6 4
N7096	21 37.4	-64 8
N7097A	21 37.4	-42 42
N7107	21 39.2	-45 2
N7098	21 41.9	-75 21
N7119A	21 43.1	-46 45
N7119B	21 43.1	-46 45
A2144	21 44.0	-21 29
I5131	21 44.4	-35 7
N7124	21 44.8	-50 48
N7135	21 45.3	-35 11
N7125	21 45.6	-60 56
N7126	21 45.7	-60 50
N7137	21 45.9	21 56
N7135	21 46.8	-35 7
N7141	21 48.8	-55 48
N7144	21 49.5	-48 29
N7145	21 50.1	-48 7
N7156	21 52.0	2 42
N7154	21 52.4	-35 3
N7155	21 52.9	-49 46
N7163	21 56.4	-32 8
N7162	21 56.7	-43 33
N7166	21 57.6	-43 39
N7162A	21 57.7	-43 23
I1417	21 57.7	-13 23
N7171	21 58.3	-13 31
N7177	21 58.3	17 29
N7168	21 58.9	-52 0
N7172	21 59.1	-32 7
N7174	21 59.2	-32 15
N7180	21 59.5	-20 48
I5152	21 59.6	-51 32
N7184	21 59.9	-21 4
I5156	22 0.4	-34 2
N7179	22 1.2	-64 18
N7196	22 2.6	-50 22
N7192	22 3.2	-64 33
N7191	22 3.3	-64 53
N7200	22 4.1	-50 15
N7205A	22 4.1	-57 41
N7199	22 4.9	-64 57
N7205	22 5.1	-57 40
N7217	22 5.6	31 7
I5168	22 6.0	-28 6
N7213	22 6.2	-47 25
N7214	22 6.3	-28 3
N7218	22 7.5	-16 54
A2208	22 7.9	-22 56
N7219	22 9.7	-65 5
I5181	22 10.3	-46 16
N7232A	22 10.6	-46 2
N7236	22 12.3	13 36
N7237	22 12.3	13 35
N7232	22 12.6	-46 5
N7233	22 12.7	-46 6
N7232B	22 12.9	-45 56
I5179	22 13.3	-37 6
N7240	22 13.4	37 2
I5186	22 13.4	-37 5
N7242	22 13.5	37 3
N7248	22 14.8	40 16
N7252	22 18.0	-24 56
I5201	22 18.3	-46 19
N7280	22 24.0	15 53
N7290	22 26.0	16 53
N7298	22 28.2	-14 27
N7300	22 28.3	-14 17
N7302	22 29.7	-14 23
N2573A	22 30.0	-89 26
N2573B	22 30.0	-89 26
N7307	22 30.9	-41 12
N7309	22 31.6	-10 37
N7313	22 32.8	-26 23
N7314	22 33.0	-26 18
N7317	22 33.6	33 41
N7318A	22 33.7	33 42
N7318B	22 33.7	33 42
N7319	22 33.8	33 42
N7320	22 33.8	33 41
N7320C	22 34.1	33 43
N7331	22 34.8	34 10
N7332	22 35.0	23 32
N7335	22 35.0	34 10
N7337	22 35.2	34 5
N7339	22 35.4	23 31
N7343	22 36.4	33 48
N7329	22 37.0	-66 44
N7348	22 38.1	11 38
I5240	22 39.0	-45 4
N7361	22 39.5	-30 19
N7363	22 40.9	33 44
N7368	22 42.7	-39 36
N7371	22 43.4	-11 16
N7377	22 45.1	-22 35
N7385	22 47.4	11 21
N7386	22 47.6	11 26
N7393	22 49.0	-5 49
N7392	22 49.2	-20 53
N7410	22 52.1	-39 56
N7408	22 52.7	-63 58
N7412	22 53.0	-42 55
I5267A	22 53.0	-43 41
N7416	22 53.1	-5 46
I5269A	22 53.1	-36 39
N7418	22 53.8	-37 17
N7418A	22 53.9	-37 1
I5269B	22 53.9	-36 31
N7412A	22 54.0	-43 4
N7421	22 54.1	-37 37
I5264	22 54.1	-36 49
I5267B	22 54.1	-44 2
I5267	22 54.4	-43 43
N7424	22 54.5	-41 20
I1459	22 54.5	-36 41
I1460	22 54.5	4 25
I5269	22 55.0	-36 18
I5270	22 55.2	-36 7
I5271	22 55.3	-34 1
I5273	22 56.7	-37 58
N7442	22 57.0	15 15
N7443	22 57.5	-13 4
N7444	22 57.5	-13 5
N7448	22 57.6	15 43
I5269C	22 57.6	-35 38
N7454	22 58.6	16 7
N7457	22 58.6	29 53
N7456	22 59.3	-39 51
N7463	22 59.4	15 42
N7464	22 59.4	15 42
N7465	22 59.5	15 41
N7462	23 0.0	-41 6
N7469	23 0.7	8 36
I5283	23 0.8	8 37
N7479	23 2.4	12 3
I5284	23 4.3	18 50
N7497	23 6.6	17 53
N7496	23 7.0	-43 42
N7499	23 7.9	7 18
N7501	23 8.0	7 19
N7503	23 8.0	7 15
N7507	23 9.5	-28 49
N7496A	23 9.6	-43 3
N7513	23 10.5	-28 38
N7537	23 12.0	4 13
N7531	23 12.1	-43 53
N7541	23 12.2	4 15
N7562	23 13.4	6 25
N7552	23 13.5	-42 53
N7562A	23 13.5	6 23
N7576	23 14.9	-5 1
N7585	23 15.4	-4 56
N7587	23 15.4	9 23
N7582	23 15.8	-42 38
N7592	23 15.9	-4 42
N7590	23 16.3	-42 31
N7600	23 16.3	-7 52
N7601	23 16.3	8 57
N7606	23 16.5	-8 46
N7599	23 16.7	-42 32
N7611	23 17.1	7 47
N7615	23 17.4	8 7
N7617	23 17.6	7 54
N7619	23 17.8	7 55
N7623	23 18.0	8 8
N7625	23 18.0	16 57
N7626	23 18.2	7 56
N7631	23 18.9	7 55
N7632	23 19.4	-42 46
N7640	23 19.7	40 35
N7671	23 24.8	12 12
N7672	23 25.0	12 7
I5325	23 26.0	-41 36
N7678	23 26.1	22 9
A2326	23 26.1	14 29
N7679	23 26.2	3 15
N7682	23 26.5	3 16
N7685	23 27.9	3 38
N7689	23 29.9	-54 22
N7690	23 30.2	-51 58
I5328A	23 30.4	-45 19
I5328	23 30.5	-45 19
I5328B	23 31.2	-45 31
I5332	23 31.7	-36 22
N7702	23 32.7	-56 17
N7714	23 33.7	1 53
N7713	23 33.8	-38 13
N7715	23 33.8	1 53
N7716	23 33.9	0 1
N7713A	23 34.5	-37 53
I5342	23 36.1	26 44
N7721	23 36.2	-6 48
N7723	23 36.4	-13 14
N7727	23 37.3	-12 34
A2339A	23 39.3	-3 54
A2339B	23 39.5	-3 50
A2340	23 40.0	-45 27
N7741	23 41.4	25 48
N7742	23 41.8	10 29
N7743	23 41.8	9 39
N7744	23 42.4	-43 12
N7752	23 44.5	29 11
N7753	23 44.6	29 12
N7755	23 45.3	-30 48
N7757	23 46.2	3 54
N7764	23 48.4	-41 1
N7769	23 48.5	19 52
N7770	23 48.8	19 48
N7771	23 48.9	19 50
N7764A	23 50.8	-40 59
N7779	23 50.9	7 35
N7782	23 51.4	7 42
N7785	23 52.8	5 38
N7793	23 55.3	-32 51
N7796	23 56.5	-55 44
A2359	23 59.2	-15 45